## Praise for the Detective Gaby Darin series . . .

'Mind-blowing'

'Keeps you on the edge of your seat'

'A great crime procedural series!'

'An amazing thriller from beginning to end'

'Couldn't ask for a better read'

'This series just keeps getting better.
I was hooked from the first page'

'A five-star read, no question'

Born in Dublin, **JENNY O'BRIEN** moved to Wales and then Guernsey, where she tries to find time to both read and write in between working as a nurse and ferrying around three teenagers.

In her spare time she can be found frowning at her wonky cakes and even wonkier breads. You'll be pleased to note she won't be entering *Bake Off*. She's also an all-year-round sea swimmer.

## Also by Jenny O'Brien

### The Detective Gaby Darin series
*Silent Cry*
*Darkest Night*
*Fallen Angel*
*Lost Souls*
*Buried Lies*

# Cold Grave

## JENNY O'BRIEN

ONE PLACE. MANY STORIES

HQ
An imprint of HarperCollins*Publishers* Ltd
1 London Bridge Street
London SE1 9GF

www.harpercollins.co.uk

HarperCollins*Publishers*
1st Floor, Watermarque Building, Ringsend Road
Dublin 4, Ireland

This paperback edition 2022

1

First published in Great Britain by
HQ, an imprint of HarperCollins*Publishers* Ltd 2022

ISBN: 9780008457099

**MIX**
Paper from
responsible sources
**FSC C007454**

This book is produced from independently certified FSC™ paper to ensure responsible forest management.

For more information visit: www.harpercollins.co.uk/green

Printed and bound in the UK using
100% renewable electricity at CPI Group (UK) Ltd

*For Ellie-Rose, may you have a wonderful time at university and a promising career in forensics.*

# Prologue

Was it the pain that woke her or a sound from outside? She didn't know and – in that second – she didn't care, as the pain ratcheted up a notch, leaving her a panting, exhausted mess spread across the middle of the bed.

It took a couple of deep, sighing breaths to manage the pain as she thought once more about what had woken her. The sound of the front door slamming. But that couldn't be right. He'd said he was going to get her a glass of water and phone for an ambulance. That would have only taken a minute – two at the most. There was no way he would have left her, not like this. He was both loving and kind. Tears, never far from the surface, started chasing down her cheeks. Nothing was ever too much trouble for him. He was the best of men, just like her father. Although there was nothing fatherly in his attentions.

With a little heave on her arms, she managed to prop herself up against the pillow. She felt woozy from the effort, which was ridiculous for a seventeen-year-old, a very fit seventeen-year-old. She needed fluids and pain relief. All the beer had done was leave a sour taste in her mouth and set up a blinding headache. But she couldn't move, not yet, even though she knew she must. He would come back. She knew he would.

It took the shadows lengthening across the duvet cover for her to realise that he'd gone. He'd left her to manage as best she could. She could barely stand. With her hand pressed to her stomach, trying to push back the pain, she furniture-walked out of the bedroom and down the hall, leaving a trail of bloody hand-prints along the pristine magnolia paintwork, handprints that would need far more than a wipe with a damp cloth to remove the stains. She didn't bother with the fluffy dressing gown he'd bought or notice the icy cold temperatures now that the wood burner had been left unattended.

The flagstones felt cold underfoot but she paid no heed. Instead, she made her way to the kitchen sink and after filling a tumbler with water, she downed it in one along with a couple of painkillers from the front pocket of her rucksack – her emergency supply to stave off the crippling period pains that had been the bane of her teenage years.

She placed the glass back on the worktop with an unsteady hand. If she didn't do something quickly, she'd die all alone and with no one to find her until the cleaners came. She bit down hard on her lower lip in an effort to ignite her anger and jump-start her determination. It wasn't over yet. Far from it. She was weak with the pain and blood loss but she was alive and young enough to get through this. The main road was her only option. It meant heading outside but what was the alternative? There was no phone – he'd thought of that. There was nothing but her sudden resolve to stare him in the face and ask him why.

The snow continued to fall, leaving a wonderland straight out of the pages of a romantic novel, the kind she'd used to read before Eli had come to rescue her. He'd laughed when she'd explained that it was a form of escapism, her way of living vicariously through the characters on the page. Now she didn't know what to think as she trudged through the snow, one step at a time, her eyes glued to the horizon and the sight of the road curving into the distance.

# Chapter 1

## Dr Lloyd

**Monday 8 February, 5 p.m. Mold**

'What's the name of the house again?'

'Hold on a sec and I'll check.' Bryony pulled out a scrap of paper from her pocket and unfolded it, squinting down to read the writing in the dim car interior. 'Edelweiss. The one opposite the bus stop. Look, there. Up ahead. The blue door,' she said, extending her gloved hand before fastening the buttons on her coat, her fingers fumbling with the toggles. 'I can get a bus back, Dad. It's late and I thought you said there was a game you wanted to watch?'

'Don't start all that again, Bry. You know our views on your safety.' He stopped the car and, securing the handbrake, turned in his seat. 'I can always get it on catch-up. Now, you have everything?' he asked, his attention on her school rucksack. 'Kitchen sink? Bath taps? Spare kettle? Teapot?'

She leant across the narrow space and planted a kiss on his cheek. 'You are silly.'

'But you still love me?'

3

'Of course I do. Now shoot. If you hurry, you might catch the start.'

She pushed the door open only to pause, her hand on the side of the frame. 'See you in a couple of hours. There's no need to wait.' And with that, he watched as she closed the door and walked up the short path to the house.

*

The house was in darkness when he pulled up outside and switched off the engine but he wasn't worried, not then. There was no sense of impending doom. No thought that tonight would be any different to the countless other nights when he'd had to act as unpaid and unappreciated chauffer to his daughters. He didn't mean that, not really, he mused as he switched off the engine and pushed the door open. He'd do anything for his girls. He only wished that they'd be a little more considerate.

With his phone in his pocket, he walked the couple of paces to the front door. As a doctor, he never went even one pace without his phone, a lesson he'd learnt while working as a junior doctor. Despite being finished for the evening he was always on call. Things went wrong. Other GPs went off sick. Cars developed punctures. The list was endless and, as he was the senior partner, important calls were forwarded on to him by the practice manager. He could ill afford a missed message even though he had no intention of staying longer than the social chitchat necessary to decant his daughter back into the car.

He heard the doorbell peal in the hall as he stamped his feet and rubbed his hands, his thoughts on the single measure of whisky he'd promised himself and not on the dim shadow approaching the glass.

'Hello, can I help you?' The voice was soft and tentative, almost as if he wasn't expected – the first warning shot across his bow that things might not be as straightforward as they first appeared.

'Hi there. I'm Lewis Lloyd, Bryony's dad,' he said, expecting an immediate response. The opening of the door. A welcome smile followed by a 'Do come in, they'll be here in a minute.' That's not what he got.

'And?'

'And, I've come to pick up my daughter.'

'I'm sorry, you must have the wrong address. There's no one by that name here,' she said, moving to close the door.

'Hold on a moment.' He stepped back, his gaze taking in the metal door sign and the little white flowers, edelweiss picked out in blue lettering, before repositioning himself in front of the door again, this time his arm rigid against the wood panelling. 'No, there's no mistake, Mrs . . . er . . . I dropped my daughter off to you earlier on and now I'm collecting her.' He watched her eyes widen briefly, the pupils large in her suddenly pale face and his pulse ratcheted up a notch.

'Please leave. Your daughter isn't here,' she said, moving to close the door and realising that his arm and then foot were preventing her. 'Hey, hold on a minute . . .'

Lewis Lloyd pushed the full force of his not inconsiderable height against the door so that it flung back against its hinges and banged against the wall. 'No, you hold on a minute. I don't know what game you're playing but I want my daughter and I want her now.'

He glanced around the hall before heading for the first room on the right, the lounge. Empty – as was the kitchen. There were only two rooms downstairs and he tore through each of them like a whirlwind, toppling over chairs, peering behind the sofa, leaving cupboards open, even cupboards that were far too small for his daughter to hide in or . . . or be hidden in. He clamped down on the thought and headed for the stairs, ignoring the screaming woman behind him brandishing her mobile.

'I'm phoning the police.'

'Please do. The only useful thing you've suggested.'

The upstairs rooms were as empty as the downstairs or empty of anything important. His daughter. There was nowhere left to look. Nothing left to do with the police on their way. He sank down onto the top stair, his elbows on his knees, his head cradled in his hands, suddenly aware of the silence both inside the house and within his heart. The screaming had stopped but that was the least of his worries. His daughter. His beautiful girl. Where the hell was she?

# Chapter 2

## Gaby

**Monday 8 February, 7.30 p.m. Rhos-on-Sea**

'I'll just pop up and check that Conor is doing his homework,' Rusty said, standing and stretching before heading for the stairs.

*Good luck with that.* But instead of replying, Gaby went back into the kitchen and put the kettle on.

Senior pathologist Dr Rusty Mulholland's relationship with his twelve-year-old son had taken a nose dive over recent months and a hot drink would be just the thing after leaving the battleground of his son's bedroom. Knowing Rusty, he'd probably prefer a glass of whisky but she'd leave him to make that decision when he returned downstairs.

Detective Inspector Gaby Darin still couldn't believe that they'd moved in with her when the lease of his rented house over in Old Colwyn had come up for renewal. But she and Rusty had been spending so much time together that it had seemed the right decision at the time. She would like to think her relationship with Conor had improved but that would have been wishful thinking. While she tried her best, all she could say was that

Conor tolerated her in the same way he tolerated school. An evil necessity of dubious benefit to all concerned.

'Working on his maths,' Rusty said, strolling into the kitchen with a broad grin.

'Seriously?'

'Nope. He's now got a major strop on because I removed his iPad and threatened to disconnect the internet. Now, where did you leave the whisky?'

'Ha, it's in the same place it always is.'

'Which is where?'

'In the brown cupboard in the lounge,' she said, swallowing back the 'it hasn't moved since yesterday' comment playing on the tip of her tongue.

'Would you like one?'

'Might as well keep you company but just a tot.'

Gaby fished the teabags out of the mugs for use in the morning before pulling open the freezer and withdrawing the ice cube tray. Rusty liked his whisky neat but it was far too strong for her taste buds. In the old days, which meant a time before Rusty, she wouldn't have touched the stuff but then a lot had changed over the last few months, including their relationship. The rows were plentiful but they usually seemed to muddle through to some kind of a happy compromise – and Gaby wasn't always the one to give in.

She checked the back door was locked, switched off the lights and followed him back into the lounge, carrying a couple of glasses on a tray along with a small jug of water and a dish of peanuts.

'At least you should be proud that he's reading,' she said, picking up the threads of the conversation. 'You'd be surprised at the number of kids his age who are allergic to books.'

'If only he was allergic to computer games in the same way.' He grimaced. 'I wish he spent as much time on his schoolwork as he does on his computer.'

8

'Which is what parents in almost every household across the land are saying at exactly this moment.'

'I know it's not just me but . . .'

'Rusty, you're doing more than most parents do for their children. You need to give yourself a break. You're a good dad, great even,' she said, dropping onto the sofa, her thoughts turning to her best friend, Amy, who was weeks away from giving birth. 'You're going to be invaluable to Tim and Amy. She was only telling me last week of Tim's intention to pick your brains. Apparently his biggest concern is making an arse of himself by dropping into a faint at the crucial moment. She couldn't stop giggling while she was telling me.'

Rusty poured a measure into each glass before joining her, his head resting back against the cushions. 'I'm not sure I'll be of much help. Pru opted for an elective caesarean in the end. Not what I wanted but then choice wasn't a factor that ever featured in our relationship. Falling pregnant, supposedly by accident, closely followed by a shotgun wedding wasn't the most auspicious of starts. Our relationship never got a chance to recover.'

'I'm sorry. I had no idea.'

'No, well, we've never really discussed that side of things, have we?' He turned his head to look at her, his expression grim. 'But while we're on the subject I do have to tell you I think that I'm too old for this parenting lark.'

'Forty isn't old, far from it. Certainly not these days.'

'Well, it feels it.' He turned back to his drink, lifting his glass to his lips and taking a moment to relish the flavours, something she'd seen him do a hundred times but this felt different somehow. This felt as if he was also using the time to choose his words.

He started to speak only to stop at the sound of her mobile belting out 'I Will Survive'. For once Gaby didn't resent the intrusion.

'Darin speaking.'

'Sorry for interrupting your evening, ma'am, but we have a situation back at the station.'

'Carry on, Mal. I'm listening.'

'We have a missing teenager. A seventeen-year-old. Bryony Lloyd. Her father dropped her off at a friend's house for a study session but when he went to pick her up she wasn't there.'

Gaby raised her eyebrows. 'Probably nothing to worry about. Most likely she's ditched the study and gone off somewhere with her mates for a drinking session.'

'It's not quite as simple as that, ma'am. We've also had a complaint of harassment from the owner of the so-called "friend's house". The homeowner says she's never heard of a Bryony Lloyd and doesn't have a teenager. In fact, there are no children living at the address.'

# Chapter 3

## Gaby

**Monday 8 February, 9.15 p.m. St Asaph Incident Room**

'This had better be good, Mal,' Gaby said, dumping her bag on her desk before unravelling her scarf and peeling off her thick padded jacket. 'It's minus bloody freezing out there and with snow flurries forecast for later. If I crash my car on the way home . . .' She left the sentence unfinished, her meaning clear.

'I know. I'm sorry, ma'am. I've put on a fresh pot of coffee if it's any help.' He strolled over to the cafetiere and, choosing her favourite mug, filled it to the top before placing it on her desk. 'I haven't added milk – it smelt funny.'

With the mug cradled between her fingers, Gaby made her way to the radiator and plonked her bottom on the top. 'So, what have you got for me then? A missing schoolgirl?' She paused. 'I take it she's still at school?'

'At sixth form college studying for her A levels.'

'That's all we need.'

She stared across the room at him, their thoughts working in tandem. A missing teenager. Another one. It had been five months since Christy Taylor had disappeared. A straight-A student with supportive parents and a glowing future ahead of her. That was until she'd upped and vanished, never to be seen or heard from again. They hadn't given up the search despite a distinct lack of clues – there weren't any. At the time they'd made the mistake of not taking her disappearance seriously enough, under the misapprehension that she'd run away from home and would eventually turn up. Gaby wasn't prepared to make the same mistake twice.

'Anything untoward with the parents?'

'No. Nothing. Pillars of the community. The father's a GP, the mother a housewife. They say the daughter has never done anything like this before. That it's totally out of character. After joining the police in combing the area and checking that Bryony hadn't made her own way home, they came straight here. I've popped them in interview room 4 with a PC looking after them.'

'Any siblings?'

'There's a younger sister. Sixteen. They left her at home in case Bryony turns up. So far there hasn't been a peep.'

'And no note left? Nothing taken?'

Mal shrugged. 'That's where there is a difference. She had her schoolbag with her and if the sister is to be believed, some of her clothes are missing.'

Gaby set her mug on the windowsill and headed back to her desk. 'I'll inform DCI Sherlock while you mobilise the search. Then we'll interview the parents.'

'What about the others?' Mal said, waving his hand towards the empty desks.

'No, leave them be for the moment. If she doesn't turn up in the next few hours, and there's every hope that she will, then they're going to have to put a shift in.'

'There is also this Lynda Checkley woman. The owner of the house Bryony was dropped off at,' Malachy explained, unfolding his frame and stretching to his full height.

'Oh, yes?'

'She went bananas when Bryony's father turned up on her doorstep. It seems as if he forced his way into the house without a by-your-leave and rampaged through the rooms like an elephant on heat. The thing is – what if Checkley is involved and it's all some sort of a cover-up? I was thinking that perhaps we should get Jason onto it? The sooner we get the CSIs involved, the better, don't you think?'

'Mal, if you carry on like this I'll wonder why you called me in,' she said, matching his grin with one of her own. 'I'll phone Jason as soon as I've finished speaking to Sherlock and, if you get this Checkley person's number, I'll give her a ring after. We'll head over there after we've met with the Lloyds. It's always better to fend off potential complaints before they have time to fester.'

She grabbed her phone from her bag then walked over to the first of the three whiteboards that filled the left-hand wall of the room, while fast-dialling DCI Sherlock. Gaby didn't like loose ends; Christy's disappearance was the biggest loose end imaginable. That's why, despite the passage of time and other cases taking precedence, the first of the boards was still given over to the teenager.

The seventeen-year-old appeared shy in the photo they had displayed, her eyes downcast as if avoiding the camera lens. Could both cases be linked? It was far too early to tell but instinct told her that it was unlikely. Teenagers went missing all the time. Most turned up within twenty-four hours, their tail between their legs and with the hangover from hell. She could only hope that it would be the same in this instance.

'Good evening, sir, we have a missing teenager.'

# Chapter 4

Gaby

Dr and Mrs Lloyd sat huddled in their coats despite the warmth of the interview room, but Gaby couldn't blame them. One glance at their shocked faces told her everything she needed to know about the distraught couple. Malachy had called them overprotective, an observation which she'd dismissed out of hand as having little factual basis. With a missing daughter, they were bound to have a whole rainbow of emotions exploding beneath their stiff smiles but she still decided to tailor her approach accordingly.

'Hello, I'm Detective Inspector Gaby Darin.' She held out her hand and shook each of theirs in turn before taking a seat. 'I know it's late but—'

'The lateness of the hour is irrelevant, Detective,' Dr Lloyd said, eyeing her across the table. 'We want to know what you're doing to find our daughter.'

'Everything we can, Dr Lloyd. DC Devine is arranging a search as we speak. We're also in the process of circulating a description of your daughter along with copies of the photograph you very

14

kindly provided,' she added, pulling out the picture tucked inside her notepad. 'I'm about to head over to Mold to start interviews, bearing in mind that your daughter is only a little over two hours late for her pickup.'

'But she's been missing nearer to six if you take into account the time I dropped her off,' he said, through gritted teeth, his hands forming fists on the table in what was probably a desperate attempt to control his temper.

'That's why we've decided not to leave it until morning, which is the usual practice for missing older teens.'

Gaby crossed her legs at the ankles, her hands relaxed in her lap, deliberately so. She was used to distressed relatives. They came in all shapes and sizes, from the hysterical to the angry like the man sitting opposite. The wife was different again: deathly pale, her shock of fading red hair dragged off her face in a hasty ponytail.

'My daughter isn't a usual teenager, Detective.'

'Which brings me on to the next question, Dr Lloyd. Do you have any idea of what might have happened?'

'Absolutely none. That's your job. Bryony is a studious, straight-A student with her eyes on medicine as a future career. She barely has time to finish her coursework let alone go out gallivanting.'

'What about friends? Anyone we can talk to who might know something? What about the girl she was meant to be meeting up with?'

He looked at his wife. 'Lesley?'

Lesley Lloyd twisted her hands in her lap, her tan leather gloves similar to a pair that Gaby had been coveting for a while now. 'I don't really know. Bryony isn't very forthcoming with what goes on at school. I ask her often enough but she rarely tells me anything of any importance.'

'Don't worry. We'll catch up with that side of things in the morning.' Gaby scribbled a note down on the A4 pad she'd brought with her. The station was trialling out a new notebook app but she couldn't get on with it. 'I believe she's studying at the sixth form centre over in Mold?'

'Yes.' Mrs Lloyd managed to flick her a quick glance before dipping her head, her chin sunk into her neck, her voice scarcely a thread of sound. 'My husband drops both girls off on the way to work and I pick them up in the afternoon. The workload is such that, apart from a quick break to eat, she spends the rest of the time in her bedroom studying.'

Gaby bit down on the end of her pencil. It sounded like there wasn't time for Bryony to have made the usual connections as she remembered the parties she'd used to attend as a teenager. She also wouldn't mind betting that Bryony wasn't the type to go out partying.

'So, there's no boyfriend then?'

'As if! She's far too young for all that nonsense.' Dr Lloyd folded his arms across his chest, resting back in his chair and balancing on the back legs. 'Her sister's just the same. We brought them up with their heads screwed on the right way, Detective. There's time enough for partying when they've got their exams out of the way.'

*Of course there is.* But something had happened to their daughter to change all that. Gaby picked up Bryony's photograph again, noting the red hair and deep blue eyes set in a freckly face, with the pallor that only came with genuine redheads, well aware that the couple opposite were watching her every move.

The girl couldn't be said to be pretty or even eye-catching. Her forehead was too broad and her eyes a wishy-washy shade of blue. And as for her build. Gaby turned the page of her notebook to where she'd jotted down her particulars. At five-foot-four and only six stone she would have been slim, thin even, none of which explained why she'd pretended to knock on a stranger's house in Mold only to then disappear into thin air.

Gaby placed the picture down with a steady hand, which was at odds with her thoughts. Either Dr and Mrs Lloyd were innocent parties in their daughter's disappearance or they should have been in the movies. Currently she didn't know either way but would hazard a guess at the former. The air was thick with shock and despair, no less than if their daughter had been a child as opposed to a near adult. The fact that Amy, their family liaison officer, was on maternity leave and her replacement wasn't due to begin until next week was an added hiccup in the process. Another thing to worry about.

'I will need to speak to your other daughter,' she finally said, again drawn to the photo.

'Cerys has been very distressed about the whole business,' Mrs Lloyd said, bristling suddenly. 'Especially when I asked her to check Bry's wardrobe to see if anything was missing.'

'That's as may be, but one of us will be over first thing tomorrow. There's no need for it to interrupt any of her lessons,' she continued, well aware of Dr Lloyd's sudden uncompromising expression. They should really send a team over now but it sounded as if the sister would need careful handling and there wasn't much they could do overnight. A few hours wouldn't make any difference. 'I believe there are two T-shirts missing? What about any electronics?'

'We can't find either her mobile or her iPad but she would have taken them with her. She never goes very far without either. Her laptop, on the other hand, is still sitting on her desk.'

# Chapter 5

Gaby

Conway Street was a narrow residential lane off Wrexham Road, with an antique warehouse at one end and the local school at the other. The houses were small and terraced with no front gardens, their doors opening straight onto the pavement. Edelweiss was difficult to distinguish from the others in the street apart from the metal name plate with a brace of small white flowers bordering the pale blue lettering, presumably to match the periwinkle shade of the door. There were many other places that Gaby would have liked to be right now instead of stamping her feet on the pavement. The station. The car. Her bed. In fact, almost any place other than here.

The door opened on the second knock, which was hardly surprising. If their situations had been reversed, Gaby would have been hanging around checking the front window for car headlights. Streets like these were breeding grounds for nosy neighbours. Often an advantage if you were a copper but not if you had any secrets to hide.

18

'I'm Detective Gaby Darin,' Gaby said, proffering her hand. 'Apologies for disturbing you, Mrs Checkley but . . .'

'It's Miss.'

'Oh. Right,' Gaby said, her face deliberately expressionless at the mild rebuke sent her way. 'Do you mind if we take this conversation inside? It's freezing out here.'

The house was both warm and comfortable. The walls painted a rich buttermilk with large bold canvases interrupting the smooth surfaces. The original floorboards were stripped and painted black with a large cream rug in the centre. Not a house for children, Gaby thought, noting the cat ornaments on the mantelpiece and the black cat curled up asleep on the cream sofa.

'Do take a seat, Detective.' Miss Checkley nodded at the red chair opposite before sinking down beside the cat and idly smoothing her hand along its back.

Gaby sat on the edge, her notebook open on her lap. Lynda Checkley wasn't what she'd imagined. She was younger for one thing. An attractive woman in a hippy sort of a way, with long straggly hair complemented by large, hooped earrings and a handkerchief-hemmed dress. Appearances were important. They set the scene and gave an indication as to the type of person Gaby was dealing with. But in this case they gave no hint whatsoever apart from the frown lines etched around the woman's eyes and brow, which had Gaby wondering who or what had put them there. They looked deep enough to predate today's little escapade. She made a brief note on the top of the pad before speaking. It would help when she was preparing the witness statement.

'I take it you live here alone?'

'Yes, apart from Midnight,' she said, tilting her head in the direction of the cat.

'And you were in this evening?'

'All evening and, before you ask, yes, there was a knock earlier while I was in the back cooking but, by the time I went to the door, there was no one there.'

'Despite Dr Lloyd telling us he dropped his daughter to your door?'

Miss Checkley shrugged, her meaning clear, her words confirming her expression and body language. 'It's got nothing to do with me. I did try and tell the father that, but he was having none of it.'

'No. Well. He wouldn't, would he? Not with his daughter missing,' Gaby said, trying to hold on to her patience along with her control of the conversation. 'What about neighbours?'

'What about them? There's Mr and Mrs Hussain on the left. A nice couple, in their mid to late fifties, I would have thought. No children. I doubt they would have seen anything.'

'And the other side?'

'That's rented or at least it's usually rented. The last tenant left, let me see, a couple of months ago now.'

Gaby was disappointed although she should have known better. The likelihood that the girl was in the house, after Dr Lloyd's thorough search, was always going to be a long shot. But it was still something that she had to follow up and the reason why Jason Moore, her head CSI, was sitting outside hunched over his steering wheel with a flask of tea cradled between his gloved hands in an effort to keep warm.

She pushed to her feet, forcing a smile. 'I'm afraid I'm going to have to ask the crime scene investigators to have a quick look at your property, just to confirm your story.'

'And if I object?'

'I do hope that you won't considering the seriousness of the situation. Obstructing an investigation is viewed in a very grave light by the courts,' Gaby said, her voice changing from warm to icy. She had far better things to do than passing the time of day with someone who clearly didn't appreciate the urgency of the situation. 'It will also make me wonder as to your motive for the delay.'

'My motive? Now hold on a minute.'

'Miss Checkley. You're wasting my time and that of one of my officers when, for all we know, the life of a young woman hangs in the balance. We can stay here arguing or I can apply to the courts for a search warrant?'

'Oh, for heaven's sake, this is ridiculous.'

'I entirely agree. So, what's it to be?'

# Chapter 6

## Gaby

**Tuesday 9 February, 8.15 a.m. Moss Cottage**

The next morning came along all too soon and started off with a visit to the Lloyds' home.

Moss Cottage was a grade-two-listed building on the outskirts of Mold, with a long sweeping driveway hidden behind remote-controlled wooden gates. Gaby felt out of her league as she drove up the drive, which was a ridiculous emotion for a serving police officer. The only thing of interest to the Lloyds was her role in finding their daughter but that didn't stop her from tugging her shirt straight and fastening the buttons on her jacket as soon as she'd stepped out of the car. She hid a smile as she watched Detective Owen Bates doing the exact same before he reached for the doorbell.

The lounge was like something out of *Country Life* magazine. The ceiling was beamed, the carpet a pale blue, which made Gaby wonder whether they'd been expecting her to take her shoes off in the hall. She glanced across at Owen but his expression wasn't giving anything away. Too late now.

'We won't take up much of your time,' Gaby said, the implication being that they had a job to do. She watched as Mrs Lloyd placed a tray of tea in front of them before joining her husband on the sofa opposite. There was no sign of their daughter. They hadn't wanted drinks but it was as good a method as any for breaking the ice.

'So, I take it that there's no useful news about Bryony then?' Dr Lloyd asked, ignoring the tea. 'You obviously haven't found her but what about leads?'

'We have a team scouring the area and officers following a trail of information but so far they've been unsuccessful,' she said, meeting his gaze. 'We've met with Miss Checkley, the owner of the house on Conway Street, and we'll be sending someone over to the sixth form centre shortly to see if any of Bryony's classmates know anything.' Gaby picked up her cup and saucer for something to do with her hands. 'In addition, we're going through all of the CCTV and doorbell footage along Conway Street in the hope that something crops up. Obviously you'll be the first to hear if we find anything.' She placed her cup and saucer back on the black minimalist coffee table without having taken a sip. 'We were expecting to meet with your daughter?'

'Cerys is beside herself as I'm sure you can imagine,' Mrs Lloyd explained, smoothing a manicured hand over her cream linen trousers. 'She's refusing to come out of her room.'

'Even so. It's important that we speak to her in case she does know something,' Owen said, taking the initiative by pushing up from the sofa. 'We're happy to see her in her bedroom and we can have a look at Bryony's room while we're at it. I think DI Darin has already explained that our investigators will also need access?'

'Is that really necessary!' Dr Lloyd exploded, his face going a disturbing shade of beetroot.

'It's all right, Lewis. After all, they are only doing their job,' Mrs Lloyd said, in a placatory tone.

'If they'd sent out a search party right from the beginning, perhaps we wouldn't be in this position.'

'It probably wouldn't have made any difference, dearest. You know that as well as I do.' She tilted her head towards Gaby. 'Bryony hasn't been herself for a few weeks now. We put it down to the pressures of studies but perhaps we were wrong in that.' She smoothed her hand over her trousers a second time, picking at a stray hair. 'Bringing up two daughters isn't easy, Detective. No matter what we do, our girls tend to have two settings: sullen and shouty.'

Owen managed a laugh, deflecting the tension in the room. 'I can well imagine. I have a daughter too and it's like walking on a tightrope covered in eggshells. I never know from one minute to the next what kind of a mood she's going to be in.'

The Lloyds visibly relaxed at his words. Here was a man who understood, a father. Little did they realise that his daughter was only six months old. Gaby wasn't going to be the one to tell them. He also managed to get the Lloyds to agree to stay in the lounge with a finesse that reminded her of why she'd wanted him to accompany her. With Amy away on maternity leave, he was the next best thing to a family liaison officer.

\*

Cerys had a large bedroom with a panoramic window looking out over a long narrow lawn, bordered by ornate laurel trees. She was lying on her bed, her legs dangling over the edge, with what looked to be a schoolbook in front of her and her mobile off to one side. Gaby suspected that the book was for show.

It took a slight knock on the open door to cause the girl to leap to her feet, a tissue in one hand and her phone in the other, the guiltiest of looks fading to oblivion when she realised that it wasn't her parents.

'What are you doing in my room?'

24

Gaby opened her mouth to speak only to be pipped to the post by Owen.

'I'm Detective Owen Bates and this is Detective Gaby Darin. We'd like to ask you a few questions about your sister, if we may?'

Cerys looked at them, very much like the rabbit Gaby had managed to avoid running over last night on the way home.

'I'm not sure there's anything I can say to help,' she said, wiping her nose with her tissue before turning and sliding back up to rest against the headboard, her jean-clad legs stretched out in front of her.

'Probably not.' Owen walked over to the window and leant against the frame, his hands stuffed deep into his pockets. 'It's just one of those boxes that we have to tick, or the boss will have a go.'

Cerys managed to force out a hoarse croak of a laugh. There was something contrived about the way she lifted her hand to push back her mop of red hair, the exact same shade as her sister's, as if she'd practised the movement in front of the mirror.

She had the same pale freckly complexion as Bryony but here nature had been kinder. Her forehead was less pronounced. Her features more defined. Her figure more like her mother's than her skeletally thin father's. Her eyes were a startling shade of green instead of Bryony's pale blue ones.

'What do you want to know? Not that I can tell you anything. My darling sister is a nerd,' she said, lifting her finger to her head and rotating it. 'Completely screwy.'

'Okay. So, how did you get on with your "screwy sister"? There's not much between you in years is there . . . ?'

'I didn't. She might have lived in another house for all I saw of her. Study. Study. And more study.' Cerys yawned. 'So boring. Just like her. Most days you'd need a crowbar to prise her away from her computer.'

'But apart from the studying. You must have met up at meal-times and on other occasions? Out for meals? Shopping?' Owen asked.

'More of the same. No conversation apart from books.' Cerys frowned. 'Even less conversation recently.' She twisted a plain silver ring round and round on her thumb.

'Less conversation recently,' Gaby repeated, entering the conversation. 'Why do you think that was?'

Cerys shrugged. 'You tell me. Worried about exams probably. There's mocks coming up.'

'So, what about the friend she'd arranged to meet?'

'No idea. She didn't have any friends or at least none that she ever talked about or brought home.' She turned her attention to her fingernails, pushing back the cuticles with the tip of her nail.

'And boyfriends?'

'Give me a break.' She flicked them a glance full of derision. 'Haven't you been listening to a thing I've been saying? We never discussed boys, ever. She could have been gay and we'd have been none the wiser.'

'And was she? Gay, that is?'

'Your guess is as good as mine.'

Owen pushed away from the wall and, pulling out his wallet, selected a business card, which he dropped onto the desk. 'If you think of anything, no matter how stupid, my numbers and email are on there.'

'Whatever.'

*

'Do you think we were like that when we were that age?' Gaby asked as soon as Owen had pulled the door closed behind them.

'Probably.'

'God. That's as good a reason as any not to have kids.' She didn't see Owen send her a quick look, a brief smile on his lips at the lie. He remained silent, which was just as well. It wasn't a conversation she was ready to have yet.

# Chapter 7

## Gaby

### Tuesday 9 February, 9.30 a.m. St Asaph

Gaby was starting to feel the after-effects of only five hours' sleep but there was nothing she could do about that apart from pump herself full of coffee in the hope that caffeine and adrenalin would pull her through. She had a 9.45 meeting lined up with DCI Sherlock but first she needed to catch up with Malachy before sending him home for some much-needed sleep.

'Remind me not to put you on nights again anytime soon, Devine,' she said, waving him to take a seat.

'Yes, ma'am.'

She waited until he'd settled in the chair opposite. He looked tired but then so did she; at least he had the attraction of a day tucked up in bed instead of a day stuck at the station.

'So, what's the news then?'

He spread his hands. 'You can have the long answer or the short one.'

'That bad, eh?'

'The girl has disappeared into thin air. No sightings. Nothing from the CCTV so far. Marie has been hard at it since six.' He grinned. 'I didn't think it would do her any harm having an early start. The only positive is that the radio stations are going to run an on-the-hour news item so, with a bit of luck, we'll get more of a response.' He stroked his chin. 'Remember there's a school at the far end of Conway Street so the likelihood is that we'll get something from that stretch of road, even if it is only camera footage. The hope is that we'll get a numberplate we can check on the ANPR system.'

'Okay. You've done well, Mal. It's not your fault that the clues aren't there.'

He nodded. 'What did the sister have to say?'

'She wasn't as helpful as we would have hoped. We still have her mates to interview over at the sixth form centre. Here's hoping they have something more interesting for us.' She left her desk and strode the short distance to her window which, one floor up from the incident room, had a lacklustre view of the car park below. The morning was cold, the remnants of a heavy frost still clinging to the pavement. 'It's a shame Diane has gone off to take her detective exams. I could have used Marie in on the interviews but she'd better keep going on the CCTV.'

'It won't be long until Diane's back among the fold with her exams under her belt, ma'am.' He followed her example and stood to his feet. 'Is it all right if I head off now?'

'Yes, thank you again. See you tomorrow,' she said, glancing over her shoulder before turning back to the view.

The temperature had plummeted again overnight, which meant that what looked like frost was more likely to be ice. There was snow forecast for later, which was all they needed. They also had the task of trying to see if Bryony's disappearance was in any way linked to Christy Taylor's. Either way, DCI Sherlock was not going to be pleased. She returned to her desk and picked up her phone.

\*

DCI Henry Sherlock was a tall, stern man with an army regulation crew cut. He'd been in charge of the St Asaph station now for ten years and had earned the respect of his colleagues the hard way by overseeing some of the most difficult cases Wales had ever come across. Gaby admired him but she couldn't emulate his autocratic style of leadership or indeed his clear-desk policy – she glanced at the polished sheen of his dark wood desk. She knew it made sense to keep on track of the influx of paperwork that landed in her in-tray at regular intervals but if she did, she'd never get anything done. She was well known at the station for using the wastepaper bin under her desk as a filing tray and her top drawer for any works in progress as soon as she smelt anything approaching management heading her way.

Gaby stood in front of him like a recalcitrant schoolgirl, her hands neatly folded in front of her, while she waited for him to finish whatever he was doing on his computer. For all she knew, he could have been finishing off a game of tiddlywinks.

'What have you got to smile about, Darin? Because from where I'm sitting there is nothing remotely amusing about your current situation.' He bit out the words, gesturing towards the chair opposite the desk with an impatient wave of his hand.

She tailored her face to match her mood, which had just taken a nose dive. Asking her to sit meant that she wasn't about to be let go anytime soon. Gaby sank down onto the chair and watched as he pushed his keyboard to one side and rested his elbows on the table. Something had annoyed him. She could only hope that it wasn't anything to do with her – she feared otherwise.

'I've already had CS Winters on the phone,' he said, his blue eyes resolute behind his steel-rimmed frames. 'He's far from amused with your lack of results on the Christy Taylor case and now you're telling us that another girl has gone missing. Please tell me that you've been able to rule out any links between the two.'

'I can't do that, sir. The simple truth is that currently we don't know but it would be wrong of us not to consider the possibility.'

'Have you forgotten that Miss Taylor's parents are close friends of the chief superintendent, Darin? I certainly haven't.'

She'd like to tell him what she thought of his comment but that would get her in even deeper water and without a life belt in sight. The truth was Gaby didn't give a damn about who the girl's parents' friends were, close or otherwise. It wasn't relevant to the case and it wouldn't make a jot of difference to the way she conducted the investigation.

'No, sir. That's one of the reasons I contacted you as soon as I did. We can't discount that both girls are a similar age. They were also both attending sixth form centres, one in Mold the other in Llandudno but that's not all.'

Gaby paused, the remainder of the links tenuous at best and difficult to quantify. Both girls appeared younger than their photos and nerdy, a word she wouldn't normally choose to use but probably more appropriate than the swot label assigned to the clever kids when she was growing up. There was also an innocence about them that added to the puzzle. Nothing to make them stand out in a crowd; in fact the complete reverse. They were girls who were either uncomfortable in their skin or didn't give a toss. Gaby shook the thought away, unsure if she was reading far too much into the photos they'd been given. It was also something she couldn't share with Sherlock. He'd laugh at her if not sack her on the spot. She decided to come up with something that he would accept.

'The other thing, of course, is that both girls come from comfortable middle-class backgrounds but with no sign of any ransom, yet. We'll have another look at Taylor's case to see if we can find anything that might tie them together.'

'There's also been no sign of a body for either.'

'Which has to be viewed as a positive sign.'

'Not to the parents of Christy Taylor, it doesn't. They've spent the last five months agonising over when and where a body might be discovered because, after that length of time, what is the likelihood that she'll turn up alive?'

Gaby knew it was a rhetorical question and one she didn't have to answer. After all, they were in magic-wand-waving-and-miracle territory. She believed in neither.

Instead of shouting – he never raised his voice – he took off his glasses and rubbed the bridge of his nose between his thumb and forefinger. 'Get out of my sight and do what you're paid for. You're no use to me here.'

He wasn't expecting a reply. She didn't offer one. Instead she slipped out of the room and pulled the door quietly behind her, one thought prominent. They'd failed Christy's parents. What were the odds that they were also going to fail Bryony's?

# Chapter 8

Gaby

**Tuesday 9 February, 10 a.m. St Asaph**

The incident room, situated on the first floor of Saint Asaph police station, was warm. The radiators that lined the walls were set on high and belting out as much hot air as their little metal bodies would allow. It was also busy with all of the desks full, the only noise coming from muted telephone conversations and the tapping of fingers on keyboards.

Gaby didn't expect her staff to greet her as she stole into the office and settled behind her usual desk. She would far rather they got on with their business while she got on with hers. There were things she needed to do, urgent things, which included assigning new tasks but first she wanted to spend a couple of minutes making a list of priorities. It was only Jax who noticed her arrival, sending her a quick smile before returning to his phone call.

She pulled open the top drawer, removed an A4 pad and started jotting down some quick notes. She ignored the report that stared back at her from where she'd placed it yesterday with a promise that she'd get to it today at the latest. If it came to it she'd rehash last month's and hope for the best.

Top of the list was a visit to the sixth form centre to meet with Bryony's peers and teachers and see if anybody had any idea of what she'd been getting up to recently. The results from the CCTV footage were of lesser importance but, knowing how efficient Marie was, she had probably already been through all of the available material. Gaby pressed down on her pencil, making a deep dark hole through the top few sheets of her pad, her mind stretching back to the end of the summer and Christy Taylor. She'd have to set somebody onto it, to see if they could find a link between the disappearance of both girls and Owen Bates was the obvious choice.

She lifted her head only to meet his gaze above the screen of his laptop. Unlike Jax, he had no smile, only a look of intense concentration to match the gravity of the situation. Two missing girls and not one bloody clue between them which, in a funny sort of a way, had to be viewed as relevant. People didn't disappear into thin air, not with the growth in CCTV and dashcam footage. There were some similarities too that couldn't be discounted. Not as many as she would have liked but enough to cause a layer of disquiet under her breastbone. Their age. Their education. Their commitment to their studies. Both girls being dropped off by their parents to meet an unnamed friend and with a minimum of belongings. The only negative as far as she could see in forging that link was the differences in the way they looked.

She threw her pencil down and pushed back from the desk, fed up with the idea of another difficult disappearance, which was so unlike her that she paused to mull over the reason for her sudden mood. She loved nothing better than the thrill of the chase. The more complex the problem the better as far as she was concerned. Her enthusiasm and drive were part of the reason she'd decided on a career in law enforcement against the wishes of her parents who'd wanted her to go into the family business in Liverpool. Why then, suddenly, at the age of thirty-three, was she feeling like this unless last night's interrupted conversation with Rusty had unsettled her more than she'd realised?

It took iron-clad courage to force the wayward thought under control but Gaby was nothing if not a professional. With a tilt of her head, she gestured for Owen to join her at the first of the whiteboards.

Missing people weren't that uncommon. With travel links it was easy for someone to disappear if they didn't want to be found. But these missing teenagers were different. It wasn't a case of kids from a troubled family, far from it, just as it wasn't a case of a romantic liaison – both sets of parents had been adamant that their daughters were more interested in studying than they were in boys. This was no moonlight flit or random abduction. There was a level of planning. Audacious planning that had seen both girls being dropped off by their parents and, in Christy's case, never to be seen again. It was too early to say the same about Bryony but Gaby feared the worst.

Despite everything, that wasn't the thing that was causing her the most concern. Gaby frowned, her gaze travelling from Bryony's red hair to that of Christy Taylor's. Black hair contained in rows of tightly braided plaits that were moulded to her scalp. Her shy smile set in skin as dark as Bryony's was pale.

Criminals were nothing if not consistent, something that she'd learnt during the profiling course she'd attended last year. Their crimes were either carried out on the spur of the moment or planned to the nth degree. With the former there would be no thought to the appearance of the victim. It was more a case of acting on an opportunity that was too good to miss. The open car door. The Christmas tree easily spotted from the roadside along with the presents underneath. The solitary woman walking home late at night in an unlit, unpopulated area.

These two cases were different but also suspiciously similar. There was planning here and lots of it. In both cases, the girls had lied to their parents. In Christy's, she'd told her mother that she was meeting a friend for a coffee in Llandudno town centre. She'd got her to drop her off on the way past. Her mother had even seen her enter the café in her rear-view mirror as she'd pulled back out into the traffic. It had been a hot summer's day, Gaby remembered, the time stamped in her mind as it fell around the time of Amy's wedding. All Christy had with her was a multicoloured slouch rucksack, not much to start a new life with. But, with no sign of a body, and no evidence of a crime being committed, that was the scenario Gaby and her team had been hoping for.

'What's your favourite movie, Owen?' she said, out of the blue, aware of the time.

He pulled a grimace, obviously uncertain where the conversation was heading. Was that a blush rushing up under his beard staining his cheeks? She wouldn't like to guess either way.

'*Dr Zhivago,*' he said after a moment, his voice unusually quiet.

Gaby raised her brow but didn't comment. Instead she checked to see if the movie appeared on the approved list of codenames before adding 'Operation Zhivago' to the top of the second whiteboard. She pinned a picture of Bryony underneath. Getting to know Owen Bates was like piecing together a patchwork quilt. A jumble of random fragments with little pattern and many gaps. The stocky, dour Welshman was a man of his word, a man to be relied on. He was also a fantastic asset to the team with his blistering insight into the criminal mind and a memory that bordered on genius. He never forgot a face and could quote verbatim an interview or witness statement without having to refer back to his notes. The only sticking point was his insistence that he was happy continuing where he was instead of climbing up the ranks.

'Do you think they're linked then?' he said, picking up a photo from the top and concentrating on Bryony's face.

'It would be wrong of us to discount that possibility,' she said, starting to count off on her fingers. 'Background. Education. Age. Similarities with the way they both disappeared.'

'But . . .'

'No buts, Owen. I know we've been on the same profiling course but that doesn't change my thoughts. It's confusing but then what case isn't until we discover all the facts?'

'I take it that this is your way of asking me to lead on Christy Taylor's disappearance, while you have all the fun with the new one?'

'I wouldn't exactly say that fun is the right word to choose, Owen,' she said, a note of censure in her tone.

'You know what I mean.'

'Yes and that's why you must agree that you're the perfect person to lead it.'

'When we've already addressed every possible scenario for Christy's disappearance with no success?'

'Owen, there are two possibilities here,' Gaby said, struggling to maintain calm. 'Either the cases are linked or they aren't but, if they are, then the hope is that more clues will be forthcoming. You know as well as I do that we're up against a complete dead end with regards to Christy's whereabouts. Working the two cases in tandem can't possibly harm and may very well lead to a breakthrough.'

'I wouldn't bet on it,' he said, walking towards the window and taking up his usual position by the radiator, his hands thrust deep into his pockets.

Gaby watched him go, his body language everything she didn't want to see in one of her officers, but there was nothing she could do about it. He was bound to be annoyed but he had to realise that she relied on his expertise. He was the right choice whether he liked it or not.

She clapped her hands together. 'Right. Everyone, stop what you're doing. We'll have a quick catch-up.' She picked up a marker and tapped the end against the nearest desk. 'As you all know, we have another missing girl to trace and there is a possibility that her disappearance might be linked to that of Christy Taylor.'

She turned back to face the board, uncapped the pen and started writing in her illegible scrawl. 'Bryony Lloyd, aged seventeen. Attending sixth form with a view to becoming a doctor like her father. She went to meet a friend over at a house in Mold yesterday evening. When the dad went to pick her up, the owner of the property, a Miss Lynda Checkley, decried all knowledge. Lynda is a single woman of around thirty or so, and she doesn't have a teenager or in fact any children living at home.'

'Probably chosen at random,' Jax interrupted.

'Maybe. Maybe not. We'll have to look into Checkley's background to see what gives,' Gaby said, recapping the marker and turning back to the room. 'There are lots of innocent reasons why a seventeen-year-old ups and disappears. We all know of teenagers of sixteen and over who have to cope on their own; but this is different or, at least, it seems different. We also know more than most that people lie, even the people who are hard-wired to love us the most. That said, we must remember there could still be an innocent explanation for all of this. Just because I can't think of one doesn't mean Bryony won't turn up with a pile of shopping and her tail between her legs. The only thing against that is it's out of character according to her parents and sister and the little issue of those missing T-shirts. Right. Down to business. Marie, did you find anything on the CCTV?'

DC Marie Morgan was reclining in her chair, her shoulder-length blonde hair pinned away from her face, a light dusting of make-up on her lids and mouth. Many people disregarded her ability because of her enviable looks but Gaby wasn't one of them. Marie had a sharp mind and an uncanny knack of hitting upon the truth even when she wasn't looking for it.

'Not a huge amount for what is a busy street, then again that's only during the school run. Outside of the morning and afternoon drop-offs and pick-ups, it's deathly quiet so I didn't really expect anything else on a miserable cold night in February.'

'Perhaps not. So it was a complete waste of time?'

'Not quite. Doorbell tech hasn't reached the road but the school car park has a camera that picks up traffic along the end. The upshot is that I have four numberplates to run through the ANPR system.'

'Okay. Better than nothing. When you've done that, I'd like you to head over to the sixth form centre and meet up with Bryony's friends.' Gaby shifted her watch strap into a more comfortable position. 'It's potentially our strongest lead.'

'Yes, ma'am.'

Gaby nodded before switching her attention to Jax. 'You see what I did there, Williams?'

'No, ma'am,' he said, a look of confusion appearing.

Jax was the youngest member of the team and still exhibited the youthful exuberance of someone who expected the best from everybody. It would be knocked out of him at some point but Gaby hoped that he'd manage to retain his good humour and optimism. She couldn't help feeling a maternal responsibility towards the rangy, blond-haired detective, something that was augmented by his periodic stutter.

'Me selecting Marie to interview a classroom full of nubile teenage girls,' she said, with a total disregard for the English language. 'That leaves you with a nice little desk job searching into the life and loves of all the key players. You can crank up your playlist while you're at it.' She turned back to the board and wrote down a list of names. 'Dr and Mrs Lloyd and Lynda Checkley for a start, Jax. Financial. Personal. Employment records and anything else you can think of. You can also be the liaison for the search while I'm out of the office.'

She placed the marker back on the shelf underneath the whiteboard and grabbed her phone and keys. 'We'll meet back here at 1 p.m. unless something happens in the meantime.'

# Chapter 9

## Owen

The investigation into the disappearance of Christy Taylor was still open and likely to remain that way, if CS Winters had anything to do with it, but an open investigation didn't mean an active one. While the team had done their best to find the girl, they had no leads or sightings to follow up on.

Detective Owen Bates wasn't in the mood for company. His usual mild-mannered demeanour had been ruffled by his six-month-old daughter's continued teething difficulties. Gaby's decision to side-line him had come after a sleepless night and an early-morning row with his wife. The last thing he needed was a dose of office banter from a group of people he had little in common with outside of the job. So, instead of heading back to the incident room after the catch-up, he'd taken his laptop into one of the spare interview rooms where he'd found absolutely nothing to add to the information they already had on Christy's disappearance.

After unplugging his device, he bundled it under his arm and headed to the coffee machine down in reception. A trip to the archives office came next and Colin, the archives officer, was a sucker for the station's hot chocolate.

'All right?' He settled the takeout cup on Colin's desk along with his laptop before brushing the back of his hand across his beard.

'Never better, thanks to you. What brings you to these sunny parts then?' Colin said, holding the cup between both hands.

'Work. What else? I take it you've heard the news about the missing schoolgirl?'

'All a bit quick to panic, though? She's barely missing at all and you know what teenagers are like these days.'

Owen nodded. 'The only problem is that it's the second disappearance on our patch and under similar circumstances. Remember Christy Taylor?'

'Ah. We never did find her, did we? I'd forgotten.'

'No and the way Sherlock keeps reminding us, we're not bloody likely to.'

They exchanged glances. As experienced officers, they knew the statistics more than most. Christy would probably be found but only when it was too late to do anything other than mourn missed opportunities and police failings.

'What do you want from me then?' Colin placed the empty cup back down on the table, pushing it to one side. 'You remember more about the case then the rest of us put together,' he added with a grin, in reference to Owen's near-photographic memory. It was a grin Owen found difficult to return.

'My memory is far from foolproof, Colin, especially on zero hours' sleep. You might remember Christy was dropped off at that café in Llandudno so that's probably the place to start,' he said, checking his phone for messages. 'You know me, I'd far rather look at photographs in my hands than peering at them on the screen. Something to do with my age, no doubt.'

'Get away with you. You're only a young whippersnapper,' Colin said, pushing to his feet and adjusting the waistband of his trousers over his large belly. 'Come on then, the box files are over on the left, second shelf down. Only a couple but then there weren't that many clues. Don't forget my records.' He nodded in the direction of his clipboard. 'There's a pen attached.'

Owen completed the top form, signing the document with a flourish. The amount of paperwork that accompanied the job was getting ridiculous but he knew that it would be futile to comment. Colin was only doing what he was paid for. All evidence had to be accounted for – whether physical, photographic, electronic or forensic – just in case its trustworthiness was brought into question in the courts: a common loophole used by the legal profession to help their clients evade prosecution.

He shifted the two box files to the long span of tables against the back wall and, donning a pair of rubber gloves, removed the lid. The photos were in a pile at the top, neatly referenced with regards to the location, date, time and name of the CSI who'd taken them. He removed them from the box and spread them across the table.

The outside of the Llandudno café. The exciting display of cakes in the window caused his mouth to water. It was actually somewhere that he knew, a place he'd been to on the odd occasion with Kate. There wasn't any CCTV in that particular section of Mostyn Street, which had been a huge disadvantage to the investigation. They'd even put out a call for dashcam footage but no one had come forward.

The next group of photos showed Christy's bedroom. A plain blue room with built-in floor-to-ceiling bookshelves and smart white furniture. It looked nothing like the kind of room he'd had when he was a teenager. There wasn't a poster in sight for one thing and far too many books for another. He knew that Christy was bright and it showed with the type of paperbacks she had on display.

Owen removed the inventory that went with the bedroom photographs and nodded his head at the book titles, which included a variety on animal husbandry and YA fiction. The inventory also included her laptop and iPad, both of which hadn't revealed anything startling. Her mobile would have been useful, he thought, and not for the first time. People didn't realise the quality of information that was stored in the small handsets even when they wiped the phone. The experts in the digital lab were still able to extract a whole wealth of material. Every website they'd ever visited. Locations if they used Google Maps. Every phone number and every message all waiting to be discovered – and the reason for the escalation in burner phones.

He stood and, pushing his hands in his pockets, strolled the length of the room and back, his mind jumping the short distance to Bryony's disappearance. They hadn't got feedback from the CSIs yet but there had been no mention of her mobile and what student didn't rely on that piece of equipment these days? The likelihood was that she'd taken it with her but it was something else to check. Likelihood wasn't fact, as he kept reminding himself. The phone was something that he needed to mention to Gaby at the earliest opportunity. He pulled out his own mobile and sent her a quick message before replacing the lid on the box and returning it to the correct shelf.

# Chapter 10

## Jax

### Tuesday 9 February, 11 a.m. St Asaph

Jax was finding it difficult to concentrate. He didn't mind holing up in the station for the morning. In fact he welcomed it. With the temperature falling and the threat of snow imminent, he was quite happy in the warm office with a steady stream of free coffee on tap and his industrial-sized water bottle at his elbow. Even the thought of one of Gaby's working lunches didn't bother him. It meant that he'd get a break from his girlfriend's home cooking. Living with a vegan was one thing, her using him as a guinea pig to try out her recipes, something completely different. The easy answer of course was for him to get off his backside and make his own meals but he didn't hate her creations *that* much.

What he wasn't enamoured with was the thought of spending his precious time on such a fruitless exercise. Looking for a missing teenager was very different to a missing child. There was a score of reasons why Bryony could have decided to leave home. They'd even made a list when Christy had originally disappeared, a list he'd saved to his C drive. He'd already scrolled down the bullet points and ruled out most of them. However that still left a few, despite the advantages afforded to her from having middle-class, professional parents. Emotional, physical and sexual abuse could happen in any household and the more intelligent the abuser the more adept they were at hiding the signs.

The most likely possibility in both cases, and one he'd tried to voice at the time of Christy's disappearance, was that the girls had decided, for whatever reason, to run away from home. The streets of London were paved with unhappy kids heaving with teenage angst. And these days it wasn't just London, he remembered. The morning news was full of a veritable horror house of bodies discovered over in Manchester, which was a little too close for comfort for anyone's liking.

He sighed at the hopelessness of trying to find the girl if she simply didn't want to be found. If her parents hadn't been so adamant that it was totally out of character . . . The truth was, over seventy per cent of runaways returned home within the first day – they had hours yet before they reached that milestone. But none of that mattered. Gaby had given him a job, which he'd do to the best of his ability. He'd worked with the short, feisty officer for long enough to realise how clever she was. If anyone could find out what was going on it was her.

It was easy enough to find information out about Bryony's dad, Lewis Lloyd. His birth and marriage certificates came first followed by his medical qualifications and finally, information about his role as senior partner at the GP practice. There was nothing outstanding. Nothing to make Jax think that he'd be involved with the untoward disappearance of his daughter and everything to suggest that he was a generous father. They lived in a large, detached four-bedroomed property on the outskirts of Mold that they'd bought, mortgage-free, eight years ago. A quick look at the DVLA showed that he had three cars registered to his address. The first in his name, the second in his wife's and the third in his eldest daughter's, which begged the question why she hadn't driven herself unless she'd yet to pass her driving test. Jax scribbled a note on his A4 pad before heading over to the coffee pot, refilling his mug and settling back behind his desk.

Police searches followed a set pattern but they also had to be tailored to each individual case. One of the most important items on his list was whether someone had a police record or not. A simple enough thing to check and as instinctive as breathing after the number of times it had been drilled into him. Driving offences rarely mattered. He wasn't interested in parking or speeding fines and mostly that's all he ever found. The majority of the public were law-abiding and rarely appeared on the system. The Lloyds were in the clear but he couldn't say the same for Lynda Checkley.

The report into the break-in to her car, almost three years ago to the day, was brief and to the point. But then again that kind of incident was becoming increasingly common. The police in Mold might have a pile of these on their desk at any one time and with little or no hope of finding the culprits. Opportunist thieves trying door handles and peering through windows in search of handbags tucked under seats were two a penny. But in Miss Checkley's case they'd discovered her medical bag, which Checkley routinely locked in the boot of her car between patient visits while performing her role as a community midwife.

It felt like a targeted attack. The only thing taken and when the car had been parked in a quiet lane outside one of her patient's homes, with no CCTV anywhere near. Jax couldn't quite work out how the break-in of a nurse's car could in any way be related to a schoolgirl going missing on her doorstep three years later. But that didn't stop him from making a note of the officer's details in the unlikely event that they remembered the incident.

Jax stifled a yawn as he continued his search. Miss Checkley had been born in Oldham, where she'd also completed her nurse training. There was no record of a marriage licence, something he made a note of before moving on. House records came next but they didn't tell him anything that she hadn't confirmed already apart from changing the house name from Chez Nous to Edelweiss. Jax wasn't big on gardening but a quick Google search told him all he needed to know about the white alpine flower, the only piece of the puzzle missing was why she'd chosen to name her house after it. Not important in the scheme of things – certainly nothing like as important as the car break-in – but something he made a note of anyway. It always seemed to be the smallest things that smashed a case wide open and Jax was determined that no omission on his part would lead to a vital clue being overlooked.

As mornings went, he'd had far better, he thought, his gaze shifting to the empty coffee pot. He made one final search on the system to check if the car theft had been an isolated incident before shoving his laptop aside. Picking up his phone, he scrolled to the BBC for an update on the news, a bad habit he'd got into over the years and one that came with a daily ribbing from his girlfriend about being a news-obsessed junkie. The top item was about the bodies found in Manchester, which was only to be expected. He read on to keep his mind off the fact that he had a worrying lack of anything—

'Bloody hell.'

The words were wasted on the empty room. Instead of preparing a fresh pot of coffee he turned the page on his pad and started taking rapid notes, his fingers barely able to keep up with his thoughts. He only reached for his phone when the page was full.

Owen replied on the first ring. 'What's up, Jax? I'm just on my way back.'

'Sorry, Owen, but we have a problem, a huge one. They've made an ID on one of the bodies over in Manchester as a runaway teenager. A seventeen-year-old who, up until recently, had been studying at her local sixth form centre. Ring any bells?'

'Bloody hell!'

'My thoughts exactly.'

# Chapter 11

## Marie

### Tuesday 9 February, 11 a.m. Sixth Form Centre, Mold

The sixth form centre was a tall, narrow, red-brick building situated on the corner opposite Tesco's. Walking through the double doors was like going back in time. It almost seemed as if she knew the receptionist who was manning the front desk. She certainly had the same hairstyle and taste in John Lennon glasses as the receptionist in Marie's old school in Llandudno.

'The head teacher sends his apologies, Detective. In his absence I'm to take you to meet with Bryony's classmates.'

Marie was shown into an empty classroom at the back of the building. Instead of taking the chair offered, she strolled to the front of the room and waited, her ears fine-tuned to the distinctive sound of an assortment of shoes echoing along the corridor outside.

Twenty pupils came traipsing into the room, an equal mixture of boys and girls, all dressed in the usual student garb of jeans and an assortment of hoodies and woolly jumpers. She waited for them to quieten down before speaking, restraining the impulse to smile at how they were shoving and pushing each other. There was nothing orderly about the way they found their seats and slumped down, their legs outstretched, their expressions ranging from disinterested, annoyed and puzzled, to nervous. Marie's interest was piqued.

'Morning, everyone. Sorry for disrupting your lessons.'

'You can disrupt my lessons any day.'

'Shut up, Cormac. She'll arrest you if you're not careful.'

'Even better, Juliet. Even better,' Cormac replied, rubbing his hands together, a distinct leer in his eye.

'Hi, Cormac. I'm Detective Morgan. I was going to ask a few general questions about Bryony but as you're so keen to speak . . .' Marie said, popping her hip on the edge of the desk, her hands resting on either side, her calm outward appearance hiding her inward grin. 'You obviously knew Bryony so . . . ?'

He shrugged his shoulders. 'We're in the same class for biology and maths but I can't say that I *knew* her,' he said with a smirk.

Marie suddenly remembered what it was like to be a teenager in a class full of pubescent boys. She'd been a late developer, both physically and emotionally, and she'd found school a real trial. For someone like Bryony who, on the surface, appeared to be painfully shy, it must have been excruciating. Perhaps instead of getting them together in one great teenage mass, she should have interviewed them one at a time, but it was too late for that now.

Cormac obviously had something to say, but nothing of any importance. She slid her gaze over to where Juliet was examining her fingernails as if they held the secret to the universe.

'What about you, Juliet? What can you tell me?'

'Firstly, to ignore everything that Cormac says. Every year has a classroom clown.' She rolled her eyes. 'He's it. I've had to listen to his rubbish right through primary school and it doesn't get any better. Bry is nice enough but totally focused on her studies.' She returned her attention to her nails. 'She never comes out with us and to be honest I couldn't say if she hangs around with anybody in particular. Every time I saw her she was either lugging books in that big bag of hers or hiding away in the library studying.'

'She's taking maths, biology and chemistry, isn't she?' Marie said to no one in particular, her gaze flickering over their faces. 'Pretty hardcore subjects.'

'Yes well, her father was ambitious for her to follow in his footsteps.'

Marie homed in on a slim redhead with blue highlights, who was slouching on the chair closest to the window.

'And you know this, er . . . ?'

'I'm Poppy. And yes. Her parents are friendly with my parents, which is such a pain in the arse. They're always going on at me about how much Bry is studying.'

'As opposed to you not studying at all?' Cormac interrupted.

'Shut up, idiot. No one is talking to you, least of all me.'

Marie hid another smile at the banter toing and froing around the room. She hadn't expected much from the visit and that's exactly what she was getting. Her only hope was that a chat with Bryony's teachers would throw up something useful.

*

Marie followed the stairs up to the second floor feeling slightly trepidatious at the thought of knocking on the head teacher's door. It had been many years since she'd left school but the fear remained.

The office she was shown into was small but with a large feature window with views over what looked like a pretty decent garden interspersed with well-managed shrubs and empty borders, presumably awaiting the onset of spring.

The man behind the desk wasn't what she'd been expecting. He was younger for one thing. Probably only a couple of years older than her. She felt her gaze instinctively travel to his left hand, an automatic reflex she'd never quite grown out of, despite her lack of interest in the male sex in its entirety since splitting up with her husband. Mr Litton could head up a harem and she wouldn't turn a hair unless there'd been a crime committed. The fact that he was pleasant-looking with a head of thick brown hair and dimples cleaving his cheeks when he smiled was immaterial.

'I'm sorry I wasn't available when you arrived, Detective,' he said, directing her to take a seat with a wave of his hand. 'This is a most unusual business. There are plenty of students I can imagine going AWOL but Bryony wasn't one of them.'

'If indeed she went willingly?' Marie crossed one leg over the other, making sure that her skirt displayed as little leg as possible.

He leant forward, a frown appearing. 'But I thought that she ran away from home?'

'We have no way of knowing one way or the other and, as she didn't leave a note . . .'

'Ah, yes, of course. A wait-and-see job. So, how can I be of help?'

'I'm not sure. I had been hoping one of the students might know something but . . .' She shrugged her shoulders.

'I probably could have told you that,' he said, with a charming smile. 'Bryony was a bit of a loner. Completely driven to get the best A levels. A product of ambitious parents, topped off by poor self-esteem. To be fair to the girl, I liked her. In fact, I'd go so far as to say I admired her. If I'd studied half as hard when I was at school who knows what I'd have ended up doing.' He smiled again, this time revealing slightly crooked teeth. 'But that doesn't mean I understand what made her tick – an ideal pupil if ever there was one.'

He paused, his eyes trained on where he was playing with his pen. 'However there's something missing from her make-up. I'm not sure what exactly but I can see that she wouldn't have been popular with the other girls and, as for the boys . . . There was an immaturity about her that I think most of them found off-putting and that's not even mentioning her superior intelligence and stellar grades.'

'Are you saying that one of them might have been jealous then?'

He lifted his head at that. 'No. Not exactly. Just that she was far from popular. A loner, as I said. But they're the rainmakers, aren't they? She was destined for great things.'

*But only if she wanted them,* Marie thought. *Bryony wouldn't be the first product of pushy parents to go off the rails.*

'So, there's nobody she hung around with especially? Nobody you can think of that I should ask to see?'

'I suppose you could try Ruby Royal simply because they were studying the same subjects. I used to see them in the library at lunchtime.' His eyebrows drew together. 'Although not for some time. Most of the students and staff make use of the garden, which made their library lunches unusual to say the least.'

Marie nodded in the direction of the window. 'You're lucky to have such a space on site.'

'Very, although the additional expense of a part-time gardener is something we can do without.'

'Maybe Bryony and this Ruby had a falling-out?' she said, prodding the conversation along in the right direction when she'd much rather be discussing gardening.

'Perhaps you're right.' He switched on his computer and tapped on the keys, his eyes trained on the screen. 'Ruby has a free period in about half an hour. You'll probably find her in the library. That's where she usually is. If not, she'll be in Lovelies Delight coffee shop around the corner.' He lifted his head, meeting her gaze. 'But first I've arranged for you to meet with Bryony's teachers. Mrs Lemon, who takes her for maths. Ms Short, our biology teacher and finally Mrs Smale, who takes chemistry although I'm pretty sure they're all going to say the same thing. Studious and conscientious to a fault.'

A comment that nudged Marie to remember that she still needed to ask him for a list of all the staff working at the school before she left.

*

Ruby Royal was easy to spot. There were hundreds of teenagers just like Ruby: uncomfortable in their own skin and wanting to merge into the background. The girl was dressed in head-to-toe black and with her hair hanging around her shoulders in a thick curtain. But this was no goth lookalike or somebody trying to make a statement. This was a young woman trying to blend into the wall behind her like some invisible shadow. And the reason for Marie's certainty? She'd felt the exact same way when she was growing up. It would take the brushstroke of time for Ruby to find her comfort zone. There was no sign of it happening anytime soon.

Marie slipped into the chair opposite, only a coffee in her hand despite the enticing display of gooey cakes, but as Ruby wasn't eating then neither would she.

'Hello, I met you earlier. I hope you don't mind me joining you? The head teacher said I might find you here,' she said, giving the teenager little choice in accepting her company. 'I can call you Ruby? I'm Marie. It all seems a little ridiculous to call you anything else.'

Ruby didn't speak. She also didn't move a muscle in acknowledgement, which didn't bode well for the rest of the conversation. Marie wasn't in the mood for chatty but she wouldn't get very far if the girl wasn't going to answer her.

'Mr Litton thought that you'd be the best person to speak to about Bryony,' she tried again, picking up her spoon and concentrating on stirring her drink.

Silence.

'He said that you used to hang around a bit in the library between lessons?'

Silence.

She tried another approach, more direct as the softly-softly one wasn't getting her anywhere. 'Did you used to hang around with Bryony between lessons?'

'Occasionally.' Ruby dropped her head, her rope of hair falling

52

forward and obscuring her face, something Marie had last seen in a movie shot in the 1950s.

'Only occasionally? That's not what Mr Litton intimated. He said that he often saw you there together?'

'But not recently.' Ruby tucked her hair behind her ear in a defiant gesture, which must have tugged at her scalp.

It often amazed Marie how much she was able to learn from a few words. But it wasn't just the words. It was the tone of voice coupled with the girl's facial expression and body language, her gaze drawn to the way Ruby was holding her mug in a death grip. The teenager was hurt and maybe even angry. It was up to Marie to peer under her heavy layer of discontent to find out why.

'Ah. Did you have a falling-out then?'

'Not so that you'd notice. There were no words spoken or anything.'

'Then what?'

She shrugged. 'I don't know, do I? We had a lot in common, or at least, I thought we did.'

Marie slipped her phone out of her pocket and, swiping the screen, brought up her notebook app. 'I'm going to take a few notes,' she said, placing the mobile flat on the table. 'So, when did you notice the change?'

'Last year sometime.'

'Can you be more specific? At the start of term or . . . ?'

'No. It was fine then. Later but not much. Maybe the second or third week of September.'

'Okay. And did she give any indication of what the problem was?'

Ruby rolled her teeth over her bottom lip. 'Nope. Nothing. We used to meet up at lunchtimes, as Mr Litton said. And then it stopped. No reason. She didn't come into the library anymore.'

'And you have no idea where she went or what she was up to?'

'We didn't really talk about anything other than study. A bit about the prats in the year if they were being particularly annoying but that's all.'

Marie tapped her fingernails against the table lightly. 'And there's no one else you can think of who she'd have confided in?'

'No one. We're different from the others, or we were.'

That continued use of the past tense as if Bryony was dead already. Mr Litton had used it too . . .

# Chapter 12

## Gaby

Gaby paused to catch her breath, one foot on the landing above, the other on the step below as she glanced at the large picture window ahead of her. She knew the stairs would be a challenge – they were always a challenge – but she refused to take the lift. She wouldn't have had to take either if Jason Moore, the crime scene coordinator, ever answered his phone. The only way to speak to him, outside of an emergency, was to beard him in his office or hope the temptation of a working lunch was enough of an enticement.

Jason was one of the most experienced CSIs that Gaby had every worked with but also the tetchiest. She couldn't be doing with his moods and snarky backhand remarks. The only reason she allowed him to get away with even half of the comments he flung her way was because she felt in part to blame, which was ridiculous by any measurement scale. It wasn't her fault that the North Wales MIT had never been busier, the spate of serious crimes over the last twelve months defying both reason and explanation. The fact that the rate had only escalated since Gaby

55

had joined the team was something Jason was keen to remind her of at every opportunity but also something that she had no answer for. She didn't go out of her way to find trouble but that didn't alter the truth. Murder and mayhem followed her around the station like a bad smell.

Jason was holed up in the fingerprint development lab, his head bent over a large tabletop screen.

'Sorry for disturbing you, Jase.'

'You're never sorry, Gaby. More's the pity.' He straightened to his full height and rotated his shoulders with a grimace. Tall and lean, he had a long serious face enlivened by distinctive green eyes and topped with wavy brown hair.

'That's where you're wrong but I'm in no mood to argue. What do you have for us, if anything?'

'Nothing to make me think that she's not what she seems. A runaway.' He strolled to the open door, gesturing with a flick of his head that she should follow him into his broom cupboard of an office, a room dominated by floor-to-ceiling shelves filled with box files and a desk bare apart from a phone and a laptop. Gaby didn't bother to sit. Instead she propped herself against the doorframe while Jason dropped down in the black swivel chair and booted up his computer, his attention on the screen.

'We spoke to Bryony's parents and they confirmed, with a little help from her sister, that she'd filled her schoolbag with a few personal items, including a change of clothing, some toiletries and her hair straighteners instead of the expected course books, which she'd left in a neat pile beside her desk.'

'What about devices? There's her laptop but her mobile and iPad are still unaccounted for?'

'Neither were found.' He shrugged. 'She must have taken them with her. We also examined the property in Conway Street. There's nothing to show that she was anywhere near it. No trace evidence. No fingerprints. We managed to pick up lots of good matches from her bedroom as a comparison. No blood spatter or indeed any blood after spraying with luminol. In fact, no sign of Bryony or pretty much anyone else in the house apart from the owner. Miss Checkley obviously doesn't get many, if any, visitors.'

'So, a waste of time and resources when Bryony has probably gone off somewhere with her boyfriend, except for one simple fact.'

'What's that?'

Gaby looked up from where she'd been staring at her shoes. 'If we're to believe her parents and sister, she doesn't have one.'

'She wouldn't be the first teenager to pull the wool over her parents' eyes though, would she?' he said, leaning back in the chair, the springs creaking under his weight.

'No. If they're to be believed, she's a straight-A student with her eyes set on a medical degree and her teachers are of the same opinion.'

'Well, that's your problem not mine.' He stood, signalling that their conversation was over.

'Jase, I know you're overworked, and mostly by me, but if I can trouble you for another minute or two . . .' she said in a placatory tone, as she tried to distribute the strands of the case together in her mind – strands that couldn't or wouldn't knit together into a workable pattern. There was always a reason for a crime and that was the problem with both Christy and Bryony's disappearances. They couldn't even establish if a crime had been committed. If it hadn't been for the determination of Christy's parents, the girl would have been added to the ever-increasing list of runaways. What they were left with was two top-performing students who had disappeared without warning or subsequent contact. Find the reason and they'd find the girls.

'What's worrying me most is the similarity between this and the disappearance of Christy Taylor,' she finally said, eying him from the security of the doorway. 'You were involved with that one too, remember? Cast your mind back. Is there any striking similarity, anything that you came across at the time that reminds you of this case?'

'You're getting paranoid, Gaby. Teenagers go missing all the time and, the truth is, if they both weren't from well-to-do families, no one would think anything of it.'

'I think that's a little harsh.'

'Maybe,' he said, brushing his hair off his forehead with one hand, the other shifting his mouse to reactivate the screen. 'I'm tired and in need of a holiday,' he added, the nearest she was going to get to an apology.

She waited, using the time to check her phone for messages – there weren't any.

'Okay, I have her file up and, there's nothing striking and, if I'm honest, I can't agree with your thinking. Okay so both girls disappeared after lying to their family about their plans. Bryony had a smattering of personal items missing that, in the normal course of events, shouldn't have left her bedroom. Fewer items were missing in Christy's case. Her make-up bag. Some underwear maybe. That's about it but there's no pattern outside of the obvious. If you're going to run away, of course, there are things that are essential, like my fishing gear for one,' he said, with a rare display of humour. 'That's common sense. What's not is why these two young women were chosen, and I think that's where you're coming from, isn't it?' He only continued at the nod of her head. 'Please don't take this the wrong way or go all sexist on me but you must have noticed that they're both a pair of plain Janes.'

Gaby's eyes widened, two bright pink spots appearing in her cheeks. 'I can't believe you said that.'

'No. Well. Diplomacy can't be a medium to disguise the facts. What would the motive be to lead a couple of er, homely girls to stray? I can't think of one, can you?'

She stared at the photo of Christy on the screen, the same photo that was pinned to the board in the incident room.

*No.* And that was the biggest problem of all.

*

Gaby elbowed the door of the incident room open before making her way to the nearest desk and depositing a tray full of sandwiches and chocolate muffins.

'Time for a break and a catch-up?'

She didn't have to ask twice. The one sure-fire way of getting her team onto their feet was an offer of eats followed by one of the canteen's famed jumbo muffins. If she hadn't had the farsightedness to hold back a sandwich for herself, she might very well have gone hungry, she mused as she eyed the empty tray.

'It's like living with a houseful of teenage boys when Mum returns with the weekly shop. I've never seen food disappear so quickly,' she said, removing the cheese roll from under her arm and placing it on the desk for later. A working lunch was one thing but she found it easier to eat after and not during a meeting.

'Let's get cracking. By the looks of things, Bryony isn't going to turn up anytime soon without the help of our illustrious team. Who'd like to go first?' she asked, picking up a black marker and slapping the end against the palm of her hand.

'Well, it's not related as such to either case but it might be,' Jax said, only to be interrupted.

'If it's not related then it can wait. We'll have plenty of time at the end,' she said, ignoring his expression and turning to the room at large. 'I've asked Owen to concentrate on Christy's disappearance while we focus on Bryony. What have you got for us, Bates?'

'I'm not a miracle worker, ma'am,' he said, his voice dry. 'I had been planning to meet with her parents straight after my morning in the archives but something has come up to interfere with those plans.'

Gaby's lips pursed. She was well aware that he was annoyed with how she'd allocated the work but there was something in his face, something that sat outside of their earlier conversation.

'I'm listening.'

'I think Jax should explain. If it's related to our case then it has huge implications.'

'Okay, Jax. It seems as if we're going to start with you after all.' She folded her arms, managing a small smile.

'I was catching up with the n-n-news earlier,' he stuttered. 'You know. That house over in Greater Manchester. There's a major search of the property underway. Two bodies so far and maybe more. The thing is they've ID'd one of the dead as a seventeen-year-old, Jules White, and I was thinking that Christy and Bryony come up as close matches.'

'How come?'

'Well they're all studious and from middle-class families with no hint of any scandal attached to their names for a start. No previous attempts to run away. Not known to any of the child mental health teams and, finally, all attending sixth form.' He stood up, a piece of paper in his hand. 'I took the liberty of finding out who's running the show over in Greater Manchester. A DCI Maureen Webb. Here's her contact details.'

Gaby drew her hand over her forehead. Up until that moment she'd still been hoping to find Bryony; however, Jax's words extinguished the flame. But it wasn't only thoughts of the dead girl that had dropped her mood. There was nothing worse than having to work alongside another force on an investigation. Every area had their own way of running things just as every station had its own unique set of personalities. What were the odds that this DCI Webb would want to take the lead? The worst of it was that Gaby wasn't precious about being in charge, far from it. It was a job to be done, only that. But she'd come up against too many tosspots in her time as a copper, not to have a wide variety of concerns about this new development.

She shifted her gaze from where she'd been staring into space, her eyes clashing with Owen's.

'It's not good, Gaby. They've started digging up the back garden.'

'Shit!' One word, a word with a wealth of feeling behind it but, instead of expanding on the sentiment, she added Jules White's name to the board with a big exclamation mark. Someone would have to go to Manchester to follow up on this new lead and Owen, with his level of experience, was the best person for the job, she thought, her pen hovering over the board before adding his name and recapping the marker pen. It might even appease him somewhat about being asked to lead on the Christy Taylor side of things. She'd phone this DCI Webb straight after the briefing and set it up.

'Right, back to business. What else have you got for me, Jax? Hopefully nothing as explosive as your most recent contribution,' she said. 'Any background on Lynda Checkley?'

'As clean as a whistle, ma'am. She took a mortgage out on the property three years ago. There's no record of any involvement with the police, apart from a report filed in relation to her car being broken into shortly after she moved to the area.'

'And her job?'

'A nurse.'

Gaby added Lynda Checkley's job beside her name.

'Nothing spectacular there then,' she said, almost to herself. 'But we didn't really think that she was involved. A house picked at random, probably due to the location.'

'The same could be said for the café in Llandudno where Christy disappeared. A busy street in the height of summer is about as anonymous as an empty one in the depth of winter.'

'Exactly,' Gaby said, sending Owen a fleeting smile for his contribution before turning back to Jax. 'And what about the Lloyds? Anything?'

'Not a thing. Both pillars of the community. He's tied up with work and on a pile of various health-related committees outside of that. I wouldn't have thought he'd have much time for a family life but, by all accounts, whatever spare time he has he spends at home. No shadow of a stain on his character.'

'And the wife?'

'A similar story. Volunteers a couple of days at the local

branch of Oxfam. Apart from a handful of parking tickets, there's nothing.'

'Thank you. Marie, how have you been getting on?'

'I've had a bit of luck with the numberplate checks along Conway Street. Having a school sited at one end is an unexpected gift,' she said, peering down at her phone. 'A 2005 Nissan Micra, in Cocoon Green, was picked up via one of the school cameras facing Wrexham Road, which leads onto Checkley's street. When I ran it through the ANPR, I discovered that it was reported stolen last week, outside of a property in Bolton. I've just caught up with the officer in charge and she's sending me over the report ASAP.'

'Great work. So if we locate the car there's a good chance we might find Bryony?'

'Exactly. I've alerted the police to keep an eye out.'

Gaby turned to the whiteboard and scribbled the car details down before recapping the marker pen. 'That's something at least. What else? You were going to the sixth form centre, if I remember correctly?

'Yes and that's where it all goes a bit pear-shaped I'm afraid. Bryony, by all accounts is a bit of a square peg in a round hole. The only friend she appears to have is Ruby, a girl in her year studying the same subjects. Ruby said that there was a distinct cooling off in their friendship at the start of the last school term.'

'Mmm. Interesting. The friendship isn't something that either her parents or her sister alluded to, which makes it even more interesting. Did she say why they'd fallen out?'

Marie shook her head. 'Ruby seems to be in the dark.'

Gaby made a note on the board. 'As you know, Owen and I went to see the Lloyds but it was a complete waste of time. Bryony was performing well at school and was hoping for an offer to study medicine in Saint Andrews, something she was excited about. The younger sister came across as secretive and possibly hiding something but what? At sixteen, and with controlling parents, there's very little we can do to make her speak if she doesn't want to.'

'Unless we get the parents to have a word?' Owen said, selecting a muffin and taking a large bite.

'Hah.' Gaby laughed. 'You should know better than that. When was the last time you heard of a girl that age taking any note of her parents?'

'What about if I try, ma'am?' Marie said. 'A different face and all that. I can mention having met Ruby and see what reaction I get from the sister.'

'Good idea. If Cerys is hiding something, we need to know what and why. She might even know where Bryony is.' Gaby paused, her attention switching between the photos of the two girls, her eyes lingering on Christy's youthful features, innocent of any embellishments from make-up to piercings. 'I managed to catch up with Jason a few minutes ago. He didn't find anything at either address, which is what I was expecting. However, he did make an observation about both young women being plain Janes – his words I hasten to add, not mine.'

'Of all the bloody cheek,' Marie piped up, going off on a tangent. 'There is absolutely nothing wrong with girls wearing loose joggers and jeans or indeed appearing fresh-faced instead of slathering themselves in make-up just as there's nothing wrong with tight clothing and a slash of lippy. It's their body and their choice. They're only teenagers for God's sake. There's plenty of time for all that nonsense if and when they decide to follow trend. Peer pressure, in addition to male expectations from the likes of bloody Jason, are half of what's wrong with young women today. Advertising companies are responsible for the rest.'

Gaby's eyes narrowed at the unexpected lecture but all she said was: 'I know exactly where you're coming from, Marie.'

She turned back to the whiteboard and studied the photos of the two girls. They were very different. Different-shaped faces. Different hair and eye colours. Different builds but, loath as she was to admit it, both on the plainer side. The most important thing though was why that could be relevant.

'What about Jules White. Anyone seen a photo?'

'There's one in today's paper, ma'am, I'll print off some copies later,' Jax said. 'Brown-haired and wore glasses if I remember rightly. I didn't really notice anything else.'

'Okay, thank you. So, what I want to know is why he picked on Bryony, Christy and maybe Jules too? I could perfectly understand if it was opportunistic. Plucking them off the street in a random act. But there's nothing random in the way Bryony and Christy got their parents to drop them off. The problem is, we don't have a motive. We mustn't forget that there was no ransom note after Christy left or any form of communication for that matter and, so far, Bryony's case is following the same pattern. So, my question is, why were they chosen?'

The sudden silence enveloping the room was telling. Gaby shifted from one foot to the other, her focus on Jax who was eying his muffin like a starving lion in search of the next kill.

'You're forgetting something,' Owen said, walking across the room and tapping on the board.

'What's that?'

'The Nissan Micra Marie was on about earlier. Bolton is a town in Greater Manchester.'

# Chapter 13

## Owen

### Tuesday 9 February, 2.25 p.m.
### Greater Manchester Police Headquarters

It took Owen a little over an hour to reach Manchester. The divisional HQ was housed in a relatively new, impressive, purpose-built building located in the east of the city. Parking was a bitch but he finally managed to squeeze in between a mini and a 4x4, which was so badly parked that he was tempted to report it for a traffic violation.

DCI Maureen Webb was tall and thin with a long straight nose and a fine set of bags under her eyes that told of long hours and sleepless nights. But her smile was welcoming and the coffee placed on the edge of the desk piping hot if the steam rising off the top was anything to go by.

'Sorry to drag you all this way but it's so much easier than the phone or even a video chat, don't you think?' she said, opening the buttons of her jacket and sitting behind her desk.

'It's no bother, really. At least the snow has held off for now.' Owen glanced over the DCI's shoulder and the window behind her chair, the dark grey clouds as ominous as the weather forecast he'd caught on the journey down.

'Snow is all we need.' The DCI shuffled through a pile of papers before finally withdrawing a photo and placing it down on the desk for Owen to see, her index finger pushing it towards him. 'Jules White. Went missing a little over eighteen months ago. An A-grade student with a place at Durham University to study maths. An only child, she lived with her parents and rarely, if ever, went out unless it was to attend school. Chetham College, an exclusive all-girls school situated locally. It was books, books and more books.'

Owen studied the photo. The square, unassuming face and thin mousy hair restrained by a narrow headband. There was nothing wrong with her looks but nothing out of the ordinary either. He wondered what went on behind her dark, intelligent eyes, partly disguised by gold-framed glasses.

'And how did she go missing?'

'She took the bus, from where she lived in Worsley, into Manchester City. She was never seen again.' The DCI picked up another photo and placed it on top. 'The last known sighting was from the bus CCTV footage but, despite an exhaustive inquiry, the trail went arctic.'

The picture was blurred, the image of the young woman distorted and without a trace of colour to add to the identification. Video footage like this was notoriously unreliable but he could make out a long dark duffel coat and satchel-type bag gripped under her arm as if it was the most valuable of possessions.

'It was the bag that led to her identification,' DCI Webb continued, tapping the image a second time. 'The family are wealthy business owners. That is a limited-edition Burberry satchel, or so they told me at the time. They look all the same to me.'

'Me also.' Owen was more of a Primark man but he withheld the comment in light of the seriousness of the situation. He had a razor-sharp wit that often showed up at the most inappropriate of times – now was neither the time nor the place, he told himself, his gaze drawn to the expensive watch and fancy diamond engagement ring worn by the DCI. 'And her body?'

DCI Webb leant forward, the images swept aside, her elbows on the desk. 'Do you know Manchester at all?'

'Only the Trafford Centre and that's because of the missus.'

'Bournville Road is a long, narrow, residential street situated in East Didsbury. The houses are terraced. Two-up, two-down, red-bricked and carbon copies of each other. Number 26 is owned by a Mr Ansel Abalos. A retired accountant who, according to his neighbours, lived alone. But they haven't seen him around for a good few months now. It's the smell that drove them to send in the council. The drains, or so they thought.' She picked up her coffee and finished it before returning it to her desk. 'And in a way they were right. With the high rainfall we've had recently, the River Mersey has been breaching its banks. Areas that run alongside its trajectory, like Bournville Road, are the hardest hit. When the man from the council turned up in his white van he found a blocked drain, a back garden floating in raw sewage and a skeletonised hand sticking out of the ground. More coffee?'

Owen nodded his head, his attention now on the small pile of photographs that the DCI handed over before getting to her feet and leaving the room. The overgrown back garden, all brown branches and weeds this time of year. A blow-up of the protruding hand photographed in all its graphic glory. An incomplete skeleton. He turned to the next photo and almost spewed his coffee across the desk.

No matter how many years he spent on the force, he never felt anything but appalled in the presence of death. It was never routine, never just a job for him. There was a person inside, someone that the system had let down by failing to guard them against the warped mind of their killer.

He examined the wizened skin that was the colour of grubby

parchment, before picking up the school photo of Jules White and comparing the features. The same-shaped face. The broad forehead. Her glasses still on her nose. It was easy to see where the DCI was heading with her on-the-spot identification. They'd need supporting proof but Owen was now one hundred per cent sure he was looking at the dead body of the girl even though there was something different about her, something he hadn't been expecting. Jules had disappeared eighteen months ago and yet he could still discern her features, her form when he'd been expecting what? He ran his hand across his beard, unable to shift his gaze from the photo. He didn't know what to think except that he'd never seen anything like it before outside of a horror movie.

'Here you go.'

He jerked in the chair at the sound of the DCI's loud, bellowing voice from somewhere in the vicinity of his left ear as she placed a fresh mug of coffee beside him. 'I've rounded up our resident forensic pathologist, Dr Maston, and I think you know Dr Mulholland?'

# Chapter 14

## Marie

**Tuesday 9 February, 2.45 p.m. Moss Cottage**

Moss cottage was the least cottage-like house Marie had ever seen. Approached through a pair of electronically controlled, wrought-iron double gates, the handsome Georgian property featured an impressive columned porch accessed via broad, sandstone-coloured steps.

By the time she'd manoeuvred her car in front of the building, the Lloyds were waiting for her in the open doorway, which was to be expected. They were obviously keen for information but there was nothing Marie could tell them that would in any way lessen their expression of tortured grief. If she was to tell them the likely truth, based on statistical evidence, it would only make things worse.

After the usual introductions, Marie followed them into the hall, her professional smile in place as she sidestepped their questions with a level of skill that had taken years to develop.

'I'm sorry to take up your time but I do need to have a word with Cerys. There are a few questions that we still need to ask her.'

'Is that really necessary, Detective?' Mrs Lloyd said, waving her towards the drawing room.

Her degree of composure was unexpected and jarred with what Marie had been expecting. In her experience, it was usually the father who was able to pull himself together while the mother struggled with her emotions. It was also very different to the picture Gaby had portrayed of the couple's behaviour during their initial interview. Now she wondered at the shift. Dr Lloyd had barely strung two words together. Instead he'd drifted towards the window, his hands clasped behind his back as if he was distancing himself from the proceedings.

'Cerys is a very emotional girl,' Mrs Lloyd continued. 'She's little more than a child really and, despite what you might think, not that close to her older sister.'

'I promise I'll go carefully. But if there's the smallest chance that she might know something, something she may not even realise the importance of, then we are duty-bound to question her.'

'Let her get it over and done with, Lesley,' Dr Lloyd said over his shoulder, his attention on the range of hills in the background.

\*

Cerys was sitting at her desk in her bedroom, but Marie would like to bet that not much work was happening despite the textbook open in front of her and the pen in her hand.

Mrs Lloyd had the sense to leave the room but was careful not to shut the door. It didn't take a genius for Marie to realise that she'd be pressed up against the frame, listening to every word. She couldn't really blame her.

'Hello, Cerys. My name is Marie. Thanks for agreeing to see me.'

'I didn't have much choice, did I?'

'No. Well. It is important to find your sister. That's why I'm here. I know you spoke to my colleagues earlier but there are always new items that crop up and need clarification.'

Marie sat on the edge of the only other chair. A peach-covered recliner set in the window recess, which framed the same view as the lounge.

'So, what subjects are you taking?'

Cerys shrugged as if to say *what's it to you* but Marie was hoping that good manners would prevent her from being rude.

'Maths, Further Maths, Physics and DT.'

Marie raised her eyebrows. 'And any idea what you want to do when you leave school? A doctor like your father?'

'No fear.' She curled her lip. 'Electrical engineering if I get the grades, which is doubtful. Not all of us can be as clever as my darling sister.'

'It certainly looks as if you're working hard enough,' Marie said, nodding in the direction of the open textbook.

'Looks can be deceiving. If it wasn't for my parents paying for extra tuition, I'd be dead in the water.'

There wasn't anything Marie could say to make her feel any better except to direct the conversation down another avenue. 'I wish I'd worked harder at school but then I'd still have wanted to do the same sort of job.'

'What's so good about being a detective then?'

'Everything.' Marie smiled. 'Every day is different. I never know from one minute to the next what's going to crop up.'

'But does that mean you're going to be able to find Bry?'

Marie should have been expecting the question and the worst of it was she didn't know what to say, especially with the thought of Bryony's mother standing outside listening to every word. She didn't want to lie to the girl but she certainly wasn't prepared to tell her the truth. What was the truth anyway? It was all down to statistics. The majority of runaways turned up within the first twenty-four to forty-eight hours. She had no idea whether Bryony would be one of the lucky ones.

'I certainly hope so. We're doing everything we can,' Marie said, deciding to change the subject again. 'Electrical engineering sounds amazing. What's the coursework like? I'll just bet you're great at design and drawing? I did DT too but my portfolio was a mess.'

Cerys smirked. 'I'm heading for a 9.'

'Wow, that's the top grade, isn't it?'

'Can't get any higher.'

Marie dropped her gaze to her mobile, well aware that she was the focus of Cerys's stare but that couldn't be helped. She was playing a risky game. It all depended on how much Bryony had taken her sister into her confidence and whether or not Cerys was prepared to throw her big sister's trust under a bus.

'It must have taken a lot of thought for Bryony to run away?'

'In what way?'

'In every way. After all, she told your parents she was only going to spend the evening at a friend's house and it's not as if she had much room in her bag for more than a few items. If it was me, I'd have found it impossible to know what to bring and what to leave.' Marie lifted her head in time to catch a guilty blush storm Cerys's cheeks. With a quick glance at the door, she moved closer and lowered her voice. 'What about her electronics? Her mobile? Your dad couldn't remember whether she had it with her, which is unusual, don't you think? Who goes out without their phone these days?'

'She told me not to tell. She made me promise,' Cerys said, her voice a mere thread of sound. 'I promised faithfully.'

'And it's important to keep your promises but not when your sister is missing this long, Cerys. I'm also guessing that Bryony would have been in touch to let you know she was safe and not to worry? She's certainly bright enough to know how much hurt she'd be causing. A quick phone call, an email or even a letter would have done?'

'She promised she'd let me know.' Tears started tracking down Cerys's cheeks. 'She also promised she'd write to Mum and Dad,' she added, her voice rising almost to a shout, which brought her mother into the room like a flapping penguin ready for a fight.

'I heard raised voices.'

'It's all right, Mrs Lloyd, nothing to worry about. Cerys is upset as Bryony promised that she'd be in touch.'

'She knew . . . ?' Mrs Lloyd sank onto the edge on the bed, her face ashen.

'Don't be too hard on her,' Marie said, turning back to Cerys. 'I know it's hard for you but all your parents want is for your sister's safe return. Isn't that right, Mrs Lloyd?'

'Of course!' She watched the woman in front of her swallow what looked like a brick before finishing the sentence. 'Sweetheart, you tell the nice officer what you know.'

*

Marie slid into the driving seat, barely able to prevent herself from banging her head against the steering wheel. She had a hunch that Cerys knew far more than she was telling but all that had stopped with the arrival of her mother on the scene. Yes. They'd got the phone. That would have to be enough for now. She'd left the girl to the ministrations of her mother, still in floods of tears and full of remorse. But she had a job to do. To take Bryony's mobile and iPad back to the digital forensics team. Staying any longer would only delay that.

Picking up her own phone, she checked for messages, only to find that the stolen Nissan Micra had been discovered languishing in a parking place along Church Walks, a well-known area of Llandudno, situated close to the pier.

Instead of banging her head, she felt like screaming. Two important clues: one straight after the other.

Go Team Gaby!

# Chapter 15

Owen

**Tuesday 9 February, 3 p.m. Manchester**

Owen was a happily married man who would never do anything to put his marriage at risk. He'd been dating Kate since he was fifteen and he'd never looked at another woman since.

One glance at Caroline Maston changed all that. Tall, Amazonian even, with a head full of honey-blonde hair that fell in waves around her shoulders and with dark, sparkling eyes to match. She wasn't young, probably touching forty, but that in no way diminished her allure.

Owen swallowed, unsure of where to look and finally opting for his shoes. He knew he was being a coward but Dr Maston was a woman who knew what she wanted and wouldn't worry about who she had to trample on in the process. Not that he was worried. His marriage was sturdier than the Rock of Gibraltar, the addition of their two children forging their vows in steel. But he felt a sudden coldness in the pit of his stomach at the way she was studying Dr Mulholland. He didn't know the man well.

Certainly not well enough to know if Rusty would have the same strength of character. He could only hope.

DCI Webb gestured for everyone to join her at the oval table, tucked into the corner of the office. Owen swallowed again, trying to ignore the way Caroline manoeuvred the seating so that she was sitting next to Rusty.

'Right then,' DCI Webb said, after introducing everyone. 'I thought this would be an ideal opportunity to call a quick meeting, given the unusualness of the case. So far the Bournville Road property has thrown up an as yet unidentified skeleton buried in a shallow, flowerbed grave. We're hazarding a guess at the remains being Ansel Abalos, the owner, but we're waiting for forensics on that. There's also what we suspect are the remains of Jules White, who was found in the locked attic.'

'Forgive me if I seem obtuse,' Owen said, leaning back in his chair, 'but I'd like to hear more about why you think our cases might be linked before we go any further. To my mind, this one seems a little different.'

'I agree that on the face of it the disappearance of the three women isn't that similar. But when we examine the evidence and, in Jules's case, the end result, you'll forgive me for being nervous about your two missing women,' DCI Webb said, her hand flat against her pad of notes. 'My current thinking is that our murderer must have started his little killing spree down here in Manchester only to move to fresh ground when the threat of discovery became too great.' Her brow pulled into a frown. 'I don't know where the body of White comes into it. He must have decided, for whatever reason, to lock her up and leave nature to take its course. We'd have to find him first and ask him the whys and wherefores. I'm going to pass you over to Dr Maston, who's performed a preliminary examination, to explain her findings and the reason she asked for Dr Mulholland's input. Caroline?'

Caroline smiled, all snowy white teeth and an absence of any visible gums. Her words were short, abrupt even but not their impact. 'Jules was mummified.'

'What?' Owen started, trying to retain his jaw in its rightful position. 'I don't get you? Surely there'd be bandages and . . . and . . . ?'

'You're making the most common of mistakes, Owen,' Rusty said, glancing down at his impeccably clean fingernails. 'We're not talking about the use of chemicals here, as seen in Egypt in centuries past. Mummification simply means the preservation of a body. This can be undertaken via a variety of means, only one of which includes the subsequent wrapping of the body in bandages. It might make more sense if we term it desiccation, don't you think, Caro?' he added, staring across at Dr Maston.

'Not technically correct, Rusty,' she said, acknowledging his comment with a sharp nod. 'But perhaps easier under the circumstances.'

*Patronising cow* was what Owen thought. 'I see,' was what he said. 'So, my questions are – how, why and where? Oh, and what's your involvement in this, Rusty? I'll need it for my records.' That was a lie but he wanted to know in case Gaby asked.

'That's easy to answer. I was lucky enough to spend some time on a body farm in the USA, where they're doing some exciting work into the mummification of animals. Caro read a subsequent article I wrote on the subject.'

'You're underselling yourself again, Rusty,' she said, placing a proprietary hand on the sleeve of his jacket. 'Dr Mulholland is the top expert in the field of mummification, this side of the pond.'

Owen ignored her, his thought processes still mulling over what a body farm could be but not wanting to sound ignorant he made a mental note to google it after.

'To answer the rest of your questions,' Rusty continued, shifting slightly in his chair and thus dislodging Dr Maston's arm, 'it's impossible to know either why or where but there are some parameters that should help with the investigation. There's a set pattern to what happens to all bodies following death. The only way to prevent the process of putrefaction, which usually starts four hours following death, is to subject the body to intense heat. As to where that might have taken place . . .' He raised both hands before flopping them back against his thighs. 'There were no clothes found on the body to test so unless we can find the killer to ask, we're left with surmises and supposition. We will obviously know a lot more after the autopsy.'

'And the other body. What about him, or her?'

'Hardly a body, Detective,' Dr Maston said with a laugh. 'Not a scrap of muscle or flesh and no clothing fragments at all.'

'Which means?'

'Which means that unless he was lying outside long enough for his clothing to disintegrate then he was buried naked. The bones have certainly weathered but only superficially. The local insect population would have had a field day stripping them clean but the bones weren't exposed to the elements long enough to cause major damage.'

Owen set his jaw, trying to distance himself from thoughts of the two victims and what they must have gone through. He'd been involved with some pretty horrendous cases recently. This by far topped the lot. He cleared his throat, his mouth uncomfortably dry from all that swallowing. 'What you're saying is that we should be able to identify the skeleton with DNA and whatnot?'

'Exactly. I'll get the lab onto it straightaway. We'll also initiate a dental records search. There's a good chance we'll get his skeleton matched.'

'You said man? How can you be sure if there was no clothing and even if there was for that matter?'

'Yes. I'm not a forensic anthropologist by any means but there are ways and means to distinguish the sex apart from the obvious,' she said, tapping her forehead. 'The supraorbital ridge above the eye sockets for instance and the shape of the jawline. I might be proved wrong but I don't think so.'

*

Owen ambled towards his car, his head bowed against the icy wind, his turned-up collar doing little to prevent the cold air streaming down his neck. DCI Webb had given him lots to think about but no actual links to Christy and Bryony's disappearance. But, if she was right in thinking that all three cases were linked, then the likelihood of finding either of the girls alive was minimal. He didn't want to be around when that news was broken to their parents, something Gaby would have to consider sooner rather than later. Uncomfortable as the truth might be, the news would be far better given from the lips of one of their officers than seeing it blaring from the front pages.

'Bates, hold up.'

Owen stopped and, turning, was surprised to see Rusty running to catch him up, his key fob in his hand.

'I thought you'd be staying on for a bit?'

'Not on your Nelly, Owen. Caroline is more trouble than a whole choir full of Gabys,' he said, opening the door of the 4x4 and flinging his briefcase into the back. 'And, before you ask, we dated way back so I know what I'm talking about. She's a grand pathologist, one of the best, but as far as men are concerned, she's far less discerning and I'm not about to be anyone's leftovers.'

'Oh. I did wonder,' he said, changing the subject. 'I still have a few questions about the mummification, Dr—'

Rusty clapped him on the back. 'I thought you would but it's Rusty as you very well know, Owen.' He leant against the Range Rover, as if he didn't have a care in the world.

'I never did ask you your real name,' Owen said.

'Ha.' He chuckled, tucking the ends of his scarf firmly under his dark navy overcoat, his hands encased in black leather gloves. 'That's on a need-to-know basis and, apart from my parents, no one else needs to know.'

'Even Gaby?' Owen asked, feeling brave. He didn't quite feel brave enough to question Rusty's inferior parking skills but knowing the eminent pathologist's gift of the gab, he'd come up with some excuse or other.

'She's under strict instructions not to divulge it.' Rusty glanced up at the heavy yellow-tinged sky and the start of snowflakes beginning to land on the windscreen. 'Why don't we continue our chat over Bluetooth? The sooner we get back to St Asaph the better. Gaby will have my neck in a noose if I'm late,' he went on, his hand on the edge of the door. 'We're having Amy and Tim around for dinner later and she's already warned me to be home on time.'

Owen couldn't prevent a laugh from exploding. 'Rather you than me. She can be as tardy as she likes but if the team is even a couple of minutes late there's hell to pay.'

Rusty's mouth lifted into the parody of a smile. 'As long as it's not only me, Owen. As long as it's not only me.'

# Chapter 16

## Jax

### Tuesday 9 February, 3 p.m. Church Walks

Jax had been born in Llandudno and knew the area around the end of the pier better than anywhere else in the Victorian-styled town. He'd been raised on a council estate situated near the hospital and, with money tight, his parents had relied on the pier and a bag of two-pence pieces to play on shove ha'penny as an affordable treat for him and his siblings.

With his hands thrust deep into the pockets of his thick parka and his beanie pulled low against the biting wind, he hurried up Church Walks, pondering the reason why the car had been left where it had. In winter, Llandudno was the same as any other British seaside resort, dead except to the locals and those hardy individuals who preferred their enjoyment spiked with all the elements in the weather's toolkit. There must have been another means of transport awaiting unless they'd decided to hole up for the night.

The problem was that there was too little information for Jax to think his way around the issue. A missing woman and a stolen car spotted in the vicinity. A car that travelled the fifty-minute or so journey to Llandudno. Why? They might not have known about the CCTV but Jax thought that unlikely. It had the feel of a highly planned operation. A change in car would have been common sense. But why Llandudno? There had to be a reason.

He pulled his beanie further down his head to cover his ears, which were beginning to sting. Did cold numb the brain to the same extent as the rest of the extremities? He lengthened his stride to quicken his pace as he marched past Snooze Wine Bar and towards Lynton House, with its closed sign suspended from its front window. The only thing he could come up for the car being left in Llandudno was the possibility of Bryony and the driver of the car deciding to break their journey, which overturned any idea that she was snatched instead of leaving willingly. He frowned. None of that explained why they'd interrupted their getaway and therefore increased their risk of discovery.

Jax hunched deeper into his coat, seeking warmth where there was none to be found. Perhaps he was overthinking it. The way the snow was settling, if he didn't hurry up, he'd never get back to the station. He hovered outside the Empire hotel, unsure of whether to go in or walk on. His gut instinct was that the four-star spa hotel wasn't the place for a teenage runaway. The truth was he didn't have a clue whether they'd stopped off to change cars, stayed for the night or had holed up in one of the many houses in the area. Combine that with the fact that he was on his own with the weather closing in and he had a decision to make. Breaking their journey to stop at a hotel or guest house didn't make sense but at least he'd have a fair chance of checking out the more likely ones.

He went with his gut and hurried past the hotel.

Church Walks was deserted, everyone having more sense than to be wandering about on paths that were starting to feel decidedly slippery underfoot. The snow was at the slushy stage, a fine coating covering every surface like the counter in a clumsy baker's kitchen. It would only take one wrong move on his part and he'd be laid out with a sprain or even worse.

The Capri Guest House was a smart, cream building with black trim. But Jax was more interested in the vacancies sign in the window than in their paintwork, the first he'd seen on his short walk. He didn't question the sense in them staying open in what was building up to be a snowstorm or the reason why Bryony might have interrupted her journey. He pushed any such concerns to the back of his mind as he headed for the front door, his warrant card in his hand, an easy smile stamped on his lips. Members of the public were a contrary lot. One false move and he'd be forced to obtain a search warrant, which would only add to the delay. A charm offensive was called for – not Jax's specialty but Mal was providing lessons.

'Hello, I'm trying to find a runaway,' he said, pulling out his warrant card.

'Happy to help any way we can.' Mrs Donavan was an attractive middle-aged woman with a ready smile and a willingness to help.

The register was an old-fashioned brown ledger, a throwback from the previous century. The couple had paid in cash so the entry was the only record of their short stay. A Mr and Mrs Jones, Lichen Cottage, Mold, which made a strange sort of irony. Jax pulled out his phone and took a photo before placing a call to the CSIs back at the station.

There was nothing else. No CCTV in the immediate vicinity, nothing to tie the couple to either the guest house or the area, apart from the deserted car. The room had already been cleaned so it was unlikely that Jason and his team would find anything but that wouldn't stop them from trying. It only took one clue to solve a case, something that had been drummed into him from the first day of walking through the door of the station as a raw eighteen-year-old recruit trying to find out about a career in policing.

'I'm afraid you and your husband will have to come down to the station, Mrs Donovan. We need to get an e-fit photo out there as soon as.'

'One of those drawing experts like on that telly programme, *Line of Duty*?' she replied, her bright eyes scrunching up to match the expression of delight on her face.

Jax's smile froze. Everyone was a sofa specialist these days. If he was being honest, it probably made his job easier but only if he had the time or the inclination to immerse himself in cops and robber shows after a long day spent catching criminals. He much preferred watching baking programmes.

'Not quite but near enough.'

# Chapter 17

Gaby

**Tuesday 9 February, 5 p.m. St Asaph**

'What are you doing back so early? I thought you were on nights again?' Gaby said, eying Mal from behind the security of her laptop where she'd been catching up on the report that Sherlock had demanded before she left for the evening.

'I wasn't up to much so I thought I might as well come in a bit early.' He stripped off his leather gloves and removed his full-length coat. 'God, what a filthy evening,' he said, blowing into his hands. 'Any news on the girl?'

'Lots but nothing of any significance.' She scanned the document one last time for any typos before pressing send and backing her chair away from the desk. 'The others should be back in a minute,' she said, glancing at her watch. 'We said we'd aim for a quick catch-up. It's lucky you'll be here.'

She watched Malachy as he rearranged the top of his desk to his liking, shifting his pen pot an inch to the right and placing his mobile just so. The differences between the desks always amused her. Marie's was a tip, with chocolate wrappers scattered over the top. Jax must have rushed out in a hurry, leaving his awash with papers, which was all very well except for their clear-desk policy. If he didn't arrive back soon, she'd have to clear his desk for him or risk the cleaners filing a complaint with the desk sergeant. It wouldn't be the first time.

'You have a lift home?' Mal said, interrupting her musings.

'I take it that's a reference to the shit weather and not my driving, DC Devine?' she said, with a raise of her left eyebrow.

'As if I'd have the nerve, ma'am. Only concerned for your welfare in that death trap you call a car; known to the rest of us as "scrapheap".'

Gaby had the exact same thoughts about her far-from-trusty runabout but refused to confirm it to anyone else, least of all herself. She knew she needed a new car. She'd needed a new car two years ago but there was always a greater demand for her money.

'For your information, Mal, Dr Mulholland is driving me home in the luxury of his 4x4.'

'Always a good plan to choose a boyfriend with a four-wheel drive, ma'am,' he replied, without a trace of a smile.

'And one of the only reasons she agreed to go out with me in the first place,' Rusty said, strolling through the door with a broad grin.

'Bloody hell. I'm outmanned two to one and by a bunch of *Top Gear* enthusiasts too.' Gaby slapped her hand to her forehead, very much in the vein of a black and white movie starlet.

'Hah, you just wait,' Owen said, following Rusty into the room and heading over to his usual spot by the window. 'I can see a five-door saloon in the wings as soon as the nippers start, Rusty.'

'Hah, yourself. I've been there and done that. The 4x4 stays,' Rusty said.

There was an awkward silence, which thankfully Owen chose to break because Gaby certainly couldn't think up the cocky, smart-mouthed reply that was called for. Her thoughts were as barren as her mind and, quite possibly, her body if Rusty had his way. With one, off-the-cuff comment Rusty had changed the whole course of their relationship. Her chin hardened along with her resolve. Only if she let him.

By the time Jax and Marie had joined them she'd managed to pull herself together. The only giveaway was the way her gaze lingered on Rusty and Owen, who were chatting by the window like a pair of reunited long-lost buddies. Part of her wanted to know what they were talking about. The other part knew that it was none of her business. The likelihood was that it had nothing to do with her or the investigation. That afforded her no respite from her thoughts.

'We'll start with Owen and the bodies found over in Manchester.'

'I thought you might,' he said, his voice resigned. 'As we already know, DCI Webb has a similar case on her books. The disappearance of a girl eighteen months ago, under what they now believe is a similar set of circumstances.' He braced his shoulders. 'However, in Jules's case they've also found a body – actually, two bodies.' He raised his hand to his beard. 'I think it would be best if Dr Mulholland explains the rest.'

Gaby switched her attention between the two men, a bunch of wrinkles making a statement about the face cream she was always forgetting to apply. She was happy that her boyfriend and her second-in-command seemed to be getting on so well but there was more to it than that. There was something about Owen's body language that had the hair on the back of her neck standing to attention. Gaby was a bit of an expert when it came to the art of nonverbal communication. Her many books on the subject were testament to that fact. But she didn't need to be an expert to notice the way Owen had flicked her a look before dropping his gaze to study his brown suede loafers. She wasn't worried, far from it. More like annoyed but also far too busy to do anything with the feeling other than to stuff it into a drawer at the back of her mind. There was a time and a place to puzzle it out. Now wasn't it.

'Manchester is a bit out of your stomping ground, I would have thought, Doctor?'

'Ah, yes. Under a normal set of circumstances I'd have to agree but there's nothing normal about this young woman's death.' He joined her in front of the whiteboards, his fingers hooked around the belt of his black jeans, his gaze entrenched somewhere in the distance. 'The field of forensic pathology is small enough for all of us to know what the other is doing. And if and when we come up with anything unusual, we like to share it with our colleagues, either at seminars or writing for publications.' He lifted his head, his face expressionless. 'A skeleton dug up in the garden is one thing, Jules's body something else entirely and the reason why I was brought in. The cause of her death is yet to be established; however, post-mortem, her body was stored at such a high temperature as to cause mummification.'

There was a collective gasp from the room but he continued regardless. 'To clarify, mummification means the preservation of tissue by the introduction of an intense, dry heat. We'll know more when Dr Maston has performed the autopsy.'

'The poor girl's parents.' She turned to Owen. 'What do we know about her?' Gaby reached for the first marker pen to hand and scribbled down Jules's details on the third whiteboard. Her name. Her age. She left out the part about the mummification and for good reason.

'When the media gets to hear about this there'll be hell to pay.' She recapped the marker and turned back to the room, deep in thought.

'Especially if they manage to link the three cases together,' Marie said, brushing her fringe out of her eyes with the back of her hand. 'I'm not sure what the policy is in situations like this?'

'Let's leave that for now,' Gaby said, simply because she didn't have an answer at present with their current workload. 'There's no way that she could have died from natural causes I suppose?' she added, thinking out loud.

'A little too convenient, although not out of the realms of possibility. However, it doesn't change that she was moved after death, which defeats your theory somewhat.' Rusty pulled out his mobile and checked his screen for messages before returning it to his pocket. 'Mummification does have some advantages though.'

'Not from where I'm standing it doesn't. I can't think of anything worse,' Gaby said, pulling a face. 'Give me a nice hot cremator any day.'

'I'll make a note, shall I?'

Instead of answering, she turned back to the whiteboard and changed the subject. After his comment about his beloved car, she wasn't sure if they'd be dating next week let alone heading for the type of relationship where such conversations featured. Six months as a couple allowed for certain liberties – none of which included discussions on funeral arrangements.

'So, how is mummification advantageous?' she said, ignoring his scowl. It seemed as if they had a long-overdue conversation waiting in the wings of their relationship. It would have been nice if he'd warned her about what was coming before and not after she'd allowed him into her home as well as her heart. Her muscles tensed at the thought.

Gaby didn't like trouble and tended to deflect awkward situations with witty banter – at least she viewed it as witty. How others viewed it wasn't her problem. But Rusty couldn't be managed that way. He couldn't be managed at all and that was part of the problem. Two strong-willed people in the same relationship was always going to end in an explosion of fireworks. As yet they'd both been on their best behaviour but she had a funny feeling that the time had passed for the velvet glove treatment. Gaby had been put in a corner and, like all animals in a threatened position, she had two choices. Claws or retreat. She'd never retreated from anything in her life and she wasn't about to start now. Part of her felt sorry for him but it was only a very small part. Her life. Her rules.

'It's a way of preserving tissue without the messy leakages, odours and insect activity that one would normally expect from a body undergoing the usual processes around putrefaction,' he finally said, back in his stride. 'In comparison, a body that's been buried for a year will present as little more than a skeleton, which results in all that layer of fleshy information lost to the crime team.'

'Charming. So it's likely that we'll have a cause of death pretty soon?'

'If there's one to be found,' he said, again checking his mobile. 'Caroline promised to call as soon as she had something useful.'

Gaby inclined her head in acknowledgement before shifting onto Jax. 'What about you? How did your little excursion to Llandudno go?'

'Actually better than expected, ma'am, all things considered. I managed to find where Bryony stayed and, as we suspected, she had a man in tow. They checked into the Capri Guest House late last night and left first thing, probably knowing full well that it would take us a bit longer to follow their tracks.' He glanced down at his phone briefly. 'I have the owner, a Mrs Donovan, upstairs with Jason and the team looking through albums of known perps and trying to make an e-fit. The bad news is there's no CCTV along that stretch of road. There is along the Prom and Mostyn Street but it doesn't stretch as far as the tributary streets, more's the pity. The man also paid in cash so . . .'

'So no clues there,' Gaby said, finishing his sentence for him. 'There's a surprise. But well done all the same. I take it that the CSIs are tearing the place apart as we speak?'

'Of course,' he replied, sounding offended.

'I didn't expect anything less.' She added a note about the guest house to the second whiteboard. 'So Bryony is picked up in Mold only to be driven the fifty or so minutes to Llandudno. Why?'

The room went quiet.

'Well there must be a reason. What about food? Did the guest house feed them, Jax?'

'Nothing mentioned but I can easily check,' he said, picking up his mobile and starting a new message.

Gaby turned to Marie. 'How was everything over at Moss Cottage?'

'As expected, ma'am, that is after I got over my surprise at finding a mansion instead of the piddly little cottage I'd been expecting. Tempers were frayed but all in all a pair of very concerned parents. The sister came up trumps though,' Marie said, toying with the thin gold bracelet on her wrist. 'She didn't have any info as such, only a promise from Bryony to contact her as soon as she'd arrived at her destination. The icing on the cake is that she left her sister in charge of her mobile and iPad, which are currently upstairs being unlocked and analysed. I asked them to pull their finger out but it's going to take most of the night apparently. Something to do with encrypted files but you know what I'm like when they go all techie on me.'

Gaby returned the marker to the shelf under the whiteboard, a thin smile in place. 'So basically we wait. Frustrating but it is what it is,' she said, glancing at the wall clock.

'Not quite,' Jax interrupted, staring down at his mobile. 'Mrs Donovan didn't feed them – she didn't have to. They'd already eaten.'

'Bingo. A name and address of the establishment would be useful?' Gaby wiggled her eyebrows at him.

'Afraid not.'

'Shame. Another job to add to the list but at least it's something! Right then. Off you all hop. Mal will keep the home fires burning and alert me of any news, won't you, Mal? The rest of you might as well try and enjoy what's left of your evening. The Met Office predicts two inches of the white stuff overnight so drive safely.'

# Chapter 18

## Gaby

### Tuesday 9 February, 6.50 p.m. Rhos-on-Sea

Gaby was well versed in Rusty's moods and it didn't take a genius to realise that his current frame of mind required careful handling. She wasn't in the best of humour herself and regretted that they'd invited Amy and Tim over for supper. But it had made sense to proffer the invitation when Amy had finally succumbed to the temptation of maternity leave. With their baby due in less than a month, it was going to be one of the last occasions when they could all get together before the birth.

The journey home was peppered with conversation about the case. There was no move on either side to discuss anything personal, which was just as well. Gaby was like a pot left to simmer on the stove too long, her disappointment having turned into something akin to anger. There would come a time to talk and soon but they both appeared to be in silent agreement to leave serious conversation until after their friends had departed home. To say that Gaby couldn't wait was wrong on all levels.

Supper was an Italian baked pasta. Gaby had prepared it the

evening before so all that was needed was for her to throw together her signature beetroot houmous and polish the glasses. She didn't worry about Conor, Rusty's son. Early on in their relationship she'd appreciated that it was going to take more than kindness – and a realisation that she wasn't out to steal his father out from under his nose – for him to accept her. Therefore an unwritten rule had crept into their little household of three. Rusty continued to take on the majority of the parenting duties while she took reluctant control of the ironing simply because she'd learnt the hard way that her work shirts weren't safe with the heavy-handed pathologist. By mutual consent, they shared both the cleaning and the cooking. It worked up to a point.

They all lived together in Gaby's two-bedroomed cottage, but with no room for a separate study, it was all a bit cramped and claustrophobic especially with the cooler evenings and little chance to escape to the summer house unless she was desperate – the way things were going, she was considering the possibility of buying a heater and perhaps a cheap desk and chair as an alternative to working on her lap while Rusty hogged the kitchen table and Conor holed up in his room. She didn't know how much work the lad managed to do in his bedroom; by the sounds coming from his games console, not much. But it wasn't her problem, something she had to remind herself umpteen times a day – in fact, every time she went upstairs and heard the loud crashes and bangs filtering through the gaps in the woodwork. The cottage was old and built from Welsh granite but it would have to be layered in thick soundproofing foam to dim the noise to a respectable decibel level.

'Cup of tea?' she said, wandering into the kitchen after slipping off her shoes and coat in the narrow hall and placing her laptop bag in the corner of the lounge.

'That would be lovely. I'll head up and check on Conor. Do you mind if I have the first shower? I'll promise to be quick.'

'Fire away. I'll pop your mug up to you when it's ready,' she replied, taking out a packet of vacuum-packed beetroot from the fridge and a can of chickpeas from the cupboard while she waited for the kettle to boil.

They were being so formal she could scream. Her fingers curled into her palms, forming deep crescents, to prevent the scream from escaping in a cacophony of noise. She should have guessed that it had been going too well. He wasn't perfect, far from it, but then neither was she. All she was asking for was someone to share both the highs and the lows but not at the expense of having her own family. Never that.

She removed a couple of mugs from the shelf above the worktop and made the drinks before heading to the stairs in the hope that he wouldn't use all of the hot water. Walking into the bedroom, she managed the glimmer of a smile at the sound of his baritone voice ringing out through the open door of the small, en-suite shower room. Rusty had a lovely voice and was far better at keeping a tune than almost anyone she'd ever met. She placed his mug on the small dressing table under the window and turned to go only to pause at the sound of his mobile.

'That will be Caroline with the autopsy results.' Rusty walked out of the shower with a towel wrapped around his waist and picked up his phone, nodding at the sight of the number. 'Wait up a mo. You might as well hear what she has to say,' he added, switching it to loudspeaker.

'Hello, Rusty darling, it was lovely to see you again. We'll have to meet up for a little drinky-poos to celebrate our reunion sometime soon.'

Gaby sent him a look, which was laden with a message he couldn't fail to interpret before she hurried out of the room and back down the stairs.

If Gaby had been upset before, now she was livid. It was there in the way she carefully closed the lounge door instead of slamming it, which was what she felt like doing. She walked into the kitchen and poured her mug of untouched tea down the sink.

There was a time for tea. This wasn't it. She reached for the cork-screw and attacked the bottle of red with more energy than the tender 2017 Barolo deserved. For Gaby, alcohol in large volumes was anathema unless she was with a crowd of friends. Even then she couldn't remember the last time she'd partied into the small hours with her glass set to fast refill.

Alcohol in large volumes was also bad news. She'd certainly never been tempted to drink more than a glass of wine on a work night, with or without Rusty. Now she didn't care. The only thing stopping her from swallowing the lot in one greedy gulp was the mellow flavour of the Barolo assaulting her tongue with its liquid grace. A wine to be sipped and not chugged despite the temptation to throw it down her neck, consequences be damned.

The chickpeas and beetroot didn't get the treatment they deserved. Instead of the carefully measured spices, she threw in a bit of this and a bit of that, whizzing it up in her small mixer and hoping for the best.

'Hey. You disappeared before Caro had a chance to tell me that she won't have the autopsy results until tomorrow. There was a double shooting in Manchester earlier so she's had to push it back,' Rusty said from the door, making her jump. 'I'll have to have a word with her,' he continued, his voice taking on a rough edge. 'She's not very good at remembering boundaries.'

Gaby lifted her head and watched as the colour stormed up his face. Rusty didn't blush. She didn't think he knew how. The next question slipped out of its own accord but she couldn't have stopped it even if she'd wanted to. She didn't.

'Have you slept with her?'

'Have I . . . ? No, of course not!' The blush deepened but the words were too quick, too sharp a denial. The truth was out there despite his denial. She hadn't been worried before. Now all she felt was a gut-wrenching sadness.

The silence lengthened, the only sound coming from the pulse drumming in her ears. He was obviously waiting for her to comment but the one thing she was unable to do right now was speak. She knew if she opened her mouth she'd never be able to pull back the words marching around the back of her tongue. The sense of disappointment and, yes, disloyalty was striving for freedom along with a tsunami of tears – tears she was determined not to shed.

Gaby had known from the very start that their relationship had felt almost too good to be true. It wasn't love at first sight – far from it. They couldn't stand each other at the beginning. When they finally did get together, she couldn't be sure which one of them had been the most surprised. Their lives were so busy, with the added difficulty of Conor. She hadn't appreciated until just now how much Rusty had crept through her ribs and infiltrated both her life and her heart. But the one thing she wasn't prepared to do was share him. It was bad enough having to pussyfoot around his son. She wasn't about to make more allowances than she was already. Kids aside, this Dr Maston was welcome to him, dirty socks and all.

Instead of replying, she wasted precious moments covering the bowl of hummus with a tea towel and planting a smile of sorts on her mouth before turning to face him. She'd never been a coward and she wasn't about to start now. Her life might be falling around her head in a shitstorm of unwanted sideswipes but there were worse things, she remembered, her thoughts turning to the Lloyds and what they must be going through.

'Good to know. I've had a shit day and, just for once, I'd like to relax with my friends and not have to think about work or . . . other things,' she managed, avoiding looking at him as she squeezed her way through the narrow gap he'd left, her glass in her hand. 'I still have to grab a shower, and Amy and Tim will be here any minute, if you don't mind setting out the drinks.'

# Chapter 19

## Gaby

### Tuesday 9 February, 9.30 p.m. Rhos-on-Sea

'There's hardly room for the baby after that lot. I'm absolutely stuffed,' Amy said, resting her hand on her stomach.

'You hardly ate anything.' Gaby started collecting the plates. 'There's strawberry pavlova – nothing exciting, only shop-bought. Rusty, if you wouldn't mind giving Conor a shout for pudding,' she added, heading into the kitchen.

'Just for the boys, Gabs.' Amy heaved to her feet and followed her. 'Decaf coffee if you have any?'

'Coming right up, lovey.'

Gaby added water to the coffee maker while Amy sliced the pavlova. 'That was the best evening I've had in ages. I know you won't agree, but you really are the most marvellous cook.'

'You should see the food my mother serves up in the restaurant. Puts my paltry efforts to shame, but thank you all the same. I don't get enough compliments not to lap them up with a spoon whenever they come my way.' Gaby leant against the worktop and watched as Amy slid enormous slices of pavlova onto the china plates she'd set out earlier. 'The boys are going to love you.'

'The way to a man's heart and all that.' Amy laid the knife down and, lifting her head, met Gaby's eye. 'You don't look happy, Gabs. I do so want you to be as happy as I am.'

Gaby didn't know what to say. She certainly wasn't prepared to tell her best friend the truth. A partner who had decided, with no consultation whatsoever, that he didn't want any more kids. Right now, that was minor in comparison to the phone call. Was it a coincidence that this Caroline Maston had phoned or was it his way of letting her know their relationship was reaching saturation point?

She'd tried to enjoy the meal. What was it her mother called it? Putting on a brave face. That was it. But she obviously wasn't as good an actress as she'd thought, if Amy was able to see through the cracks. The problem was, they weren't cracks – more like craters.

'You spotted that, eh? It's been a long day and, yes, you've probably guessed that we've had words but nothing we won't be ironing out later,' Gaby said, sticking to the fairy-tale version of her relationship that she knew Amy would accept.

'Oh good. I was hoping it was something like that. You two are made for each other.' Amy rubbed her lower back. 'Lara is sitting right on my kidney at the moment. The sooner my daughter arrives the sooner we can get back to some kind of normality.'

'I don't think you quite know what having a child is going to do to your . . .' Gaby started to say, only to stop mid-sentence, a huge smile breaking. 'Lara Dunne. What a beautiful name.'

'I know but, shush. I'm not meant to have told you.'

'Mum's the word.' Gaby lifted her hand to her mouth, twisting her thumb and forefinger forward, sealing her lips. 'I can't wait to meet the little darling.'

'You and me both.' Amy beamed. 'If only this backache would go and take the indigestion I'm expecting later with it, I'd be the happiest person in the world right now.'

# Chapter 20

Gaby

**Wednesday 10 February, 6 a.m. Rhos-on-Sea**

Gaby couldn't sleep. She lay there for hours, silently seething at the sound and feel of Rusty. The odd sighing breath. The occasional grunt. The touch of his leg when he rolled over onto his side. Every particle was as irritating as a random bit of grit in her shoe. But instead of getting out of bed and heading for the sofa, she decided to stay for no other reason than it was her bed. Her room. Her house. If anyone was going to leave it should be him.

The free-flowing wine earlier didn't help, the glass of water by her side unable to assuage even part of her growing thirst.

So, she lay there, snippets of the conversation over dinner running through her mind. The last nightcap that Rusty had offered, very much in the vein of a peace offering and one she'd refused. After that sneaky glass of wine, she'd hit the brakes on her drinking, the tempting full bottle turning into three glasses spread over the course of the evening. Any more and she'd have been tempted to speak her mind: speaking her mind was a habit she'd picked up in childhood and had never managed to shake.

If she told him what she was thinking it would be over. Game, set and match to Rusty.

Much to Gaby's dismay, most of last night's conversation had revolved around children, firstly the baby and then Rusty's son. While it made perfect sense, it also meant that she was left out of huge chunks of chat, very much in the manner of an observer. She wasn't a parent and, if Rusty had his way, she wasn't going to be. That hurt as much if not more than her suspicions about Rusty and his relationship with Caroline Maston. She could manage revelations about another woman – if Rusty was so easily swayed then good luck to him as far as she was concerned, but as for the rest . . . She had no defence for an unknown child she wasn't even sure she was ready for.

No, that wasn't true. She wanted children, even more so now that she saw how happy Amy and Tim were.

Gaby turned onto her stomach, burying her head into her arms and shifting her foot away from where Rusty was invading her space. He'd wanted to speak while they'd set about clearing the table and filling the dishwasher. It was there in the way he'd tried to catch her eye at almost every turn. She hadn't let him. Not even a single word. Instead she'd placed the tea towel carefully on the metal bar of the oven and walked to the stairs, a glass of water clutched in her hand.

'I'm tired, Rusty. We can talk in the morning,' she said, leaving no room for misinterpretation.

Gaby didn't know if this was a blip or a full breakdown in their relationship. The only certainty was that it hurt like hell.

\*

If leaving for the office at ten to seven was running away then that's what she was doing. But after a night of no sleep and a headache that was starting to bite, she wasn't in the mood for a civilised chat. Rusty was a heavy sleeper and a slave to his seven o'clock Alexa wake-up call. She was determined not to feel guilty at using that knowledge to her own advantage. Instead she switched on the local radio station as soon as she reversed out of the drive. As a method of distraction it didn't work. But at least she was up to speed on the public view of the case.

She knew it was cowardly to run away but she also knew that she had some serious thinking to do before she was ready to finish the conversation Rusty had started about their future. With the way the case was panning out, she had far too many other responsibilities to do more than tuck her personal problems out of sight. Her biggest worry was how to behave around Rusty until she'd had the time to work out what she wanted.

'Am I pleased to see you! I was just about to phone.'

Gaby shook off her padded jacket and hung it on the hook behind the door before heading for the coffee pot and reaching for a mug.

'I take it you've had a busy night, Mal? Do you fancy a top-up?' She lifted up the jug and waved it in the air.

'I'd love one but I'd better not. I've had more than my fair share as it is.'

Gaby cradled the mug between her fingers as she leant against the radiator.

'What couldn't wait then?' she said, eying his undone top button and loosened tie with an impartial expression. He looked a little tired around the edges but nothing compared to the hag-like reflection that had greeted her when she'd brushed her teeth earlier.

'I had a call from the station over at Penygroes. There was a rescue overnight for a couple of missing walkers lost on Snowdonia.' He cleared his throat before managing to raise his head and meet her gaze.

And with that look, Gaby knew it was going to be bad. Malachy Devine was hardcore. If he had a sensitive bone in his body, she had yet to find it. Something had happened on Snowdon, Wales's largest mountain range. Her mouth went dry at the growing list of possibilities colour-washing her thoughts.

'Why didn't you phone earlier, Mal? I would have come in to help.'

'I phoned Owen instead.' He had the grace to blush. 'He said not to bother you, being as you were meeting up with Amy.'

'Did he now? Okay, carry on.'

'The team were on their way back to their base after receiving news that the couple had turned up unscathed. They were halfway down Rhyd Ddu, one of the paths that scar the area, when they literally stumbled across a young woman half buried in the snow.'

'Dead?'

'Not quite but it's touch and go. If it hadn't been for one of the crew literally tripping over her, she'd still be there now. They managed to mobilise a helicopter from Caernarfon and take her to St Asaph.'

'Surely there's a nearer hospital?' Gaby frowned.

'But not with St Asaph's trauma unit. When the police over at Penygroes realised the significance of the woman's identity, they called it in straightaway. I've sent Jason a text to assemble a team of CSIs.'

Gaby swallowed the bile gathering in the back of her throat, her mouth full of the taste of stale wine and garlic. Her poor parents, was her first thought. A determination to catch the bastard, her second. There was more, much more. She could see it in the way he'd started playing with his earring. He was probably waiting for her to speak before he launched into the rest of the story. 'Poor Bryony.'

'Bryony?' Mal shook his head. 'Sorry, ma'am. I should have been more specific. It's not Bryony. It's Christy. That's the reason I phoned DC Bates first. You know. As he's heading up that part of the investigation.'

Gaby stared across the room at him, her mouth slightly open in surprise.

'Okay, I'm not sure what to make of that. How did they know it was her?'

'She had no identification on her but she matches the description exactly, right down to the mole at the side of her bottom lip.'

'I take it her parents are aware that she's been found?'

'I've already sent a car to their address.' He hesitated. 'I hope that's all right, ma'am? I didn't think it was fair to inform them by phone.'

'You did exactly the right thing, Mal. Well done,' Gaby said, reaching for her mobile. 'Get a four-wheel drive organised would you, please? I nearly lost all of my nine lives on the way over. Where is Owen?'

'On his way. He should be here shortly. There is more . . .'

'In a minute. I just need to make a quick call.'

Gaby tapped her fingernails against the top of the desk while she waited for the DCI to pick up.

'Sherlock.'

'Sorry for disturbing you, sir.'

'This had better be good, Darin.'

Gaby dry-swallowed, well aware that a mole wasn't the best of identifiers. A nice tattoo or even better, a dental match accompanied by a full DNA profile. God help Owen and Mal if they'd made the wrong call but it wouldn't be their necks on the chopping block. Her team. Her responsibility. But with a missing girl to find, one already dead and one hanging on by that proverbial thread, there was no time to waste on such incidentals.

She started to speak.

# Chapter 21

## Gaby

**Wednesday 10 February, 8 a.m. St Asaph Hospital**

'Will she make it?' Gaby asked, staring through the glass window at Christy, her parents on either side of her bed. She felt as if she was intruding. She probably was.

Gaby had rushed over to the hospital as soon as she'd heard the news. She couldn't believe that the girl was still alive. Neither could anyone else.

'That she has up to now is pretty much a miracle, suitable for the medical journals. It's only the quick action of the team leader performing CPR on the roadside and on someone with no visible signs of life that we are where we are,' the doctor said, running the rubber tubing of his stethoscope through his fingers. 'She had no pulse or blood pressure . . . We're in the realms of voodoo dolls and witch doctors,' he added on a laugh.

Gaby didn't find it amusing.

'And why is she? Alive, that is?'

He shrugged his broad shoulders. 'Your guess is as good as mine. She's a very lucky woman taking into consideration the amount of blood loss she sustained from her wounds. But the freezing conditions came to her aid, constricting her blood vessels, which stopped the bleeding while at the same time lowering her temperature sufficiently to preserve her core functions. Is that all?' he ended abruptly, stuffing his stethoscope fully into his pocket and rocking on his heels.

'Yes. Sorry. Of course. Just one more question. When can we speak to her?'

'That's not something I can answer at this stage. She's stable at the moment but by no means out of the woods. We've had to put her on life support and, as yet, we have no idea what the effect of all of this will be on her brain function.'

'So, what you're saying is she might never be able to answer our questions?' It was Gaby's turn to shake her head, her gaze resting briefly on Christy's lifeless form underneath the pristine white sheet, her face barely visible under the machinery that was keeping her alive. 'Her poor parents.' The only phrase she seemed to be able to come up with currently.

He paused, sending her a searing glance, which swallowed her whole. It left her in no doubt as to his low opinion of her. Gaby had no idea why.

'I'd say more "poor Christy".' With that he turned on his heel, leaving Gaby to watch him, a look of surprise on her face.

# Chapter 22

## Gaby

**Wednesday 10 February, 10.30 a.m.**
**Rhyd Ddu Path, Snowdonia**

Gaby wasn't a great one for sport. In fact, she'd go so far as to say she was allergic to anything more energetic than a walk on the beach followed by a nice cup of tea and a slice of cake at one of the cafés found in and around Rhos-on-Sea. The thought that someone would walk up Snowdon for fun, and in the inclement weather they were currently having to deal with, was as foreign to her as the rowing machine that Rusty had set up in the corner of their bedroom.

She also wasn't a great one for cold weather and couldn't understand why someone would consider venturing out in the depths of winter to climb a mountain that would still be there in summer. Flippant answers like 'because it was there' did nothing for either her mood or her inclination to join them in their choice of leisurely pursuits.

The snow had stopped in the small hours, leaving a trail of devastation in its wake. The journey across North Wales was treacherous and she was pleased she'd co-opted Owen to drive. There'd been an accident on the A55 at the Bodelwyddan junction, which meant they'd had to take an alternative route of interweaving minor roads, in some instances roads too narrow for two cars to pass safely. Snowmen were in abundance but Gaby had too many other things on her mind to spare them more than a passing smile. Owen was quiet, which suited her mood. A grisly murder. A missing girl. A mummified body. And yet all she could think about was Rusty.

'There. Up ahead, Owen,' Gaby said after twenty minutes of silence.

'I'm not blind, last time I checked,' Owen grunted, his usual black humour raising its ugly head. 'The tent might be white but it's not bloody hard to miss being as it's surrounded by what looks like half of the local police force in addition to a gaggle of CSIs milling around like ghosts on parade.'

'Ha bloody ha. I know you've probably been up half the night with one of the kids but that's no reason for sarcasm.'

'There's always a good reason for sarcasm,' Owen replied, shifting the car into neutral and making sure the handbrake was pulled into place. 'Come on, let's get this show on the road so I can get back to the station and defrost.' And with that he hopped out of the car.

Gaby watched him walking to the policeman at the entrance of the tent, whose job it was to preserve the crime scene from nosy parkers and the like. Not that he had to worry, Gaby thought, as she dragged her padded jacket firmly in place before removing her gloves from her pocket and slipping them over her hands. Apart from the crew the area was deserted and, with snow forecast for later, likely to stay that way.

'What have you got for us?' Gaby joined Owen and Jason just inside the tent. There wasn't a lot to see apart from the ground swathed in tarpaulin.

'Outside of a challenging crime scene that we're trying to

preserve? With the threat of more snow later I'm not promising anything,' Jason said with a snap. 'The Llanberis Mountain Rescue Team did their best when they realised the significance of what they'd found but there was only so much they could do with the resources they had available. They managed to protect as much of the evidence as they could, which is the only reason we're in such a good position now.'

'You can only do what you can, Jase,' Gaby replied. 'Is there anything at all of any use?'

'Apart from a few footsteps, which look to be from the same type of shoe she was wearing, it's primarily blood and lots of it – enough to turn the snow pink. We'll know more when we get it back to the lab for processing,' he said, adjusting his hood from where it was digging into his cheek. 'I've also sent a team up to the cottage,' he added, pointing in the direction of a stone-built building about half a mile in the distance. 'We think she must have walked as far as the road only to collapse, but that's a guess based on the blood we found on the gate and then inside the porch.'

Gaby nodded her appreciation of the difficulties the CSIs were facing. There was nothing she could do to speed things up but, the stark truth was, they were in a race against time to find Bryony before something similar happened.

'Thank you. We'll take a quick look,' she said, smiling at the policeman on her way past.

'You can take my arm if you like,' Owen said with a smirk, his attention on her flat-heeled pumps.

'My knight in shining armour.'

'Hardly. I'm only doing it in case you end up flat on your back with a broken something or other, leaving me to speak to the media.'

'As if I'll get a word in edgeways. You know what a showman Sherlock is, just as you know I hate all the palaver surrounding press conferences. But it's also a necessary evil. If we get only one response from the public as to Bryony's whereabouts then it will be more than worth it. Have you thought any more about continuing with your next lot of exams by the way?' she asked, narrowly avoiding a spot of black ice halfway up the path. 'Sherlock was asking me only last week what your plans are.'

'Kate thinks I should.' He tightened his hold on her arm. 'But I'm not so keen although the money would be helpful. We'd like another bedroom, but with four mouths to feed . . .'

'I know that feeling. Conor eats us out of house and home.'

What Gaby didn't say was that she'd recently discussed with Rusty the possibility of pooling their resources and moving from her cottage into something larger and more family-friendly. While she loved her little slice of Rhos-on-Sea, the cottage was far too small for the three of them. She disguised a grimace with a cough, annoyed that she'd once more allowed Rusty to infiltrate the crime scene. She wouldn't let it happen again.

Treasure Cottage was perfect, apart from the location, which was a bit too isolated for Gaby's liking but each to their own. After donning a pair of overshoes at the door along with a pair of rubber gloves, she entered the hall, which led directly into a small lounge with an open fireplace and a brown leather, three-piece settee suite.

'In here, Gaby,' Owen said, sticking his nose out of the room next door.

'In here' was the bedroom, the bed bare of linen, the large brown stain in the centre of the mattress difficult to ignore. Gaby stepped around one of the CSIs who was photographing the scene, to join Owen at the end of the bed.

'That's a lot of blood,' she said, unable to tear her eyes away from the stain. Blood had always been her nemesis. The cloying smell still lingered despite the overwhelming odour of bleach.

'You and your understatements, Gaby. It looks as if someone has been slaughtered only for the killer to clean up with a bucketful of sodium hypochlorite. As we all know, bleach does a good job of denaturing DNA. But that's not all.' Owen lifted up

108

a specimen bag and held it up, his gaze flickering to hers before shifting away. 'The place has been emptied, presumably by the same person with the heavy hand in bleach. The team found this crisp packet wedged behind the back of the bedside table but that's it as far as evidence goes.'

Gaby's mobile jerked into action, a welcome interruption from thoughts of all that blood until she saw who it was. She was tempted not to answer but, with Owen by her side, she had little choice.

'Hi, Rusty. I'm a little busy right now.'

'I know.' He didn't apologise, but then when did he ever? 'This isn't about the case. Is Owen with you, Gabriella?'

'Is Owen with me?' she repeated. 'I don't understand how that's relevant but, yes, he's here.'

'Good.' There was a pause, a long pause that made her turn to Owen, a look of confusion stamped across her features.

Gaby had no idea what this was about but it felt serious and so unlike Rusty's usual behaviour that her anxiety levels ratcheted up a notch. It was a surprise in itself that he'd actually contacted her after the way she'd run out on him and their promised chat.

'Gabriella,' he said finally, his voice stripped of any emotion. It was a tone she recognised all too well, his work voice. The blood in her veins turned to ice and her thoughts immediately turned to Conor. Something had happened to push everything else off the agenda. The only thing that made any sense was something to do with his son.

'Rusty, I . . .'

But he interrupted. 'You need to be strong, sweetheart.'

Gaby's fingers tightened, the knuckles white as they pushed against her skin. Her eyes slid across to Owen who, picking up on her body language, reached out and pressed his hand on to her shoulder. A myriad of images raced around her head as to what could have happened. None of them were even close to the truth.

'Tim and Amy have been in an accident. Get Owen to drive

you to St Asaph's right now. Ask one of the porters to bleep me as soon as you arrive and, for goodness' sake, make sure he drives carefully. Now, I need a brief word with Owen.'

Gaby had questions – a hundred, a thousand, a million – in the short moment Owen was on the phone. She didn't get to ask one. Instead Owen pulled her into a gentle bear hug before turning her around and walking her to the door and out to the car as if she was made of glass. She smothered a laugh, purely because it was the most inappropriate of emotions. But the analogy with glass wasn't so far off the mark. The news had shattered her to the core. She knew Rusty better than anyone. He could have said more. There was more – she could sense it drizzling in through the gaps and spaces of his words – but he'd chosen not to. Why?

Owen led her down the slippery path, his hand firmly clamped around her waist. He pulled open the passenger door with one hand and eased her into the seat before clicking the seatbelt in place. The most unusual part in all of this was that she let him.

# Chapter 23

Bryony

**Wednesday 10 February, 11.30 a.m. Blaen-Cym House**

Blaen-Cym House was a small stone building with what looked like a separate granny wing tacked onto the far corner. Tucked away on the bank of Lake Llyn Padarn, the seventeenth-century building featured deep mullioned windows, decorative plaster-work ceilings and what looked to be original flagstone flooring in the kitchen. It had an air of shabby chic, the white-painted walls in need of a touch-up. The beige carpet in the lounge showing the marks of time. The faint hint of cigarette smoke tainting the air and causing her nose to wrinkle. A long-term rental he'd said, something to tide them over until he could gather enough together for a deposit. It was everything that Bryony could have wished for and far more than Eli had promised.

She'd been concerned that he'd hide her away in some poky, out-of-the-way hole. After all, he had a lot to lose if they were discovered, she remembered. They'd blame the man because wasn't that always the case in incidents like this? She could almost hear the words bandied about. Undue influence. Too young to

111

know her own mind. Manipulation of her innocence. It didn't count that she was the one who had pleaded with him to take her away to start a new life together. They wouldn't listen to a word she had to say. No. He'd be dragged off to be paraded in front of the media and she'd be sent back to her parents. It was up to her not to let that happen.

The kitchen table was overflowing with scraps of paper, proof that the task of writing to her parents was as difficult as she'd expected. Bryony sat back in her chair, her legs curled around the bar underneath. The pad of note paper he'd produced from the top of the shopping bag was flung beside her; the finished letter lay between them. He'd even provided a pack of envelopes. Brown. Rectangular. Businesslike.

Bryony had started out writing the truth only to disregard it. Her parents wouldn't understand the truth if it jumped up and bit them on the nose. They were too wrapped up in their halcyon little world to be concerned about what it was like to live under their roof. What it was like to follow their exacting demands.

No. She couldn't write the truth. The whole purpose of the exercise, as Eli kept reminding her, was to get her parents off their back. The truth would never be acceptable. Her parents would most likely have sent her for counselling if she'd confided her fear of not achieving top A levels and the realisation that there was far more to life than studying. To someone in her father's crappy practice, with an 'ology' after their name. They'd take her aside and brainwash her into believing that university was the only way forward, closely followed by a fabulous job and the lifestyle to go with it.

She picked up her mug of tea and in between tiny sips watched on where Eli was checking his messages, a worried frown pulling at his brow.

Bryony was clever, far cleverer than either her teachers or her parents gave her credit for. That was why she'd agreed to Eli's idea of contacting her parents by letter instead of by phone and also to leaving her mobile with her sister along with her iPad: the accoutrements of her twenty-first-century life. She was also cleverer than Eli, not that she'd ever let on. She'd quickly appreciated, early on in their relationship, that he liked to think that he was the one in control and she was happy to let him as long as she got what she wanted – a new start. But with a new start came a reality check, a flickering shoot trying to break through the fairy-tale flower garden of her mind. She loved him one hundred per cent but she loved herself more. There might come a time when she needed her parents and common sense dictated that she should have a means to contact them, which was why she'd made him promise to get her a new phone just as soon as they were settled.

'Everything all right?' she said, when her mug was empty and the silence was starting to bother her.

'Yes, fine but I do need to go out in a bit.' He glanced up from his phone briefly to send her a smile only to return to his screen.

'Again! You ran out on me yesterday almost as soon as we got here.'

'It can't be helped, sweet pea. It wouldn't do for people to get wind of what we're up to, now would it?' He pushed to standing, the sound of the chair legs grating against the quarry tiles causing her to wince. 'I can post this while I'm at it. Extra ammunition against your parents trying to find us,' he continued, picking up the envelope. 'I'll grab a newspaper too. It's as well to be prepared for what might be heading our way.'

'I'm of age.'

'Not quite. You will be in a few months though.' He stooped to kiss her. 'Don't worry. We're as safe as houses here as long as you remember to keep to the garden until the furore has died down a bit. You're not the first woman to up and leave home. They'll have to accept it eventually.'

*

113

She didn't see Eli pause by the back door, his face set into lines and grooves she would never have thought possible. She also didn't see his blunt cut nails curling around the letter as he glanced down at it before folding it into four. His hand was on the brass handle before he realised what he'd forgotten. The envelope. The envelope to the letter that would never be sent.

# Chapter 24

## Gaby

'Thank you, Owen, I'll take it from here. If you can tell the DCI that Gabriella won't be in for the rest of the day. I'll try and give him a ring later with an update.' Rusty held Gaby by the shoulders, his thumb reaching out to trace her jaw in the briefest of touches.

Gaby's world shrank to the tiny space they took up in the large, bright reception area. She didn't see Rusty tilt his head for Owen to leave. She didn't even notice. She was drowning in Rusty's blue eyes, fearful about what he was going to tell her and yet needing to hear every word, every thought, every inflection in his voice: the truth hidden in the folds and crevices of his speech. She barely registered the brief conversation he'd had with Owen and she certainly didn't notice Owen slipping out of the entrance only to stand on the top step and double up as if in pain. He walked to the car, a broken man.

Rusty started to speak, his look direct but gentle. His words were anything but.

'You remember Amy and Tim were coming here today to be

115

shown around the midwifery ward, don't you, sweetheart? They were so excited yesterday when they told us, so excited,' he said. 'They were on the A55. You might have even heard it on the news earlier? An accident at the Bodelwyddan junction? Anyway, there was a lorry. It appears the driver had a heart attack or stroke behind the wheel. Tim did what he could but he didn't have a chance, Gaby love, he died at the scene.'

She knew what was coming next; she felt it in every nerve ending as her fingers clamped around the flesh of his forearms. He'd have bruises later. It was the least of her worries.

'And Amy and the baby?'

He started walking towards the lift, his hand drawing her into his side. 'Gabriella, I'm not going to lie. They've stabilised her sufficiently to prep her for theatre but it's not looking good for either of them. I've pulled all of the strings possible and have managed to get them to allow you in to see her.' He pressed the button to the fifth floor and where the theatre suite was located. 'I know you're brave, braver than most people I've ever met, but you need to be extra brave now. Amy doesn't know about Tim. She's been asking about him but they've managed to avoid answering her and I'm asking that you avoid telling her if at all possible. She needs hope. That's the only thing that's going to help her now.'

Gaby had been to many hospitals over the years. She'd even spent an extended stay as an inpatient last year while she was recovering from an attempt to remove her spleen without the benefit of a general anaesthetic. But this was different. The only other time she'd ever been close to an operating theatre was when sitting on her sofa watching an episode of *House*, one of her guilty pleasures.

This was impossible. This was the worst thing she'd ever been asked to do. Rusty had left her at the door. She could tell that he'd wanted to stay but he must have sensed something in her manner or mood that dictated that she'd wanted to be left alone with her friend. He only stayed long enough to help her into the regulation gown and cap before having a quick word with the anaesthetist, who was drawing up something into a syringe. Gaby didn't take any notice. She didn't notice anything apart from the still form lying on the trolley in the centre of the room, surrounded on all sides by machinery she couldn't begin to guess the purpose of.

Gaby approached the trolley and, touching Amy's hand, noted the cannula that appeared to be delivering blood into her body, much needed if the cold temperature of her skin was anything to go by. Amy's mousy brown hair was hidden underneath a swathe of bandaging that extended over one side of her face, so that only one eye and part of her left cheek were visible, her body concealed under a white hospital gown dotted with small pink triangles, her protruding belly driving home how very serious the situation was. Gaby's teeth clenched at the thought. Little baby Lara. Amy and Tim had been so happy the last time she'd seen them, their arms wrapped around each other, their blistering smiles impossible to forget.

Crouching down by the side of the trolley, she cradled Amy's hand between hers, trying to instil some warmth into her flesh. She had no words. There were no words to express the level of emotion weighing her down. The problem with Rusty. Her relationship with Conor. The case. All swept away at the sight of her dearest friend lying helpless in front of her. She didn't spare a thought for Tim. She couldn't. It was hard enough trying to restrain the tears creeping up the back of her throat, inch by fatal inch. Rusty had told her that she needed to be brave but there was no rule book, no guideline, no policy or protocol to guide her way. The only thing she had was her instinct and that wasn't going to get her very far. Her instinct said run. She stayed and would stay for as long as Amy needed her.

'Amy, my love. It's me, Gaby.'

Amy's left eye flickered but failed to open. Her hand squeezed around Gaby's with barely a twitch of her muscles.

'Tim. Where's Tim? They won't tell me.' Her voice was a croak, barely a whisper but full of heartache. Gaby nearly broke at the sound. The one thing stopping her were Rusty's words. She wanted to tell her. She knew that she shouldn't. She had no idea what to say next.

'Amy, do you know there was an accident? Well, you've been injured and you need to be operated on for both your sake and the baby's.'

The pressure on her hand increased. 'I always knew it was too good to be true, Gaby. The perfect life we had. I need you to promise me something.'

Gaby caught the eye of the anaesthetist. It was time for her to leave.

'Okay, my love. Anything as long as you get well.' The words caught in the back of her tongue, the muscles tensing in her throat as she tried and failed to withhold the tears seeping under her eyelids and tracking down her cheeks.

# Chapter 25

## Owen

**Wednesday 10 February, 11.35 a.m. St Asaph Hospital**

Owen made it to his car. But, instead of starting the engine and driving back to the station, he rested his head back against the seat and closed his eyes. He knew he had to be strong. But he didn't feel strong. He felt weak – weak and desperately sad. Because of course, he'd been in a similar situation. The abduction of his wife by a maniac. The near loss of both her and their baby was the worst kind of horror imaginable. It had taken him months to get over it. But, the truth was, he'd never be able to forget the gut-gripping fear. A fear that even now, a good six months after it had happened, had him stressed beyond belief if Kate and the kids were ten minutes late. He imagined that he was only one step away from disaster, for lightning to strike twice even though he knew he was being both foolish and irrational.

Now his worst fears had been confirmed. Now he knew that disaster lay hidden just around the corner. Now he didn't know what to do.

Only the thought of duty, the thought of the team, made him

finally press the ignition and pull out of the hospital grounds. He drove instinctively, the route between the hospital and the police station a well-travelled journey that needed little thought or concentration. He drove into the car park, pulled into one of the reserved spaces and slammed the door shut. The ground was slippery underfoot, which was the only reason he took his time in choosing where to place his feet. Clancy, the desk sergeant, was waiting for him at the entrance.

News travelled fast among the police. Good, bad or indifferent. The type of news didn't make any difference to the speed of relay. It didn't take rocket science for Owen to realise that Clancy was as lost for words as he was. His expression said it all.

Instead of waiting for him to cobble together some kind of a sentence, Owen decided to take the initiative.

'Amy's in theatre. That's all I know. Sorry.' He spread his hands, almost as if to apologise for something that wasn't his fault.

'You know we're all devastated, Owen.'

He nodded, his mind trying to shift from thoughts of Amy to thoughts of Christy and Bryony. It was a difficult but necessary transition, he reminded himself with a sharp mental kick.

'Oh, the DCI asked me to give him a shout when you turned up,' Clancy added. 'He's waiting upstairs.'

'Okay. Can you assemble the team please and see if you can purloin a couple of paracetamol while you're at it? I have a splitting headache coming on.'

*

'Good God, man, take a seat. You look done in.' DCI Sherlock walked around the desk and propped himself against the edge, his head tilted in the direction of the chair. 'This is a horrible business,' he continued, crossing his legs at the ankles and folding his arms. 'Dr Mulholland was kind enough to phone me with an update. He's a good man.'

120

'Yes, very good,' Owen replied, thinking of the few short words Rusty had said to him straight after speaking to Gaby at the cottage: brief but to the point.

Owen felt restless and ungrounded. He didn't know why the boss had called him in when Rusty must have told him all the key points. There was nothing for him to add surely.

'With the DI out of action, until we know what's happening with dear Amy, I'm going to need you to step up, Bates.'

'Sir?'

Sherlock leant forward, his hands holding on to the edge of the desk. 'You know the case as well as Darin and, as the most experienced of her officers, I'm relying on you to move it forward while she is out of action. I know there isn't any reason as such for her not to be here – knowing Gaby as I do she'll be chomping at the bit to get back – but until that happens I'm depending on you, Bates.'

'Yes, sir.'

*

In a funny sort of a way, the incident room was the antidote he needed for the heavy pressure that had settled underneath his shirt at the news, the very ordinariness helping him to reset his priorities. The smell of stewed coffee mingling with Marie's new perfume. The sight of Jax's navy padded jacket and woolly hat draped over the radiator. Even the box of cakes on the shelf beside the coffee maker that someone must have brought in for a special treat only to have forgotten about.

His gaze swung from Amy's old desk by the window and landed on Marie's concerned expression.

He cleared his throat. 'I know . . .' He coughed and tried again, avoiding the two worried faces staring back at him. 'Tim died at the scene and it's not looking good for either Amy or the baby. She's in theatre and Gaby will stay with her until Amy's family arrive up from Swansea.' He shivered despite the warmth of the office. 'In the meantime, I've been tasked with leading the case. I know how difficult this is but finding Bryony has to be our priority. We owe it to both Amy and Gaby to do our best, despite everything.'

'You know if there's anything that we c-c-can do for them . . .' Jax said, the sentence trailing off into the distance.

'Thank you. If I hear of anything . . . Right then.' He stepped across to the wall of whiteboards and straightened his shoulders. 'As you know, Gaby and I went out to Rhyd Ddu Path first thing, following up the discovery of Christy lying on the side of the road.' He picked up a marker pen at random and started to write. 'She was found in a puddle of blood with some kind of knife wound to her abdomen and airlifted straight to St Asaph's, where her condition is serious but stable.'

He turned, the marker still in his right hand, his left now securely in his pocket. 'However that's not all, far from it. Despite the heavy snowfall there was enough of a blood trail for Jason to guess that Christy had walked from the only cottage in the vicinity, as opposed to being dumped by a passing motorist. We can only surmise that she was going for help. Treasure Cottage is one of those quaint olde-worlde, stone-built affairs that are popular with tourists. We need to find the owners as a matter of urgency. Jax.'

'Yes, guv.'

'Enough of the guv, if you please,' Owen said with a laugh. 'Wait until I've earnt my stripes.'

Jax coloured up but remained silent.

'The cottage has all the appearance of being occupied for some time. Debris in the grate. Coal in the scuttle. Wood piled up in the log basket. The fridge was empty but the freezer was full to the brim. However, everything of a personal nature had been removed, from the clothes in the cupboards to the toiletries in the bathroom. There was also this found behind one of the drawers.'

He stepped over to where he'd placed the clear specimen bag along with his phone, holding it up by the edge, an empty crisp packet clear to see. 'I'll leave you to liaise with the CSIs, Marie. If we're lucky, there might be some latent fingerprints from the plastic wrapper or maybe even some traces of saliva. It looks like the place has been wiped clean of anything relevant but you never know.' He placed the bag on her desk. 'There's also no certainty that it wasn't left over from a previous tenant.'

'I can check on how they're getting on with Bryony's devices at the same time.'

'Good plan.' Owen's phone rang, causing all three pairs of eyes to shift in the direction of his desk and where the device was flashing out a number. He nearly tripped over his feet in his effort to reach it before it rang out.

The office was silent apart from his monosyllabic replies, the call brief.

He returned the phone to the desk, nudging it slightly so that it lined up with the edge of the laptop, well aware that Jax and Marie were watching his every move.

'That was Rusty. Amy gave birth to a baby girl.' He checked his watch. 'A little over half an hour ago. They've whisked her off to the special care baby unit, something about keeping an eye on her because she's a month early. They're waiting for Amy to come round from the anaesthetic.'

'Come round? What does that mean?'

He grimaced. 'Your guess is as good as mine, Marie. We'll just have to be patient until we know more. That's not the only reason for his call. Dr Maston has completed the autopsy on Jules White. Apparently it's not straightforward so I've been invited over to Manchester to meet with her again as opposed to her "wasting time" travelling to us,' he said, punctuating the space over his head with air quotes.

'Of all the bloody cheek,' Marie exploded.

'Remember, she is doing us a huge favour here, and it's not

as if she'll even think about our workload or know about Amy,' Jax said, with his usual calm manner.

Owen carried on as if there hadn't been an interruption. 'I'm going to head over now, which means I should be back in good time for a catch-up, weather depending. Marie, you head up to the CSIs. Jax, I need you to follow up on the work Mal was doing in trying to locate where Bryony might have eaten.' He collected his mobile and shoved it in his trouser pocket. 'If I have any more news about Amy or the baby I'll let you know.'

'Here, take a doughnut with you.' Marie raced across to the shelf and handed him the box. 'Knowing you, you won't stop for lunch.'

# Chapter 26

## Marie

**Wednesday 10 February, 12.55 p.m. St Asaph**

The laboratory was a light, bright, airy space divided by glass partitions into the different areas of forensics. Marie dropped the crisp packet off at the fingerprint section before tracking down Jason in his office, a small cupboard of a room with no natural light but black coffee on tap, which he appeared to drink by the bucketload.

Marie had known Jason for years, a serious man with a taste for chequered shirts and brown trousers. In fact she'd rarely seen him in anything else, apart from his paper bodysuit. She'd heard rude comments about his style of dress but had never been party to any of the conversations. Some of her colleagues took an eager delight in picking on members of the team but Marie had always been of the opinion to keep her mouth shut unless she had something nice to say. She did find him a little gruff but then the same could be said about her.

'I wasn't sure if you'd be back yet.'

'Only just. Pull up a seat and take the weight off. We're all sorry to hear about Amy. Any news?'

'No, not really. She's had the baby. We're still waiting to hear more.' She changed the subject. 'Any luck over at the cottage?'

'Only the crisp packet up to now. They're still working on the contents of the freezer but nothing so far. The team will probably be there most of the day and maybe into the night but early indications are that we're not going to find very much in the way of usable evidence.'

'That's what Owen said. We need to speak to Christy urgently but the hospital aren't playing ball. It's all a bit of a mess.' She crossed her legs and rearranged her skirt accordingly. 'I also came to ask about Bryony's phone?'

'Ah. Yes.' He swivelled back to face his desk and, after a moment or two of shuffling through an ocean of paperwork, finally found what he was looking for. 'I don't know about you, but as soon as I turn my back someone piles more crap onto the crap I already have to deal with,' he said finally, holding up a sheet of A4 paper like a prize. 'It didn't take long to unlock in the end. Most people are sloppy with their passwords and this was no different. She did make a half-hearted attempt to delete her internet searches by cleaning up her history but nothing that Matt wasn't able to sort out in about five minutes. The Solid State Drive never lies.'

'So she did have something to hide then?'

He gave a sharp nod. 'It's mostly to do with coursework and shopping,' he said, dropping the sheet into her lap before resting his elbows on the desk and steepling his fingers. 'But if you check around the start of September, there's a new strand to her Google searches.'

Marie scrolled down until she reached the relevant date, a sigh breaking at the memories it evoked. It might be twenty years ago but she could still remember thinking the very same thoughts.

*How to recognise when you're in love. How to attract a man. How to know when a man likes you.*

'I see she uses the term man as opposed to boy?'

126

'Yes. Obviously we don't know the relevance but can only assume that she means someone older,' he said.

'And there wasn't anything else? No photos?'

He shook his head. 'It's all there. I get the impression that something changed around November. Who knows what? Maybe the pressure of exams catching up. She was probably facing mocks by then.'

'Why do you say that?'

He tapped the paper towards the bottom. 'Her searches changed. Nothing that wasn't work-related. No music or movie downloads. No online clothes shopping. None of the sites she used to visit, albeit sporadically.'

'So, she changed. As you say maybe it was exam pressure or maybe her parents said something.'

'Or maybe she was trying to hide something from both them and her sister?'

# Chapter 27

## Gaby

**Wednesday 10 February, 2 p.m. St Asaph**

Lara Dunne looked the same as the two other babies in the baby unit. Red-faced and with a tuft of nondescript hair just visible underneath the white hat that covered most of her scalp. Gaby couldn't get over how small she was, with perfectly formed hands smaller than the dolly she'd had as a child.

Gaby had never thought she was maternal. Far from it. The dolly had ended up in the back of the toy cupboard, pushed aside by balls and racquets for every sport imaginable. One look at Lara changed all that. She couldn't put into words her feelings for Amy's child. She couldn't describe the sense of joy that had crept under her jacket, piercing through all the layers of fabric, flesh and bone. A joy that was crippled by an acute sadness for everything the poor little mite had already gone through in her short life. Lara wasn't out of danger, far from it. The next twenty-four hours were critical but Gaby had an optimism born out of desperation. Fate surely couldn't be that cruel.

*

128

The intensive care unit also looked the same. It even smelt the same, with that distinctive mixture of antiseptic underlined by a hint of bleach, common to all the high-dependency units she'd ever visited. Gaby couldn't believe that Amy was now being cared for by the same staff caring for Christy. Only one room separated the two women. But she hadn't bothered to check on the girl's progress. All her thoughts were for Amy and the baby.

Amy wasn't responding and, with the passage of time, Gaby felt the mood of the staff switch from hopeful to noncommittal. There was nothing to say, not really. The machines said it all. The apparatus in her mouth assisting her to breathe. The drip in her arm delivering an array of liquid into her veins. The pallor of her skin visible where the bandaging stopped. The stillness of her body under the thin, white sheet.

Gaby leant on the edge of the bedrail, her fingers cradling Amy's, her voice a soft mix of words. She told her about Lara, about her beautiful daughter and how strong and pretty she was. She talked about the past, their conjoined past. The cases they'd solved and the cases she hoped to solve with her in the future. She even mentioned Tim but only in passing, following Rusty's advice to the letter. Rusty had wanted to stay but she'd sent him away. There was no place for him here. Gaby would be lying if she said she was staying for Amy. She was staying for a whole multitude of reasons that she couldn't begin to break down into their meaningful parts. Amy was lost to her as her body tried to repair the damage from the accident. But hope remained.

The only interruption came from the nurses performing their routine checks and finally when Amy's parents arrived.

Mr and Mrs Potter were interesting, which was the politest word that Gaby could think of when referring to Amy's parents. As a couple, they were full of their own sense of importance, something reinforced by Mr Potter's three-piece suit and Mrs Potter's designer frock and coordinating handbag and shoes. Both retired, they'd obviously taken the time to dress for the occasion instead of grabbing their keys and racing for the door to be by their beloved daughter's side. But then Amy wasn't their *beloved* daughter, Gaby remembered. No, Amy was the daughter who'd bucked the trend by refusing to attend university, unlike her two older siblings. In marrying Tim, she'd rubber-stamped her parents' poor opinion by choosing someone who worked in a restaurant for a living, albeit one he owned.

Gaby bit down hard on her lip, suddenly ashamed of her thoughts. She had no right to judge and no way of knowing the coping mechanism of the couple staring down at the child they'd reared. She couldn't begin to speculate what they were thinking or how they were holding up. Grief was a funny business that affected everyone in different ways. Despite the number of books she'd read on the subject, Gaby still didn't understand how it worked. She only knew how it affected her.

Mrs Potter presented a carefully made-up cheek and dry eyes while Gaby's face was riven with tears, her tissue a soggy mess and the blouse she'd hastily ironed before rushing out of the door earlier now stained and wrinkled. But all that meant was that the Potters were better at disguising their feelings, not that they were any less upset.

Gaby jerked to her feet, pushing the chair back, and slowly removed her hand from Amy's. She couldn't stay, as much as she wanted to.

'I'll leave you to it.'

'Before you go . . .' Mrs Potter began, gingerly sitting on the edge of the chair Gaby had just vacated. Gaby wouldn't have been surprised if she'd taking out a tissue to wipe it first. 'What about the baby?'

'Lara. She's beautiful. Holding her own at present.'

'I suppose that's something.' She lifted a limp hand and Gaby knew that she'd been dismissed.

Christy's door was closed and the window curtained off from any casual observers keen to stare into the tragedy of other people's lives. Instead of intruding in another place she wasn't wanted, Gaby made her way back to the baby unit. Rusty had promised to come for her when he'd finished. She'd hide away there until then. After all, she had a right. Amy and Tim had asked her and Rusty to be Lara's godparents. At the time it had been a token gesture. Now it felt anything but.

# Chapter 28

Gaby

**Wednesday 10 February, 3 p.m. St Asaph Hospital**

The canteen at the hospital was quiet now the lunchtime rush was over. Gaby wasn't in need of sustenance or indeed the black coffee that she was nursing between icy fingers. But the staff on the baby unit had been right to send her away. They had a job to do and she was getting in the way.

When she'd gone back to check on Amy, she'd found the door closed and the curtains pulled. Her parents were nowhere to be seen until one of the nurses informed her that they were meeting with the doctor in charge of Amy's care. The gnaw in her gut that should have been hunger was a physical pain. She hadn't eaten breakfast after the row-that-wasn't-a-row she'd had with Rusty last night. A row meant words and she hadn't felt up to sharing even one of her many thoughts with him. His view on children. The case. That phone call. Now she wondered if she ever would. It wouldn't be the first time she'd run out on a man. It was one of the reasons for her move from Cardiff to Swansea.

She picked up her spoon only to put it back down. Stirring her lacklustre drink wouldn't make it any more palatable.

Her mind continued to flit from topic to topic, unable to settle. Even her mobile next to her bag was silent. No doubt Owen and Sherlock's way of protecting her from anything to do with the case. The problem was she had nowhere to go now that Amy's parents were here. She wasn't needed at work and sitting at home staring at four walls was the very last thing she wanted to be doing. But she also wasn't prepared to sit in front of a coffee she didn't want while her team were run ragged. With that thought, she collected her mug, handed it over the counter, and made her way back to intensive care where she could at least be of some use.

Mr and Mrs Taylor were sitting either side of Christy's bed. Gaby recognised their expression; hadn't she seen the exact same look when she'd caught sight of her reflection in the mirror on the way up in the lift? Anxiety laced with fear was unmistakable. She adapted her words and demeanour accordingly in the hope that they'd see the sense in speaking to her but there were no guarantees.

Instead of barging in, she knocked and waited until Mr Taylor joined her at the door, rolling his neck and shoulders in a movement she knew well. She'd had to free up her muscles in the exact same way earlier when the Potters had taken over from her bedside vigil. But where the Potters had dressed for the occasion it was obvious that the Taylors had tumbled out of bed and into the first set of clothes they'd laid their hands on. In Mr Taylor's case, a pair of grey trousers and a sweatshirt. In his wife's, a pair of workout joggers and a thick jumper adorned with navy and white stars.

Gaby put her hand out, hoping that he'd take it. A show of good manners was usually an indication of what her welcome would be like.

'I'm sorry to disturb you, Mr Taylor. I'm not sure if you remember me? DI Darin from St Asaph.'

The handshake was quick and begrudging. Gaby tried to remember the background. That's right. Both vets. She hoped that might help. She wasn't sure why, her gaze on Christy and the tiny rows of black plaits spread out against the white of the pillowcase, more of her face visible now that the intubation tube had been removed.

Mr Taylor fetched her a seat and waited until she'd settled before retaking his.

'How is she doing?'

'Thank you for asking. Better than we could have hoped under the circumstances.'

There was no answer that she could give to that. The police were obviously at fault for not taking their daughter's disappearance more seriously at the time, just as they were in not finding her location until it was almost too late.

'We think she's been staying at a cottage in Snowdonia, close to where she was found. I have a team scouring the area for clues,' Gaby said, in the hope that a stream of words might improve the atmosphere somewhat. 'I also need to explain the likelihood of her disappearance not being a solitary incident. I don't know if you've heard the reports about the schoolgirl going missing in Mold?' She watched the play of emotions on their faces before continuing. 'While there are differences, there are enough similarities not to eliminate the possibility that they're linked. Obviously I don't want to upset you any more than necessary but it's likely that the newspapers will pick up on the story and try and speak to you.'

'Don't you worry, Detective. I'll give them a very short shift if they start bothering us. All we want is for the man responsible to be caught and locked up for a very long time.'

'Mum.'

That one word and the atmosphere of the room crackled with emotion. Gaby was forgotten in the pandemonium of tears and hugs that followed. She headed for the door, uncomfortable with being privy to what was a very private occasion. Yes, she needed to speak to Christy and urgently but she also had the presence of mind to realise that she was far from welcome in the small room. The daughter that they'd thought lost; found by a rescue team who, by some quirk of fate, were in the right place at the right time to discover someone they hadn't even been searching for.

Gaby wasn't a sentimental sort of person. In fact she was more embarrassed than anything at overt displays of emotion. All Rusty got in public was a brief peck on his cheek if he was lucky. A quick swallow then another was all that was needed to dislodge the brick in her throat. A couple of rapid blinks and she was ready to sneak through the door and present her newly arranged features. She might even manage to pull her lips into a smile if she met someone she recognised. All that changed in an instant with Christy's next words.

'Where's my baby?'

Gaby's face blanched as she suddenly recalled the doctor's strange behaviour as they'd stood outside Christy's room. Another piece of the puzzle slotted into place but to what end? She turned back into the room in the hope that she'd be allowed to question the girl further.

# Chapter 29

## Bryony

### Wednesday 10 February, 3 p.m. Blaen-Cym House

Bryony glanced down at her watch, not quite able to believe the time. She'd decided to join Eli for a nap but once her head had hit the pillow, she'd fallen into a deep dreamless sleep.

Lifting her head, she turned to face him. The lines around his eyes and mouth had softened in sleep, making him look younger than his twenty-three years. She'd always imagined that she'd end up with an older man. Someone mature and sensible. After all, weren't those the same words attributed to her? Her mother was prone to saying she was born old, unlike her flibbertigibbet of a sister who continued to go from one disaster to the next. And yet here she was. The sensible sister acting completely out of character by deciding to run away with Eli.

She'd known the first time she'd met him that he'd be important but she couldn't have guessed what an impact he'd have on her future. It hadn't taken him long to seek her out. She couldn't believe that someone so good-looking would be interested in someone like her. To go from spending all her days studying to running her own home would have been unimaginable six months ago. And yet here she was, mistress of her own destiny. Or at least that's how she'd felt when she'd run away with him. His behaviour since then . . . His long absence yesterday, most of the night and again this morning, had diminished the excitement somewhat.

'Are we staying in bed all day?' he said, interrupting her thoughts.

'I thought you were still asleep?'

'Just resting my eyes.'

'I'm not surprised, the state you were in earlier.' She rolled out of bed and, stretching, stifled a yawn. 'Would you like a cuppa?'

He lifted one eyelid and then the other before propping up on one elbow. 'I could get used to this level of service.'

'A cup of tea is as far as it goes. I thought you'd deserted me yesterday.'

'As if.' He reached out a hand, pulling her back into bed. 'We've only just got here,' he said, stamping a quick kiss on her mulish mouth.

Bryony shifted slightly, her hand resting on his thigh.

She knew she had to forgive him but it was difficult. He still hadn't explained properly what had happened. There was also a wariness about him, something left unsaid lurking behind his eyes that made her reluctant to question him further. But she still wanted to make her feelings known.

'Seriously, Eli, I was scared out of my wits.'

'Darling, it couldn't be helped but I'm all yours now. I'm not going anywhere until at least my holidays are over.'

'You promise?'

'Of course, I promise, you silly Billy. You just try and get rid of me. You'll be sick of the sight of me and begging for a bit of peace and quiet. You'll see,' he said, neatly shifting the conversation into a new direction.

But Bryony was still worried despite his glib response. She knew he could disappear again anytime he wanted and there wasn't anything she could do to stop him. She needed a backup plan. The only problem was she couldn't think of one. She wasn't saying she'd changed her mind or that she didn't trust him but . . . she didn't trust him quite as much as she had last night or even this afternoon. Something was different. It was up to her to figure out what.

She stretched her fingers over the denim of his jeans. 'You didn't say if you'd managed to post my letter?' she said, still trying to find reassurance.

His hand covered hers, pinning her restless fingers hard against his leg. 'I posted it like I said I would. First class. If the postie does what they're they meant to, they should have it by the morning,' he said, his voice deepening into a tone she hadn't heard before.

He was still smiling but she knew that he was annoyed. No. He was angry, although he wasn't prepared to show it. Her gaze dropped to his lap and where her fingers were trapped under his hand and, for the first time, she wondered if she hadn't made a terrible mistake.

The thought of running away from her domineering parents had been the thing that had focused her mind and swung the balance in favour of leaving home. She didn't dwell on the reality of having very little choice to do otherwise. Yes, she loved him but she loved the thought of the life he had promised, away from exam pressures and a future full of study, far more. But what kind of a man would want to whisk a schoolgirl away from her parents without even letting her tell them where she was going? Perhaps that was a question she should have asked him before and not after she'd left. He'd even countered any suggestion that she could leave a note in case it scuppered their plans.

'Great, thanks,' she said, easing off the bed to standing. 'I'll make that tea then.'

She made her way into the kitchen, flicking the kettle on with one hand and reaching for a pair of mugs with the other. If she was so happy with her new life why did she suddenly feel so sad?

# Chapter 30

## Owen

**Wednesday 10 February, 3 p.m. Manchester**

Owen had decided that the only way he was going to get through the rest of the day was by immersing himself in work. They had to find out what had happened to Christy and they had to find Bryony. But first he had the meeting to attend in Manchester.

He walked into the incident room, a takeout coffee in one hand and his mobile in the other. The room was full but the only people he recognised were Dr Maston and DCI Webb. The former ignored him while the latter managed a brief smile of welcome.

'I'd like to introduce Detective Bates,' the DCI said, angling her head in the direction of an empty chair at the front. 'As you know, we think that the modus operandi over in Bournville Road has been repeated in North Wales, with the recent disappearance of a seventeen year old girl. There was also a similar incident six months ago. That's right, isn't it, Bates?'

'Exactly right, ma'am, except for the fact that Christy Taylor, the first victim, has turned up during the small hours, halfway up Snowdonia.' He stroked his beard. 'She's in a bad way, I'm afraid. Too ill to interview yet. I'll keep you informed about what happens.'

'Please do. As I'm sure you can appreciate, cross-jurisdiction working is a pain in the bum for both sides. Let's keep it clean and tidy with an easy flow of communication, eh? That way we both win.'

'Yes, ma'am.'

Owen appreciated her sentiments but doubted that her words would have any impact – not that he allowed his expression to give away his thoughts. The obdurate backs of the Manchester team, in addition to their obvious lack of a welcome, hadn't gone unnoticed, at least not by him. He hadn't expected flags and balloons but a quick nod wouldn't have gone amiss. Owen had been party to this type of operation before, where similar sentiments prevailed. Coppers as a breed were both ambitious and territorial. If they pissed on his patch, he'd piss straight back but longer and harder.

DCI Webb turned to face the rest of the room. 'To recap – over the last eighteen months three young women have disappeared: Christy Taylor, Bryony Lloyd and finally our very own Jules White. It's only thanks to our archives officer that we're here today joining the dots between all three.' She straightened her jacket, her fingers fiddling with the bottom button. 'Three women on the cusp of womanhood and, if their parents are to be believed, with no reason to desert the family home. Jules White was tied up in her studies with a shining career in mathematics ahead of her. She'd already been accepted at Durham and spent all of her spare time in her bedroom working. It's a similar situation with Christy and Bryony.'

She held up her hand to stop one of the officers at the front starting to interrupt. 'I know what you're going to say, Malcolm, about the patchy similarities but we also have to consider that none of these girls fit the profile we tend to expect in runaways.' She picked up one of the three photos lying on the table behind her and, after studying it briefly, held it up. 'Jules had no difficulties at school or major arguments at home. No problems with alcohol or substance abuse and she also wasn't known to either the social services or the Child and Adolescent Mental Health Service – it's the same story with Bryony and Christy. We've interviewed Jules's parents many times but there's nothing in their background to flag any concerns. They never had a jot of trouble with her, which is more than they could say about their youngest who by all accounts is a bit of a tearaway.'

Owen barely glanced at the photo. He didn't need to be reminded of her pale mousy looks and intelligent face. Instead he filed away the information about the sibling for perusal later as he recalled a similar comment made about Bryony – and hadn't Christy also had a sibling?

'Over to you, Caroline.'

Dr Maston walked towards the open laptop, set up in front of a white screen, her long honey-blonde locks gathered at the base of her neck into some kind of clasp. He hardly noticed her clothes, other than the colour – black. He wasn't the type of man to notice clothes, much to his wife's frequent displeasure.

Owen wasn't boorish, far from it, but he followed the stance of always complimenting Kate whatever her apparel. He still couldn't understand why she got annoyed when he didn't notice something new. Nice, as far as he was concerned was a perfectly acceptable phrase that covered a multitude of outfits from tatty joggers to posh frocks. If she'd wanted more she should have married someone else. He was only thankful that she hadn't. He couldn't imagine being married to the woman taking centre stage, with all the artifice of a prima donna mid-pirouette. Rusty might think that he could cope but it would take a very special man to outwit her charm offensive, not to mention the bait she was dangling. Owen liked to think that Gaby and Rusty had a strong relationship. He hoped it was strong enough to stand up to the temptation on offer.

'Performing an autopsy on a mummified body comes with its own challenges,' Dr Maston said. The glossy smile didn't reach her eyes. 'The body was moved shortly before death to the place of mummification, as can be seen by the torn skin where she was dragged over a hard surface.' She pressed a button on the laptop and the screen filled with a close-up of what looked like dried-up old leather. Owen swallowed, regretting the doughnut that Marie had pressed on him.

'So, she was left somewhere to die?' DCI Webb said, her look of distaste mirroring Owen's.

'Exactly. The blood stasis following death wouldn't account for the petechial blood spots seen just under the skin – here and here – otherwise,' Dr Maston said, clicking through the next couple of slides at speed. 'To be absolutely clear, the body was moved twice. Firstly to the place she was left to die and secondly to her place of discovery. Liver mortis, body discolouration caused by blood settling due to gravity, is present on her left-hand side – her left hip, along the side of her left leg and the top of her left arm, which indicates she curled up during death. When she was discovered, she was found to be lying on her right-hand side so she was definitely moved post-mortem. The normal pattern with a body such as this is rapid insect involvement but that's not the case here due to the speed in which the skin dehydrated. Because of an absence of evidence we have to make the assumption that she was placed somewhere hot and dry. A new-build with double glazing as opposed to a draughty barn.'

She clicked through the next few slides. 'The internal organs were unremarkable. All normal for a woman of her age. Again the toxicology reports didn't show up anything of note. There were no broken bones, nothing to indicate the cause of death other than an assumed complication of her pregnancy.'

'Excuse me?' Owen knew that it wasn't his place to interrupt. This wasn't his show, far from it. Despite the DCI's pretty words, he was only here on sufferance to see if he could add anything important to their case.

Dr Maston focused on him, no trace of her earlier smile on her pert lips. 'Jules gave birth shortly before her death, as can be seen by changes to her cervix.'

'So, where's the baby?'

'Your guess is as good as mine, Detective.' She propped against the edge of the table, not bothering to adjust the length of her skirt, which now revealed a considerable length of toned leg. 'Remember, there's no evidence that she gave birth to a live baby or that the baby survived for long. With no record of the birth that has to be viewed as a possibility.'

'And with no baby, there'll be no way to harvest the DNA we need to find the father?'

'Actually that's not the case, Detective,' she said with a little pout. 'With a bit of jiggery pokery, I'm hoping the brain tissue samples I've managed to retrieve from the mum will reveal their secrets. I can see you're looking a little confused. Let me explain. MFCT, or maternal-foetal cellular trafficking, is the term used to describe the two-way blood flow between parent and foetus which, luckily for us, results in the presence of foetal cells usually being discovered in the mother's bloodstream, something called microchimerism. The brain, under normal circumstances, is an excellent source. Isolating it is another issue entirely.'

Owen shook his head, his nausea returning with a renewed vengeance at the thought of the missing baby and dead mother. It was only his long years in the force that prevented him from spewing up in front of the team. He had to get on the phone and quickly. Would it be rude to walk out mid-briefing? Probably. He pushed to his feet anyway.

# Chapter 31

## Marie

Cerys opened the door after one ring of the bell, a bag of crisps tucked under her arm and her mobile clutched in her hand.

'If you wait here a minute I'll just go and fetch my mum.'

Marie hid a smile. 'Well, I've actually come to see you, if you have a minute?'

Cerys paused in the act of closing the door, her colour fading, causing Marie's detective's antennae to ping to high alert. At sixteen, the girl was still only a minor, which technically caused a whole raft of problems. But Marie wasn't worried about that in the least. Dr and Mrs Lloyd had given their permission yesterday and there was nothing to suggest that they wouldn't do the same today. Marie was more than happy to explain away the set of circumstances that had led to her standing in front of Cerys with a host of questions.

'You'd better come in then,' Cerys said, waving her into the lounge. 'I'll just go and tell Mum you're here,' she went on, her manner a little short of curt.

She returned straightaway, closely followed by her mother.

Lesley Lloyd appeared diminished somehow, shrunken, her calm demeanour now only a memory. She was even dressed differently, her smart garb forgotten as more pressing priorities took precedence. Marie wasn't a parent but she didn't need to be to recognise what Lesley was going through. She'd never felt more determined to solve a case than at that moment.

Mrs Lloyd launched straight in, ignoring any and all of the social niceties but then again Marie wasn't expecting them.

'Is there any news?'

'No, I'm afraid not. We're still following up some leads but at the minute there isn't a huge amount to go on,' Marie said, sitting on the chair offered.

She wished that there was more to tell her but she was also reluctant to give her false hope. The issue of Jules's body was ramraiding the back of her brain with the finesse of a dog on heat. There was also the unidentified skeleton. Marie hadn't been given permission to inform the Lloyds about the possible links with the Manchester case. But, on the other hand, they were only a hair's breadth away from the media picking up on the story and all hell breaking loose. She decided to drop a hint and leave it at that. 'Something has come up in relation to an investigation over in Manchester that's raised a few questions.' Marie tilted her head in Cerys's direction. 'As you know, we have Bryony's mobile, which we've managed to open and gain access to all her files.'

'What have you found?' Mrs Lloyd asked. Her daughter remained silent and still from the security of the window seat, so very still, the only part of her moving was her eyes.

'Actually it's not what we've found so much as what we haven't.'

'I don't understand?'

'And neither do we really,' Marie said, managing a small smile. 'Up until the end of September your daughter spent a fair degree of time searching the web and landing on the sort of sites a teenage girl would be expected to. I take it she had a clothing allowance?'

Mrs Lloyd flushed. 'That was my husband's idea. A way of teaching her to budget before uni. It wasn't much – £20 a week for clothes and essentials. We do the same for Cerys.'

'And she presumably drew on her own bank account?'

She nodded. 'Exactly. It's one of the things that surprised my husband when he decided to check with the bank – she has one of those junior accounts so that we can still keep an eye on things.'

Marie masked her impatience. She needed facts and she needed them quickly. What she didn't need was to know about the ins and outs of bank accounts and the like but there was little she could do to hurry her up without sounding like an unfeeling cow.

'The account had over £500 in it last time he looked, which was before Christmas,' Mrs Lloyd continued. 'Bryony had said that she was saving up for the January sales.'

'And now it's empty?'

'No, on the contrary. She hasn't touched a penny.'

Marie frowned because leaving the money untouched didn't make sense unless Bryony had been kidnapped and, if she had, why was there no ransom note? She made a mental note to discuss it with the team later, her mind already shifting on to the next question.

'Cerys, do you have anything to add? The thing that's most puzzling is, outside of the shopping side of things, your sister used her mobile for all sorts of internet searches.' Marie flicked open her phone, launched her notebook app and started to read. 'From cutting her own fringe to homemade treatments for freckles to body language and how to attract a man.' She placed her phone back onto her lap and, lifting her head, saw the expression wash across Cerys's face. Guilt. There was nothing she could do about the mother being there. It was far too late for that. The younger sister knew something important. Marie could only hope that they weren't too late to act on whatever it was.

'She had a boyfriend.'

'Cerys!' Mrs Lloyd jumped to her feet and strode across to the bay window, her hand raised as if to strike.

Marie didn't know whether Mrs Lloyd's exclamation was one of surprise, shock or rebuke – she didn't know her well enough to narrow it down. But she was ready for her, whatever the cause of her aggressive behaviour.

'If you smack your daughter, I'm going to have to take you down to the station and that's certainly not going to help in the search for Bryony now, is it?' Marie strolled over to them, her hands firmly clamped in her pockets, her expression calm even if she was feeling anything but.

The Lloyds didn't seem the type of family to use physical violence but Marie had seen far too much in her career for her to be surprised at anything. Stress did strange things to people but the look of horror and shame on Lesley Lloyd's face said more than a host of words could ever do. The Lloyds were broken and would remain so until they found Bryony. All of which added to the pressure they were under. Time was slipping through their fingers and skewing the odds for a happy resolution.

Marie waited a moment, watching as the mother settled on the window seat, her hand draped across her daughter's shoulders. But it was Cerys she was worried about. The way she was hugging her knees to her chest, her hands in a death grip with the knuckles gleaming white. The girl was little more than a child. It was up to Marie to dissuade her of the notion that she was to blame for any of this. She also had to calm her mother.

Who'd be a copper?

It was always difficult to gauge how a family worked. Police officers knew that there was no such thing as normal and what worked in one household was anathema to another. The Lloyds looked an average sort of family with perhaps a tendency to over-stress the importance of a good education. Marie also considered that exam success was important but not at the expense of being a teenager. She'd seen too many kids going off the rails when they realised what they were missing out on. That old adage of the grass always being greener on the other side came to mind. It was often too late by the time they realised that the grass was never greener, only different.

'Cerys. No one is cross with you,' Marie said. 'It's just that we're concerned about your sister. I know it's difficult but you need to tell us everything you know.'

'She was meant to write.' Cerys shifted position, her head now resting on her mother's knee, tears starting to fall. 'She promised faithfully that the letter would be waiting on the doormat along with the rest of the post.'

'Shush, it's all right. Just tell us what you know, sweetheart,' Mrs Lloyd said, starting to stroke her daughter's thick red hair.

# Chapter 32

Gaby

**Wednesday 10 February, 5 p.m. St Asaph**

'What are you doing here?'

'Hello, Owen. And it's good to see you too,' Gaby said, arranging her coat on the back of her chair before slipping into her seat.

'Sorry.' He hesitated. 'I just thought you'd still be at the hospital.'

'So did I,' she said, with a grimace. 'But Amy's parents had other ideas. They made me feel as welcome as a pile of doggy doo.'

Owen pulled a face. 'How is she?'

Gaby was well aware that Marie and Jax were tuning in, their hands resting on their keyboards, their heads tilted in her direction. She didn't mind, far from it. She'd far prefer to say what she had to only the once.

'They're waiting for her to wake up. The only good thing is Luru. She's beautiful, Owen. Absolutely perfect but also not out of the woods.'

'I can't stop thinking about Tim's parents and what they must be going through.' Owen raked his hand through his hair. 'There must be nothing worse than losing a child.'

'I haven't tried to contact them,' Gaby said after a moment. 'I wouldn't know what to say.'

'I don't think conversation skills come into it. I've never met anyone who knows what to say at times like this but I've learned over the years that the longer you leave it the harder it is. Anyway, lecture over. We were about to have a quick catch-up before I send this lot home. You can lead it if you like? Sherlock will be none the wiser.'

She flicked his comment aside with a brush of her hand, her mind still on the tentative issue of Tim's parents and what she was going to do about it. 'No. You lead. Knowing my luck, Sherlock will walk in mid-sentence. After all, you're far more up-to-date than I am.' She walked over to the coffee machine. 'Anyone for a drink?'

'Nah. Any more caffeine and I won't sleep a wink. I probably won't sleep a wink anyway,' Owen said, running his hand across his eyes. 'Angelica's got another tooth coming through.'

Gaby sent him a sympathy-laden smile. She had no idea how Owen managed to get through the day on so little sleep. Being used to shift work most likely helped but she could never imagine a situation where she had to work all day only to cap it off with staying up all night. The fact that it was his own child was probably key but that wasn't an area that she could think on. All day her mind had been pulling her back to her personal life and her problem with Rusty, despite the complexities of the case and what was happening with Amy. It was like a bite mark she couldn't resist scratching: illogical but irresistible.

Owen clapped his hands. 'Right then, a quick five minutes before I send you lot home.'

'I'll stay,' Marie said, removing the wrapping from a Cadbury's Dairy Milk. 'It will save on Mal's heating bill.'

'Count me in too. Georgie is back on nights so no reason not to,' Jax added.

Gaby smiled, picking up her mobile and scrolling through the apps until she found the one she was looking for. She'd be just the same if their positions were reversed but that didn't lessen the pride she felt. Police work was boring most of the time. Long spells stuck in front of a laptop wading through the most tedious of information. That was one of the reasons she refused to either read or watch crime programmes on the telly, unlike Owen who gobbled them up like sweeties. A nice programme like *Bridgerton* with tea on tap was her idea of pleasure.

'Pizzas all round then,' she finally said, tapping away.

'Pepperoni for me with extra chili.'

'Owen, when have I ever known you to choose anything else?' Gaby rolled her eyes. 'Two pepperoni, one ham and pineapple and one cheese. Oh, and a meatball one for Mal. They'll be ready in an hour.' She returned her mobile to the table and turned to face Owen, her meaning clear.

'I might as well go first.' Owen picked up the red marker and headed for the third board. 'I've just come back from Manchester and the results of Jules's autopsy. The upshot is that she gave birth shortly before her death.'

'How did I know you were going to say that?' Gaby lifted up her mug and downed her coffee in one.

'I don't know. How did you?' he mimicked, his expression as serious as his tone.

'Bates, you know me too well to ask that. Instinct? Second sight? Or perhaps the fact that Christy has finally woken up.'

She returned her empty mug to the table, her movements slow and controlled unlike her imagination, which was flaring in all directions. Gaby wasn't mathematical. She had a hard enough time balancing her bank account at the end of each month let alone coping with the complexities of mathematical probability. She knew what she knew and she suspected the rest. The one thing she couldn't work out was the motive and they'd need that to capture the perpetrator. It wasn't the first time she'd had to deal with crimes against women but by comparison this was off the scale. She felt like weeping but that wouldn't serve any purpose. Calm and collected thinking was needed and that meant . . . more coffee.

'And?'

Gaby pushed away from the desk and, heading for the cafetiere, fiddled around with filter paper. She needed a moment, just one, to marshal her thoughts before retelling Christy's story.

# Chapter 33

## Past
## Christy

**Wednesday 10 February, 1.05 a.m. Treasure Cottage**

'I need to go to hospital. Please, Eli. I'm really scared.'

'You'll be fine, sweetheart. Absolutely fine. I know you're scared, terrified even, but giving birth is such a beautiful, natural experience. I'll be with you all of the way.'

If she'd heard those words once she'd heard them a thousand times. They never changed, never altered. It was as if he'd learnt them off pat and refused to deviate from even a syllable.

Christy pressed both hands against the rigid frame of her stomach, another wave of contractions drowning her words and suffocating her scream. It felt as if she'd been like this for hours, days even. She couldn't think. She couldn't process anything but the pain ripping through her flesh and tearing through her dignity. It didn't matter that she was lying naked, sweat-drenched hair dripping down her back, her fingers clenched against the mattress as her nails dug into the sheets. She started to pant like the video had shown her, trying to open her mind to the pain-free seconds up ahead, before the next wave hit.

She couldn't complain about how attentive Eli was being. Nothing was too much trouble, from a back rub to iced water by the barrel load and renewing the flannel to her forehead. They'd discussed pain relief, of course they had, and like him, she was all for a natural birth. But it wasn't Eli lying there riven by pain. There was something wrong, terribly wrong, but she couldn't seem to get him to understand that she needed the attention of a midwife now. He'd done what he could but it had been too long, far too long.'

The pain disappeared, leaving her collapsed back into the pillows.

'Eli, I'm begging you,' she stuttered, tears rolling down her cheeks. 'I can't do this anymore.' Her hand smoothed over her abdomen, prodding gently. 'I think . . . No. I know I need help. I'm *begging* you.'

He looked worried, the stress visible. But she had far more to be worried about. There was something in the way he couldn't quite meet her eye that scared her more than anything before. There was no help coming. There was her and him and a baby she was beginning to think would never be born. She'd been pleading for hours now but he was as immovable as a brick and about as useful.

'If you're not going to help then you might as well go away,' she finally said, closing both her eyes and her mind to what came next. She'd accompanied her father on some of his many farm visits over the years, especially when he'd realised that she'd wanted to become a vet just like him. Most births went to plan and proved to be a glorious reaffirmation as to what she'd wanted to do with her life.

But those births weren't what she was thinking about now. They couldn't help her. She knew what she had to do: it was either that or die here with no meaningful help coming from any quarter.

She remembered her dad saying that labour was as distressing for the baby as it was for the mum. Okay, so he'd been talking about sheep at the time but now she thought of his words as she tried and failed to remember when she'd last felt her baby move. It must be half an hour or more. She spoke again, her voice a thread of sound, the words a shock even to her.

Without the pain, she was calm. Calm and resigned to what she had to do next.

# Chapter 34

## Gaby

**Wednesday 10 February, 5.25 p.m. St Asaph**

'You're kidding me!'

'I'm afraid not,' Gaby said, noting Jax's pasty skin tone. 'Remember the wound to her abdomen when she was found? We assumed it was defensive in nature but not a bit of it. She told me that she made him sterilise one of the knives from the kitchen and, in between swigs from a whisky bottle, she performed a caesarean on herself.'

'You're lucky they let you question her,' Owen said.

'Very but she was as much telling the story to her mum as she was to me. She had the presence of mind to plug the wound with a pillowcase before she collapsed. When she came to, she was expecting to find herself in hospital. The man – her partner, or so she told me, an Elijah Brown, no e – told her he was going to fetch an ambulance. Instead he hightailed it with the baby, leaving her on her own.'

'The absolute bastard.' Marie broke off a piece of chocolate and stuffed it into her mouth. 'So, he took the baby and left her for dead?'

'Certainly looks that way.'

'I'd like to fillet him in two and see how he likes it. Words fail me.'

'I think they fail us all, Marie,' Owen said, adding a note on the board before turning back to face the room. 'But your story does tie in with the autopsy report on Jules White, which confirms that she also gave birth. So, what about a description then? His mobile number and shoe size would also be helpful!'

'Hah. No such luck, Owen, but good try.' Gaby picked up her mobile and swiped the screen. 'Elijah Brown, age twenty-three. Tall, about five-eleven or thereabouts. Well-built but not fat. In her own words, he looks after himself. Dark brown hair, a little long.' She pointed to just over her collar. 'No tattoos, piercings or skin blemishes. That's all I managed to get before the nurse finally realised who I was and kicked me out.' She shut off her phone and returned it to her desk before walking towards the window. The snow had started to fall.

They'd hit pay dirt with Christy still being alive. They'd better keep her that way. Gaby blinked, putting herself into the shoes of this Elijah Brown. He'd know by now that Christy had been found alive, the only witness they had currently to what had happened on that mountainside. A witness who could pick him out of a line-up and get him put away for a very long time.

Gaby hurried back to her desk and picked up her phone, tapping in an internal number from memory.

'Evening, sir, I thought you might still be here.' She waited a moment, her expression unchanged despite his less than effusive words as to the lack of progress on the case. 'Yes, that's why I'm ringing. I need an officer assigned to the hospital. Round-the-clock protection. Yes, sir. Thank you, sir. I will.' Gaby replaced the phone back down on the cradle, her hand pressing the receiver hard against the black plastic, her eyes meeting Owen's. She knew that Sherlock was only being kind but asking her to pass on his condolences to Tim's parents was the very last thing she needed.

Owen was right. She had to contact them and soon but . . . God forgive her, it wasn't one of her immediate priorities.

She removed her hand, tucking it into the waistband of her trousers. 'I'm annoyed that I didn't think of the risk to Christy earlier but, as the only witness, it makes sense that he's going to try and prevent her from speaking to us.'

'He probably thought she wouldn't make it.'

'Exactly that, Jax. A natural assumption after everything she's been through. And with no media coverage yet he's most likely alternating between his mobile and the TV, waiting for news of her body being discovered.'

'What sicko would do such a thing?'

'What have I missed?' Mal said from the doorway, his hands laden down with pizza boxes. 'I take it you've all decided to share my shift in addition to feeding me. That's more than kind.'

'Don't get any ideas, Mal. We'll stay for a bit but not all night,' Gaby said, giving him a brief update. 'You're lucky I remembered your predilection for meatballs,' she continued, relieved at the interruption not least because Marie looked ready for tears. She felt the same but sheer bloody-mindedness wouldn't allow her even a sniff.

'You're only jealous, ma'am,' he said, unwinding his scarf and removing his gloves before taking a second to flex his muscles. 'My body is a temple, as you very well know. Any opportunity to add to my protein intake and I'll take it.'

'Are you saying that mine isn't?' Gaby asked, striking a pose. 'Remember, temples come in all shapes and sizes, Mal. I happen to be a shorter, rounded version but still perfectly formed.'

He chuckled. 'If you say so.'

She joined in with his laughter. Okay, so it was a touch hysterical around the edges but with the mood lifting, they decided on a quick pizza break while they filled Mal in on their day.

'And you're only staying until eight at the latest, Bates. And, yes, that is an order,' Gaby said, packing up the empty boxes and piling them beside the door for recycling later.

'If you say so, ma'am,' he said, mirroring Mal's words.

'Don't be like that. You said yourself that you didn't get much sleep last night. What kind of a boss would I be if I didn't take that into account?'

'One who wants to solve the case.'

'Really! And how are you meant to function tomorrow if Angelica decides on an all-night teething party?'

'Kate just messaged me.' He nodded at his mobile, his expression smug. 'The little bugger is through. It only took half a packet of rusks and a bit of raw carrot.'

Gaby stared at him, managing a smile of sorts because, of course, she'd forgotten all about Rusty and Conor. She hadn't given a thought to the cupboards being bare and that she'd been planning on doing a large shop on the way home. It hadn't crossed her mind until just now. Bugger indeed. While Rusty was a grown-up and well used to fending for himself, the very least she could do was warn him to get some food in on the way home.

'In that case, you can stay all night. I won't mention it again.' She picked up her phone and made for the door. 'I'm popping up to my office; be back in five.'

# Chapter 35

## Bryony

**Wednesday 10 February, 5.55 p.m. Blaen-Cym House**

Bryony was bored, which was ridiculous. Crazy even. The craziest thing ever considering having all the time in the world to do all the things she'd ever wanted was what she'd dreamt of over the last few months. It wasn't that she hated school. The coursework was difficult but manageable once she'd set up a study time-table. It also wasn't anything to do with her parents. She knew underneath it all that they wanted the best for her. No. It was something inside. Some thought that she was missing out. But missing out on what exactly?

She glanced around the kitchen, not seeing the pine cabinets or the coordinating ceramic tiles and worktops. She'd come into the kitchen to start preparing tea. One of those curry dishes where all the spices came pre-measured in tiny plastic packets. She'd have preferred to make her own from scratch but it was all in the way of spices that Eli had provided. He didn't seem to care and she wasn't in the mood to spend hours chopping, peeling, and slicing while he sat in the lounge messing around with the

160

TV remote. It didn't take a genius to work out that the life she'd dreamt of wasn't the one she was currently living, even as she told herself to get a grip. She'd been given a beautiful home to live in and the most perfect of men to share it with. There was nothing that she was lacking and yet the misery remained. Eli was getting annoyed with her and that was something she couldn't allow to happen. After all she was reliant on him for everything now from the food on the table to the clothes on her back.

She threw the diced onions into the frying pan with a sigh, the pungent aroma hitting the back of her throat and almost causing her to gag. She'd been lucky up to now with regards to morning sickness but she knew she had to be careful. She sighed again, much deeper this time. Her hand sneaked to her belly, which was still remarkably flat.

Pregnant at seventeen wasn't what she would have hoped or planned, especially as they'd taken precautions.

With the garlic and onions on the heat, she opened the sachet of spices and added them to the mix before throwing in a can of chopped tomatoes. Bryony had never been a great meat eater but all there was to add to the sauce was a packet of chicken pieces. The sight of the pink flesh added to her overall unhappiness.

She would have never put Eli down as a control freak but his recent behaviour only confirmed that view. He was different now that they were living together, not so much fun and far too bossy. To moan about her unhealthy diet and then force her to take a vitamin pill when he knew she struggled with tablets was one thing. He hadn't seemed bothered about her diet when they'd first met, always complimenting her on her looks when deep down she knew that he could do better. He couldn't have changed overnight but that was exactly what seemed to have happened.

Eli had disappeared only to be replaced by a stranger who looked like him but acted very differently. To take a risk at happiness only to find fool's gold at the end of her personal rainbow was almost more than she could bear. They hadn't rowed exactly but he hadn't said two words to her after the incident in the bedroom earlier. Where before he'd been kind and loving, now he was arrogant and overbearing. All she could think about was the reason for the change and what she'd done or hadn't done to instigate it.

She picked up the wooden spoon and stirred the sauce before reducing the heat and angling the lid on top, her mind looping in circles while she tried to puzzle it out.

There was nothing left to do in the kitchen. The plates and cutlery were out and the rice already in the saucepan. She should probably return to the lounge; that's what Eli was expecting, but she couldn't be bothered. Instead she slipped into the hall and headed for the bedroom, her feet barely making a sound, an idea forming.

For all her common sense and intelligence, Bryony was as insecure as an orphaned lamb in search of his mother. A lack of looks combined with a geeky mind-set had exposed her to a raft of snubs over the years. The promised sleepovers and party invites that never materialised were just part of the treatment she'd received at the hands of her peers. It was only when she'd met Ruby that she actually realised what she'd been missing. The girly chats in the library when the librarian had gone for lunch. The general feeling of camaraderie that she wasn't going through those teenage years on her lonesome. They'd formed a tightly knit unit up until Eli had come on to the scene.

Bryony felt the heat flush across her cheeks, guilt pushing up through her diaphragm to her face. She'd known at the time that she hadn't been fair to Ruby. She'd been less than fair, leaving her to cope on her own through breaks, the most difficult time for anyone being bullied. But Bryony had pushed those feelings aside while she wandered through her first relationship with her head in the clouds and her knickers in her handbag. Her blush deepened. She wasn't a tart, far from it, but it was different with Eli. Sweet and innocent. He hadn't rushed her into anything that she hadn't wanted and he was so sensible, insisting on always using a condom. He'd even asked her to marry him without prompting when she'd finally plucked up the courage to tell him about her late period. Now it was different. Now she was scared of what she'd got herself into.

Instead of stretching out on the bed, she pulled open the wardrobe and riffled through the selection of clothing Eli had put together for her. Long, floaty dresses and a selection of thick jumpers and cardigans, which would be perfect but not yet and she quite liked knowing that she was wearing her own clothes. Okay, so her jeans were starting to tighten around the waist but, with the top button undone, they were the most comfortable thing she owned and at least she'd chosen them. Restless, she turned to the second wardrobe even though she knew that it housed none of her clothes.

Eli was a snazzy dresser with a fine taste in suits and smart casuals. She ran a finger down the fabric of one of his fitted T-shirts, the one he'd been wearing when she'd first seen him. She couldn't say that it was love at first sight but she'd certainly felt something twinge under her breastbone at the way the cloth had stretched across his shoulders.

The plastic bag stuffed right at the back was incongruous with everything she knew about him. All his clothing was either hung up or neatly folded, his socks and boxers following suit. His shoes neatly aligned against the wall. Bryony flicked a cautious glance over her shoulder. She wasn't doing anything wrong and even if he did burst in, she could easily explain away that she was on the hunt for dirty clothes to make up a full load for the washing machine.

The bag was heavy, heavier than it looked, the handles tied in a knot that only took seconds to free. She frowned at the contents. A pair of mucky trainers that had seen better days on top of a bundle of clothes. The only thing unusual about the trainers was that they looked like a supermarket brand instead of the Nikes

Eli usually wore. Unless the previous tenants had left them by mistake. The old clothes were unlabelled. A full complement of jeans, shirt, jumper and thick jacket. But it wasn't the clothes or the shoes that caused her heart to dip and her temper to flare.

She sat back on her heels, the bag safely refastened and back in place, the letter to her parents scrunched up between her fingers. The letter he'd promised he'd posted. The most unsettling thing – she didn't have the guts to ask him why he hadn't.

# Chapter 36

## Gaby

### Wednesday 10 February, 5.55 p.m. St Asaph

Gaby ended the call, her hand lingering around the receiver. The difficult call to Rusty, which had been anything but. They'd glossed over the fractures in their relationship, instead discussing the mundane, which made her feel a fraud about all the bitchy thoughts she'd been having about him all day. But after years on the force, she was well versed in the art of compartmentalising her life into work and after-work segments.

The incident room was exactly as she'd left it five minutes before except for the sudden silence closely followed by a spurt of activity, which nearly drew a smile. Not quite. They'd either been talking about Amy or Rusty. Perhaps both. Her mood dropped a notch. She'd like nothing better than to spend the evening beside Amy, willing her to wake up, but Bryony had to take precedence.

'Sorry about that.' She settled back in her swivel chair. 'I'm all ears.'

'No need to apologise.' Owen picked up the TV remote. 'I

thought we should probably see what kind of a hash I made of the press conference. Ah, here it is. Hold on a sec and I'll just turn up the sound.'

The discovery of Jules's corpse in such gruesome circumstances was now mainstream news as was Bryony's disappearance. George Alagiah seemed suitably shocked when presenting the piece while Owen looked terrified, making what was his first appearance on national television.

'Great tie, mate,' Mal shouted across the room.

'Thanks, I got Kate to—' Owen stopped abruptly, noting the snigger on his face. 'Why? What's wrong with it?'

'Nothing. Nothing at all. I spotted something similar in the window of Primark only last week.'

'Which isn't surprising as that's where it's from.'

'Hey, you two. Stop it. We have work to do or have you forgotten?' Marie snapped. 'The tie is suitably restrained, which is more than I can say for your *avant-garde* nonsense, Mal. Unless you know something about the killer that's neckwear-related then ties aren't really relevant, are they!'

'Thank you, Marie,' Gaby said, biting back a comment about posturing peacocks and their relevance to the male egos in the office. 'Let's carry on, shall we, before I pass an edict that allows sleeping bags at work.'

'Good idea. Not about the sleeping bags. That's pants,' Owen said, dropping his hand from where he'd been fingering his tie with all the aplomb of a teenager meeting his prom date. 'So, has anyone found anything about this Elijah Brown then or is it an alias?'

'I'd go with the latter,' Jax said, his gaze still on the screen. 'A few Elijah Browns out there but nothing on the system so he's not known to us under that name.'

'Hmm. What are the odds that he has a criminal record, if only for some random misdemeanour? It would be unusual if he didn't.'

'Exactly what I was thinking. Should I get in touch with Manchester to see if they're doing any better?'

'Good idea.' Owen turned to Marie. 'What about your visit to the Lloyds? I think you said it was the sister that interested you?'

'That's right,' Marie said, sweeping her blonde hair over one shoulder. 'I don't remember leaving an interview feeling more helpless than I did this afternoon. Cerys mentioned the boyfriend but that's something we suspected. There's also Bryony's savings. Common sense should dictate that she would have emptied her bank account before disappearing but that's not what happened.' She picked up her biro, rolling it between her thumb and forefinger. 'The girl hasn't touched a penny for months, apart from purchasing her Christmas presents. It doesn't make any sense.'

'Unless she was scared stiff that someone would guess at what she was up to,' Owen said, making a note on the whiteboard.

'I didn't get that impression at all. On paper, she sounds like the ideal daughter – that is, for the Lloyds – completely focused on her studies. The mother is a car crash and I'll bet the father is only holding it together by putting a shift in at the practice. The sister knew about the boyfriend in so far as she guessed and badgered Bryony into telling her. But she didn't know anything much. A name would have been good for a start.'

'With Christy under police protection and by all accounts stable, we might be able to start filling in some of those gaps,' Gaby said. 'What we need is a media blackout for another twenty-four hours or so until her doctor gives us permission to interview her in earnest and—'

'Too late for that, ma'am,' Jax said, glancing up from where he was checking his mobile. 'Someone somewhere has just let the cat out of the bag. It's all over Facebook – I'd be very surprised if the news channels don't pick up on it, not to mention the DCI . . .' He paused to stare at Gaby's ringing phone.

Gaby sighed at the sight of DCI Sherlock's name flashing

across the screen. They'd been lucky in forging the connection with Manchester, but their luck had just run out. If the media had got hold of the story then so would Bryony's abductor. And who knew what he might do then?

# Chapter 37

## Gaby

**Wednesday 10 February, 9 p.m. Rhos-on-Sea**

The very last thing Gaby needed right now was for special treatment from Rusty and Conor, particularly Conor.

Conor was a nice enough lad. Well brought up and grounded, despite a long-distance relationship with his mother and a father who often worked round the clock. But that's as far as it went. He'd never bothered to hide his animosity towards Gaby, and most days they were barely on speaking terms. Oh, he was polite up to a point but only when Rusty was at home; on the odd occasion when it was just the two of them, he went out of his way to be an insufferable little git. If she was lucky, he'd hide away in his room on his computer until Rusty came home, only drifting out for food and the occasional side-swiping comment. As she wasn't his parent, she let him. Gaby was wise enough not to take it to heart but maturity didn't lessen the impact of his behaviour.

It had come to the stage where she didn't bother to tell Rusty even when he asked. The truth was, Conor was still very much a child. There was nothing that Rusty could do to change his son's

169

attitude that didn't involve either disciplining him or shouting, neither of which would improve matters.

When she arrived home, the first thing she always did was step out of her shoes before sliding them under the crescent-shaped hall table. On this occasion Rusty and Conor met her in the hall.

'Conor was worried about you.'

'Oh.'

Conor ran across the small space, burying his head somewhere in the vicinity of her shoulder. 'Dad told me about Tim. I thought that the same might have happened to you.'

Gaby had learned a lot about child rearing over the last six months, not least that it was far more difficult than policing on a good day and, up to now, there had been no good days in her relationship with Rusty's son. She certainly didn't know what to say to him now to make him feel better. There was no better and there never could be.

Instead, she hugged him back, relishing the smell of his freshly washed hair with the faint undertone of bubble gum. She'd never been party to their bedtime ritual and this was the first time that Conor had let down his guard with her. She was only sad that it had taken a tragedy for it to happen.

She drew back, smoothing her hand over his springy hair one final time before giving his shoulder a little squeeze. 'I didn't realise how tall you'd got, Conor.' She glanced down at the hem of his school trousers. 'You'll soon be as tall as your dad.'

'I'm nearly as tall as you already,' he said, with a smirk.

'Well, that wouldn't be hard, would it?' she replied, her voice dry.

Part of her was pleased that he seemed to be bouncing back to his usual form but only a small part. While she didn't like to see him unhappy, she'd enjoyed the hug despite the reason behind it. Straightening her shoulders, she finally felt ready to meet Rusty's gaze. 'Sorry I'm late and that the cupboards were bare.'

'Don't give it a second thought,' he said, taking her laptop bag from her. 'Mother Hubbard to the rescue. We opted for fish and chips as a treat.' He paused, his fleeting expression difficult to read. 'They're in the oven.'

'You mean Conor didn't decide to eat mine too?' she said, grinning across at where he was now glued on the sofa glued to the television.

'It was a closely fought battle.' Rusty placed her bag on the hall table and, lifting up his hands, cradled her face. 'I'm sorry about last night and that you've had a shitty day,' he said, dropping a gentle kiss on her upturned mouth. 'Come on, let's eat in the kitchen. Conor won't miss us.'

'I thought you would have eaten?'

'And leave you to a solitary tea?' He shook his head. 'You should know me better than that, Gabriella.'

Gaby followed him into the kitchen, a wave of tiredness spreading across her skin and lodging somewhere in the vicinity of her muscles – all of them. It had been a difficult day yesterday followed by an impossible one today. All she wanted was to switch off the lights and retreat under the nearest duvet. Instead she had to sit in the kitchen and make small talk.

'You don't have to talk if you don't want to,' he said, with uncanny insight as he placed a plate in front of her along with a glass of water. 'But feel free to vent if it will help. I've got broad shoulders.'

Gaby didn't want food, especially after the slice of pizza she'd consumed earlier before sliding the box in Jax and Mal's direction, the taste like sawdust. She didn't want anything apart from the last twenty-four hours not to have happened. But the clock was insatiable in the way it chewed up time, leaving bitter memories of their dinner party lingering along with her best wine glasses, which she'd yet to put away. She shook the thought aside and, picking up the glass, watched him over the rim.

'What was your day like?' she said, her eyes trained on where he'd started to dissect his fish.

'Oh, you know.' He concentrated on removing a bone from

171

the pile of white flesh. 'The usual. Most of it was writing reports and in meetings. I also had an interesting email from Dublin.'

'Dublin?' She took her time in choosing the perfect chip. Gaby wasn't a foodie, far from it, but she knew what she liked and for her the perfect chip was golden brown with a crunchy outer coating. She finally found it under the mountain he'd piled on to her plate.

'Yes. The Justice Department. They've offered me a job,' he said, his attention still on his fish.

The chip caught in the back of her throat and took two attempts to swallow. She had the weight of the world on her shoulders and now this. If this was Rusty's way of telling her that it was all over then he had the worst timing imaginable.

'And are you going to take it?'

'What do you think?' He lifted his head, meeting her gaze square on.

'I don't know. That's why I asked.'

'I can't deny that it's not tempting but unless you have a hankering to move to the Emerald Isle then no, I'm not.'

'I thought . . .' Gaby rarely cried if ever and certainly never over a man, despite having had plenty of reason to in the past. Now the tears came in a torrent of emotion when she least expected them. She'd remained strong throughout the day. She didn't know how she'd managed to negotiate her time spent at the hospital or later at the office. The sight of Lara. The beauty of that small combination of Tim and Amy in one tiny package. The hope in her forget-me-not-blue eyes.

'I'm sorry, I didn't mean to . . .'

He pushed away from the table and was by her side in an instant. 'I'm not sure what you thought but I'm not going anywhere unless you tell me to,' he said, wiping her tears away with some of the kitchen roll he'd used in place of napkins. 'You're not, are you?'

Gaby stared back at him, noticing his look of uncertainty, an expression she'd never seen on his dear face. What could she say? She wasn't convinced that she could ever be content without a child of her own but was that her being greedy? There were plenty of good relationships where children never featured. Look at Lara and what kind of a life she faced without her father, she remembered, closing her eyes briefly. And at least they had Conor. She opened her eyes again, coming to a decision, which wasn't a decision at all. More of a delaying tactic. She also wasn't going to be forced into making a decision because it suited Rusty, whatever his motive. They hadn't talked about Caroline Maston. Okay, so she wasn't convinced that there was anything to tell but she couldn't live her life being scared of every femme fatale that came Rusty's way. She trusted him up to a point. That would have to do.

'You're stuck with me for the moment. Now, about these chips,' she said, directing the conversation onto safer ground. 'You're not going to be offended if I can't eat them?'

'Conor, are you still hungry?'

After Conor had scoffed the remaining chips and half of the fish, after Gaby and Rusty both saw him up to bed, at his behest, and after all the dishes had been washed up and put away in their respective cabinets, Gaby curled up on the sofa next to Rusty.

'What do you think I should do about Tim's parents?'

'I can't tell you what to do, Gabriella,' he said, placing his hand on her knee even as he stole the remote and started flicking through the channels. 'You know them better than me.'

'I barely know them at all but Tim was a good friend.'

'Then that's your answer.'

'I'll leave it until the morning. Half nine is far too late to be phoning.'

'That's up to you but I think it's unlikely that they'll be asleep. I certainly wouldn't be.'

'If you're sure . . . ?'

'I'm not sure about anything anymore but it's probably the right thing to do.'

Gaby picked up her mobile and pulled up her phone numbers. As Amy's chief bridesmaid last year she'd a whole host of new contacts; Tim's mother was one of them.

'Faith, it's Gaby. Gaby Darin,' she said, barely leaving room for his mother to reply before going into a far from original speech. 'I'm so sorry for your loss. Rusty and I are devastated.' She waited a moment, her mobile pressed hard against her ear, her free hand reaching out and grabbing Rusty's in the tightest of grips, her nails causing untold damage to the skin on the back of his hand. He'd have a few awkward moments of explaining over the next few days – not that Gaby cared. She didn't notice anything apart from Faith's next words, an image of Lara popping into her mind and staying there.

# Chapter 38

## Bryony

**Wednesday 10 February, 10.05 p.m. Blaen-Cym House**

'You're not going out now? Not after leaving me last night,' she said, following him into the hall.

'I don't have any choice, Bry.' He collected his jacket from the coat rack and, pulling his scarf from out of the pocket, proceeded to wind it around his neck. 'Why don't you head up and I'll be back before you know I've even gone?'

'If I'd known it was going to be like this, I'd never have agreed to come with you.'

'If I'd known you were going to be such a nag, I'd never have invited you,' he retorted, without a trace of his usual cheeky grin.

Bryony didn't know whether he was joking but the way he was clenching his keys was a pretty good indication that he wasn't. If she hadn't been so annoyed, she'd have found it funny but it was no laughing matter. He was deserting her for the third time in two days and there was nothing she could do about it.

The door banged behind him, the noise echoing around the empty room. Instead of doing what he'd told her, she wandered back into the lounge and dropped onto the sofa. He'd been fine after tea, more than fine. Full of plans for tomorrow and beyond, so much so that she'd almost forgotten what had gone before. After all, anyone could forget to post a letter. She'd done it herself on occasion. She'd left the room to make them a hot drink, which had only taken her a few minutes. But in those minutes, everything had changed.

Now she concentrated on what could have happened in the lounge to make him run out on her. He'd been in the lounge playing with his phone but she hadn't heard it ring and she was well known for her acute hearing. So it had to be something on the television. Maybe even something to do with her. She picked up the remote, part of her surprised that he'd left it behind and then ashamed at the thought. She wasn't a prisoner, even if his attitude had changed.

The news was still on. She'd curl up on the sofa and wait for the recap of the headlines that always came at the end.

# Chapter 39

## Mal

Malachy Devine was the newest member of the team but also the most determined. With no dependants or partner to distract him, he threw himself into his job. The work he was doing was all very well but he had every intention of managing his own team in the near future. Gaby was a good enough DI but he knew he could do better.

Last night had been a disaster for many reasons but mostly because it had interrupted his research into possible restaurant venues. Jax had managed to uncover that Bryony had stopped to eat somewhere between Mold and Llandudno from the guest house owners, but that wasn't particularly helpful unless they could expand on that titbit of information.

The reason the couple had decided to stop off was what was puzzling him the most. Mal liked things neat. His desk was the tidiest in the incident room, his ironing pile non-existent, his apartment pristine. Stopping off didn't make sense. Doing so meant they'd increase the chance of someone spotting them. A

177

random person in the street. A CCTV camera. A stray fingerprint or particle of DNA. And yet they'd ignored the risks. Why?

He pushed the thought aside to play around with later as he continued working his way through the phone book. Looking for the right restaurant was always going to be a difficult if not impossible task, except for one vital fact. Bryony had disappeared on a Monday, when most restaurants were closed. He was left with two possibilities. After phoning them both, he ruled out the exclusive French restaurant as being an unusual choice. That left a pizzeria.

Mal sat back in his chair, the printout in his hand as he ran through a breakdown of both the bookings and the bills. It hadn't been a busy night at Johnny Dough's pizza restaurant, far from it. The party of ten that had paid by credit card. The table of four that had pre-booked months before. The smattering of drinks paid for at the bar. The two pizzas and drinks paid for in cash. He slapped the sheet down on the desk in annoyance, the last item highlighted in red. People didn't use cash anymore. Certainly not for a full meal and drinks. The trail once again had gone cold and he was left with the feeling that they were dealing with someone who had all the cards stacked on his side.

The only error the man had made – choosing a restaurant on a Monday when most were closed – was wiped out in an instant. There wasn't anything Mal could do . . . or was there? His brow creased as he reached for his keyboard and searched for the file that Jason had sent on the man they were looking for. The guest house owner had only seen the man twice and on each occasion Brown had been wearing a woolly hat pulled low over his forehead. But, despite that, the image almost exactly matched the description they'd been given by Christy Taylor. Thank God for the station's e-fit artist. Now all they needed was a miracle or, in this case, someone recognising him. He pressed the print button before reaching for his coat and car keys. It was all he had so it would have to do.

# Chapter 40

## Gaby

**Thursday 11 February, 7.10 a.m. Rhos-on-Sea**

Despite everything Gaby fell into a deep dreamless sleep as soon as her head hit the pillow. A drug-induced sleep facilitated by Rusty who'd sneaked a sleeping tablet into her mug of hot chocolate – not that he'd ever admit to it. As a pathologist, Rusty didn't have a capacious black bag full of medical delights. He wasn't that sort of doctor. He'd found what he'd needed tucked in the back of Gaby's bathroom cabinet.

She woke with a thick head and a dry mouth, which made a mockery of her alcohol-free evening but a mug of tea on her bedside table, along with her mobile, distracted her from the thought that Rusty might have done something to aid her sleep. She'd remember later but by then it would be far too late to question, the importance diluted to a faint shadow by everything that followed.

'You should have woken me,' were her first words when she raced down the stairs, fresh from the shower.

'It's only a little gone seven. You have plenty of time,' Rusty said, waving a hand in the direction of the table, where Conor was munching on a bowl of his usual cereal.

She was about to refuse breakfast only to stare across at his son, her mouth closing in surprise.

'I have a volleyball match at four, if you're free to make it, Gaby? Dad said that he'd try and be there.' Conor's eyes narrowed. 'You know what he's like when he gets stuck into those dead bodies of his.'

Gaby nearly laughed despite her current mood, which had sadness entrenched in all four corners. She was swamped in grief but still able to appreciate the innocent black humour from a twelve-year-old.

The thought curled and died, like paper over a candle flame, leaving a bitter taste in her heavy heart. But it wasn't Conor's fault, far from it. For the first time, he was trying to bridge the chasm in their relationship. It was up to her to provide the bricks and mortar.

Taking the chair beside him, she reached for the butter and started slathering the slice of toast Rusty had placed in front of her, taking care to spread it to the edges. 'I can't one-hundred-per-cent promise, Conor, in case I let you down – if one of your dad's bodies misbehaves – but I'll do my very best. Thank you for asking though; it means a great deal.'

She felt Rusty's fingers squeeze her knee and, slipping her hand under the table, placed it on top. It was the first time she felt they might become a family. The cloud shifted to reveal a chink of light. How could she be so happy and yet so desperately sad?

Gaby picked up her toast and took a bite.

Her phone rang.

The bread turned to ash in her mouth.

\*

Gaby almost felt as if the incident room was her second home. Some days she spent longer in the room than she did in her own house. Today she wanted to be anywhere other than the bright, warm space, with one square window looking down over the car park.

At ten past eight, Mal was still propped up in front of his keyboard, black stubble shadowing his jaw. Marie was in the process of hanging up her coat on the rack behind the door while Owen was filling up the coffee pot. Even Jax, who was usually the last to show, was lounging in his chair, busily texting on his mobile. It was as if a shutter had come down in her mind. The image of her team forever captured in their usual places. A before shot. She wondered what the picture would be like in a few brief seconds. How would they cope with the news? Her gaze landed on Marie before flickering across to Owen – the two people she was most concerned about.

There was a pause, an intense silence, the walls contracting around the tight space. The world outside shrank, the case unimportant as the reality of life and death took precedence. There was no easy way to tell them. As their boss, it was her responsibility. Gaby was a great believer in the power of foreshadowing. Her team knew something was up by her behaviour alone. Now she had to colour in between the lines.

'I'm sorry to have to inform you that Amy passed away last night,' she finally managed, her voice deliberately devoid of any expression. 'I know you'll join me in offering our condolences to both her and Tim's families.'

# Chapter 41

## Bryony

### Thursday 11 February, 12.50 p.m. Blaen-Cym House

Eli was different, so very different. Less caring. Less romantic. Just less. He still wanted sex but that was also different. More mechanical. Going through the motions. She could be a lump of meat in the bed for all the care he took about her feelings, her needs. To wake up with him pounding on top of her had wiped away any last excuses she'd been making for his behaviour. She'd made a mistake, a terrible mistake. But with no way of contacting her family and the snow continuing to fall, Bryony had no chance of putting it right.

Conversation was out of the question now. The last time she'd tried, all she'd got for her efforts was a monosyllabic grunt of a reply. She knew he wasn't interested in her and that was the most confusing thing of all. What was she doing here if he didn't want her? Surely he should have dumped her when she'd told him about the baby. She'd read enough true-life stories to know that that's what a lot of men did. Dumped their partner before running into the distance as fast as their vile legs would carry them. But not Eli. As far as the baby was concerned, he was ideal father material. Only this morning, he'd made Bryony sit at the breakfast table and watched while she spooned cereal into her mouth along with the vitamins he'd set out with a military precision. After, he'd wandered into the lounge and sat in front of the television, leaving her to her own devices. She'd decided to stay in the bedroom out of his way and that's where he found her.

'Time for lunch.' He didn't even bother with calling her sweetheart. That was one of the things that hurt the most.

'I'm not hungry.'

'Tough. I don't care if you're stuffed to the gills,' he said, from his position in the doorway, his hand on his hip. 'You have a baby to look after or don't you care about its welfare? Just how selfish are you, Bryony?'

'You know that's not true,' she said, her voice a rasp of sound as tears gathered. 'Why are you being so mean to me all of a sudden?'

'Perhaps because I'm sick of your whining. Eli do this. Eli do that,' he said, in a weak imitation of her accent. 'What about what I want?'

'What do you want? Tell me?'

'I want you to shift that scrawny excuse for an arse of yours into the kitchen and get us some lunch. Don't make me have to come and get you.'

Bryony lowered her feet to the floor, conscious of his rapidly retreating footsteps and the sound of the door slamming behind him. There was nothing she could do apart from follow his orders but there'd come a time when he'd slip up, a time when the snow would have melted sufficiently for her to make her escape. She pressed her fingers under her eyes, removing any trace of tears. She wasn't prepared to give him the satisfaction. There was a lot to think about, not least what could have brought about such a change. She knew he was worried about something. She could almost smell the fear.

She placed her hand to her stomach, which was still flat

although she was now well over four months gone. Her baby came first. Not theirs. Not his but hers. How could she have been so blind? She didn't like this version of him, a version she was beginning to realise was the real Eli; all the smiley flirtatious banter stripped back to reveal the man beneath. She certainly wasn't going to let her child be born under his roof. She'd find out what was going on and act on it. Until then she'd wait. The news item last night had told her that her family were still searching for her. She could only hope that they'd find her.

# Chapter 42

## Gaby

### Thursday 11 February, 3 p.m. St Asaph

The atmosphere in the incident room wasn't worth mentioning. Owen had returned late from lunch, lacking his customary dry wit, which he must have left at home along with his smile. Jax and Marie didn't even bother leaving their desks, instead living off the supplies of sandwiches and snacks they'd had the farsightedness to bring with them now the weather had again taken a turn for the worse. Gaby hadn't remembered food – even the thought of it turned her stomach. Rusty had passed through at midday to drop off a sandwich but it remained unopened on her desk along with her unwashed coffee mug, stained from the frequent refills she'd relied on to get her through the shift.

The case had come to a standstill and none of them had the wherewithal to shift it into motion. With Amy's death, they'd not only lost a colleague and a friend, they'd lost the heart of the team. She might have been on maternity leave and with a replacement due to start next week, but that had only been a temporary measure. Amy had already negotiated a part-time contract with the DCI, which would have allowed her to work a couple of days a week to, as she'd put it, stop her going stark-raving baby bonkers.

Gaby's phone pinged through a message from Rusty, which drained what little colour she had from her cheeks. But it also gave her the push needed to put everything into perspective. They needed to move on from Amy's death and fast if they were going to find Bryony. There was a time to grieve and that wasn't in the middle of an active investigation. She reread his words with a sigh. He needn't have told her that he was about to perform an autopsy on Amy. She was angry that he had but only for a moment. Wasn't she the one who'd insisted on complete honesty from the start? She couldn't criticise him for keeping to his side of the bargain.

'Right, everyone. Stop what you're doing and let's focus.' She shifted from her chair to her resident spot in front of the white-boards, a random marker now in her hand, which she rolled between her thumb and forefinger in a continuous motion. 'Believe me when I say that I know what you're all going through but Amy wouldn't have wanted this.' She took a second to look at each of them in turn. 'She'd have told us to move on until at least the wake.' Gaby smiled, the first proper smile since she'd laughed herself silly at the dinner party. 'Even if the family balk at the idea, I suggest we go ahead anyway. We're going to give Amy and Tim the best of send-offs but that's for the future. Now we have Bryony to find and we have to find her soon. I've been trying to get the doctor looking after Christy to return my call but he's been in theatre all day, some kind of an emergency. Our main priority has to be an interview with the girl as soon as we're allowed.'

She turned to face the board and started writing. 'As we all know Mal was working on background checks last night, some-thing we didn't get around to discussing in the end. That's what I'd like us to concentrate on. You all have copies of the file he emailed us before heading home. The pizza restaurant was a good call but, in the end, inconclusive. But some of the other stuff he worked on after might bring up something. Shout out some suggestions.'

'Well, he said he was trying to find a common denominator,' Marie said, peering down at her screen.

'Mmm. Okay. So, what do the girls have *in* common?' she said, stressing the in. 'We'll discuss their differences after.'

'They're all young and studious for a start,' Marie said.

'Yes. All undertaking A levels with their sights on top universities,' Owen said, from his usual spot by the window.

'You can add innocent to that and probably naive,' Jax added. 'Both sets of parents did say that they were home birds with no boyfriends in sight.'

'True enough,' Owen said, taking up the thread. 'It's the same with Jules over in Manchester. Led a very protected life by all accounts and, like Christy and Bryony, had parents in high-powered jobs.'

'Not so innocent,' Gaby said. 'Remember, Christy and Jules were both pregnant. We don't know yet about Bryony.'

'Which could well be a motive,' Owen interrupted. 'Although I'm not sure how.'

'Let's keep to the facts. We can get to possible motives later.' Gaby ran Owen's words through her mind. The problem was that they didn't have enough evidence to do more than guess at the reasoning behind Elijah's behaviour. 'The one thing we haven't discussed is where they were picked up. Three women, two in North Wales, the other in Manchester. Not that far away but far enough to be problematic for him. There must have been a reason for him to switch locations but we don't know enough about that yet to speculate,' she said, making a note on the board with an exclamation after. 'As far as we know, none of the families knew each other. The Lloyds didn't keep any animals so wouldn't have been in need of a vet. We also know that the

Taylors weren't registered with Dr Lloyd's medical practice. What else am I missing, apart from the obvious?'

'The obvious?'

'The schools or sixth form centres, or whatever they're called. Jules attended sixth form in Manchester while Bryony was at the centre in Mold. Do we know where Christy went to school?'

'St Michaels. They have their own sixth form.'

'Thanks, Jax.' Gaby made another note on the board then took a moment to study the new entries before turning back to the room. 'So, what are we looking for. A teacher?'

'Unlikely unless they're a supply one. They don't tend to move around that much do they,' Marie said, glancing at Owen.

'Don't look at me. Pip doesn't start until September, thank God.'

'Okay. A supply teacher or someone else who works in the school.'

'It could be anyone though, couldn't it, from a receptionist to a cleaner and beyond.'

'But the one thing that they'd all have in common would be a police check, which means that either our man is new to the criminal scene or using an assumed identity.'

'Or maybe both.'

Gaby nodded at Marie. 'Good point, maybe both. Let's move on to the girls' differences.'

'Different ethnicities, Jules was mousy brown, Christy black-haired and Bryony a redhead. We also can't dismiss Jason's comment, despite wanting to.'

'What was it he said again?' Owen asked.

'The one where he was disparaging about their looks,' Marie snorted, much to Gaby's amusement.

'I understand where you're coming from, but you must agree that he does have a point and one that is supported by what we know about serial killers, Marie. There's Ted Bundy's preference for petite brunettes and John Edward Rogers for redheads and that's the two I can remember,' Gaby said, studying the photos of the three women. 'Opportunistic criminals don't tend to be fussy with who they snatch but in planned crimes like these are,' she went on, tapping each photo in turn, 'the perp usually has a type that they stick to and desirability is part of that.'

She turned to face the room, the lid now back on the marker, her head angled to take in the time on the silver-framed clock above the door. 'Speaking of which, I think the sooner we bring in a profiler the better, unless anyone has anything else to add?'

'Only that I'll start comparing the employee lists from the three girls' schools,' Marie said. 'Might as well see if there are any common denominators.'

# Chapter 43

Gaby

**Thursday 11 February, 4 p.m. Rhos School**

Gaby arrived with only seconds to spare but the sight of Conor's anxious face breaking into a grin made up for the quick dash to the car and frantic trip across town. She wouldn't have made it if Rusty hadn't insisted on swapping cars earlier, his four-wheel drive making all the difference to the journey.

She settled on one of the wooden benches that edged the sports hall, well aware of the number of eyes turned in her direction. School gate politics had changed little since she was a child. Small-minded individuals with far too much time on their hands had been less than welcoming to her Italian mother and it looked as if history was going to repeat itself if the frowns sent in her direction were anything to go by. But Gaby wasn't her mother, far from it. She was a strong, independent woman with no thought other than to support Conor. She sat back, crossing her legs in an effort to get comfortable and, apart from a gentle all-encompassing smile, which wasn't returned, ignored the lot of them. Her eyes watched the game while her mind flipped between thoughts of Amy, Lara and the case.

Later, she waited in the car rather than hanging out with the parents milling around the entrance. She'd kept her promise to Conor but there was still work she could do until he was ready to be dropped home. Top on the list was a call to Angus Ford, professor of criminal profiling at Liverpool University.

'Hello, Gaby, long time no speak.'

'Indeed it is, Angus. How are things?'

'All well, my dear. I hear on the grapevine you and Dr Mulholland are finally an item?'

'That's a very far-reaching grapevine,' she responded, her voice brittle.

'Well, you know. I was interested enough to find out. You can't blame me. Now, back to the business in hand, dear lady. I do take it that you didn't phone to wish me a safe journey home in all this snow?'

'I'm sorry. Yes. It's work,' she said, eying the main entrance for any sign of Conor. 'I have an interesting couple of cases on my books, both of which might be linked to that news item last night in Manchester.'

'The mummification?'

'That's the one.'

'Very distressing all round. I'm all ears, m'dear.'

'I have three young women, all intelligent and with great futures ahead of them. By all accounts, they were committed to their studies with little or no time for partying or even social media. We also know that two of them fell pregnant and subsequently gave birth. But, and here's the big but. They're all completely different with regards to their outward appearance, including their ethnicities and this is hampering our ability somewhat in finding a common denominator.' She spotted Conor up ahead and pushed the car door open.

'Give me a moment to make a couple of notes, Gaby. Back-of-a-cigarette-packet profiling isn't how it's done, you know,' he said, a note of reprimand creeping in. 'I'll do what I can – stay on the line.'

'Of course.' She cradled the phone into her neck and got out of the car to take Conor's bag. 'Well done. You certainly put those long legs of yours to use. Let's stop off at the shop and get some snacks. I'm sure you're starving.'

'You could say that. Shame Dad couldn't make it. You reckon he's found any more dead bodies to carve up?' he blurted out, with all the ghoul-loving tact of a pre-teen.

'Conor, shush now.'

Gaby wasn't paranoid, far from it but it would have taken a complete dimwit not to notice the sudden drop in conversation or the heads swivelled in their direction. Bloody great! That's what she got for trying to blend into the background like a proverbial Victorian wallflower.

'I do hope that "shush" wasn't meant for me, dear lady?' Angus chuckled somewhere in the vicinity of her left ear. 'Now, back to your little problem,' he continued, on a far more solemn note. 'You're lucky that I read the *Guardian* earlier, the unfortunate issue in Manchester made the front page and, reading between the lines, there are very few clues.'

'I think that's an overestimation, Angus. One of my officers attended the post-autopsy briefing and it's more like none,' she said, indicating with a tilt of her head that Conor could play on his phone, in the faint hope that his earphones would drown out her words somewhat. The car park was clearing, the other parents having to manoeuvre around her stationary vehicle, but she had far more important things on her mind.

'Which leads me to hazard that you're looking for a highly intelligent young man with time on his hands. I suggest young because he must have had the wherewithal to entice teenage girls into his net unless he went catfishing, of course?' he added, a query in his tone.

'Unlikely. By all accounts these young women weren't into

social media and the like. I hate to use the term socially inadequate but that's the picture we're getting.' She popped open the glove compartment and removed a small notebook and biro along with a packet of mints, which she dropped into Conor's lap.

'Mmm. Interesting, very interesting indeed. And again we see that intellect is no guard against pluralistic ignorance.'

'Pluralistic what?'

'Sorry, I forgot who I was talking to for a moment. Social psychology is a bit of an obsession. Basically here we have a group of women who've set themselves apart from normal societal behaviours. They've stood back and observed their network partying and drifting into mating pairs and, on some basic level, will have regretted their decision. That's where pluralistic ignorance comes into it. The need to not miss out runs deep within all of us, Gaby. Those poor girls were ripe for the picking, by someone clever enough to see their vulnerability under the thin veneer they presented to the world. Therefore I'm putting my neck on the line by theorising that you're probably looking for someone with an antisocial personality disorder. There's no remorse or guilt in his actions. He'll come across as charming but drill down through the layers and you'll find a loner living on the edge of society. No family or friend networks. Someone interested in self-gratification on a purist level. The end justifies the means and all that.'

Gaby bit down on her lower lip, feeling the taste of blood. She preferred straight talk over pussyfooting around any day but for Angus to tell her that she was looking for a psychopathic serial killer was exactly the kind of news she could do without.

'And what about their differences?' she said after a brief pause, scribbling a note down on her pad. 'I thought that the criminal fraternity were set in their ways with regards to who they picked? These weren't opportunistic abductions, Angus. We're talking about well-executed disappearances, which takes lots of planning.'

'Hah, at least I know you were listening in those lectures, Gaby.

Yes, you're right but also wrong in that you're focusing solely on their physical attributes. In essence your team is at risk of being bogged down by skin tone and hair colour while to the killer it may be irrelevant. He chooses his prey using a completely different rulebook. Find out that and you'll find out his motive.'

Gaby finished the call with a promise to catch up on a less formal footing soon, all thoughts of where she was and what she was meant to be doing forgotten. She'd been using work as a panacea but there was no magic bullet. No idea or action that could push aside the image of Amy on Rusty's slab, that is until Conor's words pulled her back into the car.

'I thought you said we were going to get something to eat?'

'Yes, yes we are.' She laughed, the sound filling the small space. It wasn't joyous but it was all she could manage. 'Snap on your seatbelt, Conor,' she said, mirroring his actions before switching on the engine. 'And do you know what? I think I'll join you.'

# Chapter 44

Gaby

The hospital drew Gaby back like a moth to a flame. With Conor full of cupcakes and happily ensconced in his room, she'd texted Rusty and arranged to collect him rather than let him drive her rust bucket of a car home. It could stay in the hospital car park for the duration of the bad weather as far as she was concerned. Her opinion on cars had taken a nose dive since yesterday. One of the first things on her list was a reliable vehicle, especially if she was going to be ferrying Conor around the place.

There was still work to be done back at the office but, with Owen happy to pick up the reins, Gaby didn't have a moment's hesitation in deserting her desk for a short while. The case would be there later and that was her plan. With dinner sorted – Rusty was planning on throwing together a lasagne when he got home – she was going to head back into the station and knock out a few hours in the quiet of her office. The crime was starting to take form. She could almost smell the pieces untangling and coming together. All they needed was some luck, topped off with a sprinkling of inspiration, to catch the bastard. But for that to happen she also needed to put in some serious thinking along with complete silence and a piece of blank paper, neither of which she'd get sitting in the baby unit.

She'd never been more thankful of her warrant card and the power it had for getting her into places the public would never generally be allowed. Lara was doing well, better than she could have ever expected. They'd removed the feeding tube and had started to bottle-feed, her rosebud of a mouth taking gasping little breaths around the teat, her tiny hands bunching into fists.

Gaby sat off to one side, her hands hidden under the PPE the nurses had asked her to don before letting her into the room, sending her curious looks from over the top of their masks. They knew she was working on the case of the woman they were starting to call the snow angel. Gaby didn't know when or where the moniker had started but, like most things of its ilk, the label had taken wings, spreading across all forms of media faster than a bullet out of a gun. She much preferred Operation Zhivago. Her gaze swept over Lara as the nurse settled her back in her cot. It seemed to fit – now more than ever.

'I thought I'd find you here,' Rusty whispered, throwing a quick nod in the direction of the nurse's look of enquiry. 'Ready?'

'Yes. All done.' She picked up her bag and, pulling back her sleeve, was surprised at the time. 'Sorry, I didn't realise.'

He placed his arm around her shoulders. 'No need to apologise. I've only just finished.'

Gaby stopped, catching his eye. 'Amy . . .'

He nodded again. 'I don't know about you but I could murder a quick coffee before . . .' He ran his hand through his hair, not bothering that it was now standing on end. 'Not the kind of day I want to repeat.'

The snappy retort on her lips stayed just where it was. It wouldn't help in the scheme of things. She took his arm and directed him towards the set of lifts. 'Conor won't even notice we're not there.'

The canteen was full of doctors and nurses taking their supper break but Rusty directed her to a table in the corner, partially concealed by a tall artificial rubber plant. 'You sit there. I'll be back shortly.'

The coffee was strong and hot. After two sips, she felt a return to her normal equanimity. Rusty was anything but. The way he couldn't quite meet her eye set up a range of notions fluttering around her head like butterflies trapped in a jar; their little wings echoed the beating of her heart as adrenalin, laced with a heavy dose of fear, kicked in. He had something to tell her. She had no idea what.

Gaby didn't speak, she couldn't, which was an unusual turn of events for someone who always knew what to say, whatever the circumstance. That didn't include the death of her friend.

Ignoring his drink, he picked up a packet of sugar and started flipping it between his fingers, something he'd learnt in med school. The words started to pour out, one after the other, words that turned her heart to stone and her blood to ice.

'I shouldn't be telling you this but what the hell . . . I performed the autopsy earlier, not the easiest of procedures.' He cast her a quick glance before returning to his sugar flipping. 'It took longer than I'd hoped but I took my time, Gaby. I wanted there to be no doubt with my findings so I checked and double-checked. I've just returned from ICU where I spoke to the manager and, after contacting the staff nurse responsible for her care, my findings have been confirmed. This isn't the case of a cover-up. The nurse responsible acted with speed when Amy went into cardiac arrest.'

'I don't get you?' Gaby interrupted. 'Why would you need to check with the staff?'

'In short, Amy died of hypoxia, a lack of oxygen to her tissues, caused by someone deliberately messing around with her respirator. The team did everything they could when the alarm sounded but they couldn't guard against murder. By the time they realised what was wrong it was too late.'

Gaby froze.

'She was murdered?'

'It certainly looks that way.' He took away her mug, replacing it with his hand. 'All indications are that she would have survived the accident. There was nothing wrong with her that time wouldn't have healed.'

Gaby couldn't speak. She couldn't think. She couldn't move. Her body shut down into a form of statis. It was over in a second, maybe two. It was a feeling she never wanted to experience again.

She dropped her chin into her chest. 'Why, Rusty? Why would anyone want to hurt Amy?'

'I'm going to help you to find out.' He pushed back from the table and, with his hand still ensconced in hers, grabbed the mugs and placed them on the trolley provided before drawing her to the bank of lifts. 'You'll need to speak to the DCI. It might as well be now.' But she held back, refusing to move another step.

'You know better than that, Rusty. Sherlock would never allow me, or indeed any of the team, to be part of an investigation into one of their own.'

'You still need to make him aware of what happened,' he said, softening his tone. 'You owe it to Amy.'

# Chapter 45

## Gaby

**Thursday 11 February, 7 p.m. DCI Sherlock's office**

'Murdered, you say? But why?'

Henry Sherlock was a consummate professional, a career copper who'd devoted the last twenty years of his working life to law enforcement. His calm demeanour in the face of adversity was legendary. Now he was flustered, his glasses skew-whiff where he'd pushed them up his domed forehead, his cheeks flushed, his gaze unable to settle.

'All we have is guesswork, sir.'

'You don't know for sure but you do know something?' He leant across the desk, in full glare mode. 'You also know that you can't be involved in this, Gaby. God.' He slumped back in his chair as the implication of her death sank in.

'I'm sorry, sir.'

He lifted his hand in dismissal of her comment. 'Not as sorry as I am. You know how the detective superintendent operates as well as I do. Before I know it, I'll be on the doorstep clutching my P45 in one hand and the address of the job centre in the other.'

Gaby wanted to say something but she knew her words wouldn't be welcome.

He raised his head. 'You might as well tell me what you know and I'll take it from there.'

*

Gaby had planned on spending the evening holed up in her office thinking about the different strands of the case. Instead she was back in the incident room with her team but this time it was worse, far worse. There was only so much she could cope with in one day. A day that had started out having to tell them about the death of a dear friend and colleague. Now she had to tell them about Amy's murder.

She was proud of her team, never prouder. They were closer than most families and supported each other, both inside and outside of the station. Her gaze landed on Malachy before switching to Marie, who was busy sharing around a block of chocolate. Owen refused; he'd told her in confidence that Kate had been nagging him about his weight. Jax's face was a picture, his cheeks with a perfect chipmunk bulge as he scoffed his portion in one bite. But then she'd heard rumours that his girlfriend had turned vegan so who could blame him the odd slip-up. Certainly not her – she thought of the huge chocolate muffin she'd eaten earlier.

Gaby turned away, her nails forming deep crescents in her palms as she remembered that it had been Amy who'd told her about Jax's girlfriend.

'Right then, time and tide and all that. I've heard that you all have homes to go to or is that not the case?' she asked, with a cutting edge; her razor-sharp wit was the only thing that would get her through the next five minutes. 'Yes? Good. I was thinking I'd have to arrange for a night in the cells at this rate and, as you know, the porridge isn't up to much.' She perched on the edge of her desk and studied her shoes, not that they were anything special – low-heeled, black brogues bought to match her black Zara suit – but she couldn't look into their expectant faces. She might be strong but it would take someone a lot stronger to stare them in the eye until after she'd said what she had to.

'Firstly an apology. I know. Don't get any ideas. It will be a one-off occurrence. I had thought to be back earlier but something cropped up.' She shifted slightly, her hands now holding on to the sides of the desk. The office was silent, so silent that she could hear the clock ticking above the door. Everyone was waiting. She closed her eyes and jumped.

'I met with Dr Mulholland. He had to perform an autopsy on Amy.' Her hands drove into the wood, the pads of her fingers aching under the pressure. She welcomed the pain. 'Contrary to opinion, Amy didn't die from the injuries she sustained in the car accident. It's Rusty's view that she would have made a full recovery in time if someone hadn't messed with her respirator.' She lifted her head finally, looking at each of them in turn, well aware that they wanted to interrupt. She lifted her hand and stopped them. 'Just give me a minute, please. There's more.'

Gaby hopped down and headed over to the water cooler. She only continued when the paper cup was empty and squashed between her fingers. 'As you know, we had a PC stationed at Christy's door, which is all very well but some bastard, and I think we all know who it was, set off a small fire in one of the rubbish bins situated in the corridor outside the unit. In the panic that ensued our man must have slipped inside Amy's room and . . . it was an easy mistake to make, I suppose. Amy was wrapped almost head to foot in bandaging. He might have even seen me coming out of her room. Who knows how it happened but we think he switched off the wrong machine,' she said, concentrating on straightening out the cup back into its former shape. 'Amy didn't deserve to die and I'm determined to catch her killer if it's the last thing I do. Which brings me on to the next item,' she said, gesturing to her mobile. 'I've just come off the phone with Christy's doctor, who's allowing us in to talk to her briefly this evening. I know it's a big ask but I don't think I can do this alone,' she said, showing her vulnerability for the first time in her thirteen years on the force.

'I'll accompany you, ma'am, and before you start on at me, you must allow me to do this one thing. Kate will understand when I tell her.'

Gaby nodded, unable to speak for a moment. She'd always suspected that she had the very best of teams. Now she knew it as fact. 'Thank you, Owen. The rest of you shoot off, all apart from you, Mal,' she said, sending him a quick smile. 'I'll see you bright and early in the morning.'

# Chapter 46

## Eli

Eli climbed out of the car and headed for the entrance, still unsure about what could have happened to force another round trip across North Wales. He'd have bet his fortune on Christy being dead but that's not what the news had said. Being downgraded from critically ill to seriously ill was the worst of news and necessitated another visit to the hospital, despite the weather. The only positive was that the downgrade came with a ward shift and a surgical ward would be far easier to sneak into than ICU.

The word *carbolic* came to mind when he walked up the steps. He never walked when he could run – he was that sort of bloke. But this was different. He wasn't here on a mercy dash to see a loved one. No. He was here on a completely different mission and for that he had to act the part. CCTV cameras were everywhere these days. In hospital car parks and receptions for a start. He lowered his head over his phone, pretending to text as he made for the bank of lifts. It didn't help that he hated hospitals with a passion. He'd been forced to visit them as a child. Since then he'd never been able to get the smell out of his head or his nostrils. If it wasn't for Bryony and the baby he wouldn't have bothered.

He knew what Bryony thought of him – a bit of rough to mould into the type of man she wanted – they all thought it until it was too late to think otherwise. But there were different types of intelligence. The sort that got you a place in a revered university only to spend your days slogging your guts out on some fancy degree, capped off by a life working all the hours – for the same sort of pay he could earn in a few months, and have all the fun imaginable while he was doing it. With a bank balance tipping the million mark, he was thinking of retiring to somewhere hot. No. He stopped the lift on the third floor and made his way to the set of stairs that ran parallel to the lift shaft. He was the smart one, which was why he'd had his eyes peeled to the television for any news about the case. The item about Christy Taylor regaining consciousness was like a kick in the teeth. His wonderful world, which he'd built up from scratch, was about to come crashing down unless he did something to prevent it. The wastepaper bin fire yesterday was a gift but one he was sensible enough to know he wouldn't get away with it a second time.

The corridor outside the female surgical ward was still well lit despite the time but then he hadn't been expecting anything less. It had been the same yesterday outside the intensive care unit. He couldn't work out what had gone wrong last night but obviously something for Christy to still be alive. The flowers dangled from his hand with no thought for the heady blooms, chosen for impact. Twelve tightly packed red roses and a tear-laden smile to match. But he didn't get as far as the entrance. He didn't get anywhere near it because of the bearded man heading towards him, holding two overfull cups by the rim so that he wouldn't burn his fingers.

'Here, let me help.' He stepped forward with a smile, pushing the door with the flat of his hand.

'Thanks. Need the caffeine to keep me awake.'

'I'm sure.'

'Are you coming in or . . . ?'

'Me. No.' He didn't hesitate, his gaze resting on the detective's beard briefly. 'I'm waiting for my wife.'

'Well, have a good evening. Hope the missus likes the flowers.'

'Oh, she will.'

Elijah turned on his heels, returning the way he'd just come, the flowers now poking out of the nearest bin. Someone somewhere was having a laugh at his expense. By the look of things, Christy was now out of his grasp. He was only thankful that the detective wore a beard or he might not have recognised him as the person being interviewed on the television. What was his name again? Bates. That was it. Instead of heading for his car, he could be facing a night in the cells and a lifetime behind bars with no hope of parole. The thought of what might happen if he'd been arrested wasn't worth thinking about. He'd always known he was taking a huge risk with the game he was playing but that was part of the thrill. It wasn't all about the money and the image of what his future was going to be like, living off the fat of his offshore bank account. Life was boring. Mediocre. Predictable. He had his cake and was eating it even if it wasn't quite to his palate, as an image of Bryony's scrawny body popped up in his head.

He sat in the car thinking, ignoring the fog of breath misting up his windscreen and the intense cold seeping in through the seams of his thick woollen overcoat. He had money in the bank and a huge promise of additional funds but was it a risk he was prepared to take? Christy could identify him, not that he was all that bothered now he had Bryony tucked away at the cottage. It would have been a different matter if she'd still been living with her parents. The weather was a huge bonus as it would hinder any thoughts she might have of escaping. But what about when it thawed? She wasn't quite as loved up as Christy had been – nothing like it. He might have to lock her up if it continued. Relationships were all about trust and the sharp truth was that

Bryony didn't trust him anymore, which was unfortunate but surmountable.

He smiled, revealing unnaturally white teeth. He should have targeted her younger sister; after all she'd have served the same purpose just as well and, being a little younger, would have been far easier to manage. But it was too late now. His smile turned into a grin. He didn't have long until he could retire. Not bad for twenty-eight. Not bad at all. He glanced down at his empty hands. Damn. He could have used those roses, not that it mattered. He didn't need to worm his way into her bed now.

The gloves were off.

# Chapter 47

## Gaby

**Thursday 11 February, 9 p.m. St Asaph Hospital**

'I thought you'd gone to China for my tea.' Gaby took the cup from Owen, wrinkling her nose up at the grey-coloured liquid.

'It's nowhere as good as the coffee and that's not great either,' he said, taking a small sip. 'But it's hot and wet, which will have to do for now.'

Gaby held her tongue along with her opinion on the subject of drink dispensers. Coppers by necessity were experts on the quality of the machines. Haranguing Sherlock to upgrade theirs had been one of her first tasks when she'd moved up from Swansea. It had been a decision she'd yet to regret.

'When did they say we'd be let in to see her?' Owen asked.

'Shortly. Something about her dressing leaking. Poor kid.'

'Poor kid indeed. At least she's now out of intensive care. I hate that place with a passion.' He straightened from where he'd been propping up the nearest wall as the door to Christy's room pushed open. A nurse backed out with a dressing trolley, a large yellow bag placed dead centre.

'You can go in now but only ten minutes – she's exhausted.'

'Saved from a fate worse than hospital tea,' Gaby said, pouring her drink down the sink and discarding the cup. Owen followed her example.

Christy was resting against a mountain of pillows, her black hair collected in a thick plait running down the right-hand side of her hospital gown. She looked drained of both energy and determination. She also wasn't alone. Her mother was sitting beside the bed, holding on to her hand. Gaby moderated her words accordingly.

'Hello again, Christy. Mrs Taylor. This is Detective Owen Bates, a colleague. I know you've been through a bit of an ordeal but we do need to ask some questions,' she said, dropping into the chair that Owen had carried over from the pile under the window.

'Mum says that there's another girl missing?'

'That's right and we need to find her,' Gaby said, watching the fleeting expressions on the girl's face before fastening on the fat tears sneaking down her cheeks.

'I'll do my best. What do you need to know?'

'How did you meet for a start?'

'At school,' she said, launching into what appeared to be a prepared speech. 'He said he loved me and I believed him. I believed everything he said including that he'd take care of the contraception. Hah. That's a laugh for a start. I must have fallen pregnant pretty much the first time we . . . Sorry, Mum. You and Dad brought me up much better than that. Talk about being naive. Bloody condoms.'

Gaby glanced across at Owen, her eyebrows raised, but decided not to interrupt her rambles.

'I only started to doubt him that last morning when he arrived back from God knows where, only to refuse to take me to hospital. He said we'd be fine. That giving birth was one of the most natural things in the world.' Christy's hand tightened around her mother's. 'He's so good-looking and charming. I still can't believe that this

208

is happening.' She turned her head, grimacing as her hair caught behind her neck. 'He wouldn't even let me see her. He told me I had a beautiful girl only to take her away . . .'

'It's all right, sweety. It's all going to be fine. The police are here to help find her.' Mrs Taylor lifted her head, her eyes narrowing. 'Isn't that right, Detective?'

'Absolutely.' Gaby was used to dealing with relatives of all sorts and as such was wary of making assumptions as to how someone might behave in any given situation but Mrs Taylor was busily earning herself a gold medal for mum of the year. Gaby only hoped that her positivism would continue. It would make all the difference. The strong possibility of PTSD was glaringly obvious and, while they might be able to find the man, the baby could be anywhere by now, if indeed she was still alive. Gaby blinked, shoving the thought away to the very back of her mind. Positivism wasn't just for relatives.

'You said his name was Elijah Brown?' She glanced at her watch, well aware of the time speeding by. If they overstayed their welcome there'd be hell to pay.

'The Brown should have alerted me. Probably a fake name, right?'

'Probably. And you said you met him at the sixth form college?'

'Yes. In Llandudno. He's the odd jobs man or he was. There's always things that need fixing, walls that need touching up. That sort of thing.'

'How old is Eli, Christy?'

'Twenty-three.'

Gaby made a note on her pad. 'And what about the day you left? Tell me about that?'

'He was waiting for me in the café. We left as soon as Mum pulled away and he drove me straight to the house. No. That's not quite right. He said that we should celebrate so we stopped off in Ruthin before going on to the cottage.'

'You say he *was* the odd jobs man,' Owen said, from his station by the window. 'What about now?'

Christy shook her head. 'He gave up in July, shortly after finding out about the baby. Said he wanted to start a new life together,' she said, tears forming two tracks down her cheeks. 'He got a part-time job instead, only three days a week. He told me he couldn't bear to be apart from me for longer. I've been a fool, haven't I?'

'No more than any young woman in your position when faced with a serious con artist.' Gaby softened her tone. 'I can't promise I'll find him or your baby, Christy, but I promise that I'll never stop looking.'

*

'Owen, you go back to your missus. We've earnt our pay tonight,' Gaby said, once they were out of earshot of the ward. 'There's not a lot we can do at this time of night and in this weather. Now that we have his place of work he should be easy to track down. I'll ask Devine to continue working on it.'

'Not until I've dropped you home and, before you start having a go, I promised Rusty that I wouldn't let you drive tonight of all nights. It's only twenty minutes out of my way.'

Twenty there and twenty back, but instead of throwing in one of her snippy comments she squeezed his arm. 'Thank you. I can't say that I was looking forward to it.'

'Don't thank me. It's that man of yours. He was in a right tizz, probably because he knows what you're like.'

'Enough said. Any thoughts on what Elijah Brown is up to?' Gaby asked, tugging on her seatbelt to make sure it was tight.

She didn't think that she'd ever get into a car again and not think about Amy and what had happened to her on what was the most routine of journeys. The day had marched on and her grief with it. The sadness had shifted from her stomach and along to her muscles and bones where she reckoned it would remain for some time to come. It was only the case that was keeping the lethargy from reigning supreme. She still had that conversation with Rusty to face but she was hoping he was in tune enough to know that tonight wasn't the night for anything apart from curling into a tight ball and hoping for sleep.

She felt rather than saw Owen glance in her direction, reminding her that she'd asked him a question, which he'd probably replied to.

'Sorry. I missed that.'

'I said that there's two motives I can come up with.'

'Only two? You do surprise me.'

'Harumph. Either Brown is a psychopathic serial killer with a penchant for babies or—'

'God, really!'

'You're interrupting me again, Gabs,' he said, his voice taking on a stern note. 'I think it's more likely that he's come up with some devious money-making plan. I'm not normally a guessing man, but I'd hazard the latter.'

Gaby leant against the door, her eyes trained on his face. 'Why?'

'Why? Because it fits. We both know the motives for murder,' he said, proceeding to recite them off. 'Jealousy doesn't come into it. He had them in the palm of his hand so what was there to be jealous about? The same goes for love. Hatred of women? Then why take the babies unless he really did hate them that much? No, that doesn't work for me. Power? That's a possibility. Perhaps something worth discussing with Professor Ford. But I still think it has to be financial gain with the babies being the bargaining point.'

'So, he's selling the babies. An interesting concept but to whom and for how much?' She swiped her phone. 'While I agree that you may have something, there is one huge problem with your current thought processes, Owen.'

'What's that?' he said, slowing down to avoid a patch of black ice on the slip road leading to the A55.

'Simply that Elijah is left with a baby without a birth certificate and no means of obtaining one. If that's his plan it would be far easier – and quicker – to steal one but he chooses instead to make his own. Why? It's not that difficult for parents to get a baby legally in the UK,' she added, switching off her phone and resting it on her knee. 'If he were to set up some kind of a surrogacy system, he'd be working inside the law but that's not financially viable.'

'I can't agree, Gaby. The babies cost him nothing. Surrogacy costs the parents . . .'

'Reasonable expenses only in the UK. No. Owen. There's more to this than we're seeing. Far more. The only problem is that I have no idea what.'

# Chapter 48

## Bryony

**Friday 12 February, 3 a.m. Blaen-Cym House**

Bryony was wide awake. Fear had a tendency to do that to a person. She lay in bed considering her options. There weren't any. There was nothing she could do until the weather had abated to such an extent that she could walk the distance back down the hill to the nearest property. Now she wished that she'd been more observant on the journey but, from what she could remember, it was at least a good two miles in treacherous conditions and with only her slippers on her feet. That was right. She couldn't find her Reeboks, which was one of the reasons her fears had escalated to fever pitch. The only truth left to her was that he'd taken her prisoner. With no phone and no shoes, she was stuck even if she found a way out of the house, which was looking increasingly unlikely. She was stuck until he was fed up with her but what then? Would he let her go? She snuffled back a small cry. No. She knew his name. She also knew his face, probably better than her own. She'd certainly studied it enough in the first throes of passion. He couldn't and wouldn't let her go.

Her hand crept to her stomach and the swell that seemed to have blossomed since she'd taken off her jeans earlier. That was another thing. When she'd wandered out of the bathroom, draped only in a towel, her clothes were nowhere to be seen. She'd even checked in the wardrobe and under the bed. No. They'd gone the same way as her shoes, leaving her with the floaty dresses she knew she was going to hate. It was bad enough having fallen pregnant but to announce it in maternity clothes at not yet five months was pushing it somewhat.

She rolled on her side, hugging her knees to her chest. The only thing she could do was wait for the weather to moderate. She'd watched the news but it hadn't said much, not about her anyway. Something about a missing girl being found but she'd switched off the television then. She had far too many of her own problems to be worried about someone else's. The way Eli had been earlier. Demanding, more demanding than she'd ever known him but also gentle despite his harsh words. Still considerate once she'd given in to him. She'd had little choice despite feeling that she was letting herself down. She should have refused. Pushed it to the limit just to see how far he'd take it but she hadn't.

Despite everything that had gone before. The loss of her innocence during her lunchbreak. The tokens from their budding romance that she'd grown to treasure. A flower from the sixth form centre garden, which she'd pressed between the pages of one of her heavier books when the leaves had started to droop. The label from their first bottle of wine, which they'd sipped in his frankly dingy bedsit instead of attending the after-school discussion on the nuts and bolts of university life. Despite all this she was beginning to see the truth now that he'd let the mask slip. He didn't love her. He didn't even like her very much. All he wanted was sex . . . but that couldn't be all he wanted. Could it?

# Chapter 49

Gaby

**Friday 12 February, 7.20 a.m. Rhos-on-Sea**

'You have to eat,' Rusty said, reaching for the bread.

'Not if I feel like throwing up, I don't.' Gaby sent Conor a smile of apology over the top of her mug of tea.

They were sitting around the small kitchen table, their knees almost touching while Rusty was standing in front of the hob, piling rashers of bacon between thick doorstop slices of bread. She felt her stomach rumble in protest as she remembered the chocolate muffin and little else. When she'd finally arrived home it was far too late to think about food. She'd done exactly what she'd planned, which was a bath and a glass of red resting on the rim. She'd stayed there until the water had gone cold and the skin on her fingertips had wrinkled. She'd probably still be there if Rusty hadn't rescued her with a large fluffy towel, hot from the radiator.

Gaby watched him out of the corner of her eye, remembering the sleepy hug that had shifted into far more. It was what they'd both needed, a reaffirmation of everything that was right about their relationship and, if the last two days had told her anything, it was never to take what she had for granted. Yes, she still had a choice to make, a huge one, but the scales had shifted in Rusty's favour without her even realising it. With a gentle sigh, she pinned the image of a red-haired baby with startling blue eyes to the back of her brain to gather dust. The decision had been made.

'Now that you mention it I could—'

'Good!' He placed two plates on the table before sliding into the chair between them. 'Sure you won't change your mind, Conor? It will only take me two minutes to whip up another.'

'I'm good thanks, Dad.' He paused, his spoon hanging in front of his mouth and dripping milk back into the bowl. 'Isn't that your mobile, Gaby?'

'Finish your breakfast first – they'll ring back surely,' Rusty said, eying her barely touched sandwich with a frown.

But she shook her head and pushed away from the table.

The call was brief, the content confusing.

'That was Faith, Tim's mum,' she said, after a moment, picking at a sliver of bacon and popping it into her mouth before lifting her head and staring across at where Conor was rushing around the lounge in search of his homework.

'And?' Rusty took her hand, squeezing it gently.

'They're meeting up with Amy's parents later and want me to attend. Something about the funeral arrangements,' she said, sweeping her tongue around her cheeks to clear her mouth. 'You wouldn't like to accompany me, would you? I'm not sure I can do this on my own.'

'You don't have to ask, Gabriella.' He turned her hand over, staring down at their linked fingers. 'I know I didn't explain myself very well about Caroline . . .'

'You don't have to—'

'I want to. The truth is we went out a few times. We even came close to ending up in bed but something always held me back. I like to think it was you arriving on the scene.'

216

'But you couldn't stand me.'

'That's not true. I just wasn't ready for the implications of what a relationship with you would mean. I have your back and—' He stopped, a rosy blush sweeping up his neck. 'I always will if you'll let me?'

Was that a proposal? She didn't even know, which went to prove how crap she was at this relationship business.

Before she could think up how to answer, Conor was back, his satchel in one hand, his lunchbox in the other. 'Enough with the smushies or I'll be late for school – and don't you both have jobs to go to?'

Gaby sent Rusty the sort of smile that said everything and nothing. She had a lot of thinking to do but there was no room in her head for anything apart from the case. Her mind veered away from the one, heart-breaking part about all of this. Amy would have been the first person she'd have told about Rusty's words.

# Chapter 50

Gaby

**Friday 12 February, 8.40 a.m. St Asaph**

Malachy Devine had the kettle boiled and a teabag waiting in the bottom of her favourite mug when she strolled into the incident room and dumped her laptop bag on the desk before pulling off her gloves.

'If you're looking for brownie points, Mal, you've just earnt yourself a shedload.'

He threw back his head and laughed, revealing a thick column of throat. 'I'll have to remember that. The weather's no better then?'

'The snow's stopped if that's what you mean,' she said, taking her usual spot on the edge of the desk. 'But the roads are like an ice rink. I've never been more thankful for Rusty's choice of vehicle even if I need a ladder to climb into the ruddy thing. So, what's the news then from the school? Start at the beginning.'

Gaby knew from his expression that he had something to tell her but she always liked the full picture instead of jumping straight to the grand finale. It was a trick she'd learnt when pounding the beat as a rookie copper in Liverpool. Never skip to the end or you might just miss out on that one vital clue necessary to split the case wide open.

Mal picked up his drink and took a quick sip before answering. 'In short, an Elijah Brown was employed by the school last year to look after the gardens on a part-time basis. Litton was very pleased with his work but, generally, Brown kept to himself. Didn't attend any of the after-school functions despite being invited. The pay was minimal but the job came with a small bedsit tucked away at the back of the grounds. I've arranged for you to visit at ten o'clock, if that's all right, ma'am? I'm happy to stay on if that helps?'

She waved his suggestion aside with a shake of her head, her fingers tapping away on her phone as she recorded the appointment. 'What else?'

'I've asked the head teacher to email through copies of his CV and employment records. I've also emailed the Department for Work and Pensions to see what they have on him.'

Gaby frowned. 'Okay, bear with me while I think out loud,' she said, playing with the end of her plait. 'We need this in chronological order. So, he decides to leave Manchester. Probably chancing his luck in staying, with the body count piling up.'

'And Jules's parents did kick up more than a stink when she went missing.'

'Hardly surprising. So, he hot-foots it to Llandudno where we know that, after talking with Christy, he takes up temporary employment. They start a relationship. She falls pregnant. He sets her up in a love nest while he plans his next move. A different school. A different girl. Another baby.'

'Sounds about right.'

'I'd like to wring his bloody neck.'

'And me.' Mal emptied the remainder of his drink down the sink. 'I've also arranged for Jason to send a team over to his flat in Mold,' he said, glancing down at his watch. 'In fact they'll probably be there by now. Who knows what they'll find?'

'Knowing Elijah like I'm starting to, probably nothing.' She lifted her head in time to see Owen sauntering down the corridor, closely followed by both Jax and Marie.

'Ah. Just in time. The kettle has boiled. Make yourselves a drink and I'll have another tea while you're at it,' Gaby said, handing her mug to Owen. 'What about the background on Brown, Mal?'

'Well, as you know, we couldn't find him on the database, which meant we were looking for someone without a criminal record. I thought that unusual.'

Gaby picked up on his use of the past tense straightaway. 'I take it you've had a breakthrough?'

'Not me, ma'am. It was that DCI in Manchester who joined the dots up with someone on their patch. An Elijah Brownley.'

'Okay. A not very original alias but I suppose it doesn't have to be. So tell us about Mr Brownley.'

'I started with his birth certificate. Born Elijah Peter Brownley, June 1994.'

'Are you sure about that?' Gaby frowned, using her fingers to work out the maths.

'Positive. Why?'

'Because that would make him twenty-eight, which is a bit odd. He told Christy he was only twenty-three.'

'Are you surprised? There's a wealth of difference between someone clinging to their twenties by the skin of their teeth and a twenty-three-year-old,' Owen said.

'Okay. Good point and he wouldn't be worried by the odd lie. His whole life is a lie. Keep going, Mal.'

'Brownley's father was a car mechanic, his mother a housewife. She died shortly after his younger brother, Mo, was born. Both boys lived with their father until he also died in an accident at work when Elijah was eight.' Mal glanced up from where he was reading from an A4 pad. 'After that they were taken into care and it's the usual story; the brothers were unable to find a family that would take them both.'

'Tragic,' Marie said, retying her hair into a high ponytail.

'But more so for the younger brother who was found unresponsive in the room he shared with Elijah. It was put down to sudden death syndrome. After his death, Elijah was accepted by a family with whom he lived until he was eighteen.'

'You're choosing your words carefully all of a sudden, Mal, which is unlike you. Are you ill? I'm assuming that the poor lad had an autopsy?'

'I thought you said for us to assume nothing, ma'am?' he countered with a return of his smile, albeit fleeting. 'No autopsy. And now no body – Mo Brownley was cremated.'

She stared at him, trying to read between the lines. 'So, what you're intimating is that the reason Elijah was placed was because of the death of his brother, bearing in mind we know how much easier it is to home a single child? Ergo he could have been implicated in his brother's demise and, with no parents to answer to and presumably Elijah acting the bereaved brother, the children's home were happy to accept it at face value. Mmm. You're nearly as cynical as the rest of us. What else?'

'Not a lot more. I did try to get in touch with his foster parents but they've left the area.' He picked up a Post-it Note. 'A Joe and Maggie Banfield and details of their last known address.'

'Okay. Thank you. Very well done. You shoot off and get a good sleep. We might see you back here tonight,' she said, having absolutely no doubts on that score. With Rusty planning on picking her up at lunchtime to visit Tim's parents, she was going to have to make the time up somehow. 'Jax, I'd like you to chivvy up social security please. Marie can take over with trying to contact the Banfields. I don't care how you do it but I want a complete breakdown of this Elijah Brownley's work history on my desk after I've bearded Sherlock in his den.' She turned to Owen, who was in the process of returning his mobile to his pocket. 'What do you think? Still some kind of baby-making operation? Elijah certainly seems to tick most of Angus's criminal-profiling boxes.' She made her way to the middle whiteboard and created room at the bottom. 'A loner with no family to speak of,' she said, making a list. 'Lives alone, and to all intents and purposes works alone. Someone who targets teenage girls. Gets them pregnant. What next?'

'It has to be financial, surely?' Jax interrupted, warming his bum against the radiator.

'Still doesn't make sense, sorry. I've already had this conversation with Owen. Why make them when he can steal them? Why steal them when parents can arrange for surrogacy, which is within the law, cost-effective and comes with a birth certificate? All the surrogate gets is reasonable expenses, which is neither here nor there. There has to be another motive.'

But that was the problem because there wasn't one or, at least not one that she or any of the team could think of that would let them sleep at night. There were many dubious reasons for abducting a child, some of them truly despicable. It only took a quick dip into the dark web to appreciate just how sick some members of society really were. They lingered in the shadows ready to pounce on any and all unsuspecting and innocent victims, and who was more innocent than a baby? But it didn't fit the picture they were building and that was a huge part of the problem. Unless this Elijah Brownley was a complete and utter looney, he'd know that there were far easier and quicker ways to harvest a baby and with far fewer risks involved. Parents were renowned for getting distracted, especially if they had more than one child to look after. It would only take seconds to unstrap them and hightail it in some fast car. There had to be some other reason.

'Hold on a minute,' Jax said, shifting from the radiator and back to his desk where he lifted some papers to reveal his iPhone. 'What about Lynda Checkley?'

'The owner of the house in Mold where Bryony was dropped off?' Gaby said, trying and failing to follow Jax's thought processes. 'She's a nurse, isn't she?'

She watched as he shuffled around his desk before finally pulling out a pad, a coffee stain on the centre of the cover.

'She trained as a nurse then went on to become a midwife, which means that she has dealings with new mums and . . .' He paused again, flicking through a raft of pages. 'Here it is. Three years ago, almost to the day, her car was burgled outside her house. The items taken included unspecified medical items relating to home births and a folder full of documents.' He paused a second. 'She was also born in Oldham which, as we know, is a town in Greater Manchester, lived there until a few months before her car was broken into.'

The room went silent for a second, the only sound to be heard the ticking of the clock. 'Okay, change of plan then. Jax, you continue what you're doing with regards to background but I'd also like you to see what you can find out about the Banfields. Owen, I need you and Marie to track down Checkley while I catch up with Sherlock. What are the odds that she knows something?'

# Chapter 51

Bryony

**Friday 12 February, 9 a.m. Blaen-Cym House**

'Why did you do that?'

Bryony stared down at where Eli had tipped the contents of her make-up bag onto the bed and was rummaging through the items.

'Why do you think, dearest?' he said, his voice dripping sarcasm as he removed a small pair of scissors and a nail file. 'Wouldn't want you to get any ideas now, would I?' he went on, grabbing her chin between his free hand and pressing his hot sticky mouth against hers, his tongue darting in and out like a snake on heat. He finally pushed her away with no regard for where she landed, the back of his hand swiping away the remnants of his kiss. 'I'll be in shortly with your lunch. You'd better eat it this time if you know what's good for you. And again, have a shower for fuck's sake or I'll do it for you.'

She refused to watch him as he headed for the door, but her ears were tuned to even the slightest of sounds. The noise his feet made against the carpet. The slight squeak of the door on its hinges. The rasp of metal against metal as the key turned in the lock. Instead of relief at him leaving all she felt was frustration as she followed his example by searching through her paltry array of cosmetics. She'd asked for her rucksack and all he'd brought instead was the small make-up bag she'd tucked in the bottom. A lipstick and a tube of mascara wouldn't help her to escape unless she decided to stab him with her mascara wand, she thought, unscrewing the top and pulling out the gloopy brush before slamming it back into place with a cry of indignation. Even the plastic pencil sharpener wasn't going to be much good to her unless she could think of some way to use it. The truth was that he was far stronger than her; one of the first things she'd noticed about him was the way his biceps strained against the fabric of his shirt. He'd whisk the minuscule blade away faster than stealing candy from a baby. Now a knife or a pair of scissors – then she'd be able to do some real damage.

She'd laugh if it wasn't so ridiculous. Bryony Lloyd, the brightest star by far, turned into a baby factory. Yes. It hadn't taken her long to realise that his small cruelties never went as far as her belly. The odd pinch and slap, which seemed to be escalating with a rapidity that defied explanation. She'd annoyed him with her small token resistances. The untouched toast lying on the side left to grow cold. Last night's wasted chiller counter bolognese. He'd threatened to force-feed her but she wasn't about to give him the satisfaction. She'd eat the toast later only because she knew that she had to look after herself if she was ever to escape. She'd even had a plan. It hadn't been much of one and had been dependent on having access to her nail file but that was as dead to her as her love for the cruel monster next door.

The make-up bag was one of those purse-sized ones sold in chemists across the country. A fabric outside in fetching red and white polka dot and a plastic-coated interior, but it wasn't the inside she was focused on. It was the zip or, to be accurate, the zip pull.

The one thing about Bryony was that she was careful with money, a trait she'd inherited from her father, who was always banging on about the cost of things. There was always something to buy that was far more important than make-up. Hence the gloopy nature of her mascara that she eked out by watering it down with a drop of hot water, much to the amusement of her spendthrift sister. A make-up bag wasn't important in the scheme of things. It wasn't as if it was on show and there were always things she needed more. So when the zipper broke on her old one she picked up the cheapest she could find, something she was reminded of every time the metal of the flat-edged zip puller snagged at her skin.

With one eye on the door, she headed for the bathroom, which wasn't anything special. Standard white with steel fittings and a plain white toilet seat and a matching bath panel. Utilitarian at best. She had an idea. It wasn't great. In fact, it was far from great. But, with shutters bolted across the windows and Eli now locking her in, it was the only idea she had. She had to run with it or suffer from the consequences of her inactivity.

Bryony ran the bath as a precaution, setting out a fresh towel on the side from the pile available and, slipping off the kaftan, draped it over the towel rail before kneeling on the bathmat. She wasn't an exhibitionist, far from it. She'd have to think she had a good body for that and with no boobs to speak of, and narrow hips more commonly found in boys, she'd had lots of peers rubbing away at her body confidence. Romping around the floor on bended knees in the buff was something from her nightmares but needs must if she didn't want Eli to catch her. This way she could quickly slip into the bath when she heard his footsteps and he'd be none the wiser.

The screw caps covering the bath panel pinged across the room, which had her scrabbling under the sink to find them. The screws were flat heads and, with the make-up bag clutched in her fist like a handle, she set to work. It was a laborious task with the improvised screwdriver slipping between her damp fingers. But with a steely determination honed by fear, she soon had four screws and four screw heads set to one side in a tidy pile.

The space under the bath was dark, dusty and quite frankly terrifying but she forced herself to crawl inside and curl around the underside of the bath like a cat in search of sunlight. If she'd been as tall as her mother or as well built as her sister, she'd never have managed but for the first time in her life she welcomed the fact that nature had endowed her with a reed-thin body. The bath panel was another issue but, with the sound of the key scraping against the lock, she didn't have time to do more than twist back onto the floor, balance the bath panel back in place, slide into the bath and drop the towel onto the pile of screws.

He stalked into the room, a plate in one hand and a mug in the other. But it wasn't the sight of the food that had her stomach flip or caused her mouth to dry. It was the way he paused in the doorway to survey the room as if he knew what she'd been up to. Instead of following his gaze, she reached for the shampoo and poured a dollop into the centre of her palm. There was no need for words. He'd won – or he thought he'd won. Bryony needed to keep it that way until the time came for her to act. She still hadn't worked out quite how yet but there was nothing for her to lose.

# Chapter 52

Gaby

**Friday 12 February, 9.30 a.m. St Asaph**

'You wanted to see me, sir?'

'Just a quick update on the case, Darin. The press and the superintendent are on my back about this one along with the DCI over in Manchester.' DCI Sherlock tapped a Post-it Note with his long bony forefinger. 'Webb has been bending my ear for the last ten minutes about poor communication. Apparently, she's sent you numerous emails but is yet to receive a solitary reply and getting Bates and Devine to do your dirty work isn't good enough. Get a grip, Gaby, or I'm going to have to think again about your fitness to head up the team.' He picked up his gold-topped fountain pen and swivelled it between his fingers. 'I know this is difficult and that you were close to Amy. We're all sad about that but you can't let it interfere with your job. Now get on the phone to DCI Webb and start eating humble pie. Got it?'

'Yes, sir,' Gaby said, making her way to the door and back to the incident room.

Not the kind of set-down she relished but he did have a point.

It was all very well letting Owen deal with the Manchester side of things but she should have realised that DCIs had mammoth egos along with their shiny buttons and highly polished shoes. She'd have to deal with it before anything else, which was the biggest bugbear of all.

'Everything all right, ma'am?'

'Apart from getting a bollocking from Sherlock about not keeping Greater Manchester in the loop I'm fine. Couldn't be better, Marie,' she said, heading for her desk and picking up the phone.

'Rather you than me.' Marie slid her arms into the sleeves of her coat. 'We're heading out to see Checkley now. I'll call you if there's anything pressing.'

'You do that,' Gaby said, the receiver angled in the crook of her neck while she checked her mobile for any messages. There weren't any.

'Is that DCI Maureen Webb?'

'Speaking.'

'Gaby Darin here, apologies for not being in touch earlier,' she said, eating as much humble pie as she was going to. 'You wanted to speak to me?'

'Thank you for the call, albeit belated. As a matter of fact, I was just about to contact you.' Gaby heard a muted conversation taking place where presumably Maureen had placed her hand over the mouthpiece. 'Sorry about that. Right, where was I? Oh yes. Our man. Eli Brown, or Elijah Brownley as he's known. He's one of ours. A Mancunian. We've traced him back to the house in Bournville Road – it wasn't that difficult considering that he did little to hide his whereabouts – and we've uncovered more evidence than you can shake a stick at. It's a virtual emporium of forensic delights that is going to keep my lead CSI happy for weeks.'

'Oh. Right.' Gaby was both surprised and shocked at how easy it had been to join the dots once both teams were working on the same picture. In this case, Elijah Brownley's alias, which wasn't a surprise at all. Most criminals chose to adopt pseudonyms close to their own name for no other reason that it was probably easier to stick to the truth than confabulate something that they'd never remember.

'We've turned out the house and are in the process of excavating the garden. So far, in addition to Jules's body, we've also identified the body of the homeowner, a Mr Ansel Abalos.'

'Any thoughts on their cause of death?'

'Too early to say.'

Gaby finished the call and after returning the receiver to the cradle, left her hand there a second, deep in thought. Criminals changing their MO wasn't unheard of. They honed their craft, adapting to changes in the environment and improving their techniques. But there was always an incentive. Some reason for their response. She had a feeling if they were to find out what Brownley's reason was for switching location from Manchester to North Wales they'd be well on the way to catching him. It was all about understanding the mind of the killer, a trail that had taken her to some very scary places in the past and no doubt would continue to do so in the future.

She chose a pencil at random from the pottery pot that Conor had made and which she'd rescued from the bin without him realising. But she didn't see the pot, or even realise that it was in front of her. Instead she drew a circle in the centre of her jotter and quickly added a head, closely followed by a fine set of chubby arms and legs. A spider diagram was one of her quick and dirty ways to get to grips with a case and within seconds she was shooting off additional points in a stream of thought. It didn't take her long to come up with an answer – but it was the same answer Owen had come up with already. She threw her pencil down in disgust, unable to join the dots.

# Chapter 53

## Owen

**Friday 12 February, 11.30 a.m. Edelweiss Cottage**

Lynda Checkley directed them into the lounge while she disappeared into the kitchen to grapple with the task of providing tea and biscuits. The room was small, with just the one window looking out onto the busy street covered in cream nets; a necessity but one that limited the amount of light entering the room.

'There you go. Sorry for making you come all this way but I'm on call for a home birth not far from here. It would be Sod's bloody law that they'll need me as soon as I step outside the front door.'

'I didn't realise that home births were allowed these days?'

'There's nothing to stop you,' she said, her gaze dipping to Marie's washboard stomach now she'd removed her coat. 'We don't usually recommend it for the first but after that it's down to personal choice and on the advice of your midwife.' She crossed one leg over the other, dragging her cardigan more securely around her middle. 'Now, what can I do to help? Still no news about that poor girl and the other women in the news today?'

she said, nodding in the direction of the paper, folded up on top of the coal bucket presumably to help with the fire later.

Owen sat forward in his chair, his hands resting on his knees. 'Do you know someone called Elijah Brownley, Ms Checkley?'

Lynda was an attractive woman with brown hair tied back in a Gaby-style plait and an arresting pair of large silver hooped earrings. But it wasn't her looks that interested Owen now. It was the colour fading from her cheeks only to be replaced by twin spots of red.

'Ah, I see that you do,' he said, his tone as mild as his manner as he reached for his mug and took a sip. 'He's a person of interest in the inquiry. Any help you can give would be most welcome.'

Owen was an expert in getting the reluctant to divulge their secrets. Gaby was always telling him that he should have trained as a priest instead of going into the constabulary. He could see where she was coming from, up to a point. Policework relied on good groundwork. It was a bit like fishing, with Lynda Checkley currently working out the pros and cons of the worm dangling in front of her nose. The collapse of her shoulders along with her gaze told him that she'd swallowed the bait whole.

'I grew up in Manchester, in a children's home if you must know. Elijah was a sort of friend, although friend is perhaps stretching it. He left when his brother died, went to live with a foster family.' Her chin dropped further into her neck, her hands wrapped into two tight balls of angst. 'I was two years older, ten. No one was interested in a ten-year-old. I didn't see or hear from him for years. In fact, I'd forgotten all about him until I came upon him at work.'

'You were nursing, right?' Marie said, her mobile open on her lap where she was taking notes.

'Yes, the Manchester Royal Infirmary. I was on placement in Accident and Emergency, oh, about ten years ago now. He came in following an injury at work. I didn't recognise him at first.' She started picking at the skin around her nail. 'But of course he recognised me. He asked me out and I accepted for old times' sake but it didn't last, only a few weeks. That's all.'

'Can you tell me a little about him then? What was he like?'

'Strange. I'd never liked him if I'm honest. There was always something about him that I couldn't trust. Something around the eyes,' she said. 'His brother, Mo, was lovely, a real dote but then you know about that.'

'Only in so much as he died,' Owen said, placing his empty mug on the table and resting back against the sofa in the hope of an answer. It came straightaway.

'He was found in bed. Sudden infant death syndrome or something. He was only five and one of the reasons I ended up going into nursing.' She wiped her fingers under her eyes. 'There was no talk of foul play but Elijah didn't seem worried or even upset at his death, which we all thought odd. He was placed with a family shortly after.'

'And when was the last time you saw him?'

Lynda reached across the coffee table to the wooden box in the centre and, flipping open the lid, withdrew an e-cigarette. 'Sorry, I'm trying to give up but . . .' she said, wrapping her hand around the casing and taking a couple of deep puffs. 'He turns up every few months or so. It's almost as if he thinks there's a connection simply because we shared the same space all those years ago. There truly isn't and he's one of the reasons I decided to move to Wales.'

'And he followed?'

She nodded. 'He keeps popping up now and again, always out of the blue and always with a plea to give him another chance. I've even considered taking out a restraining order but he hasn't threatened me or anything. He says he likes to look out for me but it freaks me out.'

'Can you think of any reason for Eli to arrange to meet Bryony outside your house?'

She shook her head. 'None whatsoever. I don't even know the

girl and anyway isn't that all a bit creepy? He must be twice her age.'

'Not illegal but certainly on the verge of being socially unacceptable, especially for her parents. Can I take your mind back to three years ago, Ms Checkley, when you moved in. There was a break-in?'

'My car. Yes. But there was nothing much stolen.' She laughed. 'Nothing much to steal. A bag with a few cord clamps and a folder with some papers but no patient details. I keep all that on my handheld device.'

'And what did the folder contain exactly?' Owen said, pressing her.

'Blank forms. When a home birth occurs, the parents are issued with a notification form, which they then take to the registrar who will issue a birth certificate. They're no good to anyone but new parents.'

Bingo!

Owen paused on the doorstep, his attention drawn to the white flowers underneath the unusual house name. 'Dutch?'

'No. Austrian. Not my choice but then not a priority. The previous owners were fans of *The Sound of Music* or so I'm told.'

Another loose end banged to rights.

# Chapter 54

## Gaby

**Friday 12 February, 1.05 p.m. Llandudno**

Tim's parents' hotel was situated along the West Shore in the shadow of the Great Orme. It had been open all over Christmas and into the New Year, only closing again on the second of January. Gaby and Rusty parked around the back, slotting in between Faith's Jaguar, the Potters' Saab and a Mercedes she didn't recognise. The black four-by-four added to the run of high-end vehicles. She wasn't a car person but even if she had been she was too tense to notice. Rusty reaching for her hand as they made their way to the staff entrance helped as did the soft words of encouragement. Gaby was here for Amy and Tim, only that.

Tim's dad stood to greet her, drawing her into a big hug.

'You remember Rusty?' she said, stepping back while they shook hands.

'Of course. Come and take a seat. I'm sure you must be busy, both of you,' he said, sweeping his hand around the lounge. 'You know Amy's parents and Faith, of course,' he went on, taking his place next to his wife. 'The only one you probably won't know is Alan Boyd, Amy and Tim's solicitor. You might as well start, Alan, now that we're all here.'

Gaby sat on the edge of the chenille-covered sofa, her handbag touching the side of her trouser leg, her thoughts in free fall as to why she'd been asked to join them. Quite frankly she had no idea and was growing more confused by the minute. They'd mentioned funeral arrangements but this seemed more than that – far more.

Alan was tall and lean with a fine taste in striped shirts and gaudy ties, the cacophony of swirling patterns reminiscent of Gaby's grandmother's 1970s curtains in her back room. His voice was melodious, his words obviously well prepared.

'Thank you all for agreeing to meet under such awful circumstances and can I again repeat my commiserations as to your loss. But there are things that need to be discussed as a matter of urgency,' he said, readjusting the cuffs of his shirt. 'I'm not sure whether you're aware that Amy and Tim came to see me in order to write a will, shortly before they got married?' He paused, using the conversation break to hand out copies of the document. 'You'll see overleaf that I've made a list of the key items. They were well within their rights to make whatever provisions necessary even though I did suggest that they discussed it with all the parties first.' He paused again, this time to run a handkerchief underneath his nose before returning it to his trouser pocket. 'I can see from your expressions that that's not the case.'

He lifted his briefcase and, propping it open on his lap, withdrew three letters, which he subsequently handed out. 'I believe Amy had a near-death experience last year, which coloured her viewpoint somewhat. She told me she wasn't prepared to rely on the hope of a happy ever after, although no one could have quite predicted the tragedy that would befall them both.'

Gaby wasn't listening. She'd stopped listening as soon as she'd unfolded the thick cream notepaper and started to read.

*My dearest Gabriella,*

*You see . . . I'm spending so much time with Rusty that his vagaries are starting to rub off on me!*

*I'm not one for letter writing and I had hoped that this one would grow yellow with age. But obviously something drastic has happened to scupper that plan.*

*Mr Boyd is a good man, despite his awful taste in ties, and he's promised to help you in every way possible now that I can no longer help myself. I could sit here writing pages on how much our friendship has meant to me but you should know all that. Now I need your help like never before. My parents aren't much cop and as for Tim's . . . well, as much as I love them, they're too old to be tied down with bringing up a child, our child. With any luck, he or she'll be eighteen and independent when this lands in your hands. But if not, my plea is that you'll do what you can for our child. That's it. All I ask is that you love them as we already do . . .*

# Chapter 55

## Gaby

**Friday 12 February, 1.50 p.m. A55**

'We need to talk about this, Gaby.'

She threw him a look, more surprised at his use of the short-ened version of her name than by his words. Yes. They had to talk but why did it have to be now? She needed time to untangle what it meant first. What it meant for them.

The token opposition from Amy's parents was heart-wrenching but it wasn't anything that Gaby hadn't expected. The Potters were far more in love with themselves than almost anyone she'd ever known. Amy joining the police force and then marrying a restaurateur was viewed as a direct sully to their name, some-thing that had upset Gaby far more than it appeared to upset her friend. Amy had got the measure of her family at an early age and had jumped at the chance to join her when Gaby had left Swansea for North Wales. Faith and Max were visibly upset at the turn of the conversation and Gaby was hard pressed not to give in to their overtures straightaway. But Amy was right. Tim's parents were well into their sixties and busy from dawn to dusk with running the hotel. Tim wouldn't have wanted them to give all that up and Gaby certainly wasn't prepared to let them, now she knew her friend's wishes. The only problem was Rusty.

'I agree we need to talk,' Gaby finally said, her hand on the door handle as she reached for her bag. 'But not now. I have a team meeting due to start in five minutes and a need for a strong black coffee with about ten sugars first.'

He smiled, the first smile she'd noticed touch his face in what felt like ages – or had she just stopped noticing? A salutary thought that had her pause in the act of unclipping her seatbelt to plant a kiss on his cheek.

'I'll pop in and check on Lara when I get back. I'll text you,' he said, curling his fingers around her jaw.' And with that he was gone, leaving Gaby with a host of conflicting emotions as she made her way into the station.

The incident room was exceptionally quiet, with all the usual suspects huddled around the whiteboard in what looked like an impromptu discussion.

'What's up?'

'Oh, you're back. Good.' Owen ambled over to the coffee machine and, shaking the pot, poured her a mug of what resembled syrup. 'Here, that will put hairs on your chest. There's a sandwich too if you haven't eaten. Courtesy of Sherlock, would you believe?'

'Maybe later.' Gaby cradled the warm mug between her fingers, the smell of stewed, dry roast nauseatingly good and exactly what she needed after the side-sweep of a conversation that had turned all her plans and good intentions haywire. Just when she'd decided to accept that she'd never have a child, one was presented to her on a plate. She was only beginning to realise what the big lummox of an Irishman meant to her and now she'd have to give him up. The one thing she knew about Rusty Mulholland was that he stuck to his guns. She'd yet to see him recant on anything. But she wasn't about to let Amy down. Stalemate.

'So, what's happening?' she repeated, settling against the edge of the desk.

'Trying to fill in the gaps. We had a decent enough interview with Checkley and she's confirmed a lot of our thoughts on the subject of Brownley's motive.'

'And?'

'And we've come up with a scenario as to what might have happened,' Owen replied, making his way to the window. 'One that seems to fit the bill anyway. But let's fill you in on the Banfields first. They weren't that difficult to find, once Jax worked out that they were well past retirement age and had a married daughter living in Sheffield. They also weren't surprised by the phone call, were they, Jax?'

'Said they'd been waiting for something all these years,' he said, undoing the top button of his shirt as if it had suddenly grown uncomfortably tight. '"A bad un" was the phrase they used but always smart enough to practise just within the confines of the law, that is until their own daughter fell under his spell and became pregnant. She was only thirteen at the time. When they tackled him he disappeared along with all their ready cash. They never saw or heard from him again.'

'And the girl?'

'She went on to give birth. They cared for their grandchild until their daughter was mature enough to set up her own home.'

'Okay. Thanks, Jax. So Brownley is an unsavoury individual but with no criminal record to speak of.' Gaby stared down at her shoes and the tide mark stain from walking through slush earlier. If she didn't polish them later they'd be ruined. The very least of her concerns. 'What else?' she said, lifting her head to where Owen was now jingling coins in his pockets.

'Lynda Checkley knew Brownley from her time spent at the same children's home. She came across him again during her nursing training in Manchester and, using her words, he creeps her out. She's even thought of taking out an injunction although there's nothing specific to hang it on. The most telling aspect is the theft from her car, which included a file containing forms that she fills out when there's a home birth.' The sound of coins chinking together stopped. 'They're essential when a parent goes to register a birth.'

Gaby pulled a face. 'We seem to find ourselves back to that old problem of motivation. Why go to all the trouble and risk of making a baby when it's far easier to steal one, and financially it doesn't make sense?'

'Artificial insemination.'

'Excuse me?' Gaby made an extra effort to manoeuvre her jaw back into its rightful place. 'What was that, Marie?'

Marie coughed, clearing her throat, her voice rising up a notch. 'Don't you see, all of you? We have three women abducted. Two that have given birth. One left for dead and one missing.'

'I know I'm being a bit thick, but I still don't get where you're coming from?'

Marie's cheeks pinkened. 'I . . . I have a friend who's trying for a baby. She doesn't have a partner so I . . . I . . . I've been helping her look at other ways. A sperm donor,' she finally blurted out, booting up her laptop. 'And that's not all. I've been doing a bit of research on the net. Did you know for instance that while surrogacy in the UK is regulated, the same doesn't go for the likes of America? There, a couple can be charged upwards of a hundred and fifty thousand dollars for the privilege.'

'So, what you're saying is Brownley is selling babies to the highest bidder?'

'Actually what I'm thinking is it's a whole lot worse than that.'

Gaby forced out a laugh. 'What could be worse than deliberately impregnating someone only to then go and sell the baby on?'

Marie blushed but carried on speaking. 'I know all that, ma'am, but Jason, for all his chauvinistic comments, opened up a new train of thought. As much as I objected to what he had to say on the topic of physical beauty, I think we all have to agree that he

241

was onto something. Brownley wanted to make as much money in as short a timeframe as possible, so he comes up with a new plan, probably influenced by Checkley training to be a midwife. Egg donation and artificial insemination are both services available in the UK whereby you can choose the characteristics of the donor. All you have to do is log on and you're immediately taken to a page. It's like shopping online but easier. Your baby's race, hair colour, height, even their eye colour. You can even choose the donor's career from vet to doctor to anything you can think of,' she said, emphasising both professions like the bullet from a gun. 'I think Brownley created his own shopping list for his clients, probably people he cultivated on the dark web,' she continued, counting out on her fingers. 'In all cases the egg donors had to be young, innocent and intelligent. Perhaps in Jules's case the client was looking for a dark-haired mother whereas in Christy's they were looking for a black mother. We know that Bryony is a redhead. He's selling on designer babies without all the messy uncertainty of IVF or women reneging on their surrogacy commitment, which as we all know isn't unheard of. For a price, parents get the child of their dreams produced on a platter along with all the necessary documents to boot.'

'He must be making a mint,' Owen said, his hand on his beard. 'Blood money of the worst sort.'

'He probably has a Swiss bank account, which makes tracing him almost impossible,' Marie added with a sneer.

'Hold on a minute, Marie,' Gaby said, a frown in place. 'That's all very well but wouldn't the babies all be fifty per cent Eli? Surely not so much of a bargain.'

'We might be able to ask him shortly,' Jax said, scrolling through his mobile.

'You have a lead? Come on, Jax. Don't leave us in suspense or I'll put you on nights for the next month.'

He grinned back at her. 'I don't think you'll do that, ma'am. While you've been out galivanting, I've been playing around with how Brownley might have tripped himself up and, as you know, I was the one who followed his footsteps around Llandudno. He's clever but only up to a point. He knows that bank notes are untraceable and in all cases that's how he's escaped detection. He paid in cash at the guest house, which was unusual but, as it was only for one night, not outside the realms of possibility that someone would have that amount of cash in the back of their wallet. Anyway I'm digressing. You asked me to do a background on the cottage over in Rhyd Ddu where Christy turned up. You'll never believe who owns it?'

'Go on, surprise me,' Gaby said, automatically reaching for a sandwich and taking a bite.

'Ansel Abalos, the same man found buried in his own back garden over in Manchester.'

'And if he owns one cottage, what else might he own?'

'Er, not quite. The land registry search only brought up the two properties owned by him I'm afraid. Apparently it's quite common to own a little retreat. Walkers and the like.'

'I wouldn't know.' She swallowed the remainder of the sandwich, washing it down with a swig of cold coffee. 'Only helpful up to a point, Jax. We need to find Bryony, and soon.'

'I believe even sooner than you think, Darin.'

She turned to find DCI Sherlock standing in the doorway. He didn't look happy, far from it. She rarely saw him smile but the seriousness of his expression had the blood freezing in her veins and the bottom falling out of her world for the second time in as many days. 'I've just been speaking to CS Winters. He's been given the heads-up that the BBC are going to report on the links between the Manchester mummy, as it's been coined, and Operation Zhivago.'

'And if Brownley sees that, he's going to know that we're onto him. You can't do anything to delay, even half a day?'

'It's out of my hands, Gaby. They say it's in the public interest to know that there's a maniac on the loose.'

# Chapter 56

Gaby

**Friday 12 February, 2.55 p.m. St Asaph**

The mood in the incident room had changed from muted optimism to deep depression at Sherlock's words. They all returned to their computers, desperate to find the missing link that would reveal Brownley's current hiding place.

The phone rang into the growing silence.

'Hold on a second, Rusty. I'm going to put you on loudspeaker,' Gaby said, covering her hand over the mouthpiece. 'He's got the results back from Jules.' She removed her hand. 'Okay, carry on. We're all listening.'

'Basically I can confirm that we've been able to isolate foetal DNA from the body of Miss White over in Manchester. We also have some comparative DNA to compare with samples collected from the shower in Brownley's flat at Mold Sixth Form Centre and from the crisp packet found at the cottage. I don't know what you were expecting, Gabriella, but they don't match.'

'They don't match? How can they not?' she said, staring across at Owen who was looking as shocked as she was feeling. Their

244

carefully planned scenario had just come crashing down around their ears.

'I can't answer that,' he said with a lack of his usual snarky response. 'The only scenario that comes to mind would be if he somehow managed to inseminate them with someone else's sperm but it all sounds a bit far-fetched. Surely the girls would have noticed.'

'Not necessarily. Remember these were innocent young women in the first throes of romance. It's not far-fetched at all. The evil bastard.'

'Do you remember Christy when we interviewed her?' Owen said. 'She couldn't understand getting pregnant when they always used a condom. All he'd have needed would have been a turkey baster after she'd fallen asleep . . .'

'Really! I don't think I'm ever going to be able to cook a Christmas dinner again without that particular image popping up,' Gaby said, her stomach turning. 'You can ignore Bates, doctor. Anything else?'

'I've passed the results on to Jason who's going to run a search on the database to see if they pick up anything. Just because Brownley isn't the father of Jules's baby doesn't mean to say that we can't still find him. Jason has come up with a scenario though for why Jules's body was moved, albeit unprovable due to lack of evidence.'

'Oh really?'

'Yes. He thinks that the bedroom in Treasure Cottage would have been the ideal environment for Jules's mummification. With the heating turned up on full it would have made a perfect closed environment . . .'

'Stop!' Gaby held up her hand even though she was speaking to Rusty on the phone. 'I get the picture. So, he takes Jules there until she has the baby then, like Christy, leaves her to die. He then moves her back to Manchester so that Christy can take her place.'

'That's about it.'

'Okay, thank you, I'll message you later.'

She returned the mobile to her desk, unable to quite believe how brutal this Elijah Brownley was turning out to be but before she could pick up a pen and start making notes on her already crowded pad, Marie shouted across the room.

'I think I'm onto something, ma'am,' she said, carrying her laptop and depositing it on Gaby's desk. 'I've been in contact with the head teacher about Brownley's bank account and he finally agreed to send me over the details.'

'I'm amazed,' Gaby replied, her tone tinder-dry. 'It usually takes far more than a missing girl to allow for a break in GDPR regs. You must have wrapped him around your little finger, well and truly.'

Marie didn't reply but her flooded cheeks spoke volumes. 'He's only being kind.'

'Yeah, right! I'm delighted for you and all that but what have you got?'

'I've been onto the bank and asked them to launch a suspicious activity report, or SAR, to the National Crime Agency, which means that . . .'

'You've frozen his bank account. You clever thing. If that doesn't bring him out of the woodwork, I don't know what will.'

'Not only that, ma'am. It looks as if he's been transferring large sums of money to a Swiss bank account. I've just come off the phone to the team in Manchester. They've agreed to share Ansel Abalos's bank statements. Interestingly, last month he transferred a large sum to pay for the rental on a winter let in Llanberis.'

'When most likely the man was up to his neck in earthworms,' Jax said, thumping the air with his closed fist. 'Well done. We've got him. We've got the bastard.'

'Not yet, Jax. Don't let's scupper our chances, eh.' Gaby glanced at her watch. 'Owen, speak to Clancy about getting a four-by-four. Where's Llanberis again?' she asked, heading over to the map of North Wales that filled the right-hand wall of the office.

'In Caernarfonshire, not that far from Rhyd Ddu,' Owen said, joining her and pointing out both locations. 'It wouldn't have taken him long to go between the two properties.'

'Okay. Let's go. We have a long drive ahead and in pretty awful weather conditions.'

'What about that news flash?'

'That just makes it more important than ever to leave now. You can let us know what it says on the way down,' Gaby said, shrugging into her coat and pulling her scarf and gloves from the pockets. 'Marie, phone our colleagues over in Llanberis to arrange for backup.'

# Chapter 57

Bryony

**Friday 12 February, 4.10 p.m. Blaen-Cym House**

'Gather your stuff. We're leaving in five minutes.'

'We're what?'

Bryony lowered her mug back onto the bedside table, swiping the back of her hand across her mouth. 'Why?'

'You don't need to know why.' He flung her padded jacket on the bed along with her trainers and rucksack. 'Don't get any ideas, Bry. I'll carry you out if I have to. Now shift. I'll bring the car round. If it doesn't fit in that bag, it's staying. Got it?'

She'd never seen him like this before. His cheeks were flushed, his eyes unable to settle. He strode out of the room failing to close the door behind him.

Bryony sat still for a moment, her eyes on the door as her mind raced through the possibilities. Something had happened to freak him out. She had no way of knowing what. The obvious answer was that someone had discovered their location because why else would he think of running away and in this weather? The house was isolated – she'd seen that much when they'd arrived. There wasn't another property in walking distance and the parking was around the back. No one would have even known that the building was occupied and the risk of them investigating on the off chance was minimal at best. She should just grab her trainers and jacket and go, but there was the snow to think about in addition to her baby. He'd be bound to find her and then what. She'd be back where she started but in an even worse predicament.

So, instead of doing what most people would have done under the circumstances, she ran into the bathroom and removed the panel before sliding underneath. Trying to manoeuvre the bath panel was a nightmare and resulted in broken fingernails and scraped arms but she finally managed to slip it back into place.

She lay on her side, the bottom of the bath digging into her spine, her fingers stretched out against the smooth underside of the bath panel in order to try and keep it in place, tears streaming down her face as she tried to regulate her breathing and maintain her sanity.

He tore through the room like a tornado, wrenching the bathroom door so that it smashed against the tiles. She stopped breathing then, her eyes scrunched closed at the inevitable but the noise died away, his footsteps retreating down the landing. The hope was that he'd think she'd done a runner and waste precious minutes in searching outside. With a bit of luck he'd slip and break something on the way.

She could still hear him shouting her name but in the faraway distance. She knew it wasn't over. Far from it.

# Chapter 58

## Gaby

**Friday 12 February, 4.10 p.m. A55**

'Bloody marvellous. Talk about idiotic reporters giving the game away. They might as well have phoned Brownley and told him that we're on our way,' Gaby said, switching off her phone and resting it on her lap, her fingernails tapping away at the case. 'We can but hope that he doesn't listen to the news.'

'We can but hope that you won't reside in cloud cuckoo land for long, Gaby,' Owen said, sending her a fleeting glance as he continued to navigate the almost deserted A55.

Gaby ignored his comment, well aware that if she'd been in Brownley's shoes she'd be glued to all of the news channels. It was only common sense to be alerted to the dangers.

She stared out of the window at the bleak and barren landscape. It hadn't been as difficult a journey as she'd feared, with the gritter trucks working overtime, but emotionally she was a car crash waiting to happen. She sat in the growing silence, almost hypnotised by the string of white up ahead, her mind flipping between thoughts of Amy and Tim and little Lara, a tiny bundle of responsibility that had been thrust in her path. Rusty had surprised her when he'd offered to check in on Lara again before she'd ended the call but it was also a syringe shot full of home truths. If she couldn't find five minutes in her day to pop into the hospital to see the poor mite where was she going to find the time for full parental responsibility? Something had to change but fitting a career in policing around childcare wasn't as simple as that. It wasn't as if she could rely solely on the assistance of a childminder. She worked long hours, often right through the evening and sometimes into the night. Did she want that kind of a latch-key life for Amy's daughter and if not, what was she prepared to do about it?

The thoughts went round and round in an unending circle with one central theme. Her days as a detective were numbered.

'It's up ahead, if that sign we passed is right. I'd like you to block the drive and cut the engine. That way he'll have to try and escape on foot.'

'You think you'll be able to manage the track up to the house in those shoes?' Owen said, pulling a face at her slip-ons.

'I'll have to. And anyway, I have your arm to lean on. Why do you think I asked a fine strapping man like you to drive, Owen? It certainly wasn't for your personality or good looks,' Gaby said, injecting a well-needed dose of humour into the proceedings.

# Chapter 59

## Bryony

### Friday 12 February, 4.15 p.m. Blaen-Cym House

Bryony didn't know how long she'd been lying in the tight space under the bath. Her hipbone and elbow took the brunt of her weight, her head pressed up against the ceramic underside as she struggled to hear despite the thickness of the wood and the solid nature of the stone-constructed building. After the initial door-slamming and the sound of the stairs creaking right under the bathroom floor, there was silence apart from the thudding of her heart and the rasp of her breaths. Time had no meaning for someone who was well on the path to petrified now that she realised exactly what Eli was.

She'd always been interested in psychology, not that any kind of label would help her now. Knowing that Eli was a cold-hearted psychopath was only of fleeting interest, something to pass the time while she waited for him to give up. She almost laughed, the anxiety and stress causing a thick bubble of noise to build in the back of her throat only for her to swallow it back at the last second. He wasn't going to give up. He wasn't the type. No. He'd find her. It was only a matter of time as she again regretted with every breath and heartbeat that she hadn't decided to run. At least whatever he was about to do to her would be swift. She didn't think about the baby; she couldn't. She barely had the strength of character to look after herself let alone to be worried about the little scrap. To think would be to remember the joy and happiness she'd felt at the thought of a little piece of Eli growing inside. Now the mere flicker of the budding idea filled her with terror.

Her thin kaftan was no protection from the stone flooring or the cold seeping into her bones. She was numb from the waist down and with the threat of pins and needles a whisper away. There was no comfort. No plan for freedom. Her brain was too caught up with the futility of her situation for that. There was no hope.

# Chapter 60

## Gaby

### Friday 12 February, 4.15 p.m. Blaen-Cym House

'Thank heaven the snow's stopped,' Gaby said, staring out of the window at the house up ahead. 'The sooner this lot thaws the better. What time did Marie say backup would get here?'

'Any minute now. We'd better wait. Remember what happened the last time? A bollocking in triplicate is something I can well do without, now you've forced me to take my exams. Sherlock would be quite happy to use something like that to stop my promotion.'

'You're being paranoid and where did you get the idea that I could force you to do anything, Owen?' She half turned in her seat, facing him. 'I feel desperately sorry for your wife. You must be impossible to live with, if you come up with fairy stories like that. I'll have to make sure to give her my commiserations next time I run into her in Asda.'

'Kate's the happiest woman in Wales,' he said with a huff.

'If you say so.'

The car fell silent. Gaby tapped her fingers against her watch face, willing for signs of any kind of a vehicle on the deserted road. It shouldn't take the local constabulary that long to get here. All was silent and calm, almost as if the world and his wife were waiting for all hell to break loose.

Gaby banged her head against the car roof when the scream came. The picture-perfect postcard scene broken by the blood-thirstiest of cries.

# Chapter 61

Bryony

**Friday 12 February, 4.20 p.m. Blaen-Cym House**

'You silly bitch. You thought you could escape, did you? It didn't occur to you that I'd know that you were in the house some-where. Snow doesn't lie. Remember that next time you try and run away – although, believe me when I say that there will be no next time. I'm going to make sure of that even if I have to tie you to the bed.'

Eli flung the wooden panel across the room and half dragged, half lifted her out from under the bath. There was no thought for the cramp that gripped her calves with a vice-like intensity or the fact that she could barely put weight through her legs.

'Eli, please.'

'Eli, please,' he mimicked. 'No Eli, please. You'll walk or I'll drag you.'

'The baby.'

'At this stage in the proceedings I don't give a flying fuck about the baby. It's on its own as far as I'm concerned. Now get a move on,' he said, his fingers clenched around her upper arm as he propelled her in front of him down the stairs.

'My bag. My coat. I'll freeze.'

'Shut up, you silly cow. You don't get it, do you? I don't care if you freeze. I don't care if you die where you stand. I simply don't care. You're an inconvenience, only that. I'd be half inclined to leave you here if it wasn't for . . .'

'If it wasn't for . . . ?'

He shook his head. 'Never mind. It doesn't matter.'

But Bryony knew it mattered. It mattered deeply. She could see it in the way moisture was beading on his forehead and the stench of stale sweat emanating from his skin, despite the temperature. He needed her, otherwise he'd have left her and driven away without a backward glance. And with that thought, she decided to make a stand. For herself. For her baby. For the stupid young woman she'd been only four days before. She'd make a stand and be prepared to die from the consequences.

They were in the hallway and he was grappling with trying to hold on to her with one hand and grab his mobile and keys from the small half-moon table with the other. With a sudden jerking movement, she dropped her shoulder and escaped his grasp. She wrenched the front door open and ran through the porch and down the steps, her bare feet sinking into the soft snow. But she didn't feel the icy cold invading her skin and numbing her muscles. All she felt was the slap as he swung back his hand and connected with the side of her head.

'You stupid fucking woman. I'm going to kill you with my bare hands and relish every second.'

# Chapter 62

## Gaby

### Friday 12 February, 4.20 p.m. Blaen-Cym House

'Shit.' The expletive slipped out without her even being aware of it.

Gaby wasn't known for her swearing but it was the only word that came to mind. 'Owen, phone the backup team and tell them we're going in.'

'No!'

'No?'

'No! I'm not prepared to go through this again, not after Amy and Tim. And—' He grabbed her arm, preventing her from opening the door. 'What about me, hmm? You can't go in gung-ho as if you're James bleeding Bond. I won't let you. You won't be only putting yourself in danger, remember that.'

She stared back, his words seeping through the cloud of mist that had shrouded her mind. Someone needed help.

If Gaby had been a different person, she'd have struggled with the decision he was forcing on her but she wasn't. She'd made a promise all those years ago when she'd signed up to join the force and it wasn't in her make-up to back down now that her life had changed. She spared a thought for Lara but the baby would be fine. The little girl had a host of grandparents and aunties who'd always make sure that she received the best of care, even if Gaby wasn't around to fulfil Amy's wishes. And as for Owen – she wasn't asking for him to follow. He'd done that far too many times in the past for her to expect it.

She peeled Owen's fingers away, her mind finally swerving to Amy. She'd have been the first to understand that it was impossible for Gaby to make any other choice.

'I'm sorry, Owen. Make that call, eh?'

Gaby stepped onto the drive, cursing with a passion that far outstripped her previous expletive. She needed to follow the drive around the back of the property to locate the source of that scream and yet here she was like a new-born foal with what felt like ten limbs to control instead of the usual two.

The screech of tyres spinning up ahead was the first indication that something else must have happened along with that scream. She managed to step out of the way of the path of the car, with only seconds to spare.

A cacophony of noise ripped through the air, the sound of metal wrapping itself around metal causing her to wince. There was nothing she could do to prevent the unfolding scene except to watch open-mouthed as the BMW slammed into the side of the unmarked police car with Owen still inside. The last sight she had of him was of his shocked face as he tried to shift across the handbrake into the passenger side, his legs trapped beneath him.

She was unable to move, unable to think, the image of Owen's face splitting into a thousand facets. His smile. His grin. His frown. Owen in a bad mood. Tired Owen. All the pictures she'd built up in the filing cabinet of her mind, which she'd labelled friend in a rare moment of sentimental madness. She didn't have enough friends to fill more than part of a drawer, even less since she'd lost Amy.

After what seemed like an age, she grabbed her phone from her pocket and dialled 999. Time contracted and the normal rules of the space-time continuum didn't apply in this tiny slice of Wales. She had no way of knowing that only one miserly second had ticked past in the space between seeing the crash and pressing those well-known numbers.

'Officer down!'

The message was garbled but then so was her brain. However, this wasn't Gaby Darin speaking. This was an experienced officer inhabiting her body, mind and soul, as routine kicked in.

She slipped and slid down the drive, unconsciously stepping onto the deep trench carved out by the car. She wasn't worried about Brownley. If truth be known, she barely spared him a thought.

# Chapter 63

Bryony

**Friday 12 February, 4.20 p.m. Blaen-Cym House**

The boot of the car was colder than the floor of the bathroom, the sopping kaftan doing nothing to prevent the chill air from stealing through her layers of flesh and bone. There was no insulation to be had and the stress of the last twenty-four hours, compounded by the horror of the last two, blended into a great big ball of fear. Bryony had started shivering in the bathroom but now she was too cold to do anything apart from curl up in a tight ball and pray for it to end. She'd heard about hypothermia during one of her biology lessons and the need to keep moving. Stay awake and keep moving but what was the point? She'd accepted that she was going to die. The sooner the better was now her silent mantra as her limbs stiffened and her breaths shortened, the slap around her head adding a burst blood vessel into the mix.

Bryony was unconscious before the large hand on her watch managed to complete another round trip. She didn't hear the crash. She didn't see the boot of the truck flip open, the power of the accident causing her to somersault through the air and land on the snow beyond. She didn't see a dazed Eli climb out of the car and make his way over to her and start kicking her wherever his steel-capped shoe landed.

# Chapter 64

Gaby

**Friday 12 February, 4.25 p.m. Blaen-Cym House**

There was nothing that Gaby could do to free Owen from the tangle of metal and, with the sound of wailing sirens in the distance, she decided to check on what Brownley was up to. He wouldn't get far on foot but something as inconsequential as snow hadn't stopped him up to now.

Gaby had a temper, something that very few people knew about outside of her family. In fact, no one knew apart from Owen. She'd let it slip one evening at the end of a particularly harrowing case when he'd nearly lost his wife along with his baby. It was the one aspect of her life that she religiously kept under control. But now she shed her professional persona as quickly as if she was shedding her coat. She had no weapon apart from her mobile and that's what she used when she saw Elijah Brownley assaulting Bryony. There was no thought as to what she was doing or that it contravened a whole host of rules and regulations. She simply didn't care.

'You absolute bastard. You think that we don't know about

you and what you've been doing in Manchester and now Wales?' she said, slamming the mobile against the side of his face, where blood was already dripping from a cut on his forehead. He turned and in that instant she lifted up her foot and aimed her pretty useless shoes, bought because she quite liked the pointed toes, in the centre of his groin and rammed it home. She didn't see the backup car arrive and two police officers hurry to her side but, if she had, it wouldn't have stopped her from continuing to lift her foot and repeatedly slam it against Brownley's now prostrate body.

'Ma'am, stop.'

'That's for Amy and that's for Owen, you complete and utter piece of shit.'

She only stopped when she was forced to, and then only when they grabbed both her arms and lifted her off Brownley's body and placed her in the back of the car, one of them standing guard in case she tried anything else.

Gaby was spent. She'd had her say. Now there was nothing left apart from tears. She'd lost Amy. She'd quite possibly lost Owen. She'd most certainly lost her job and who'd let someone like her look after Lara? There wasn't room in her narrow focus to even begin to think about what this would mean for her relationship with Rusty.

She dropped her head in her hands, tears seeping through the gaps in her fingers. Gaby was the strong type. Someone who people relied on to stay calm in a crisis and to never break down, no matter the situation. She didn't see the ambulance arrive or the paramedic's shocked face as she immediately radioed up for assistance before starting to work on the blood-covered young girl lying unmoving in the snow. Gaby was well past thoughts of Bryony, Owen or even Lara as the pressures of the last few days finally breached all of her defences.

The police officers were at a loss, as were Mal and Marie when they arrived on the scene shortly after.

'Call Rusty. As a doctor, he'll know what to do,' Marie said, sitting in the patrol car beside Gaby and taking her hand.

'I'll need to file a report on the way she was attacking . . .' the policeman began, with a mutinous glare.

'It's DI Darin to you, Officer, and yes, I suppose you must.'

The words flowed over Gaby but didn't register.

What a mess. What a bloody mess.

# Chapter 65

Rusty

**Friday 12 February, 10 p.m. Rhos-on-Sea**

'Will Gaby be all right?'

'Hopefully after a good sleep. See you in the morning, Conor.' He bent down and ruffled his hair. Night-time kisses had gone the same way as bedtime stories and cuddly toys. He missed them.

The house was quiet, deathly so. Gaby had taken herself off to bed when they'd arrived back, refusing to eat but, more importantly, refusing to talk. Jax had been wrong when he'd said on the phone that, as a medical doctor, he'd know what to do. How do you make someone open up, especially when they were barely talking? He knew he'd made a blunder about not wanting more kids but he'd assumed she'd felt the same way. One look into her face and he'd realised his mistake – by then it had been too late to backtrack. Far too late.

Like Gaby, he wasn't one for fancy words or overt displays of affection. A life spent among the dead compounded by a disastrous marriage meant he said what he wanted to, at a time and in a way that was convenient to him. That didn't mean he was insensitive, just inured by the way his life had panned out. None of that helped.

He sat on the edge of the bed, staring down at her tear-ravaged face, her nose red and shiny, her hair an uncombed mass of knots. He had made his mind up about Gaby almost the first time he'd seen her, at some staff meeting or other. There was something in her strength, drive and enthusiasm that had snagged his attention. It had been snagged ever since.

'I bet I look a sight?' she said, her eyes still closed.

'I was wondering if you were pretending. Too much on your mind to sleep?'

She propped open one eye. 'Something like that.'

'Well, they say that it's good to talk.'

'What?' She opened the other eye. 'You mean a problem shared is a problem doubled?'

'If you like.' He managed a smile. 'So, what do you intend to do?'

Gaby shrugged. 'Too late for that. I assaulted someone so I'm finished as a copper. The end.'

Rusty wanted to draw her into a hug but he didn't. 'What will Sherlock do?'

'He's no choice but to suspend me, pending an investigation by the IOPC, for gross misconduct. They may even try and go for a conviction through the courts, depending on how Brownley plays it. As I said, I'm finished.'

'So, to repeat. What do you intend to do?' he asked, his voice soft.

She shifted away. 'What are you after? Blood? There's been enough shared over the last week to sink the *Titanic*. I don't know what I'm going to do, all right? Go back home probably. I certainly can't afford to pay the mortgage on this place.'

'And Lara . . . What about her? You owe Amy.'

Gaby's face flashed with rage. 'You think I don't know that? But there's no way Mr Boyd is going to agree to Amy's wishes now!'

'Oh, I don't know. I'd be proud to have you as her co-parent.'

He took her hand in his. He wasn't quite brave enough to do more. 'You're strong, resilient, honourable and you do happen to be the woman I want to spend my life with,' he said, concentrating on their hands before meeting her gaze. 'Yes, our life is going to be a little different to perhaps the one we were planning but so be it. Will you marry me, Gabriella?'

# Chapter 66

Gaby

**Saturday 13 February, 9 a.m. St Asaph Hospital**

'We'll have to stop meeting like this, Bates.'

Owen tried to raise his head off the pillow at the sound of her voice but she put her hand out to stop him. 'No, don't move. You're fine the way you are. What if you damage the plaster casts?'

He slumped back, resigned. 'The wife as well as that Tartar of a sister would have my guts for garters.'

Gaby leant forward on her chair, unsure of how to begin the conversation. Visiting Owen had been top of her list but now she was here she had nothing to say. She'd again put his life in danger. Okay, so broken bones would heal but it was more than bones that had been broken yesterday.

'I'm sorry, I should have brought grapes. I didn't think.'

'Can't stand the things – the pips get caught in my teeth. I'm just happy to see you. Going out of my tiny mind stuck in bed. With a bit of luck they'll be able to fit me up with a wheelchair.'

'God help us all, you in charge of a wheelchair.' She paused, plucking away at the blue coverlet. 'Sherlock has called me in to see him first thing Monday.'

'And?'

'I'm going to resign. It's the only honourable thing I can do.'

'Always the martyr. Brownley deserved everything he got and more.'

'But it wasn't up to me to deliver the punishment.' She managed a grin. 'It does mean Sherlock will be on your back to complete your exams pretty smartish.'

Owen grimaced, changing the subject. 'Jax and Marie popped in, no grapes.'

'Oh?'

'They have Brownley in St Asaph. He's employed Marie's ex to defend him.'

'Lordy. Poor Marie.'

'I wouldn't say that. Jax whispered something about a hot date on the way out. That head teacher over at the sixth form centre, which isn't a surprise to perhaps anyone except Marie.'

'Well, I'm glad something good has come out of all this.' Gaby gnawed at her bottom lip. 'Please tell me that Brownley doesn't have a chance of winning, Owen?'

'With two bodies in Manchester,' he said, ticking them off his fingers, 'and the two here as witnesses, I think it's highly unlikely. Did you hear Bryony lost the baby?'

'God. No. That poor girl.'

They sat in silence, mulling over the case and all the strands yet to be tied off. The newspapers were full of the story. The search for Christy and Jules's babies filling the front pages. Brownley's refusal to speak. It was going to be a long, drawn-out process with no guarantees of success.

# Chapter 67

## Gaby

### Monday 15 February, 9 a.m. St Asaph

'Take a seat, Gaby.'

'I'd prefer to stand, if that's all right, sir.'

He waved away her comment and crossed over to the window, his hands clasped behind his back.

'I really don't know what to say.'

'There's nothing you can say, sir,' she said, placing her warrant card on his desk. 'If it's any consolation, I don't for a minute regret one second of what I did to Brownley, apart from the damage to my shoes. I'd do it again in an instant.'

'And that's what makes it so tragic, Gaby, because if I'd been in your position I probably would have felt the exact same emotion. The only difference being, I'd have taken it out on the golf course after.'

'I don't play golf, sir.'

'Perhaps you should think of taking it up!'

'Is that because of all the time I'm going to have on my hands?' she said, managing a smile.

He dropped into his chair, ignoring the warrant card. 'I'm

271

afraid I don't have any choice. Brownley is going to press charges and the worst of it is, he'll probably get help towards the costs.'

'I don't care about that. He can do his worst. If the people at the top are stupid enough to let him prosecute me then so be it. I'll clear my desk but if I could be allowed to say goodbye to the team?'

'Of course. You know, I'd sweep this under the carpet if I could but . . .'

'But that would make us as bad as the criminals,' she said, ending his sentence for him.

'Have you any plans?'

*

She'd left Rusty in the corridor outside the DCI's office. Now they strolled into the incident room, side by side.

The office was quieter than the local graveyard at midnight. When she walked through the door, the silence pulsed against the walls of the room, pressing and pushing. No one quite knew what to say. The sight of Owen with both legs stretched out in front of him was the thing needed to slash the quiet wide open.

'What the hell do you think you're doing back at work?'

He blushed, the colour flowering against the brown of his beard. 'That's why we have lifts, Gaby, in case some of the staff are stupid enough to break both legs in more than one place.' He paused, now not quite meeting her gaze. 'We're not sure how we're going to manage without you.'

'You're going to do fine, Bates. More than fine,' she said, swallowing a lump in the back of her throat. 'With your brain, Mal's charm, Jax's eye for detail and Marie's heart, you're going to be a team to reckon with. You just take your exams and in no time you'll be managing the station. I wouldn't want it any other way.'

'Talking about my eye for detail,' Jax interrupted, hurrying over from his desk.

'What is it, Jax?' Gaby and Owen said in unison, only for Gaby to step back out of the way. This wasn't her investigation anymore. Rusty took her arm, giving it a little squeeze.

'I really should go.'

'No. Stay, at least until Jax has had his say,' Owen said, shifting slightly in his wheelchair. 'Carry on.'

'Remember Mal was looking into the list from that pizza restaurant? The thing that had us all stumped? The reason Brownley chose to break off the journey when there was no need?'

'Okay. I'm not sure where you're going with this but . . .'

'I've been reading through the notes you made from that interview with Christy. There was a comment about stopping off in Llanrwst for a meal, in way of a celebration. What if the prospective parents were there? What if it was his way of screwing as much money out of them as possible with his perfectly filled shopping basket of both inward and outer characteristics? What if they wanted proof before they parted with any if their readies . . .?'

'That's a lot of *what-ifs*, Jax,' Owen said. 'Any facts to go with it?'

'I've been in touch with the restaurant behind the clock tower; there's only one. They've sent me the receipts for all the meals served on the day in question. I have them here.'

'And? The suspense is killing me, man.'

'And it was a very busy day in the height of summer. They served over fifty customers during lunch alone but there was only one cash taking. I'm hoping Christy and Brownley's. It's all here. Credit and debit card sales. It's going to take a bit of work and involve getting in touch with all of the banks and credit card companies concerned but . . .'

'All we have to do is trace the rest. My God, Jax, I could kiss you, but you'll be pleased to know that I won't,' Owen said, a broad grin splitting his face in two. 'Suffice it to say, bloody well done. A handshake and a pint will have to do.' He turned to Gaby. 'Not a bad bit of news to exit on? If Jax's hunch works out then we'll only have Jules's baby to find. With a bit of luck this will

273

spur the Manchester team into looking in the right direction.' He leant back in his chair, his expression exuberant. 'At least I'll know you're only down the road if I need any advice.'

'Er . . . not quite.' Gaby linked her arm through Rusty's. 'Dr Mulholland is going to try and make an honest woman out of me. I'm not sure he'll manage but I have accepted his proposal. I do need someone experienced to help with Lara.'

Rusty's laugh rang out. 'I can see romance is well and truly dead in our household.'

After the laughter had died down, after Marie and Jax had hugged her, after Owen had added his own quiet but heartfelt congratulations, he asked, 'But you're still only down the road?'

# Acknowledgements

Firstly, an apology. I know this book will be a shock to some of you. The loss of a well-loved character like Amy was difficult enough to write let alone read but it felt the right thing to do. I also have to apologise for ending the series but, while there won't be any more Gaby Darin books in this format, I haven't ruled out a return of the team at some point.

Back to the business in hand.

I'd like to mention the dedication, which was raffled as a fundraiser for 2021 BBC Children in Need. Thank you, Emma Bennett, for your generous bid. I also raffled off a character's name to raise funds for Les Borges Hospice. Thanks goes to Alan Boyd.

A big thank you to my editor, Abi Fenton at HQ Digital, Dushi Horti, Helena Newton, Audrey Linton and the team for turning a one-line idea into *Cold Grave*.

I also must thank my daughter, Freya. Writers are inspired in many ways. Plots come out of nowhere and everywhere. If I hadn't dropped Freya off on a sleepover and checked my mirror to see that she'd entered the house safely there'd be no book! Her two brothers both deserve a mention too as does Alan. Couldn't do it without you.

Thank you, Valerie Keogh: my support network. My writing

whip when I really don't feel like writing. My confidante when I feel like jacking it in. My friend.

Thanks to Caroline Maston, from UKCBC on Facebook for bravely agreeing to be a character in my book. Maureen Webb also makes the shift from Facebook friend onto the page as does Lesley Lloyd and Lynda Checkley. Amy Potter, a nursing colleague and friend, thank you!

I also use real places where I'm allowed. *Cold Grave* features The Capri Guesthouse, Johnny Dough's Wood-Fired Pizza Restaurant and Lovies Delight Tea House. Thank you for agreeing to be included.

Thanks too to Gareth Thomas, ASART secretary, Llanberis MR team, for help with Snowdonia Mountain rescues. Also to Huw Evans, Aberdyfi Search and Rescue Team, for pointing me in the right direction.

Twitter has been amazingly supportive, particularly the local network found at #CHOG. Thanks too to all the bloggers who have supported me over the years and continue to do so, particularly those who have helped with my blog tours. I also would like to thank my small but select band of super fans who have been with me pretty much from the beginning. Thanks Beverley, Michele, Susan, Adele, Elaine, Daniela, Tracy, Clare, Hayley, Amanda, Pauline, Terri, Sany and Maddie. You rock.

Thank you again, dear reader, for your support for Gaby and her team over the last two years. I hope you've enjoyed a peek into their lives as much as I've enjoyed writing about them. I'm currently working on something completely different but that's another story.

Jenny x

Below are some links if you'd like to keep in touch with my latest book news.

Twitter https://twitter.com/scribblerjb
Facebook https://www.facebook.com/JennyOBrienWriter/
Instagram https://www.instagram.com/scribblerjb/

Dear Reader,

We hope you enjoyed reading this book. If you did, we'd be so appreciative if you left a review. It really helps us and the author to bring more books like this to you.

Here at HQ Digital we are dedicated to publishing fiction that will keep you turning the pages into the early hours. Don't want to miss a thing? To find out more about our books, promotions, discover exclusive content and enter competitions you can keep in touch in the following ways:

### JOIN OUR COMMUNITY:

Sign up to our new email newsletter:
http://smarturl.it/SignUpHQ

Read our new blog www.hqstories.co.uk

🐦 https://twitter.com/HQStories

📘 www.facebook.com/HQStories

### BUDDING WRITER?

We're also looking for authors to join the HQ Digital family!
Find out more here:

https://www.hqstories.co.uk/want-to-write-for-us/

Thanks for reading, from the HQ Digital team

If you enjoyed *Cold Grave*,
then why not try another
gripping thriller from HQ Digital?

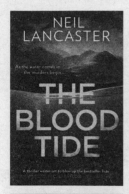

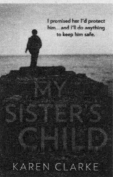

Munro Smith.
1929.

( For Review
in "Reform" ).

# HISTORICAL THEOLOGY
## An Introduction

# HISTORICAL THEOLOGY
## An Introduction

*by*
**GEOFFREY W. BROMILEY**

T. & T. CLARK LTD.
36 GEORGE STREET, EDINBURGH

*FOR PETER*

# Acknowledgments

In various ways many people have contributed to this work, and it is no less a pleasure than a duty to thank them for their help.

High on the list stand the many publishers who have readily and graciously given permission to use the excerpts from original authors which give color, vitality, and authority to the text. In particular thanks are due to The Catholic University of America Press: Volumes 25, 33, 37, 61, and 64 of the Fathers of the Church series; T. and T. Clark: Volumes 1 and 2 of Barth's *Church Dogmatics;* Fortress Press: Volumes 25, 35, and 37 of Luther's Works; Harper and Row: Harper Torchbooks, Kant and Schleiermacher; Oxford University Press: four volumes of the Library of Protestant Thought; Pilgrim Press: *The Marrow of Theology: William Ames 1576–1633* (Copyright © 1968 by United Church Press); Stanford University Press: Lessing's *Theological Writings;* and Westminster Press: Volumes I-III, V, VII-XI, XIX-XXI, XXIV-XXVI of the Library of Christian Classics. Full details of the works cited will be found in the Bibliography, and volumes that are available should be used in collateral reading.

At another level students have also played a notable and even an essential part. They not only provided the first impulse to assemble the materials but also endured their early transmission in oral form and added their own verbal and written questions and appraisals. Without those who made up the classes the enterprise would never have been initiated, let alone completed.

Books cannot see the light of day without a publisher, and a special tribute is due for the courtesy and efficiency with which the work has been received and handled by a house whose friendly cooperation has been much appreciated for the past two decades.

Finally, I owe an inestimable debt to my wife Isobel, not for undertaking mundane chores such as copying, typing, and reading, but for the less tangible yet far more valuable contribution of loving support and spiritual and theological companionship that has made the task of reading and writing so much the easier and the more enjoyable across the many happy years of married life.

*Pasadena*                                          Geoffrey W. Bromiley
*Advent 1977*

# Contents

## PART III. MODERN THEOLOGY

# Introduction

An ideal historical theology — or even an introduction to it — lies beyond the limits of human possibility. Indeed, even ideas of the ideal differ so broadly that what might approximate the ideal for some falls hopelessly short for others. Writing a historical theology involves a venture and rests on a series of choices of aim, method, matter, and approach, choices which are in some sense arbitrary and all of which are open to dispute. Even at best, then, the product will do justice neither to the subject, nor to the intention of the author, nor to the expectations of readers.

In these circumstances modesty and candor are primary demands. Modesty will dispel the illusion of mastery, recognize the boundaries of the attainable, and therefore avoid the pathetic error of supposedly definitive statements. It will also set a curb on the brilliant but speculative theorizing which does more to advance reputations than to promote authentic knowledge or understanding. Candor calls for an acknowledgment of the specific choices which are in fact made, with a frank admittance that they might be wrong, and that even if they are substantially right execution of the choices poses even greater difficulty than making them.

**1. Aim.** The aim in this historical theology is openly one of introduction. Those who have already worked their way into the field will probably find here little that is new, the more so if they have learned the wisdom of consulting primary instead of secondary sources. Experts who probe into backgrounds and connections and contexts can pass by on the other side, for even if the study is to them like the man wounded and robbed and half-dead by the roadside, they can no more give help than receive it. Teachers of the discipline are unlikely to profit except perhaps by finding comfortable confirmation that theirs is a better way, for after all teachers are like those in the days of the Judges, each of whom did what was right in his own eyes. The work is composed for beginners, for inquirers, for those who know nothing or very little of the history of theology but who want to know something, or something more, and who, if they are students, may be required to do so whether they particularly want or not. Hence what is presented is rudimentary. It moves at no exalted level. Its purpose is not to impart complete or even advanced knowledge but to give the initial knowledge and understanding which will lead to further study and reflection, or at least leave a reminder that further study and reflection lie beyond. Introduction here should be taken in the literal sense. Some outstanding theologians and some of their works are introduced. Once the introduction is performed, the true and fruitful conversation — the direct conversation of theologian and student — can begin.

**2. Method.** The aim necessarily shapes the method. Historical theologies can come in various shapes and packages. One possibility is the rapid survey which attempts a sketch of everybody and everything. Another possiblity is the detailed and multivolumed study which with greater ambition, but at the greater risk of boredom, tries to say everything about everybody and everything. A third possibility is the interpretative one which advances a series of interesting theories or theses according to which the material is grouped and which form the starting point for the interminable and inconclusive analyses, antitheses, and syntheses beloved by specialists. A fourth possibility is that of explanation, which always tries to show the root and reason of what is said or written, so that what finally emerges is a nexus of influence and interaction. All these methods have their validity, but they all serve different purposes from that intended here. The closest are the survey and the detailed presentation, but whereas the former of these is too cursory to fulfill the present goal the latter is too exhaustive and exhausting. Too little is said on the one side, too much on the other.

Instead, the method adopted in the present work is that of choosing a few theologians and making the introduction by a fuller exposition and discussion of selected pieces. As compared with the general survey this has the disadvantage of leaving out a great many people and writings. Yet what it does deal with, it handles more thoroughly and seriously, and this is the advantage. In contrast to the full and detailed treatment, it is better adjusted to the time which beginners can give and the interest which they have. If the stock of information imparted seems to compare unfavorably, a good deal is left to be explored at first hand instead of secondarily. Nor is there the same risk that students will be overwhelmed, or bored, by the excess of erudition. The excitement of broader theorizing is missing, but perhaps this is more than compensated by the relief at being able to read what is written without having to find support or refutation for the audacious thoughts of commentators who lived many hundreds of years later, and whose schematizations were totally unknown to the original authors. The lack of a more adequate presentation of the background or context forms a serious drawback. Yet even this defect can also be a virtue. For now the theologians can step forth as living persons who just possibly might have had an original idea or two and are not simply the product of other forces or a repository for current notions.

**3. Matter.** The aim and method obviously impose selectivity and here particularly onerous choices have to be made. The choices lie at two levels: Which theologians is one to introduce, and which of their works is one to use for the purpose? In neither sphere can any definitive criteria be found by which to make the selection. Nor can there be any single regulative principle. Hence the final choice has an arbitrary element in which circumstances and preferences play a major part. If other scholars in other circumstances and with other preferences disagree, one can only concede that they have every right to do so, while reminding them, of course, that their alternatives share a similar vulnerability.

Among the crucial factors governing selection in this volume is the importance of the theologian and his work either in his own time or in the ongoing history of theology. Yet the theologians should be representative too. On the other hand this principle clashes with that of more immediate pertinence. For Coptic or Eastern Orthodox or even Roman Catholic students an introduction would have to take a different course as the story unfolds. Availability of texts, pragmatic though it be, forms another criterion. When a knowledge of Greek, Latin, or German cannot be presupposed, English versions must be accessible. An element of prophetic judgment also arises, especially in the modern period when the verdict of history is not yet in. Here the danger of falsification by events is highest, but an introduction of this type hardly expects the longevity which would make the risk too high. Hand in hand with judgment comes a strong element of theological preference. No matter how objective we try to be, certain thinkers and their works seem to be more significant because they have a greater attraction in virtue of personal convictions, enthusiasms, and expectations. Finally, a mundane matter like space imposes its own limit. Desire outstrips possibility. Much that should be included has to be omitted. If those who deplore the exclusions feel strongly enough about the matter, let them not waste their energies in complaint but make their own supplementary introductions within the confines of their own space.

**4. Approach.** A final choice — by no means the least important or agonizing — lies in the sphere of approach or understanding. What, after all, is meant by historical theology? What is its relation to theology as such? What indeed is theology? What should be the relation of the historian, or the church historian, to it?

These are big questions which plainly need a book of their own. The most that can be done in the present context is to indicate the two main possibilities and to show which of them is adopted, and why, in the chapters that follow. A point worth remembering is that the validity of both approaches, within their own terms of reference, is accepted.

*By and large I would endorse this view rather than Hartley's.*

The first approach sees the historical theologian primarily as a historian and interprets historical theology by and large as the history of Christian thought. It views the ideas of Christians in the first instance as a branch of the intellectual history of the race. Its main business is thus to trace them in their origin, growth, interactions, and modifications. It also tries to assess them to some degree as a contribution to the stock of human thinking. It seeks to be scientific in its establishment of facts and also in what it attempts by way of evaluation. It assigns no specific function to historical theology as part of the theology of the church. For theology is Christian thought, and its historical side is simply the recording of this thought across the centuries. If others take a different view, their concepts come on the scene only as part of the story. The same applies to the word of God which looms so large in some Christian writers. This arouses interest only insofar as various thinkers have had various ideas or made various statements about it.

Three forms of this approach may be briefly noted. According to the first an unfavorable view is taken of the Christian contribution. Many Christians as well as humanists take this line. Theology complicates the simple truths of Christianity. Even if influenced — and not always for the better — by philosophical forces, theologians show up poorly in comparison with the thinkers of other traditions. Enlightened thought has had to struggle against the shackles of impoverished but dictatorial dogmatics. To be sure, individual writers have made important and helpful contributions, but in the main the story of Christian thought has been that of a negative influence on the intellectual development of the race. At a more radical level, theology can even be presented as the rationalization of an illusion or as the ideological superstructure of a corrupt and alienating economic and social system.

A second form of the approach amounts almost to an apologetic. It adopts a positive attitude, drawing attention to the great achievements of Christian thinkers and stressing their formative role in intellectual history. Theology again forms part of the philosophical and religious story, but in this instance it forms a key part. Christianity emerges as the highest, or as one of the highest, of human achievements. In spite of every failure, its exposition by the great theologians demands approval both for its intrinsic merit and also for the service it renders in the general human search for reality and truth.

Both these forms naturally raise a claim to objectivity. As they see it, they are simply presenting the facts as any reasonable and unprejudiced observer will see them. Now since the facts seem to be so strongly colored by the spectacles through which they are seen, one is tempted to dismiss the claims as false. Yet surely this is a mistake. For one thing, when Christian thought is set forth in this way, the story is in fact an ambiguous one, so that there is truth as well as distortion on both sides. For another, a forceful interpretation from a distinctive angle is all to the good so long as the basic premises are clearly and candidly set forth. The conclusions might be misleading or even preposterous, but what is the good of a purely annalistic history in which one hardly dare voice any opinion at all for fear of being thought prejudiced or of meeting with too stiff opposition? To be sure, partisan histories can degenerate into obscurantism and even violence. When they do, their valuelessness quickly comes to light. But they need not take this course. In the hurly-burly of divergence they can stimulate thought, interest, and engagement which will finally mean more fruitful study. Along these lines they do not lack validity.

The third form, in contrast, claims the authenticity of a purer objectivity. It tries to tell the story without overmuch evaluation. For good or ill these theologians have held these views. They have worked them out under these influences. They have stated them in this context and interrelation. The teachings have had this effect on contemporary and later thinkers. They have interacted in this way with other ideas of the same or other times and places. They thus occupy this particular place in the history of Christian theology and the more general development of human religion and thought.

For two reasons one would not question the validity of this approach. First, Christian theology undoubtedly does have the aspect which is emphasized here. No matter what other facts are seen, it can and should be studied in this way. Second, objectivity is of the essence of all true investigation. If it is more easily claimed than achieved, it is still to be sought. No scholars, not even those who represent a distinctive point of view, want to distort the facts deliberately to commend their particular reading. When there is no ax to grind, the chances of real objectivity rise.

Nevertheless, while this in no way affects the validity of the approach, it should not be forgotten that trying to play the role of a neutral observer also involves the adoption of a point of view. This means that the neutrality, even if it can be achieved, can hardly be regarded as authentic neutrality. It also means that other options, even other valid options, demand recognition. As the other two forms of the historical approach show, one can be a protagonist even as one is an observer. In addition, a totally different approach is possible whereby historical theology is not just a history of Christian theology but is itself theology. Hence the observer ceases to be mere observer and becomes participant. He is himself a Christian doing theology in its historical dimension. Now it might be argued that in spite of himself every writer about Christian thought becomes in some sense a participant as well as a spectator. The point is, however, that those who seek to be neutral observers are refusing participation. They have every right to do so. But since there is this implicit or explicit refusal, a claim cannot be made to absolute neutrality. The resultant account, for all its validity, will rest on certain presuppositions: a view of what theology is, a view of what historical theology is, a view of the self and its role in relation to both. These presuppositions cannot be dismissed as invalid, yet by the same token we have to recognize that other presuppositions which lead to a totally different approach have the same validity. It is this second and more strictly theological approach that is taken here.

**5. Theology and Historical Theology.** According to this second approach the historical theologian is theologian and not just historian. Historical theology is not history but theology. It is not even to be equated with the history of theology. It is itself theology. But what does this mean and what are its implications?

Theology can be defined in many ways, but across the centuries there has persisted the view, recently revived and more closely defined by Karl Barth, that it is essentially the church's word about God in responsive transmission of the Word of God to the church. When seen in this way, theology can cover all that is said about God in the church by all Christians, not only in preaching, teaching, and writing, but also in prayer, worship, and personal conversation. Yet a more specific use should also be noted. At the technical level, theology is the investigation of the church's word about God with the intent of testing and achieving its purity and faithfulness as the responsive transmission of God's Word in changing languages, vocabularies, and intellectual and cultural contexts.

At this technical level theology plainly has two integral components. First comes biblical theology in the broad sense, which attempts to establish with accuracy the Word of God to which the church's word must conform in its reponse and transmission. Second, we find dogmatic theology (paralleled by pastoral theology in the field of action), which wrestles with the immediate problems of the different idioms which the church must use and of conforming them to the biblical criterion. The necessity of these two components needs no demonstration.

Historical theology forms a third and, it would seem, a less unequivocal component. It fills the gap between the time of God's Word and the present time of the church's word by studying the church's word in the intervening periods. In so doing it has a triple function. First, it shows how the church and its word, moving across the centuries and continents, have come from there to here with an ongoing continuity in spite of every discontinuity. Second, it offers examples of the way in which, and the reasons why, the conformity of the church's word to God's Word has been achieved or compromised in the different centuries and settings. Third, it brings to the church of today a valuable accumulation of enduring insights as well as relevant hints and warnings. It plays, then, a substantive, if for the most part auxiliary, role which dogmatic and pastoral theology will quickly accept if they are about their proper business, although they must be careful not to equate the role of historical theology with their business, as dogmatic theology in particular is constantly tempted to do.

Working along lines such as these, the historical theologian participates actively in the church's theological enterprise. He is no less committed to objectivity than the historian in a more rigorous sense, for to do his work properly he must deal with what is there. Finding heroes and villains constitutes no part of his task. Even if he sometimes forgets this, his purposeful evaluation differs sharply from the last judgment, which is the divine prerogative. At the same time, he enjoys freedom in respect of both attack and apologetic. On his approach the criterion will not be whether theologians make what he takes to be a negative or positive contribution to human thought, but whether they help the church of their own times and other times to speak faithfully and responsibly about God in conformity with God's Word. Observance of this criterion will in fact demand a critical mind, for who among Christians can ever achieve full responsibility and faithfulness in this regard? Yet the criticism will be constructive, not condemnatory. It will also be tempered by approval as some writers in some works seem to achieve, at least in part, the desired result. And both criticism and approval will be undertaken with humility, for is not the historical theologian himself a participant whose work comes under the same test and whose aim must be the attainment of the same purity?

**6. Implications.** Some implications of this approach must be briefly considered. The first is that a real speaking of God's Word is acknowledged. This Word is indeed adopted as the criterion of historical assessment. Naturally, this does not mean that the church's word is itself viewed as God's Word: the writings of theologians cannot, then, be abstracted from the common thought of the race. On the other hand, it does mean that the church's word lies in the context of what God himself has said. Hence, even while forming part of the intellectual history of mankind, it has another dimension as the responsive transmission of this Word of God. An important point arises here. If God's Word has no reality but arises only as a human notion, then obviously there is something shockingly unhistorical about this whole approach to historical theology. If, however, God's Word is an authentic historical factor, a history of human thought which leaves it out or finds a place for it only at the level of hidden immanence will itself prove to be shockingly unhistorical, not unlike a history of the Napoleonic Wars which finds no place for Napoleon as a true participant but only as a force immanent and active in others. To be sure, historians have to try to determine as best they can what are facts and what are not. But facts, not ideas about them, are ultimately determinative. The historical theologian accepts God's Word as fact.

A second implication is that historical theology, as distinct from intellectual or religious history, is to be viewed as predominantly a discipline of the church. Naturally one cannot say dogmatically that non-members of the church cannot participate in theology. But if they do, they contribute to the work of the church. Theology in all its branches arises out of the concern and context of the church. The church pursues it and bears responsibility for it. Others may contribute, either directly or through ancillary research in religion, philosophy, history, or sociology, but it is the church that consciously engages in it and serves its own purposes through it. The difference between the seminary and the university department of religion comes into clear focus when this is perceived.

The third implication is that the historical theologian will have a specific Christian commitment. It is not argued, of course, that those who approach theological history differently can have no such commitment, nor that those who have no such commitment cannot contribute to historical theology. What is meant is that the task of historical theology will normally be undertaken by people of Christian faith. For faith is the basic axiom of all theology. The question of the validity of historical theology, or of theology in any form, is ultimately the question of Christian faith. Those who do not have it, or even some who do, may prefer a different course. They are free to do so, and what they do is valid on its own terms. On the other hand, they display a curious and irrational intolerance if, as so often happens, they then refuse validity to the work of those whose faith leads them to theology, or, more specifically, to historical theology. The crucial issue at this level is not in truth the validity of the approach. It is faith itself.

A fourth and final implication is that historical theology, like all theology, serves the ministry and mission of the church. Thus a higher and deeper purpose emerges beyond the immediate aim discussed earlier and also beyond the goals of a historical approach, such as the establishment of factual truth or the advancement of human thought, or, more prosaically, the making of a reputation. The historical theologian works to a specific end. Participant in theology, he contributes in his own particular way to the understanding of God's Word and to the forging of its proclamation in authentic contemporary terms. He thus helps in the church's task of instructing and upbuilding its members and gathering in those who are as yet outside by the pure and effective ministry of God's Word through the church's word. He may do this at different levels, whether as the technical theologian who serves the whole church, the trained minister who uses such knowledge as he has acquired to develop a full and authentic ministry, or the ordinary member who builds up his own understanding and participates as he can in the general constructive scrutiny of what is said about God in and by the church. The possibilities are endless but the purpose is the same. Historical theology is no abstract or purely theoretical and intellectual matter. It does not take place in a vacuum. It enjoys no domination and shuns all elitism. Like all else in the church it has a servant role. It exists in and for the church and through the church for the Lord of the church. Those who pursue it have to realize that their job is in a true sense their calling. Brilliant success avails nothing if the service of faith and love is not rendered.

# PART I
## *Patristic Theology*

## CHAPTER I
# *Apostolic Fathers and Apologists*

### A. APOSTOLIC FATHERS

The earliest Christian writings outside the New Testament, apart from some Gnostic compositions and various fragments, are a miscellaneous set of letters, sermons, and other works which for want of any better title are usually called the apostolic (or post- or sub-apostolic) fathers. Only at isolated points do these authors engage in anything approaching technical theology. They do, however, write theologically in the sense of talking about God and about Christ on the basis of their knowledge of scripture and their Christian faith. They thus form a suitable starting point for historical theology as it asks its twofold question: *What do these Christians say?* and *Does what they say authentically respond to and transmit the Word of God in the situation, context, and idiom in which they write?*

Obviously not all the apostolic fathers can be discussed, nor is there any convincing reason for preferring some to others. The two selected here, Ignatius of Antioch and 2 Clement, are chosen partly because they differ from one another and partly because they both handle important themes. But the same could also be said of others. Readers interested in this period so close to the age of the apostles may well extend their studies to these others, whose works are mercifully brief compared to later writings.

Since the works are so short and deal for the most part with specific issues, a word of caution must be uttered. We must not be too dogmatic about matters which the writers do not address. Within the context of what they do, hints may be found concerning what they do not, but these are only hints. Only very precariously can their position in such matters be inferred. Nor does it follow that because a subject is not dealt with, it is little known to the author or unimportant for him. The point is that these early writers do not compose doctrinal treatises or full-scale dogmatic theologies. They write as occasion demands, and it is best to stick to what they say in context, evaluating it as it is intended and not in hypothetical reconstruction of a total theology.

## 1. Ignatius of Antioch

Ignatius passes like a meteor through the skies of early Christian history. He was bishop of Antioch, or Syria, in the first decades of the second century. At a time of persecution he was arrested and for some reason sent under guard to Rome for martyrdom. On the way he stopped at Smyrna, where he wrote letters to the churches of Ephesus, Magnesia, Trallia, and Rome, and then at Troas, where he wrote to the churches of Philadelphia and Smyrna, and also personally to Polycarp of Smyrna. Most of what we know of him is gleaned from these letters, and no certain information is available about the rest of his journey or its outcome. The letters are usually put in the second decade of the second century.

Textual problems have arisen due to different recensions with additions and abridgments. Other sources should be consulted on this question. Scholars are now agreed that the seven letters listed above constitute the authentic corpus. On these, then, we shall draw for what Ignatius says in some important areas.

More, perhaps, than most of the apostolic fathers, Ignatius engages in theological statement. He has intensely practical concerns, but these relate to dangers arising out of careless or heretical doctrinal utterances. Ignatius' main fear is that doctrinal divergence will destroy the church's unity. In contrast, a solid teaching structure will guarantee orthodoxy and promote unity. He thus makes his famous plea for consolidation under the bishop, presbyters, and deacons. He also suggests what must be said about some central issues in the church's faith and teaching. It is to these that we must turn.

### a. The Incarnation

(1) Christ as God. Ignatius has a fine grasp of the importance of the incarnation in the Christian message and mission. For him incarnation means that Christ is God. He insists on this in answer to the Jews and Judaizers of his day who were rejecting or modifying it. As he puts it, Christ the "one physician" is "God incarnate" (Ign. *Eph.* 7.2). The term "Son of God" (Ign. *Eph.* 20.2) thus has a strict sense: the Son shares the Father's being. The striking phrase "the Christ God" (Ign. *Smyrn.* 10.1) expresses this in a way which, while not found in the New Testament, seems to conform closely enough to it.

(2) Christ in the Flesh. If, however, incarnation points to Christ's deity, it also involves a real being in the flesh. The threat in this regard comes from thinkers who attribute to Jesus only the appearance and not the reality of a human body. Early Gnostic tendencies may well be

reflected here, for the dualism of bad body and good soul seems to underlie this position. In answer, Ignatius simply affirms the authenticity of Christ's humanity. In *Magnesians* 11.1 he asks for full conviction concerning "the birth, passion, and resurrection, which occurred while Pontius Pilate was governor." *Trallians* 9–10 warns sharply against "any talk that ignores Jesus Christ, of David's lineage, of Mary; who was really born, ate and drank. . . ." For "if his suffering was a sham . . . in that case I shall die to no purpose." *Smyrnaeans* 2–4 speaks similarly: "He genuinely suffered, even as he genuinely raised himself. . . ." "Unbelievers who say the passion was a sham are themselves a sham . . . and their fate will fit their fancies — they will be ghosts and apparitions."

(3) Christ's Unity as God and Man. While he does not try to explain the incarnation, Ignatius realizes that the Christ God who took true humanity remains one and the same. He is the "one physician," "of flesh yet spiritual, born yet unbegotten . . . Jesus Christ our Lord" (Ign. *Eph.* 7.2). He united flesh with spirit (Ign. *Magn.* 1.2). After the resurrection he was "still in flesh," so that "he ate and drank with them [the disciples] as a real human being," but "in spirit he was united with the Father" (Ign. *Smyrn.* 3.1–2).

Two interesting points may be noted in this connection. For Ignatius, Jesus Christ, while in every sense authentic man, is also the "new man" (Ign. *Eph.* 20.1). Ignatius also uses a trinitarian formula: "In Son, Father, and Spirit" (Ign. *Magn.* 13.1). Unfortunately, he does not develop these statements. It might also be noted that the birth of Mary is important for Ignatius, since, along with descent from David, it establishes the real humanity of Christ.

### b. Soteriology

(1) The Blood of Christ. As might be expected in view of the situation and intent of Ignatius, he offers no doctrine of the atonement. Yet he does have some interesting statements with a soteriological bearing. He refers twice to the blood of Christ (or God), although it should be observed that what he has in view here is subjective response rather than objective achievement. Thus *Ephesians* 1.1 speaks of God's blood as a spur to action, while *Trallians* 8.1 fancifully and moralistically exhorts the readers: "By faith (that is the Lord's flesh) and love (that is Jesus Christ's blood) make yourselves new creatures." More general references to the passion and resurrection (see Ign. *Phld.* 9.2) make it clear that something special has been done to provide access to God; because of this "the gospel is the crowning achievement forever."

(2) Fellowship with Christ. Significant for Ignatius is the truth of identification with Christ (based on Paul and, possibly, John). The thought is not as common in his writings as one might suppose, but he expresses it so vividly and forcefully that it makes a sharp impression.

Thus in *Magnesians* 5, dying willingly in union with Christ's passion is integral to having his life in us. Again, *Romans* 4.2 finds real discipleship in martyrdom, for it brings emancipation and a rising to freedom by union with him. (Suffering is also a means of "getting to him" [*Romans* 5.3].) *Smyrnaeans* 4.2 speaks of sharing Christ's passion, but one can also share his resurrection, this time by love (7.1). Finally, fellowship can mean sharing God's reward (Ign. *Pol.* 6). Here the military metaphor leads Ignatius to speak not too felicitously of pay for satisfactory service and to describe deeds as deposits from which we eventually get back considerable savings.

(3) Christ Our Life. A strong orientation toward Christ marks Ignatius' letters. *Smyrnaeans* 4.1–2 calls Christ our "genuine life." He has power to bring heretics to repentance, and in his name nearness to beasts and the sword means nearness to God. *Ephesians* 11.1 tells us to let our lot be "genuine life in Christ" and to set our eyes "on him alone." The might of Christ — this time to establish unity — is again referred to in this connection. A variation in *Magnesians* 2 calls Christ our "perpetual life." The power of Christ's indwelling life brings moral renewal: "You are not conceited, for you have Jesus Christ within you" (Ign. *Magn.* 12.1). "Having Jesus Christ" is another phrase used by Ignatius (Ign. *Magn.* 7.1). He sees a relation between this and unity of prayer and mind and hope, in love and unsullied joy.

### c. Jesus Christ and Judaism

(1) Negative Aspects. The Judaizing problem still existed in Ignatius' time, and he comes out with many warnings against it. He argues in *Magnesians* 8.1 that "if we still go on observing Judaism, we admit that we never received grace." The Smyrnaeans must pay no attention to those who preach Judaism (6.1). At times Ignatius seems to press this to complete antithesis. "It is monstrous to talk of Jesus Christ and to live like a Jew" (Ign. *Magn.* 10.3). If written to Gentile Christians this makes sense, but in relation to Jewish Christians it would require ceasing to be Jews in order to be Christians. The New Testament had not said this, but for centuries it was a common view, reinforced by the synagogue's ban on Christian Jews.

(2) Positive Aspects. Ignatius did, however, see a fulfillment of Judaism in Christianity. *Magnesians* 10.3 traces a movement from Judaism to Christianity, not vice versa. *Magnesians* 9.1 finds a similar movement from the sabbath to the Lord's Day and the life ruled by it. Ignatius also claims in *Magnesians* 8.2 that the Old Testament prophets "lived Jesus Christ's way." According to *Philadelphians* 5.2, the prophets "anticipated the gospel in their preaching . . . and were saved by believing on him." That Christ is Savior in the Old Testament, too, comes out in *Philadelphians* 9.1, where Christ as High Priest is contrasted with the earlier priests and is called "the door through which

enter Abraham, Isaac, and Jacob, the prophets and apostles and the church." For Ignatius, Jesus Christ is the true theme of the prophets as well as of the apostles. If Jews or Gentiles "fail to talk about Jesus Christ, they are to me tombstones and graves of the dead." In the last resort it might seem that Jewish Christians could still follow Jewish practices so long as they trusted and proclaimed Christ.

### d. Conclusion

Ignatius has been criticized on three main grounds: (1) he uses New Testament expressions but gives them a different sense; (2) his theology has obvious gaps; (3) he employs many Gnostic expressions such as "medicine of immortality" in *Ephesians* 20.2 or "silence" in *Ephesians* 19.1 and *Magnesians* 8.2. The third of these criticisms probably has least merit, since his material opposition to Gnosticism is so plain. The other two can hardly be refuted, but their significance can be overrated. Writing under great pressure and in response to specific situations, Ignatius can hardly be expected to reproduce all that Paul and others said or always to give their phrases the same meanings. For all his omissions and misunderstandings, Ignatius displays a good feeling for the New Testament message as well as an intense personal faith. He also relates the message to the situation of his day with insight and vigor. In detail he may not always stand up so well, and he certainly offers little in the way of dogmatic development, but all in all the theological task of relating the divine Word to new contexts gets off to a creditable start with the Syrian bishop.

## 2. Clement

Shortly after Ignatius wrote his letters, an unknown preacher, possibly in Alexandria, composed an important sermon. Somehow a copy of this became attached to the letter from Clement of Rome to the church at Corinth (c. 96 A.D.). It has thus come to be known as Clement's Second Epistle, although, as wags observe, the title is wrong on every count: it is not by Clement, it cannot then be his second letter, and it is not a letter anyway. Nevertheless, for purposes of reference it needs to be called something, and since the name of the preacher is lost beyond recall, "2 Clement" will do as well as anything to describe both sermon and author.

Comparatively long, the sermon manages to touch on more doctrines than most homileticians would dare to contemplate. Basically, it appears to be a call to repentance, perseverance, and the shunning of Gnosticism. Theologically, however, its main interest lies in its doctrinal elements. The hortatory setting of these elements should not be forgotten; it raises the important quesion of how far the needs of sermonizing should control theological content.

### a. Soteriology

The sermon has no developed section on the atonement, but it contains some interesting soteriological statements. The very first sentence stresses Christ's deity: we are "to think of him as we do of God." This is given an eschatological application: he is the judge. But then the preacher sets in view the greatness of his suffering for us, the nature of his work as giving us light and rescuing us, and the depth of his pity and tenderness. Christ emerges as "the only hope of salvation" (1.9). This salvation extends to the flesh, for "Christ the Lord who saved us was made flesh." The incarnation, thus linked with salvation of the whole man, is in direct opposition to Gnosticism, which views the body as irremediably evil and thus rejects the reality of Christ's being in the body (cf. 9.1ff.).

### b. The Christian Life

If Clement rightly stresses the need to repent and persevere, he does so with a notable lack of theological discretion or awareness. Keeping baptism pure and undefiled is an urgent concern in 6.9. It ties up with the problem of post-baptismal sin and its consequences, which weighed so heavily on the life and thought of the church from the second century on. This maintaining of purity — especially purity of the flesh (8.4) — is presented as a condition of obtaining eternal life. This life is freely granted at baptism; the statements about grace and faith apply thus far. After baptism, however, the retaining of baptismal purity becomes a prerequisite of finally entering into life. As 11.7 puts it, "if we have done what is right in God's eyes, we shall enter his kingdom and receive the promises." Repayment of God plays a part here. "We can pay God back by speaking and hearing with faith and love" (15.2; cf. 1.5). But this pales before the threat of judgment, of which the preacher confesses that he is afraid (18.2). Few, if any, can be confident of retaining their purity. For this reason, repentance is demanded: "We must wipe off from us our former sins and by heartfelt repentance be saved" (13.1). "I beg you to repent with all your heart, granting yourselves salvation and life" (19.1). At this point one may see the same moral earnestness, uninformed by theological reflection or perception, which later misled the British monk named Pelagius and which still results in disastrous pulpit theology today.

### c. The Church

2 Clement offers some novel if obscure talk about the church. Platonic influence is usually detected in the distinction between noumenal form and phenomenological copy. But again the homiletical concern takes its toll. The hearers, if they do God's will, "shall belong to the first church, the spiritual one, which was created before the sun and moon" (14.1). To this church of life we must "choose to belong . . . in order

to be saved." As Christ's body, it existed from the first (14.2) but was manifested in Christ's flesh (14.3). A moralistic statement follows which aims to show that violence must not be done to the flesh. We must guard the church in the flesh to "get it" in the Spirit. The flesh being the antitype of the spirit, corruption of the antitype is corruption of the reality. Since the church is in the flesh, doing violence to the latter means doing it to the former and thereby losing any share in the Spirit which is Christ. The flesh can share in life and immortality "because the Spirit cleaves to it." One feels that the Platonic background itself, in spite of the problems it raises, need not have worked against a useful contribution to ecclesiology, but the elusive transitions of thought and the enslavement to a moralistic concern rob the passage of any positive theological merit. It renders its best, if confusing, service as an antidote to Gnosticism. Beyond that, the preacher seems to be fitting his theology to moral needs instead of, like Paul, letting his exhortation flow out of his theology.

### d. Scripture

Some interesting points arise in 2 Clement regarding holy scripture. First, he proves to be a pioneer in introducing a quotation from the gospels as scripture — "another scripture saith" (2.4). Yet he also includes some non-canonical sayings as dominical pronouncements (see 4.5; 5.2ff.; 12.2ff.). They are usually thought to come from the Gospel of the Egyptians. A prophecy from an unknown work (possibly Eldad and Modat) also occurs in 11.2ff. Some sense of the unity of scripture may be seen in 14.2. The Old Testament (the Bible) and the New (the apostles) both witness to the pre-existence of the church. A high view of scripture is taken in the phrase in 19.1 where the exhortation follows "God's truth," that is, the scripture reading. Though he may have hazy views of the canon, the preacher sees that the New Testament is scripture, shows some grasp of the unity of the Testaments, and equates the written word directly with the truth of God, or the God of truth. His most glaring weakness is his incompetence in the theological exposition of scripture — or his inability to subject the problems of the time, and his homiletical answer to them, to more rigorous theological control.

## B. APOLOGISTS

Like the apostolic fathers, with whom they overlap, the so-called apologists of the second century can hardly be regarded as technical theologians. They write in attempted vindication of Christianity and its right to toleration in face of the reactions of rulers, philosophers, common people, and Jews. They employ all possible arguments and naturally try to compare Christianity favorably with the best thinking and practice of the day. In exposition of Christianity they impinge on doctrinal themes, and in view of their philosophical connections they have an interest in the intellectual implications of the gospel. Their main interest for us, however, lies in the relation between the way they go about their business and the theological criteria and controls they employ.

Whether the apologists are technical theologians or not, they do profoundly influence theology. They initiate trends and set patterns which continue long after their own time, especially among those who regard apologetics as a primary or even the most important part of theology. They offer an example of how apologetic interests can affect theology as much as pastoral interests can, in 2 Clement. Do they, perhaps, allow their purpose to influence their theology instead of letting it be controlled by their theology? To the extent that this might be so, the theological problems in the apologists might need to be taken very seriously indeed.

## 1. The Epistle to Diognetus

These problems are least apparent in the enigmatic epistle which can be named only after its recipient, Diognetus. This work has raised many severe questions concerning text, date, and authorship. It is obviously divided by a gap at 10.3 which has led many scholars to postulate a double authorship. Tentatively, Quadratus (c. 125) has been identified as the writer of the first part, the apology proper, while what seems to be an appended homily has sometimes been ascribed to Hippolytus. The work clearly has a threefold structure, the people of God being depicted in Chapters 1–6, the revelation and reconciliation of God in Chapters 7–10, and the Logos, life, and knowledge in Chapters 11–12. No reader should miss the vivid and impressive account of God's people as they are in the world but not of it, every foreign land a fatherland and every fatherland a foreign land (chaps. 5–6). In the present context, however, our focus will be on the later chapters.

### a. Revelation and Reconciliation
(1) The Word. God, the ruler and creator of all things, the invisible God, makes himself known to us by sending the Word (7.2). Christian truth does not derive from men but from God, who establishes his truth among men. He does this by sending, not a heavenly intermediary, but the designer and maker of the universe, by whom he created the universe and whose hidden purposes are carried out by all its elements (7.2). He sent him, not to rule by tyranny, but "out of gentleness and kindness, like a king sending his son who is himself a king." "He sent him as God, yet also as man among men," persuading — not compelling; calling — not pursuing; in love — not in judgment, although one day he will be sent again in judgment (7.4–6). Prior to his coming, men had no

true knowledge of God but "only the ideal nonsense talked by plausible philosophers with their equation of creature and creator" (8.1–3). The author finds no philosophical bridges to the true knowledge of God. As he bluntly puts it, "no man has ever seen God or made him known." Only God makes God known: "he has manifested himself" (8.5). This manifestation is not merely by reason and sense. It is "through faith, by which alone it has been made possible for us to see God" (8.6). In this self-revelation God makes himself known in his goodness, long-suffering, and friendship (8.7–8). He does it through "his child," to whom his loving design is first communicated (8.9) and who makes known to us the good things that have been prepared and grants us "all things at once," in terms not only of understanding but also of participation (8.11).

In this brief declaration the author succeeds in combining in simple statements thoughts of no little theological profundity: the gospel as God's Word, Christ as Word, Christ as God and man, Christ as the message and method of God, the second sending of Christ to judge, the futility of man's philosophical and religious talk about God, the human confusion of creature and Creator, the revelation of God as the knowledge of God through faith, and the relation between knowledge and participation, or the revealing and reconciling Word. The themes obviously are not developed, nor can they be in what is meant to be a kerygmatic apology. Their compression in such a short compass is probably a more astonishing achievement than a more detailed elaboration of any one of them could ever have been.

(2) Reconciliation. The author follows up his account of revelation with a brief but equally impressive statement on the work of God. He first discusses the delay in sending Christ, attributing this to the purpose of God whereby, even as he was preparing the present age of righteousness, he allowed man's unrighteousness to come to its full term so as to show us that we are "incapable of entering the kingdom of God by our own efforts" and that we are "made capable of doing so only by the power of God" (9.1). Once it was apparent that man could expect only the recompense of punishment and death, the time came "in which God had determined to show at last his goodness and power." The time of Christ's coming, then, gives evidence of the divine teleology. The manifestation of man's sin and need accompanies the manifestation of God's righteousness and salvation. Even in God's apparent harshness and aloofness, one may see the forbearance of his "overflowing kindness and love toward man" (9.2).

This came fully to light in the objective work of atonement. God in his mercy "took up the burden of our sins." He gave his Son "as a ransom for us — the holy one for the unjust, the innocent for the guilty, the righteous one for the unrighteous, . . . the immortal for the mortal" (9.2). Only his righteousness could cover our sins, only in him could the "lawless and impious . . . be made righteous" (9.3–4). Reconciliation,

then, has the form of the "sweetest exchange." "The sinfulness of man is
hidden in the Righteous One, while the righteousness of the One justifies the many that are sinners" (9.5). To this "unfathomable work of
God" the response is faith in God as "Nurse, Father, Teacher, Counselor,
Healer, Mind, Light, Honor, Glory, Might, Life" (9.6). Nor does reconciliation stop there, for as knowledge of the Father brings this faith, it
also teaches man to live a life of burden-bearing as an "imitator of God"
(10.6). It gives him, too, both a joyful task of witness ("you will begin to
talk of the mysteries of God") and a new perspective in which true life is
in heaven and the real death to be feared is not "apparent death here
below . . . but that of eternal fire" (10.7). On this solemn note the short
but comprehensive account of the gospel concludes.

### b. The Logos, Life, and Knowledge

(1) The Logos. In the appended homily, the opening thought resembles that of Chapter 7. The Logos, whom unbelievers do not recognize, is he who explains the mysteries of the Father. This is why he came
(9.2). The Logos is seen to be "from the begining," but in a striking
phrase he is said to have "appeared new" and to be "ever born young in
the hearts of believers" (11.3). He is the "eternal one" who "today [Does
this denote an Epiphany or Easter sermon?] is accounted a Son" and
who multiplies grace to the church (11.5), conferring understanding so
that "the reverence taught by the law is hymned, the grace given to the
prophets is recognized, and the faith of the gospels is made secure" (11.6)
— a fine testimony to the unity of scripture.

(2) Life and Knowledge. The aim in Chapter 12 is to make it plain
that knowledge may not be isolated from life. The writer uses a typology
of Eden to do this. The garden includes the two trees of life and knowledge which God planted at the beginning "to show that life is attained
through knowledge" (12.3). The problem arises, of course, that Adam
and Eve were not to eat the fruit of the tree of knowledge. The author
solves this problem by seeing in this a snatching after false knowledge
disobediently and with unclean hearts. He finds a parallel in the knowledge which, according to Paul, puffs up because it is not genuine or
borne out by life. His exhortation, then, is this: "Let your heart be
knowledge, and your life the true teaching that the heart contains"
(12.7). True knowledge cannot be abstractly intellectual, nor can an
authentic Christian life be lived apart from knowledge. When the happy
union of the two is achieved, the fall is reversed (the Eve/Mary antithesis occurs), "salvation is displayed, the apostles are interpreted . . .
and the Logos rejoices as he teaches the saints" (12.8–9).

### c. Remarks

Chapter 7–10 and 11–12 are alike in that they compress much
deep theology into very short statements. While they do not develop this

theology, they do open up important lines of thought from a substantially biblical starting point. Their purposes differ, for the first section is apologetic whereas the second seems to be homiletical. Yet neither allows the intention to dominate the thought or expression. The authors have evidently thought through what they say, and they utilize their powers, not to change wine back into water, but to provide suitable skins for the true wine of the gospel.

The main difference, perhaps, is that the appendix, while offering excellent theological insights, obviously has a more speculative aspect. It does not have so much material content, and especially in the Eden typology it takes a fanciful turn, so that while its theology would be hard to fault, its expository relevance is slender. A rhetorical swing also appears in the perorations in 11.5 and 12.9, so that what is said sounds well enough but lacks at points any preciseness of meaning. All the same, one may say of both sections that they provide good examples of theology at work, namely, of church words which effectively reflect and convey God's Word, whether to pagans on the one side or believers on the other.

## 2. Justin Martyr

Justin Martyr may rightly be regarded as chief of the apologists. A non-Jewish native of Palestine and a converted philosopher, he continued his philosophical career as a Christian both by oral teaching and also by his two *Apologies* and the *Dialogue with Trypho*. He finally sealed his apologetic with his blood when he was brought before the prefect Rusticus in Rome and executed on his refusal to recant and offer sacrifice.

In making a case for Christianity, Justin did not pursue theology as such but he certainly could not avoid theological statements. He made these on the difficult border of philosophy and theology. His background, which included some attraction to Plato, provided him with intellectual tools, techniques, and arguments. But it also tempted him to philosophize the gospel or at least to put it in the dangerous framework of philosophical understanding and presentation. For this reason his work has a particular interest in historical theology, and some points in the *First Apology* will be tested to see how far Justin maintains kerygmatic fidelity within his stated purpose.

### a. Reason

Justin appeals to the pagan world for reason in its dealings with Christians. The use of reason will take the double form of (1) honoring the truth and (2) speaking and doing what is right. By implication Justin espouses here the truth and rationality of Christian teaching and practice.

*b. God*

In Chapter 10 Justin presents his doctrine of God the Creator, which certainly has biblical content but which should also find ready agreement among intelligent pagans. (1) The fact that God provides all things shows the pointlessness of pagan offerings. (2) The link between doctrine and life comes out in the assertion that God accepts "only those who imitate the good things which are his." (3) God "in his goodness formed all things out of unformed matter." While this has a Greek ring, Justin undoubtedly has in mind the biblical doctrine — creation out of nothing. As he says next, "He made us when we were not." He may have related "unformed matter" to Genesis 1:2. (4) Although we did not create ourselves, we may choose the things dear to God "by the rational powers which he has given us." This belief underlies the *Apology*. Pagans can be won over by an intelligent exposition of Christianity and supporting arguments. The activity of the Word, however, also seems to be presupposed in this passage.

*c. The Kingdom of God*

Dispelling the suspicion that the church had political aims formed an essential part of early apologetics. Hence Justin insists (1) that "we do not place our hopes on the present," as is shown by our readiness to die. The kingdom of God means (2) "a kingdom with God." Christians, then, can speak of it openly. (3) They are in fact the state's best helpers and allies in "securing good order," for they teach that no evil can be hidden from God or escape his punishment. Civil authorities, however, tend to "respect reputation rather than truth," and Justin boldly denounces the authorities of his day as "public executioners, not good rulers" (chaps. 11–12).

*d. Christ*

(1) Christ has for Justin the role of teacher, but as such he is "the Son and Apostle of God the Father and master of all." (2) The fulfillment of Christ's predictions backs the truth of his teaching. (3) As Son of the true God he is "in the second place and the prophetic Spirit in the third rank." (4) His power may be seen in the changed life which follows persuasion "by the Word" (chaps. 12–14). Examples of his teaching are given, with some emphasis on the sin of second marriage, possibly remarriage after divorce, which was common at the time (chaps. 14–17). Justin cannot accept as real Christians those who confess with their lips but disobey the Lord's teaching in their lives.

*e. General Resurrection*

(1) Justin believes that "consciousness continues for all who have lived." (2) Yet he also states that "we look forward to receiving again our own bodies." (3) If this seems incredible, it is only because we have never

seen or experienced resurrection. Even birth would seem incredible if we considered it apart from our knowledge of the event. Ultimately, Christians "have learned that it is better to believe things impossible" than to disbelieve, "since they know from Christ that the things that are impossible with men are possible with God." (4) For Christian ideas such as the destruction of the universe by fire, Justin appeals to the analogous beliefs of pagan thinkers and writers, questioning why pagans are honored while Christians are despised for the same ideas. He argues, however, that on many matters Christians teach "more completely and worthily of God" (chap. 20).

### f. The Work of Christ

(1) In relation to the virgin birth and passion, Justin walks a sharp ridge. To show that these beliefs are not incredible or unworthy, he adduces parallels in pagan myths. Yet he cannot let Christian beliefs be put in the same category as the mythical parallels. Stress must be laid, then, on the uniqueness of Christ in his incarnation and crucifixion. The myths are finally assessed as demonically inspired imitations and counterfeits — a distinctive angle in comparative religion (chaps. 21–29). (2) Fulfillment of Old Testament prophecy, even in detail, supports the truth of the gospel; things that happened "were prophesied before they happened" through "the divine and holy prophetic Spirit" (chaps. 30–53). Oddly, this Spirit is equated in Chapter 33 with the Word or First Born of God who, coming on the virgin, "made her pregnant." According to this account, the Word incarnated himself. (3) For Justin, prediction does not entail "inevitable destiny." Man has responsibility for his acts and "walks upright or falls by free choice" (chap. 43), even if "God foreknows what all men are to do" (chap. 44). Early rumbles of later storms about free will and grace may be heard here. (4) The prophecies indicate two comings. The first is in the past, when Christ came as passible man; the second is in the future, when he will come again as judge (chap. 52). (5) Justin finds curious support for the crucifixion and its significance in the occurrence of the shape of the cross in many human phenomena: the ship's mast, the farmer's plow, the posture of man with outstretched arms, the very nose on one's face, and the cross-shaped objects on trophies and standards (chap. 55). This flight of fancy reminds us of the later hunt for vestiges of the Trinity.

### g. Christ as Reason

Like the author of Diognetus, Justin faces the problem of Christ's late appearance on the human scene. His solution differs. Christ has always been here in some form. (1) He is the Reason (Logos) of which all partake. (2) Thus, men are always responsible before him. No matter when they live, those who do so in accordance with Reason "are Christians even though they were called godless," while those who live without Reason are "ungracious and enemies to Christ." Justin does not expound further on the difference made by the incarnation since he thinks what he has said already should make it self-evident "to any intelligent man" (chap. 46).

### h. Christian Worship

To clear up common misconceptions, Justin gives an account of Christian rites. (1) Baptism, administered after persuasion and instruction, is a rebirth by washing with water in the name of God the Father, our Savior Christ, and the Holy Spirit (chap. 61). Pagan sprinklings imitate this (chap. 62). Justin also manages at this point to work in a peculiar polemic against the Jews for failing to see that Christ, not the Father and Fashioner of the universe, spoke to Moses at the bush (chap. 62f.). (2) During worship, "eucharistized" bread and wine and water are distributed; they are not received as ordinary bread and drink but "as Jesus Christ . . . being incarnate by God's work took flesh and blood for our salvation, so also we have been taught that the food just consecrated by the word of prayer which comes from him, from which our flesh and blood are nourished, is the flesh and blood of that incarnate Jesus." Justin thus perceives a close relation between Christ's taking flesh and blood, his institution of the Eucharist, and the use of physical elements in the Christian's feeding on Christ. Demonic imitations are again mentioned, this time in Mithraism (chap. 66).

### i. Summary

The problems raised by Justin's work are plain to see. They arise out of his philosophical background and his apologetic purpose. He rightly uses the style of presentation and argumentation with which he is familiar and which he thinks will best serve his readers. He clearly does not wish to change or weaken Christian teaching in any form. Unfortunately, however, he seems to have little awareness of the way in which this orientation to his intention and audience can affect the material content of what he says. If theology must study the transmission of God's Word in the church's contemporary words, one must say of Justin that he does well with the contemporary words but at some cost to the transmission. He recasts the message overmuch in terms of his own understanding and intention.

The instances of this need only be listed here; they speak eloquently enough for themselves. He employs arguments which form no part of the message. The prophets and apostles, unlike Justin, do not seem to care that Moses preceded Plato or that pagan parallels can be explained as devilish imitations. Fulfillment of prophecy certainly looms large in the New Testament, but not with the more rational slant it is given by Justin. When John uses the term "Logos," his point is that the Logos is Jesus, not Jesus the Logos. What Justin says about Christ as God, the relation of Word and Spirit, and the order of the three in the Godhead lacks coherence and clarity. The strong emphasis on free choice makes philosophical sense but entails theological complications and leads to odd sayings such as that in Chapter 61: "There is named . . . over him who has chosen to be born again." God the Fashioner of the universe largely replaces God the Creator, giving a potentially misleading impression. The apologetic of Justin runs the constant danger of being self-defeating. Some may be won, but to a large extent only to what they can accept in the Christian message in view of what they believe already.

Nevertheless, Justin has two points in his favor. First, he hardly seems to be adopting a deliberate theological stratagem of accommodating his message to his hearers. His very naivety constitutes his defense. Missionary zeal outpaces theological discretion. Secondly, for all the defects, Justin still manages to put over in his own way the authentic message. He presents all the main themes of Christian teaching, life, and worship and backs them up with a fine array of biblical quotations. Justin is not expounding his own ideas; he bases all he has to say on the kerygma. Even his confused Trinitarianism rests on the biblical testimony to Father, Son, and Spirit. The Logos teaching, too, has a starting point in scripture. He draws his doctrine of God the Fashioner from the doctrine of creation. He recognizes the primary role of God in bringing people to knowledge, faith, and righteousness. He sees that prophetic fulfillment means the continuity of Old Testament and New and provides a rational argument. His theology has gaps, but from it one can learn a good deal of what Christianity is all about. Thus, even if it does not come through unscathed, the message survives the medium. Certainly, it would have been better if Justin had more closely adapted the medium to the message. But not by a long way does he allow the medium to engulf the message.

# CHAPTER II
## *Defenders of the Faith*

⸲ While Justin avoided the dissolution of the gospel in its apologetic defense, the teachers usually grouped under the title of "Gnostics" so intermingled Christian teachings with current speculations that nothing distinctively Christian remained. Whether they did this as Christians accommodating the gospel to other concepts or as pagans adopting bits and pieces of the gospel makes little difference in the result. Either way they concocted what Paul would have called "another gospel." They also made inroads into the Christian congregations with their obscure jargon, their heady speculations, and their hints of a secret tradition for initiates.

The Gnostics developed complicated theosophies which varied widely in detail. Some generally shared convictions, however, underlay the individual outworkings. According to them, the true God lies at a great distance from this world, the gap being filled by a strange host of intermediaries. A lesser power, the Demiurge, created the material universe. Spirit and matter, sometimes also identified as good and evil, stand in dualistic antithesis. Man's plight consists in the alienation of his spirit or soul, which is from the true God, in his body, the work of the Demiurge (who is for Marcion the Old Testament God of judgment in contradistinction to the gracious Father of Jesus Christ). The true God sends Christ down to rescue the soul. Christ, however, cannot be truly incarnate; he either associates himself temporarily with the man Jesus or simply takes the appearance and not the reality of a physical body. Salvation means rescue from imprisonment in the body and entails a life of asceticism in maximum abstraction from bodily wants, although some Gnostics allow licentiousness on the ground that the body cannot be saved itself, nor can it affect the redeemed soul. Gnostics view their own teaching as knowledge (*gnosis*) at a higher stage than faith. They try to give it credit by linking it with a secret tradition derived from the apostles. The Old Testament must either be allegorized or rejected altogether, as in Marcion's remnant of a canon. The New Testament, too, demands reinterpretation when the movement is made from faith to knowledge. Gnostics recognized, of course, that many believers may be incapable of this transition and hence three classes of people are sometimes acknowledged, those of the body, the soul, and the spirit.

Sometimes today open-ended theologians suggest that, since the gospel was hellenized in any case, Gnosticism was one of many valid forms of early Christianity. Only because it lost out in the struggle against less free-ranging thought did it come to be categorized as heresy in the later sense, that is, heterodoxy in contrast to the newly established orthodoxy. Pastors and theologians of the time, faced with the dissolution of the tradition and the disintegration of the communities, do not seem to have viewed it in this light. They saw a breach being opened in life and mission as well as in doctrine. As they understood it, this breach, if not blocked, would mean the end of the gospel, church, and ministry to the world. They therefore sprang into the breach as defenders of the faith.

## A. IRENAEUS

Irenaeus of South Gaul emerged as one of the most important of the defenders. He came originally from Asia Minor where he had heard the venerable Polycarp of Smyrna, who claimed to have been taught by the apostle John. This personal connection between the days of Christ and the end of the second century should not be ignored. By way of Rome, where he might have been a pupil of Justin Martyr, Irenaeus came to Lyons. As a presbyter of the church at Lyons, he took a letter to Rome in 177. This mission enabled him to escape the savage persecution of that year, and on his return he was chosen bishop to fill the vacancy caused by the martyrdom of his predecessor. He remained at Lyons until his death c. 200, traditionally considered as one of witness to the faith. Apparently he knew Gnosticism largely as it was taught in Rome, with some local touches from his own area. He composed an answer to it in his *Refutation and Overthrow of the Knowledge Falsely So-Called*, more commonly known as his *Five Books against the Heresies*. The core of his own theology may be found in various sections of this analysis and rebuttal.

### 1. Book III

*a. Scripture*

In meeting Gnosticism, Irenaeus argues that the gospel came from the apostles both orally and in writing. (1) These "first preached it abroad, and then later by the will of God handed it down to us in writings (*in scripturis*), to be the foundation and pillar of our faith" (chap. 1). In Irenaeus' time, New Testament scripture was still in process of collection, and therefore he attaches great significance to the perpetuation of the oral witness as well as to the written Word. He opposes Gnostics (2) because they "will not agree with either scripture or tradition" (chap. 2). When referred to scripture, they say that the tradition was handed down orally, but when referred to the tradition they claim greater wisdom than the apostles, "who mixed matters of the law with the words of the Saviour," and even than the Lord himself, who "spoke sometimes from the demiurge" (chap. 2). As Irenaeus sees it, (3) the apostles handed over their teaching position and all their teachings to their successors, as may be seen at Rome or Smyrna (3.1–3). Irenaeus does not set scripture and tradition in antithesis, but seems to see them as two forms of the same apostolic deposit. Each is valuable, but in the struggle with Gnostics, (4) oral tradition has special significance in view of its uniformity in the apostolic churches. "Even if the apostles had not left their writings to us," we ought still "to follow the rule of the tradition which they handed down to those to whom they committed the churches." Indeed, illiterate peoples "who believe in Christ follow this rule, having salvation written in their hearts by the Spirit without paper and ink" (4.1–2). All the same (5) Irenaeus turns for demonstration to the writings of those apostles who recorded the gospel. In using scripture to back up the truth as found in Christ and in the apostles as the disciples of truth, Irenaeus draws on an extensive knowledge of both Testaments. He also makes the extremely significant observation that as we see Christ and the apostles in scripture, they did not adapt their message to what "different individuals could grasp," which would "aggravate disease and increase ignorance." Christ brought life and healing just because he did not speak to people "in accordance with their previous ideas . . . but in accordance with the sound teaching, without any pretense or respect for persons" (5.1–2).

### b. Christ in John

John plays a special role for Irenaeus, partly because of the link through Polycarp, but primarily because his gospel is seen as a direct refutation of Gnostic offshoots. (1) In the opening verses of John 1 all distinctions between the Fashioner and the Father of Jesus Christ or between the Son of the Fashioner and Christ from on high (the Son of the Only-Begotten or Beginning) are plainly refuted. For John teaches one God who made all things by his Word. Nor can these "all things" be referred only to what lies within the Gnostic Pleroma. Logically, Irenaeus finds difficulty with a Pleroma which comprises all things but still leaves things outside it. Exegetically, John's text makes it plain that all things include "this world order of ours," for verse 11 states: "He was in the world, and the world was made by him. . . . He came to his own (things) and his own (people) did not receive him" (11.2). Against this witness, Gnostic ideas of the creation of this world by angels or the Demiurge cannot stand.

(2) John 1 proclaims a true incarnation. Gnostics try to evade this. Some say that the Savior descended on Jesus like a dove, proclaimed the unknown Father, and then ascended back to the Pleroma. Others say that "he passed through Mary like water through a tube." Others again say that Jesus descended on the son of the Demiurge. Others still find in the Word a transfigured man. But all fall short of incarnation. For them Christ always has to be "without flesh and free from suffering." John, however, says simply in 1:14: "The Word was made flesh" (11.3). By relating the witness of John the Baptist to that of Elijah (1:6–8), the apostle also shows that the Word is that of the God who is the Fashioner of this world (11.4). Two planks in the Gnostic program are thus knocked out at a single stroke.

(3) The fruits of God's first creation, symbolized by the original wine at Cana, are good and not evil. The Lord himself partook of them. If the new wine which the Word makes directly from water is better than the first wine, which was made by the Father, this does not set God and the Word in opposition, for the Lord uses the materials of the world (water or loaves and fishes) to provide wine for the feast or food for the hungry. "Thus he showed that God who made the earth . . . also in these last times through his Son gives to the human race the blessing of food and the favor of drink" (11.5). As Irenaeus understands it, incarnation follows the same pattern. Far from there being antithesis between the spiritual and the physical, "the incomprehensible [acts] through the comprehensible, and the invisible through the visible." In himself God can be seen only by the Son. But the Son declares him so that "he is known by those to whom the Son has revealed him." One may also reverse this and say that "the Father through his Son gives knowledge of his Son to those who love him." Nathanael and Peter are adduced as examples, and Matthew 12:18–20 (Isa 42:1–3) provides supporting scripture (11.6).

## 2. Book V

### a. The Atonement

(1) For Irenaeus the incarnation necessarily underlies the atonement even in terms of knowing Christ and living the Christian life. He thus begins his statement on redemption with two significant theses. First, "we could in no other way have learned the things of God unless our Teacher, being the Word, had been made man." And second: "Nor could we in any other way have learned than by seeing our Teacher, that we might become imitators of his works and doers of his words, and so have communion with him" (1.1).

(2) New creation in the image of Christ forms for Irenaeus an

essential part of salvation. The image itself, which is linked to "the gift of incorruptibility," is "with Christ." Made according to it, "we were predestined to be what we were not yet." This making according to the image amounts to "the beginning of creation," and comes "with the dispensation of the Word, who is . . . the mighty Word and true man." Intimated here already is the theme of recapitulation, whereby salvation through the incarnate Word entails a new image and creation, restoring and yet also surpassing the original creation and image. In this regard, Irenaeus shows keen awareness of the purposiveness of God and the operation of the Word running across both the old creation and the new.

(3) The mighty Word effects this restoration by his saving work, which Irenaeus explains in the familiar category of ransom but with a different emphasis. In accordance with his "logical" nature the Word (or Logos) shed his blood to ransom us from captivity. The "apostasy" held us unjustly, having unnaturally alienated us from God when we belonged by nature to him. The Word, however, did not violently redeem us but dealt justly with the tyrant. He thus carried through his purpose but in so doing did not incur a charge of injustice. "So neither was the standard of what is just infringed, nor did the ancient creation of God perish" (1.1).

(4) This redemption, which covers both soul and body ("he gave his soul for our souls, and his flesh for our bodies"), has as its goal "the union and communion of God and man." The incarnation makes this plain. It has a twofold movement of descent and ascent, "bringing God down to man by the Spirit, and again raising man to God by his incarnation." Communion with God means incorruption. All this loses its validity, however, if "his appearance was a mere fiction." Irenaeus has two arguments here. First, an unreal incarnation could be only a prophetic vision, the fulfillment being still future. Second, if he had taken nothing from Mary, "he would not have had real flesh and blood, by which he paid the price." Within the totality of the recapitulatory work, "a recapitulation of the ancient making of Adam" had to be included. No true incarnation means no true atonement (1.2).

(5) Irenaeus adopts Paul's comparison of Adam and the new Adam, but he gives it a slightly different twist by speaking more of created Adam than fallen Adam. In the beginning Adam was animated and made a rational animal as "the breath of life from God" united "with the created substance." Similarly, at the end the Word and Spirit, "united with the ancient substance of the creation of Adam, made a living and perfect man, so that as in the animal we were all dead [the Pauline stress], in the spiritual we are all made alive." Linking the beginning in Adam with the end in Christ, Irenaeus stresses that "Adam never escaped those hands of God," who made him after his own image and likeness — the hands would seem to be the Word and Spirit.

By the Father's decree the same hands "perfected a living man, so that there might be a (second) Adam after the image and likeness of God" (1.3).

(6) Significant insights occur in 2.1. Here Irenaeus emphasizes that God deals with his own creation and does not covetously invade the work of another. He insists once more on the need for incarnation, since "through the being made man" God restores his own creation in his own image. He adds that all this is grace: "With reference to the apostasy, he justly redeemed us from it by his own blood, but with reference to us, who have been redeemed, he acted graciously." We, not God, had need of communion. To meet this need "he graciously poured himself out," thus gathering us together "into the bosom of the Father."

(7) Salvation of the flesh is connected with the work of redemption (a) by the blood of Christ and (b) by nourishment through the Eucharistic bread and wine (2.2). The thoughts here are closely intertwined, for Irenaeus combines, compresses, and interrelates several themes: God's use of his first creation, Christ's body and blood through the receiving of the Word of God, the inclusion of the body in the gift of eternal life, and the church as the body of Christ, of which real and not just spiritual and invisible people are members (2.3). The pattern is a rich one, but unraveling and stating the themes in isolation proves to be a difficult and delicate task, as may be seen from the appeals to Irenaeus in Eucharistic debates.

(8) Irenaeus concedes that our bodies "fall into the earth and are dissolved therein." But as the grain of wheat "rises with great increase by the Spirit of God . . . so also our bodies shall rise at the proper time." God's Word enables them to rise again. Survival in any case comes from his greatness, not from our own nature. We thus see from our resurrection "what God can do, and what man receives as a gift." Our dying prevents us from being puffed up, "as if we had life from ourselves," and from being exalted against God and ungrateful to him. Thus, "being ignorant neither of God nor ourselves," we can be definite about these things (2.3).

(9) Recapitulation means reversal as well as restoration. Coming to his own, the Lord "by his obedience on a tree renewed [and reversed] what was done by disobedience in a tree." Similarly, Mary obeyed the Word where Eve rebelled, so that "as the race was subjected to death through a virgin, so it was saved by a virgin." "The sin of the first-formed man was amended by the chastisement of the First-begotten" (chap. 19). Hence the Lord "renews these things in himself, uniting man to the Spirit and placing the Spirit in man" (20.2). Genesis 3:15 teaches us that the enemy was justly conquered only by a man made of woman, since he had gained his power over man through a woman (chap. 21). The final antithetical parallel forms a fitting conclusion to this whole line of thought, for which an implicit basis may be found in passages like

Philippians 2. Declaring himself to be the Son of Man — Irenaeus plainly refers this to Christ's humanity — the Lord "renews in himself the primal man . . . that as our race went down to death by a man who was conquered we might ascend again to life by a man who overcame; and as death won the palm of victory over us by a man, so we might by a man receive the palm of victory over death" (chap. 21). Extensive quotation may be pardoned here, for no paraphrase can make these points as succinctly or forcefully as Irenaeus himself does.

### b. The Last Things

(1) Irenaeus supports the early millennialism which later theologians abandoned and even disparaged. He thus sees two resurrections separated by the reign of the righteous, who are raised first. "The righteous must first rise again at the appearance of God to receive in this created order, then made new, the promise of the inheritance . . . and will reign in this order. After this will come the judgment" (chap. 32). Since Irenaeus focuses mainly on the destiny of the righteous, and since his doctrine of the incarnation has sometimes been taken to imply universal salvation through Christ's identification with mankind, it should be pointed out that judgment definitely has a place in his eschatology. The statements which are made in the final chapters about the destiny of reign and the new creation clearly refer to the just alone.

(2) Irenaeus offers two main reasons why there must be an intervening reign on earth. First, it is right and fitting that the place of toil and suffering should also be the place of rule. Second, it is right and fitting that God should restore the created order "to its pristine state," in which it can "serve the just without restraint." Romans 8:19–21 is adduced in biblical support (32.1).

(3) Fulfillment of the promise to Abraham also entails a millennial reign. Since Abraham never entered into the promised inheritance of Genesis 13 and 15, he "will receive it with his seed, that is, with those who fear God and believe in him, at the resurrection of the just." In Christ, the true seed, Gentiles as well as Jews have been included. But so far "neither Abraham nor his seed, that is, those who are justified by faith," have the inheritance. They will receive it at the resurrection of the just in fulfillment of Matthew 5:5 (32.2).

(4) Irenaeus stresses the reality of this reign in various ways, such as by reference to Jesus' saying about drinking the fruit of the vine in the kingdom and about receiving a hundredfold in this world. The time of the kingdom will be the seventh day (or thousand-year span?), "the true sabbath of the just" (33.1–2). It will be an age of peace and plenty. "The created order will be made new and set free, and will produce an abundance of all kinds of food" (33.3). Even animals, in obedience and subjection to man, will live at peace, eating "the food

which God gave them at the first, the fruit of the earth" (33.4). Papias, "a fine old man," is cited as a witness.

(5) When the time comes for this temporary order to pass, the righteous will not lose their reality but advance "[to a new stage] among things that are." With man's flourishing in incorruption there "will be new heavens and a new earth" in which he "will always remain new, in converse with God" (36.1). Different levels are seen in this life, namely, heaven, paradise and the city, according to different levels of worthiness, but advance will be made "by the Spirit to the Son and by the Son to the Father." The culmination will come when "the Son will yield his work to the Father" (36.2).

(6) In support of what he says Irenaeus appeals to the words of John in Revelation, to the witness of the prophets, to our Lord's promise of the cup in his kingdom, and to Paul's assurance that "the creature would be free from the bondage of corruption into the freedom of the glory of the sons of God" (36.3).

(7) In and through all these things Irenaeus finds the one God at work, first in creation and the promise, then in the fulfillment in the kingdom of the Son and final glory. He also finds the one Son doing the Father's will and the one human race in which it is done. The overruling purpose of God is finally set forth again. God perfects what he has fashioned by conforming and incorporating it with the Son. He does this through the incarnation in which the Word "could descend into his creature . . . and be contained within it, and the creature again should lay hold on the Word and should ascend to him, passing beyond the angels, and be made [anew] according to the image and likeness of God" (36.3).

### 3. Evaluation

The work of Irenaeus has come under severe criticism. To some, his desire to present and defend the tradition makes him a dull establishment figure. Again, his tapping of different sources suggests a theologian of little enterprise or originality. In his accounts of the Gnostic deviations he goes into tiresome detail so that the trees threaten to obscure the wood. His argument from tradition, while not without a certain cogency, can hardly bear, either historically or theologically, the weight he himself places on it. Many of his biblical expositions raise as many questions as they answer. Even his incontestable flashes of insight tend to be lost in the prevailing monochrome of his total presentation.

These criticisms obviously contain elements of truth. Nevertheless, they do serious injustice to Irenaeus, who might credibly be called the first theologian of stature in the post-apostolic church. Over against them some positive points also demand consideration.

a. Irenaeus does not lose touch with the pastoral function and responsibility of theology. He sees it as no part of his task to be novel or exciting. His work has its source in his ministry as presbyter and bishop. He has to protect the flock and the gospel, not for the sake of an establishment, but the sake of the life, message, and mission of the church. This orientation of his theology shows a fine understanding of its role.

b. Irenaeus perceives that the gospel cannot be adjusted smoothly to current thought. He is not without appreciation of the need to use contemporary terms and concepts. It would not be hard to show that he owes something even to his opponents. Yet between the truth of God and the human ideas of any age an incompatibility will always exist. Christians have to learn, not to accommodate divine revelation to human thinking, but to bring human thoughts into captivity to Christ. Irenaeus states this insight and successfully tries to exemplify it.

c. The very fact that his theology has something of the form of a reaction can be an advantage. It is almost a truism that heresy, or exploratory theology, serves a useful purpose by forcing orthodoxy to formulate appropriate responses. The church without heresy may ultimately be in the greater danger of heresy. Irenaeus offers an early model, not of mere reiteration of past formulae, but of constructive wrestling with the Gnostic problem and of the consequent attainment of valuable insights into the gospel.

d. In this process Irenaeus surely does more than achieve a few ideas of brilliance. He wins through to an exciting theological construction which has stimulated thinkers of status across the centuries and the churches. The Gnostics raise central, not peripheral, issues. Irenaeus, then, cannot play around on the outskirts. He plunges into the heart and center of theology. Tackling the main themes of the unity of God and his purpose and work and the reality of the incarnation, he develops the rationality and coherence of the biblical message with striking force and perspicacity.

Naturally, within the compass of his book, Irenaeus cannot work out his themes and the questions they raise in any detail. His severe compression carries with it problems of expression and meaning. Nevertheless, he packs more food for thought in many of his brief chapters than later writers do in the much lengthier chapters of their time. In what he does say, he relentlessly forces us to consider the basis, essence, and logic of the biblical message. Even though one might not accept what he says or like the way he says it, he leaves us in no doubt that his theme is in fact that which has to be pondered and expounded. He also impresses upon us that unless our theology is to be just anything we decide it should be, his perceptions, rethought and restated though they may have to be, will have to have a place in any authentic expression of the Christian message.

## B. TERTULLIAN

Tertullian added strong support to the opposition to the Gnostics and Marcion. Born in about 160, a native of Carthage, he received a good training in rhetoric and possibly in law. Converted as an adult, he devoted his energy and gifts to apologetic, polemical, and moral writings. All these are marked by his vigorous and caustic style. If sometimes obscure, Tertullian is seldom dull. Some of his brilliant phrases have come down through the centuries. In his militant *Apology* he mocks at the popular cry of "The Christians to the lion": "What, all of them to one lion?" (40.2). Speaking of the growth of Christianity, he says Christians are now to be seen everywhere: "All we have left you is the temples" (37.5). Writing against the modalist Praxeas, who opposed Montanism, he coins the striking phrase: "He put to flight the Paraclete and crucified the Father" (*Against Praxeas*, chap. 1). In later life, Tertullian joined the Montanists, attracted strongly by their rigor, and his famous condemnation of Callixtus' policy of readmitting penitent adulterers belongs to this period: "Even the earthly temple of God can sooner have been called by the Lord a den of robbers than of adulterers and fornicators" (*On Modesty,* chap. 1). According to Jerome — though it is debated today — Tertullian was a presbyter. He wrote in both Greek and Latin but only the Latin works have survived.

In relation to Gnosticism, Tertullian's main essay is *The Prescription of Heretics*. Prescription seems to be a legal term, but its precise meaning is hard to pin down. What he is doing, perhaps, is putting in a demurrer. Tertullian also wrote a special work *Against Marcion*. In his moral works he dealt with the important question of being a Christian in a non-Christian culture. His rigorist position does not blind him to the fact that some adaptation must be accepted in spite of the sharp differentiation required at sensitive theological and ethical points.

### 1. The Prescription of Heretics

*a. Heresies*

(1) Tertullian first considers the teleology of heresy. God's purpose in permitting it is "to prove faith by testing it" (chap. 1ff.).

(2) Defining heresies, he describes them as "human and demonic doctrines" opposed to the divine truth of faith (chap. 7). They are engendered by human wisdom. They draw their opinions from the various philosophies. Representing Athens or the Academy, they have nothing to do with Jerusalem or the church. They rest on speculation and endless inquiry. Tertullian concludes: "I have no use for a Stoic, Platonic or dialectic Christianity. After Jesus Christ we have no need of speculation. . . . When we come to believe, we have no desire to believe anything else" (chap. 7).

### b. Seeking

The distinction between true seeking and the endless questioning of heresies calls for some discussion. (1) Faith is not an ongoing search for truth and certainty. Unbelievers begin by searching, but the search has promise of success: "Seek and ye shall find." The quest ends with faith. Truth does not recede before us. It is "a single definite truth," the Christian teaching we believe and keep (chaps. 8–9).

(2) Tertullian, however, does not shut off theological inquiry. Certainly the rule of faith admits of no questions, but so long as the rule is not disturbed, "you may give full rein to your curiosity" (chaps. 13–14). Tertullian may be sarcastic here. He fears the heretical spirit. He can even say that it is better not to know than "to come to know what you should not know" (chap. 14). Yet in a different setting from that of heresy, he leaves the door ajar for a theological task on the basis of faith. Faith's implications may be constructively explored, as in Tertullian's own contribution to the doctrine of the Trinity.

### c. Scripture

Gnostics caused much difficulty by using scripture to their own ends. In answer (1) Tertullian took the strict line that they should not even be admitted to any discussion of scripture. "Arguments about scripture achieve nothing but a stomachache and a headache" (chap. 16).

(2) Three reasons are given for this rejection of dialogue. First, scripture does not belong to heretics (chap. 15). Second, they do not have a true canon but add or substract to suit their own teaching. Third, they invent "different interpretations from ours." Dialogue, then, can lead nowhere (chap. 17), and waverers may "go away from the argument even more uncertain than before" (chap. 18). Only where true faith is present will we find true scripture and true interpretation (chap. 19).

### d. The Apostolic Rule

(1) Like Irenaeus, Tertullian contrasts the divinely given rule with Gnostic innovation. The first step in the argument is that the rule comes from the apostles, who, being taught by Christ, taught everything necessary and handed it down to the churches, not "entrusting some things openly to all and some things secretly to a few" (chap. 25). Indeed, the apostles themselves refute the Gnostics by plainly opposing legalism, denial of the resurrection, enforced celibacy, and genealogies (chap. 33). Between the apostles and the heretics lies a deep and open gulf.

(2) The next step is that the churches, as distinct from Gnostic groups, may rightly be called apostolic. Historically they can show their apostolic origins (chaps. 32–36). Theologically they have kept to the teaching handed down to them. All teach the same things (chaps. 27–

28). To prove this, Tertullian invites his readers to consult the apostolic churches in their own areas — Corinth in Achaia, Philippi in Macedonia, Ephesus in Asia Minor, or Rome in Italy. Everywhere they will find the same rule and gifts and discipline (chap. 36).

(3) In clear-cut contrast, the Gnostics are newcomers. Having no claim, either historical or theological, to be apostolic, they are trespassers when they use the scriptures. We are thus to challenge them sharply: "Who are you? When and whence do you come? . . . What are you doing on my land? By what right are you cutting down my timber, Marcion? By whose leave are you diverting my waters, Valentinus? . . . This property belongs to me. . . . I am heir to the apostles. . . . As they bequeathed it on trust, so, on their terms, I hold it" (chap. 37). Heretics, in their appropriation of scripture, are taking what does not belong to them and putting it to an alien and illegal use.

(4) In so doing they corrupt scripture, as noted earlier, by either mutilation or falsification. "One man perverts scripture with his hand, another with his exegesis." "Marcion used the knife, not the pen, massacring scripture to suit his own material. Valentinus spared the text, since he did not invent scriptures to suit his matter but matter to suit the scriptures." These procedures rule out any hope of fruitful conversation. They also constitute their own condemnation, for they are plainly of the devil, "whose business it is to pervert truth" (chap. 40).

*e. Heretical Disorder*

Tertullian argues finally that by their lack of order, heretical conventicles are self-judged. Catechumens and the baptized are not differentiated. Women exceed their functions. Ordinations are careless. Novices are put in office: "Nowhere can you get quicker promotion than in a camp of rebels where your mere presence is a merit." Many of them have no churches at all. They mix freely with magicians. In Tertullian's eyes all this is tied up with their false teaching. "You can judge the quality of their faith from the way they behave. Discipline is an index to doctrine" (chap. 43).

## 2. Idolatry

In a Christianized society it is easy to forget, or not to realize, what it meant that the early Christians lived out their faith against an explicitly pagan background. In trying to express Christianity where they were, in the idioms and culture of their time, they had to reckon with the serious problem this posed. How far could they go in fitting into the idolatrous setting? How far did the biblical rejection of idolatry impose apartness on them? Could some middle way be found which might perhaps further the cause of the gospel, either by dedivinizing the gods or by achieving compromise in neutral matters? Should some toleration be accorded to false religions even if a high degree of aloofness was required? Tertullian dealt with specific aspects of this problem in his treatises *On Shows, The Soldier's Crown,* and *Women's Dress.* He tackled the problem on a broader front in his work *On Idolatry.*

### a. Idolatry as the Chief Sin

(1) He opens the treatise by showing that idolatry holds a pivotal position as "the principal charge against the human race, the world's deepest guilt, the all-inclusive cause of judgment."

(2) Idolatry holds this position because it involves all other faults, including murder, fornication, and fraud. Even sins such as ostentation, gluttony, injustice, and vanity may also be called idolatry. "All offences are against God. . . ." Hence "every offender commits idolatry, for what he does belongs to the owners of idols" (i.e., demons) (chap. 1).

(3) Idolatry has its own form, too. Nor can this be limited to the external rites of incense or sacrifice. As with adultery or murder, the real sin lies in the inner being. Even without idols or temples, idolatry can still be there as the choice of a false god and rejection of the true God (chap. 2).

### b. Ramifications of Idolatry

(1) Idolatry does, of course, find outward expression. It may be seen in the making and worshiping of idols. Idols, attendance on them as well as their manufacture, come under the biblical prohibition of images, whether they be in human or any other form. What Tertullian is stressing here is that the whole craft of idol making falls within the scope of idolatry. The idol maker must renounce his trade to be a Christian, and the Christian cannot in good conscience be an idol maker. Isaiah 44 and Psalm 115:8 are adduced to show that the Spirit condemns the makers no less than the worshipers (chap. 4).

(2) Tertullian makes short work of four objections. Some plead their dependence on the craft for a living but the answer is: "If you are living on your own terms, why do you come to God?" Others refer to Paul's saying that we are to continue in the state which we are in (1 Cor 7:20). This obviously does not mean continuing in sin. Others cite 1 Thessalonians 4:11 to the effect that we must work with our hands for a living. But this does not cover burglars even though they undoubtedly "get their living with their hands." Finally, the making of the brazen serpent offers no precedent. This was "for a hidden purpose" (as a type) and "by an extraordinary command." Hence the prohibition stands. "Hands that have mothered idols" must not "touch the body of the Lord" or, as those of presbyters, "harass the Lord's body" (chaps. 5–7).

(3) Indirectly, many other trades are implicated, too, such as building, plastering, and decorating. Christians in these lines of work must avoid involvement. If need be, they should work on other projects

even for smaller profits. "Anyone who can carve a Mars can quickly knock up a cupboard" and "extravagance gets through more wreaths than ceremonial" (chap. 8).

### c. Related Practices

(1) Astrology comes under the condemnation of being "intrinsically idolatrous." Tertullian follows here the common patristic idea that the angels of Genesis 6 "were the inventors of this curious art," so that it comes under divine judgment with them. If the magi were astrologers, Tertullian maintains that "their science was allowed only until the gospel came" (chap. 9). (2) Magic, which God had had patience with earlier, also came under a curse with the excommunication of Simon Magus. Magic is the genus of which astrology is a species, so that both are punished together (chap. 9).

(3) Teaching raised a more complicated question, especially as Christians had as yet no schools of their own. While teaching could not be called intrinsically idolatrous, Tertullian claimed that its "affinity with all manner of idolatry is really beyond question," since schoolmasters must "praise the gods of the heathen" and "keep their feasts and celebrations" (in which they also have a vested financial interest). Yet study in pagan schools need not be condemned, for whereas teachers commend the gods, Christians do not have to "accept or admit them." Hence "it is more allowable for Christians to learn letters than to teach them" (chap. 10).

(4) Digging deeper, Tertullian finds avarice and deceit underlying the involvement of Christians in idol-related businesses. Those who help manufacture idols cannot honestly condemn them. An indirect role is just as bad, as in the case of pandering or training gladiators. Purveyors of sacrificial victims and incense merchants should, therefore, renounce their jobs or suffer excommunication. The plea of economic necessity Tertullian again rejects. It comes too late. It resists our Lord's sayings about poverty and provision. It will not take seriously the need to choose between two masters (chap. 12).

(5) Participation in pagan festivals cannot be condoned, since it entails a concession to wantonness and an antithesis to faith and discipline. Christians are on trial and must not act as if they were not Christians. Doing as the world does in order "that the name be not blasphemed" stands everything on its head; it stops the name being blasphemed only by having Christians stop being Christians. Being all things to all men does not mean being "an idolater to idolaters." Having to live with pagans does not mean having to "sin with sinners." "We share the world with them, but not their error." Pagans are more consistent: "They would be afraid of being taken for Christians" (chap. 14). The things of Caesar must be rendered to him, but "if everything is Caesar's, what will be God's?" (chap. 15).

(6) Tertullian takes a more lenient view of what goes on at family ceremonies such as weddings. These may carry with them "a whiff of idolatry," but in view of their causes "they are innocent in themselves" (chap. 16). Even if offerings be made, attendance can be allowed so long as it is for family reasons and not for worship of an idol, and so long as the Christian does not make the offering. Similarly, slaves and clients may attend sacrifices with their masters and patrons but should not be active participants (chap. 17).

### d. Civil Problems

In conclusion Tertullian discusses three areas of civil responsibility. (1) As regards public office, he finds difficulties but no intrinsic incompatibility (chap. 17). Even ceremonial robes may be worn unless there is an idolatrous link. In this case the robes have for Christians no point: "What will you gain by wearing the dress without performing its functions?" Indeed, they defile: "No one can look clean in dirty clothes" (chap. 18).

(2) Tertullian rejects military service in a famous passage. He offers two basic reasons. (a) "There is no compatibility between the oath to serve God and the oath to serve man." (b) "The Lord unbelted every soldier when he disarmed Peter." Hence even enlisted men, who do not have to offer sacrifices or impose capital sentences, should not be admitted as Christians without leaving the army, and Christians should not "turn to military service" (chap. 19). It might be noted in relation to those who applaud Tertullian here but deplore his narrowness elsewhere that his thinking on this matter is all of a piece with his thinking on the other issues.

(3) Tertullian cannot allow that Christians may swear by the gods. To name them neutrally is one thing; to recognize their existence runs contrary to the faith. A stand must be made: "sufferance is idolatry." If cursed in Jupiter's name, they must not curse back in the same name, or even in God's name, but bless. Being blessed by pagan gods, however, must be resisted (chaps. 20–22).

### e. Final Admonition

Tertullian concludes by comparing the church to a ship crossing treacherous seas. Falling back into idolatry means suffocation and drowning in the depths of hell. Hence every precaution must be taken. Seekers must be told plainly that idolatry has to be renounced. Believers must be instructed concerning it. The ark includes unclean as well as clean beasts but "no animal is the figure of the idolater. What was not in the ark can have no place in the church" (chap. 24).

### 3. Survey

Tertullian's rhetorical style adds pungency to his work but also lays him open to obvious criticism. Is he not guilty of exaggeration? Why should philosophy and faith be so opposed? How can Christianity be seen as a finished search? What sense is there in rejecting biblical dialogue with heretics even if they do adopt a different type of interpretation? Can one rest on the authority of teachers simply because their churches happen to have been founded by apostles and they have been regularly ordained? Does the rule of faith have to be so sacrosanct? Can detailed rules be laid down about every idolatrous practice? Should the issues be forced so drastically when the gospel has to be taken to pagans and it is among pagans that Christians have to live out their lives? Does not Tertullian leave us with a new law instead of the gospel?

There can be no disguising the validity of these questions. Tertullian has a harsh dogmatic streak which, combined with his knifelike pen, achieves what modern jargon might describe as overkill. Even apart from his Montanist extravagances, few would be prepared to support either his general position or all of his individual statements. Nevertheless, the evident defects should not blind us to an important qualifying factor and to the many points of lasting value in his work.

#### a. A Qualifying Factor

The qualifying factor is the contextual element in Tertullian. To a large extent he conducts *ad hoc* arguments, so that what is said in one context may not represent his total view. Thus his famous saying about believing a thing because it is "absurd" seems itself absurd in isolation but makes sense in context. His antithesis between Athens and Jerusalem must be seen, too, in relation to the philosophical elements in Gnosticism. Tertullian personally both advocated secular learning and made considerable polemical use of philosophy. The rejection of inquiry offers another example. He has in mind the endless questioning which leads nowhere, so that what he advocates does not have to be an obscurantist dogmatism. Detached from Gnostic speculation, proper theological investigation may well be pursued. Along with the contextual factor, of course, the literary manner must also be taken into account. Striking sayings and crisp overstatements abound in Tertullian. Readers can enjoy these even when outraged by them. But the words should not be pressed too literally. The rhetorician's art, while serving the content, may do it a disservice if not seen for what it is.

#### b. Points of Lasting Value

(1) Thought. Tertullian sees certain things very clearly as he surveys the interaction of Christian teaching and current thought. (a) While theology and philosophy often address the same themes, they

differ in both content and nature. (b) Because of the difference in content, philosophy can easily corrupt the gospel, as Gnostic theorizings show. (c) As regards nature, philosophy is man's intellectual quest, but theology begins with the datum of revelation on which it then reflects. (d) Theology may for apologetic or polemical reasons use the terms and concepts of philosophy (as Tertullian himself does in his thinking on the Trinity), but not to the loss of its distinctive character. Philosophical theology, which offers immediate but illusory advantages, must yield before a theology of revelation, which may use philosophy but which in any case brings solid and lasting results.

(2) Norm. Tertullian faces squarely the question of a theological norm in contrast to an ultimately normless Gnosticism. (a) He locates the norm in the apostolic tradition. (b) This may be known in the threefold form of scripture, the rule of faith, and the teaching of the apostolic churches. (c) If the norm tends to become a set of theses, it rests finally on God's revelation in Christ. (d) The final object of theological study is not, then, an abstraction, and theology can have a scientific character which Gnostic philosophizing neither has nor can have.

(3) Conduct. Tertullian realizes that paganism, which is idolatry, has extensive ramifications. (a) He offers a good analysis of these ramifications. (b) He sees a basic incompatibility between Christianity and idolatry which prevents Christianity from easy translation into the forms of an idolatrous society. (c) He does not press this absolutely, making exceptions where possible. (d) He appreciates, however, Christianity's radical criticism of pagan society and the inescapable call for Christian reorientation and renewal. (e) If he tends to express this legalistically, he also faces up to concrete issues and recognizes the need for some disciplinary measures in the church. Here, as elsewhere, the solutions of Tertullian may be overly severe. Yet they take seriously the meaning of the cross in the Christian life and the need for mortification and renewal, not just in individual piety but also in practical conduct. They thus counterbalance the facile cultural adaptations and compromises which evade or soften the claims of authentic discipleship.

# CHAPTER III
## The Alexandrian Way

### A. CLEMENT

Contemporaneously with Irenaeus and Tertullian, a more flexible approach to Gnosticism and pagan culture was adopted in the great cosmopolitan Egyptian city of Alexandria, which already had a long history of Jewish and Gentile interaction. Here, under the initial direction of Pantaenus, a school had developed for wealthier and more cultured inquirers. Instruction was fashioned not so much for ordinary converts, who were taught by catechists, but for those of higher abilities to whom the gospel might be more appropriately addressed in the terms and concepts familiar to them and who might thus be regarded as orthodox "gnostics."

Around the year 180, Pantaenus left Alexandria to evangelize in the east, but in his student Clement a capable and highly suitable successor was quickly found. A native of Athens, Clement had engaged in a long search for truth that had led him through many philosophical schools. He found help in various places but finally ran his quarry to earth in Egypt, where he seems to have been converted through Pantaenus. By training and temperament he fitted admirably into the Alexandrian situation. Two of his books, the *Protrepticus* and the *Paidagogos*, probably embody his apologetic and ethical teaching. A third, the *Stromateis,* may include material from his courses as well as much of his basic thinking. In his treatise on whether the rich man can be saved he seems to be vindicating the whole movement among the educated and affluent in answer to the problems posed by the New Testament approach to wealth.

Clement believes no less than Irenaeus or Tertullian that there is a fundamental message which must not be renounced. He also aims at a distinctive life-style which, if intended to avoid extremes, tends nevertheless toward simplicity and even a certain severity. At the same time, Clement has greater confidence than the westerners that positive

35

use can be made of philosophy on the road to faith, that Christianity can be presented and understood as true *gnosis*, and that Christians of higher social rank can work out a way of life which will not isolate them from their peers. In his thought and practice, then, the stress lies on being able to be in the world while not of it, rather than on being apart from the world while still in it. Some extracts from the *Stromateis* will help us to see how this works out at the intellectual level.

## 1. Introduction

### a. Vocabulary and Content

Clement himself explains his method. He will not at first use biblical quotations since the phraseology might not be familiar. Yet he insists that his words "draw their life and breath" from scripture. His aim is to set forth, not the phraseology of the scriptures, but "their meaning." Biblical testimonies will be added later for believers (vii.1.1).

### b. The True Gnostic

For Clement, the Christian is the real gnostic. He worships "the true God as befits him." He serves others both melioratively (like the presbyter) and also ministratively (like the deacon) (vii.1.3). "He is above all things a lover of God" (vii.1.4).

## 2. The Son

### a. Ruler of the Universe

Clement goes on to introduce the Son as the most perfect and holy being who "approximates most closely to the one almighty being." As "the highest preeminence" he "steers the universe aright." He sees, hears, and knows all things, and all men belong to him, "some by way of knowledge, while others have not yet attained to this" (vii.2.5).

### b. Teacher

Boldly adopting Gnostic phrasing, Clement describes the Son or Word as the one who "educates the gnostic by means of mysteries and the believer by means of good hopes and him who is hard of heart with corrective discipline acting on the senses." His pedagogy extends to all. "He bestows on the Greeks their philosophy" and makes believers "the Lord's portion." His bounty covers Greeks and barbarians and also "the faithful and elect" (vii.2.6).

### c. Savior and Lord of All

God's Word or Wisdom can be called not only Teacher but also Savior and Lord of all. He is the Savior of believers who "have determined to know" and the Lord "of those who have been disobedient until they . . . have received the grace which comes through him, in the way adapted and corresponding to their state" (vii.2.7).

### d. The Incarnation

The Savior loved us so much that "he scorned not the weakness of human flesh" but "has come into the world for the common salvation." Revelation seems to be the primary purpose of the coming. He could not be seen in his true nature "because of the infirmity of the flesh." He thus took "a body which could be seen and handled" and showed "what was possible to man in the way of obedience to God's commandments" (vii.2.8).

### e. Divine Power

Clement underlines the power of the Son to draw whom he wills to himself. He compares this to magnetic force. "Through the attraction of the Spirit the virtuous are adapted to the highest mansion." Others do not move up so high. Indeed, some who have "fallen into an evil habit" may crash to the ground and perish. Clement leaves a place for final loss, for the power of the Son or Spirit does not abrogate the primal law that "he who would have virtue must choose it." The inertia of sin can counteract the divine pull (vii.2.9).

### f. Source of All Commandment

All commandment comes from the Son. He gave both Jewish law and Greek philosophy to "confine unbelief" until his coming and to make possible advance to faith's perfection. The Greek, however, does not have to learn philosophy to become a Christian. If "he hastens straight to the true teaching," then, even though uneducated, he "at once outdistances all competition, having chosen the shortcut of perfection, that of salvation through faith" (vii.2.11). Clement's conclusion is that "in the wise and good ordering of creation" God "made all things to be helpful for virtue . . . without hindering the freedom of man's choice."

## 3. Gnostic Progress

### a. Development

The theme of movement or progress has a special place in Clement. He accepts the idea of the gnostic ascent. This takes place by "communion with God through the great High Priest." It consists in assimilation to God, which means assimilation to him who by nature is free from passion. Gentleness, kindness, and devoutness are the canons of this assimilation (vii.3.13).

### b. Sacrifices

These virtues Clement affirms to be "an acceptable sacrifice with

God." God neither needs nor enjoins cultic offerings. "He takes pleasure only in our salvation." His impassible nature means that sacrifices can neither propitiate nor allure him. "We glorify him who was consecrated for us by consecrating ourselves also to ever higher degrees of freedom from want and passion" (vii.3.14ff.).

### c. The Divine Image

With his care for self and neighbors, and by taming the wild elements in human nature, the gnostic achieves a likeness to God. In him, then, the image of God is seen "in a third embodiment." The Savior, as the Only-Begotten, is "the express image of the glory of the heavenly King and almighty Father." He "stamps on the mind of the gnostic the perfect vision of the divine likeness." Hence the gnostic also, by copying his example and by assimilation to him, manifests the image of God (vii.3.16).

### d. The Gnostic Task

Since the gnostic "makes a genuine approach to truth, having a firm hold of divine science," he has the double task of (1) investigating and (2) teaching both theology (matters relating to God) and anthropology (matters relating to man and his nature and conduct). In all this (3) he acts as both "lover of men" and "friend of God." (4) From God he derives his virtue and also the faith which is the basis of his knowledge. (5) He also derives from God his mode of presentation. In this regard philosophy can "provide for the soul the preliminary cleansing and training required for the reception of faith," but faith itself is the foundation on which "truth builds up the edifice of knowledge." Clement, perhaps, is not so far from Tertullian as a superficial reading might suggest (vii.3.19). "Man's work is submission to God" in receiving his blessings and reciprocating by doing what is pleasing to him (vii.3.21).

## 4. God

### a. God as Spirit

In discussing God, Clement favors philosophical terms, but his points have an incontestable biblical basis and are in fact set in antithesis to both Greek and barbarian views of deity. Thus God shares neither human shape nor passions. As Clement acutely observes, "each nation paints their shape [the gods'] after its own likeness." Thus "the conceptions which the wicked form . . . must naturally be bad." On the other hand, the gnostic may have excellent perceptions, although ultimately, no doubt, Clement would see these as originating in God, not in man, as the true original (vii.4.22ff.). Not having bodily shape, God cannot be circumscribed. Idolatry shows serious folly in trying to localize him in a shrine. Using a philosophical argument, Clement tries to show that enshrinement presupposes the non-existence of God. His themes are still biblical for all the philosophical dress, namely, God's eternal self-existence, his being as Creator and not creature, and the fact that he cannot be confined in temples of human construction (vii.5.28ff).

### b. Worship of God

Since God does not have a human body or human passions, material sacrifices are pointless (vii.6.30). Instead, Clement commends the sacrifice of prayer: "Our altar here on earth is the congregation of those who are devoted to prayers" (vii.6.32). True worship, which includes honoring the Son and Word as Savior and Ruler, takes place "continuously all our life through," "in all possible ways," and "in every place." "Persuaded that God is everywhere present . . . we praise him as we till the ground, we sing hymns as we sail the sea" (vii.7.35). Prayer, as converse with the God who is "all ear and all eye," derives its strength from a worthy conception of God according to which he does good of his own free will to those who turn to him of their own accord. Involved here is a discipline which does not regard God as a slot machine to meet human desires but asks no more than is necessary and believes that God "supplies whatever is expedient to the good" even without our asking. Public prayer has its place, but for Clement real converse with God takes the form of constant prayer even if only as "a thought in the secret chamber of the heart" (vii.7.42ff.).

## 5. Faith and Knowledge

### a. Beginning and Perfecting

Relating faith to knowledge obviously constitutes an important task for Clement. He stresses knowledge, for disposition and conduct are perfected "by the science of divine things." Nevertheless, faith, described as "a certain inward good" and "a compendious knowledge of the essentials," must be seen as the beginning: "A man must start with this faith." Clement apparently has in view a threefold process leading from faith to love by way of knowledge, which is handed down by teaching. Christ himself is both foundation and completion; through him "are both the beginning and the end." Teachers, however, impart knowledge, which is "a sure and firm demonstration of the things received through faith," which is built up "by the Lord's teaching on the basis of faith," and which leads to "unshaken conviction and scientific certainty."

### b. Threefold Conversion

Clement thus characterizes Christian experience as one of threefold conversion. First comes the turning from paganism to faith. The turning from faith to knowledge follows. Yet Clement avoids intellectualized abstraction, for from knowledge there should then be the final turning to love, in which is established "a mutual friendship between knower and known." Upward progress through and even beyond the flesh is postulated until "through the holy Hebdomad" the gnostic reaches "the Lord's abode" and security "from all vicissitude" (vii.10.55ff.).

### 6. Hermeneutics

#### a. Scripture's Role

For Clement, scripture holds a key place in the search for knowledge. Being given by God, it constitutes "the first principle of instruction." As such it needs nothing else; if it needed anything else, "it could no longer be really maintained as the first principle." Clement does not fear a circle here. The circle is virtuous, not vicious: "Having apprehended our first principle by faith, without proof, we get our proofs about the first principle from the principle itself." He can say this because in scripture "we are trained by the voice of the Lord for the knowledge of truth." We rest neither on human assertion nor personal opinion but listen to "the voice of the Lord, which is more to be relied on than any demonstration." A taste of scripture brings faith but with further study we become "accurate judges of the truth," obtaining "from the scriptures themselves a perfect demonstration concerning the scriptures" (vii.16.95ff.).

#### b. Interpretation

(1) Criteria. Clement briefly mentions the criteria of interpretation. First, those common to all men should be considered. Then come the technical criteria acquired by education. Most important, however, are the moral criteria: avoidance of self-conceit, readiness to persevere, and energy of soul to take the canon of the truth from the truth itself (vii.16.93ff.).

(2) Heretics. Surprisingly, perhaps, Clement agrees with Tertullian, not that scripture should be ruled off limits for heretics, but at least that it is barren for them. Heretics "wrest scripture to suit their desires." Failing to take the canon of the truth from the truth, "they go wrong in particulars also. . . . because they have no criterion of truth and falsehood." While using scripture, they come to it with their own systems, "picking out ambiguous phrases . . . plucking out a few scattered utterances, perverting the bare letter as it stands." They "attend to the words alone, while they change the meaning, neither understanding them as they are spoken, nor even using in the natural sense such extracts as they adduce" (vii.16.96).

(3) Hermeneutical Rules. In rebuttal, Clement advances the primary rule that the scriptures be used "in their entirety," those of the

Old Testament as well as those of the New. He then argues that scripture must be used to confirm scripture. He supports, too, a doctrine of congruity. We are to consider "what is perfectly fitting and appropriate to the Lord and Almighty God" (vii.16.96). Clement agrees with Irenaeus and Tertullian that "the orthodox doctrine of the apostles" will be guarded by the true gnostic who grows old in the actual study of the scriptures (vii.16.104). For those who fall through ignorance and weakness because they do not know where God leads, that is, "by way of the inspired writings," Clement recommends the twofold discipline of (a) "plain proof derived from the witness of the scriptures" and (b) "training according to reason controlled by faith and fear." "Both of these grow up into perfect love" (vii.16.102). Incidentally, Clement's closing exposition of the clean and unclean beasts (cf. Tertullian) shows that for him allegorizing counts as a valid hermeneutical mode, "at least for the benefit of the more speculative members of the church" (vii.18).

### 7. Evaluation

Clement's theological presentation leaves the initial impression that, with his love of philosophy and in his zeal to win over "cultured despisers," he goes dangerously far in assimilating Christian teaching to pagan thought. He adduces few quotations from scripture. He likes to refer to pagan authors. In vocabulary and style he subjects biblical terms and concepts to extensive translation. Many leading biblical themes hold no prominent place in his exposition. Knowledge receives a higher rating than faith. The gnostic on the second stage of the soul's ascent seems to have qualities and ideals which ordinary believers could hardly be expected to achieve. This knowledge is more highly intellectualized than that which Paul prays for on behalf of his churches. Clement appears especially to be in sharp antithesis to Tertullian, for, while the Carthaginian finds in philosophy the parent of heresy, the Alexandrian extols it as a possible preparation for the truth of the gospel.

On this understanding of Clement readers tend to polarize. For some he is a praiseworthy pioneer breaking free from a hampering traditionalism, boldly putting the gospel in contemporary forms, and making possible a breakthrough into educated circles. He has the breadth to find a place for the best in pagan thought and to wed it to Christian teaching to the enrichment of both. He shows a good understanding of the theological task and offers a promising example of its fulfillment. For others, however, he is a man of intellectual compromise. Well-meaning, he attempts more than can be done. The words and concepts of pagans weaken the impact of Christian truth. His adoption of the heretical notion of the gnostic transforms the disciple of the Galilean into the Christianized cosmopolitan of upper-class Alexandria.

Flirtation with philosophy brings about a mismatch, to the ultimate disadvantage of the gospel. What success Clement achieves is a hollow one which counts for little compared to the long-range losses of both Christian theology and Christian life.

Yet a question remains. Is the interpretation which underlies these opposing reactions correct? Certain points call for discussion before too hasty a conclusion is reached. First, Clement knows what he is doing in his effort to use pagan or heretical phraseology. He apparently discounts the risk since he will turn to the more directly biblical material later. Second, he can be very critical, not only of popular paganism, but even of the best of philosophy. In this he had found help but no final answer to his questions. Third, he does not regard philosophy as a necessary stage to faith. Faith itself is necessary, however, if there is to be movement to knowledge and love. If Clement does not lay too heavy a stress on faith, neither does he question its indispensability. He also relates it very closely to Christ, who is both foundation and crown. Fourth, coming to faith, while it involves free decision, depends all the same on the revelation of truth in Christ and the persuasive ministry of the Word and Spirit. Clement does not place it, then, in the category of options of human insight. Fifth, scripture has for Clement an astonishingly central place as the first principle in virtue of God's speaking through it. He sees no reason for a prior justification of the principle. He also finds in scripture a rule by which interpretation is governed. In this regard he stands in close enough proximity to Irenaeus and Tertullian.

Unlike Tertullian, who writes specifically against heretics, Clement writes positively for the educated. Hence he makes a different appeal. But this appeal includes a characterization of Gnosticism as bad philosophy and poor exegesis, precisely the points which Tertullian also makes. Certainly one may see a difference of aim and emphasis in Clement. One can also see personal differences of outlook, temperament, taste, and talent. But is the difference of basic theological orientation so vast as is often assumed? May it not be that Clement's different approach has ultimately a strategic rather than a material character? The point deserves closer attention before his work is made a starting point either for grandiose generalizations or for a battle of categorical judgments and counterjudgments.

## B. ORIGEN

In 202 the emperor Severus issued a decree designed to halt conversions. The persecution which followed hit the Alexandrian church hard. Clement, following the evangelical counsel, fled to another city. To fill the vacancy the teenager Origen, a brilliant pupil whose father, Leonides, had suffered martyrdom, was appointed head of the catecheti-

cal school. He thus commenced a long life of scholarly activity, first in
Alexandria and later in Caesarea, which in many ways excelled that of
his predecessor.

Origen brought to the task gifts of zeal, dedication, learning, and
unusual intellectual ability. He followed an ascetic mode of life and
worked prodigiously, giving ordinary instruction to catechumens and
adding advanced classes even in secular subjects for more highly educated students. In the early days he did not write so much, but output
steadily increased, and when a break with the bishop Demetrius led him
permanently to Caesarea, Origen kept a large staff of copyists busy with
his literary projects. Across the years these included his famous
*Hexapla,* the important doctrinal treatise *De Principiis,* several commentaries, the works *On Prayer* and *On Martyrdom, Contra Celsum,*
and the *Homilies,* which were based on shorthand versions of his extem-
porary sermons. During the Decian persecution of 249 Origen underwent severe tortures. Although he lived for some years after, these seem
to have undermined his health. He died at Tyre in 255.

Although Origen's explicit work of theology is *De Principiis,* his
essay *On Prayer* covers many theological themes while also setting them
in a characteristic devotional context. The work arose out of a request
from his friend Ambrose and a woman called Tatiana for guidance as to
the point and purpose of prayer in the light of God's sovereignty. Origen
answers this question, but with his speculative mind and vast resources
of scholarship he ranges over many related matters as well. Always,
however, he preserves a sense of the gracious revelation of God in
Christ. For support he also refers constantly to passages from holy
scripture. Indeed, he undertakes the work with a prayer that the Holy
Spirit may be granted to him so that he may have "a very full and
spiritual word" and give a clear exposition of "the prayers recorded in
the gospels" (2.6).

## 1. God

### a. Transcendence

(1) Origen acknowledges plainly the inability of man to understand divine themes. He rests this on the distinction, not between sinful
man and the holy God, but between what is perishable and what is
transcendent. (2) Nevertheless, God makes the impossible possible
through Christ and the Spirit. Christ, being made God's wisdom for us,
enables us to know God's wisdom even though "a corruptible body
weighs down the soul." (3) The gracious character of this work of God
receives emphasis: "This impossible becomes possible by the exceeding
grace of God" (9.2).

### b. Fatherhood

(1) Much of the work *On Prayer* Origen devotes to an exposition of

the Lord's Prayer. The address "Our Father" leads him to a discussion of the divine fatherhood in which he first points out that, while the Old Testament calls God "Father," one does not find in it "a firm and unchangeable affirmation of sonship." (2) He links this to the stage in revelation history when, before the appointed time, the heir is "under guardians and stewards" (22.2). (3) Origen realizes, of course, that we have to be true sons to dare to call on God as Father. This means that we must be able to say "Jesus is Lord" in the Spirit, that we must have the Spirit's witness to our sonship, and that heart and works and mouth must join in faith and confession (22.3).

### c. Immateriality

(1) Like Clement, Origen stresses that God cannot be localized or "circumscribed in bodily fashion." (2) Thus even while we say "who art in heaven" we understand that heaven does not contain God; instead, "all things are contained and held together by him" (23.1). Localizations, as in John 13:1, are not to be taken literally. The real ascension of Jesus must be construed in a mystical sense (23.2). (3) As Origen sees it, localization would imply that God has a divisible, material, and corruptible body. This is an absurdity and passages such as Genesis 3:8 should not be used to support it (23.3–4). The point of "who art in heaven" is to separate the essence of God from all created things.

## 2. The Image and Kingdom of God

### a. The Image

(1) In connection with divine sonship Origen has an interesting passage on the image of God in believers. He points out that "every deed and word and thought of theirs, being formed by the only-begotten Word after his likeness, imitates the image of the invisible God." (2) The image in Christians is indirect, since it is the image of the heavenly Son who is himself the image of God. The saints are thus an image of an image. (3) For them this involves being conformed to him who is in the body of glory and being transformed by the renewing of their minds — the refashioning in the likeness of Christ. Origen brings to light here the important implications of Christology for the Old Testament doctrine of the image. (4) In a further application to sanctification he argues that the seed of God becomes the reason that he who is conformed to the Word cannot sin, for the works resulting from the seed of the devil are destroyed (22.4).

### b. The Kingdom

(1) In the petition for the coming of God's kingdom Origen sees a prayer that it may come in the believer as he "takes God as his King and obeys the spiritual laws of God." (2) He thus defines the kingdom neither

politically nor eschatologically but morally and spiritually as "the blessed state of reason and ordered condition of wise thoughts." (3) Christ's kingdom, in contrast, consists in "the words of salvation and works of righteousness" (25.1). (4) Yet Origen does not view the kingdom as merely in the present. It has a progressive and future aspect too, for by unceasing advance it will reach its supreme point only when all enemies are subjugated, Christ delivers up the kingdom to the Father, and God is all in all (25.2). "The kingdom of God cannot co-exist with the kingdom of evil." (5) Hence we must let the Lord reign in us even now in sanctification. As we "are reigned over by God," we may "share in the good things of regeneration and resurrection" (25.3).

### 3. Subordinationism

*a. Prayer to the Father*
(1) The proper direction of prayer gives Origen occasion to present indirectly his subordinationist Christology. He insists that prayer be made, not to men, nor even to Christ, but to the Father alone. (2) In support he adduces the difference of the Son from the Father in person and the absurdity of praying either to Christ alone or to both.

*b. Prayer through Christ*
(1) He recognizes, of course, that prayer should be in Christ's name, for we receive God's favors through him and also enjoy his priesthood and advocacy. (2) Yet since we, too, are God's children by adoption, "it is not reasonable that we should pray to him as a brother." We pray in him and through him but not to him.

*c. Conclusion*
(1) Those who pray to the Son, either with or without the Father, "sin with great simplicity through ignorance of the subject." (2) It is through the access that Christ has won for us to the Father that we may approach God in sonship, not servitude. (3) Nevertheless, a distinction between Son and Father exists whereby in the proper sense only the latter may be addressed as God (15–16).

### 4. Universalism

*a. A Problem*
(1) Expounding *epiousios* in the Lord's Prayer, Origen winds up the discussion with some remarks on "Today" in scripture. (2) He takes this to represent an age (26.13–16) and he thus runs up against the problem of an apparent conflict between two New Testament sayings: "Jesus appeared once at the end of the ages to put away sins," and "That in the ages to come God's grace will be shown in the saints." How can there be ages to come if the ages are ended? (26.15).

*b. The Solution*

(1) Origen's answer to the riddle is that "end of the ages" is used in the sense of the last age of a series of ages, just as we speak of the last month of a year. (2) Thus, as new months will still come, ages to come may also be expected. "The present is the end, after which certain ages to come will ensue" (26.15).

*c. The Ages to Come*

(1) These future ages will be the period of the display of God's kindness. Origen concludes, then, that in them sinners will undergo a process whereby they are brought to God. "The greatest sinner who has spoken ill of the Holy Spirit and is under the power of sin throughout the present age will, I know not how, be under treatment from beginning to end in the ensuing age that is to come" (26.15). (3) Origen expands on this when he later speaks of the function of the fire and the prison. In these sinners do not receive "the recompense of error," which they have experienced already in their abandonment to vile passions. They receive instead "a benefaction to cleanse them from the evils committed in their error together with salutary sufferings that follow lovers of pleasure." The progress is purgative and remedial and the goal is that, even if with difficulty, those who undergo it should "perceive the ugliness of evil and willingly, not of necessity, hate their reprobate mind." If we do not have here a distinct universalism, two points are plain. Hell must not be regarded as retributive, and a possibility is accepted that sinners will be brought to a better mind in which they "freely attach to the good" (29.15).

## 5. Free Will

*a. Foreordination and Prayer*

As noted earlier, *On Prayer* arose out of the question whether prayer makes sense in view of the divine sovereignty. The objections spring readily to mind. God foreknows all things, our needs included; why, then, set them before him? He has also ordained what will be done, and so prayer seems to be absurd; why pray for the sun to rise? Finally, God has elected those who will be saved; what difference can prayer make, since God in his immutability "abides in what he has pre-arranged"? (chap. 5).

*b. Origen's Reply and His Assertion of Freedom*

The threat to prayer obviously poses a threat to freedom, too. Now for Origen, as for all the early fathers, freedom was vital as the antithesis of fate or necessity. He thus took pains to answer the objections point by point. He began by discussing movement in relation to inorganic things, which are moved from outside, organic things, which may move from within themselves, and rational things, which may move also through themselves. The movement through the self implies free will. To deny freedom, then, is to say that we are not living creatures, that we do not have reason, and that we are not what we appear and experience ourselves to be, as in the choice of opinions or the handing out of praise or censure. This freedom does not have to be in conflict with God's foreknowledge or foreordination because it is included within it: "With all else it has been known to God," and it is "a reasonable consequence that it is arranged by providence suitably for every person." Prayer and the individual petitions made in it also constitute data in the divine overruling. Nor does this have only an individual application, for in the divine wisdom "each act of free will is adapted to such an arrangement of the whole as the settled order of the universe demands" (6.1–5).

### c. Value of Prayer

Apart from specific answers to the petitions made, Origen sees great subjective value in prayer. Prayer demands the right approach to God. This carries with it spiritual growth. Proper prayer makes us more capable of union with the Spirit of the Lord. It also entails participation in the prayer of the Word of God (10.1–2). Hence no one should stop praying just because God's sovereignty might seem to rob prayer of meaning or purpose. In Origen's view, it is not trivial earthly things which earnest seekers after the spiritual life ask of God. Certainly, since all acts come within God's disposing, material requests may confidently be made to him. Yet earthly benefits, when given, symbolize spiritual blessings. As Elijah's prayer brought rain after long drought, so through prayer we may receive "the rain of the soul, having been formerly deprived of it by reason of sin" (13.5).

## 6. Appendix: Death

### a. Immortality of the Soul

In his work *Dialogue with Heraclides*, which did not come to light until 1951 and cannot be dated with precision, Origen has an interesting passage on the different meanings of death. It arose out of problems relating to Christ's death and Origen's belief that the body, soul, and spirit of Christ were temporarily severed at the cross, the body going to the tomb, the soul to Hades, the spirit to the Father. A questioner, Dionysius, asked whether in view of the saying in Leviticus 17:11 ("the soul of all flesh is the blood") the soul did not also undergo corruption along with the body. Origen's spiritualizing answer seemed to leave him open to the charge that he was teaching the Greek view of the immortality of the soul instead of biblical theology, and to save himself Origen offered an exposition of the threefold meaning of death in the Bible.

### b. The Threefold Death

First comes the blessed death when a man lives to God and dies in sin. The death of Christ can be set in this category in view of Romans 6:10. Here, obviously, is a death which the soul can die, too.

The direct opposite of the death to sin is the death to God. Ezekiel 18:4 has this in mind when it says "the soul that sins shall die." In this respect again we have to speak of the mortality of the soul.

Finally, death may be the natural process of separation from the body. Origen does not believe that the soul dies this death in which the body dissolves. "If it did so, it would not be punished after death." At this level, then, the human soul has immortality.

Now Origen's reply might easily convey the impression of mere quibbling. It certainly suffers from the difficulty of trying to apply biblical data to a not very biblical problem. Yet it also shows that for all his philosophical leanings Origen does sincerely try to be a biblical theologian. Furthermore, it shows that he has some grasp of the theological meaning of death. Death has dimensions other than that of the cessation of physical life. It stands related to God, the fall, and Christ's atoning work. Death to sin, the death of Christ, the second death, and life through death cannot be dismissed as though the only issue were the mortality or immortality of the soul. The passage affords at least a passing glimpse of Origen working at the theological level. It also leads on to a fine peroration in which he urges his listeners to seek immortality by taking up the eternal life which may be enjoyed already in shadow, because it is in Christ, but which will be known in fullness when Christ is seen face to face.


### 7. Survey

Origen's combination of the theological and the philosophical is highly individual. He quotes extensively from scripture, yet embarks on speculations for which only minimal scriptural support can be found. His fertile mind can leap off from texts or even single words in heady flights which set his basic orthodoxy in strange juxtaposition to his less than orthodox suggestions and conclusions. No surprise need be felt that in Christian history he has been both lauded as a contributor to orthodoxy and also condemned as a fountain of heresy.

At the level of personal coherence or consistency, putting together the different pieces may not be too difficult. The key lies in ideas which Origen took over from Clement: that of the stages of faith, knowledge, and love, and that of the corresponding levels of biblical interpretation. At times, perhaps, Origen tends to show a scorn for simple people who remain at the stage of faith and literal interpretation. Yet he acknowledges the necessity of this stage. He does not make the mistake of viewing the stage of knowledge and the accompanying intellectualized exposition of scripture as final. For knowledge must yield to love, and the first form of allegorizing must yield to a higher spiritual form. On this scheme Origen begins with faith and scripture and finds scope for more speculative ventures with knowledge and allegorical reading, but he always orients himself to a mystical or spiritual goal. He can readily enter into discussions raised by philosophical thought. He can no less readily accept ideas which come from outside, especially at the second stage or level. At the same time, the beginning and end of his thought keep him within the framework of orthodox teaching and piety.

As regards his impact on others, however, Origen's theology has an obvious tendency toward fragmentation. Different aspects, dimensions, and individual statements can make independent appeals and exercise independent influences in which the totality of his approach is lost. By its very nature his distinction of stages or levels introduces at least the possibility of dichotomy in which extraneous factors overwhelm the biblical center, or the different elements are left at odds with themselves, or the scriptures, variously used, seem to be turned against themselves.

Origen raises again — and perhaps even more acutely — the problem posed by his teacher and predecessor. He also pinpoints more clearly the basic flaw in the Alexandrian pattern. Assuming that the three stages and levels be accepted, the Alexandrian presentation can be reconciled with the more immediately orthodox approach of an Irenaeus or Tertullian. Even wilder conjectures might be included as pious opinions arising out of an outworking of possible implications of faith. The critical question, however, is whether the distinction is inherently justifiable, and, even if it is, whether it is developed in the right way. For one thing, a distinct Platonism seemingly underlies Origen's concept of the distinction, and this introduces a fatal hierarchical ordering. For another, the speculations are not just pious opinions since they supposedly have the backing of scripture on an allegorical or fanciful exegesis. Naturally, a fundamental affinity to orthodoxy remains. The Alexandrians do not take a totally different path. Nevertheless, philosophical thinking has a bigger and more basic influence than perhaps they allow for. It also gives a different slant to things undoubtedly biblical in themselves. So, then, substantial divergence does in fact take place. At the crucial middle points of knowledge and intellectualizing exegesis the theology of Origen in particular takes on an open-ended character over which the beginning in faith and the ending in love can no longer exercise a wholly adequate control, even if their presence and force are never to be discounted or minimized.

*Not really very illumined!*

# CHAPTER IV
## *Early Ecumenists*

Like any movement, Christianity experienced disruptive pressures from the very first. Even in the New Testament a variety of issues threatened the unity of the church. Discrimination in the distribution of support caused grumbling in the primitive community at Jerusalem. Doctrinal problems and a factional spirit plagued the Corinthians. Judaizers caused trouble in Antioch and Galatia. A denial of the reality of the incarnation had to be dealt with in 1 John. At the same time a concern for unity found equally rapid manifestation in the New Testament writings. One may see this especially in John 17, where Jesus prays that his people may be one, and in Ephesians, where stress is laid on the making of one new man out of Jew and Gentiles, and also on the roots of unity: "One Lord, one faith, one baptism, one God and Father of us all" (Eph. 4:4–6).

With the church's expansion, the possibilities of tension and disruption naturally increased. The Judaizing problem did not go away quietly with Paul's vigorous writings on the subject. Doctrinal aberrations took on a new intensity with the rise of Gnostic and Marcionite teaching. Even innocent matters like observing the anniversary of the Lord's resurrection could give rise to foolishly impassioned controversy. Disciplinary questions loomed large. When the baptized became guilty of such flagrant offenses as adultery, murder, or apostasy, should they be received back into communion, and, if so, on what terms and how often? With what many took to be a relaxation of discipline from the late second century onward, and then with the wholesale defections under Decius and Diocletian, differences on these matters tore the church apart as the Novatianists and Donatists carried their dissatisfaction to the point of schism.

Nevertheless, the church consistently sensed the constitutive importance of unity. Attempts had to be made to safeguard or restore this. Divergent groups had to be won over or declared no part of the church. Steps had to be taken to protect believers against seduction. Common decisions had to be reached on controverted issues. The theological problems involved in divisiveness, or in the alleged reasons for division, demanded exploration. The history of patristic theology includes, then, an ecumenical element in which the problems of unity and disunity are handled in various ways. Ignatius of Antioch might serve as a representative of ecumenical thinking in the early second century, Cyprian of Carthage in the third century, and Augustine of Hippo in the early fifth century.

## A. IGNATIUS OF ANTIOCH

### 1. Letter to the Ephesians

#### a. God and Unity

Ignatius sees dangerous, if sometimes only incipient, threats to the churches which he counsels. These come particularly from Judaizers, who are still trying to force Jewish law on Christians, and from Docetics, who deny the reality of the bodily life of Christ. In his primary answer to these perils Ignatius insists that instead of following our own minds we should seek "the mind of God" which will be found in Jesus Christ: "For Jesus Christ is the Father's mind." As we harmonize our actions with the divine mind, we shall also achieve harmony with one another (3.2).

#### b. Unity and the Ministry

Ignatius takes a further step when he finds a reflection of the mind of Christ in "the bishops too, appointed the world over." Hence in practice harmony will be achieved as we act in accordance with the bishop's mind. Ignatius, of course, associates the presbyters with the bishop, the latter being as it were the harp and the former the strings. When tuned to the mind of the ministers the congregation forms a choir. Their "love is a hymn to Jesus Christ" and they can "sing in unison and with one voice to the Father through Jesus Christ" (4.1ff.; cf. Ign. *Rom.* 2.2; Ign. *Phld.* 1.2).

### 2. Letters to the Magnesians and Trallians

#### a. The Ministry and God

Ignatius presents much the same argument in *Magnesians*. To achieve unity we obviously have to be in harmony with God. Ignatius, however, can see no way to this except by "godly agreement" with the ministry. He thus argues, in a not wholly consistent scheme, that the bishop should "preside in God's place, the presbyters take the place of the apostolic council, and the deacons be entrusted with the ministry of Jesus Christ" (6.1).

*b. The Ministry and Validity*

To put this "godly agreement" into effect Ignatius commands that "as the Lord did nothing without the Father, . . . you must not do anything without the bishop and presbyters." Independent action is forbidden. "Only what you do together is right." In this way there will be "one prayer, one petition, one mind, one hope" (Ign. *Magn.* 7.1), and also "one temple and one altar" (7.2). Similarly, the Trallians are told to "obey the bishop as if he were Jesus Christ" and "to act in no way without the bishop" (Ign. *Trall.* 2.1ff.). Apart from the bishop, deacons, and presbyters, who represent the Father, Jesus Christ, and the apostolic band, "you cannot have a church" (Ign. *Trall.* 3).

## 3. Letter to the Philadelphians

*a. Schism*

Early in his Philadelphian letter Ignatius gives the abrupt advice: "Flee from schism and false doctrine" (2.1). It seems likely from the text that there had been actual schism there. Hence the plea is urgent: "Keep away from bad pasturage" (3.1). So, too, is the warning: "If anyone joins a schismatic he will not inherit God's kingdom" (3.3). Later Ignatius points out that where schism and bad feeling exist, "God has no place," although he "will forgive all who repent" (8.1). The simple way to steer clear of schism is "not to do things in cliques" but always to act together as the one people of God.

*b. Unity*

Acting together means being "on the bishop's side" (3.2). It takes concrete shape in the Eucharist: "Be careful to observe a single eucharist" (4.1). This suggests another train of thought. Unity finds an ultimate ground in the one flesh of Christ and the one cup of his blood that makes us one. Hence "one flesh, one cup . . . one altar, just as there is one bishop along with the presbytery and the deacons" (chap. 4). Unity is to be valued, so that true Christians will "do nothing apart from the bishop" (7.2).

## 4. Letter to the Smyrnaeans

*a. Avoidance of Schismatics*

The letter to the Smyrnaeans has a lengthy warning against Docetic teachers. Ignatius urges his readers not to receive them and even, if possible, "to avoid meeting them" (4.1). All one can do is pray for their repentance. Even heavenly beings, Ignatius claims, are doomed "if they fail to believe in Christ's blood" (6.1). Those who "have wrong notions about the grace of Jesus Christ" will be betrayed by their conduct. They have no concern for the poor and "hold aloof from the eucharist" (6.2; 7.1). "The right thing to do, then, is to avoid such people and to talk about them neither in private nor in public" (7.2). "Flee schism as the source of mischief" (7.2).

### b. Role of the Bishop

The way of unity and truth is that of following the bishop, presbyters, and deacons (8.1). Episcopal authorization offers the only guarantee. "Nobody must do anything that has to do with the church without the bishop's approval. You should regard that eucharist as valid which is celebrated either by the bishop or by someone he authorizes" (8.1). "Without the bishop's supervision no baptisms or lovefeasts are permitted." "Whatever he approves pleases God as well. In that way everything you do will be on the safe side and valid" (8.2). Ignatius sums it up in two clear-cut affirmations: (1) "Where the bishop is present, there let the congregation gather, just as where Jesus Christ is, there is the catholic church" (8.2); and "He who pays the bishop honor has been honored by God. But he who acts without the bishop's knowledge is in the devil's service" (9.1).

### 5. Remarks

Ignatius does not reflect with any theological depth on the problem of unity. He has a sound basic premise, namely, that unity demands the renouncing of self-opinion and attuning to the mind of God. He has, however, only a rough and ready answer to the question of how this is to be done. The bishop, supported by other ministers, represents God's mind. Hence conformity to the bishop in teaching or church activity will bring about the desired result, while all else will be following one's own mind. Episcopacy thus constitutes the key to ecumenicity.

In the simpler circumstances of Ignatius' day, with fewer and smaller churches, greater proximity to the apostolic teaching, and more intensity of fellowship, this could probably work out quite well. But historical developments quickly expose it to greater strains than it can bear and bring to light its biblical and theological inadequacy.

Historically, the advice of Ignatius offers little help when larger bishoprics arise, when bishops come into mutual schism, when they are guilty of gross negligence and ineptitude, or when they depose the orthodox or are themselves deposed for heresy. Only a century or so after Ignatius, Antioch would know the infamous Paul of Samosata whom to obey and follow could ensure no safety but only a formal and meaningless validity. With strict enforcement, the principle of Ignatius could bring an organizational and administrative unity, but this might even be at the cost of the unity of faith and truth and love which he so patently desires.

Ignatius' program could not work out historically because it rested on a naive and unsupported assumption, namely, a supposedly self-evident equation of the mind of the bishop with the mind of God. God did indeed choose apostles, and through them pastors and teachers, both to evangelize and also to instruct and guide the church. God also gave them spiritual gifts and the Spirit's help in the discharge of their task. God ordained that church members should respect and obey them. But God also laid upon them a responsibility of faithfulness to the spoken and written tradition. Far from enjoying a direct identity with the mind of God and a consequent infallibility, they had thus to be subject to God's own Word in the apostolic testimony. Their thought, like those of all Christians, needed to be brought into captivity to the mind of Christ.

A qualification needs to be added to the advice of Ignatius to give it depth and reality. The bishop reflects the mind of God as he proclaims and does what is consonant with the Word of God. Perhaps this could be taken for granted in Ignatius' day. It cannot always be taken for granted today. Hence the principle needs to be stated, explored, and practiced. Authentic unity can hardly be effected merely by following the ministry. No doubt an authorized ministry has a place in unity. The apostolic gospel itself, however, has a more basic and central place. Apart from this one might even achieve a unity in error. With it, unity might sometimes have to come apart from and even in spite of the bishop, presbytery, and deacons. Most happily of all — and finally, of course, this is what Ignatius has in view — it will come through a ministry which is itself renouncing self-opinion and humbly and faithfully attuning itself to the mind of God in the apostolic and biblical teaching.

## B. CYPRIAN OF CARTHAGE

Cyprian, a wealthy convert (c. 245), became bishop of Carthage in 248 or 249. At once the church came under the fierce and systematic persecution of Decius, and vast numbers, being caught unprepared, fell into apostasy. Cyprian's real problems began, however, when many of the lapsed repented and sought readmission, for this led to a confused struggle between a lenient party and a severer party. Cyprian inclined toward severity, and when a decision was reached allowing readmission only after prolonged discipline, the more lax group, oddly making common cause with the extremely rigorist Novatian in Rome, set up a rival assembly under a rival bishop named Fortunatus.

The emergence of this body, which naturally claimed to be the true church, led Cyprian in 251 to write his famous work *On the Unity of the Catholic Church*. His concern here is not with the disciplinary issue. Unity is the true and dominant theme. He clearly accepts this as an unshakable reality. But what does it imply when another body, teaching the same doctrine and following the same practices, also claims to be the church? Can unity embrace many churches in one place? Can divided bodies validly do what the church does? Are their members among the saved? Is the baptism they give to be accepted? How is unity to be recognized? What is its center? These are some of the matters that Cyprian briefly explores in his searching and provocative study.

### 1. Schisms

#### a. A Demonic Stratagem

Cyprian makes his position plain at once. The adversary is at work in schisms. Schisms are more cunning but no less dangerous than persecutions. "We must guard against wily trickery and subtle deceit no less than open and obvious perils." As "a new trick to deceive the unwary," heresies and schisms have been invented by the enemy "to undermine faith, pervert truth, and break unity" (pars. 1–3).

#### b. The Danger of Schism

The particular peril in schism is that it gives a false sense of security. Though walking in darkness, schismatics "think they are in the light." Truth does not meet here the direct opposition of falsehood. It is frustrated by "a lying show of truth" (par. 3).

### 2. The Basis of Unity

#### a. Unity in One Man

To show the unity of the church, Cyprian argues, the Lord builds it on the one man Peter. The other apostles, of course, are equal to Peter. They "were exactly what Peter was; they were endowed with an equal share of office and power." Yet in demonstration of unity, Christ arranged that the church should "take its beginning from one man" (par. 4).

#### b. Scriptural Proofs

Throughout his work Cyprian makes a strong appeal to scripture. Both the Old Testament and the New teach the unity of the church. "My dove . . . is but one" (Cant 6:9) can be adduced from the Old Testament, for Cyprian sees in it a statement of the Holy Spirit "in the person of the Lord." More patently Paul "gives the same teaching and declares the same mystery of unity" in Ephesians 4:4–6.

### 3. Episcopal Responsibility

#### a. Championing Unity

Like Ignatius, Cyprian closely links the episcopate with unity. He differs, however, in that he stresses not the people's duty to follow the bishop but the bishop's duty to uphold unity. In this regard it is of the utmost importance that the episcopate should be seen "to be itself one and undivided" (par. 5).

### b. Individual and Corporate Aspects

Cyprian thus sees for the bishop a responsibility which is both individual and corporate: "Each bishop's share gives him a right to, and a responsibility for, the whole" (par. 5). This enigmatic saying seems to mean that while the local bishop has full rights and responsibilities in his own church, he also carries responsibility for the whole church. Local unity cannot be divorced from ecumenical unity; at the same time there can be no diminution of local responsibility. Possibly Cyprian fears that bishops elsewhere might recognize schismatics whom the local bishop does not recognize.

## 4. Metaphors and Symbols of the One Church

### a. Metaphors

(1) Sun, Tree, and Spring. The unity of the episcopate reflects that of the church, for which Cyprian produces a series of metaphors. He begins with three from the natural world. The universal church resembles the sun, a tree, or a spring. The sun has rays; the tree, branches; and the spring, streams — namely, the local churches. But there is one light, one trunk, one source — namely, the church. For all the appearance of plurality, unity is preserved, for rays have no light without the sun; branches, no buds without the tree; streams, no water without the source. The churches cannot just be churches; they have to be the church (par. 5).

(2) Bride. The biblical description of the church as Christ's bride suggests to Cyprian the idea that schismatic gatherings are adulteresses. The true bride "guards the sanctity of the one bed-chamber" and "seals us for God." Only by association with the one church can one be associated with Christ's true bride. To leave it and join an adulteress is to be "cut off from the promises" (par. 6).

(3) Mother. The idea of bride slips easily into that of mother when the individual believers come under consideration. One bride obviously means one mother. To belong to Christ we have to be children of this mother. Hence the decisive conclusion: "You cannot have God for your father unless you have the church for your mother" (par. 6).

(4) Ark. The example of the ark confirms this. Only those who were in the ark escaped. No other boats rode out the flood. God has provided the one church — and it alone — as the ark of salvation. Those who seek refuge in pseudo-churches will perish (par. 6).

*b. Symbols*

(1) The Seamless Robe. Cyprian backs his argument with an appeal to scriptural types or symbols. Thus the robe of Christ, which was woven in a piece from the top, contrasts with the garment of Jeroboam, which Ahijah tore to signify the division of Israel. Trying to tear Christ's robe, schismatics lose it. "Undivided, conjoined, coherent, the robe proves the unbroken harmony of our people who have put on Christ" (par. 7).

(2) The Flock and Shepherd. Scripture does not tell us to look for many flocks and many shepherds in one place. The very idea is "unthinkable." Christ and his people are one shepherd and one flock, and they are represented at the local level by the one pastor and the one church (par. 8).

(3) Rahab. Cyprian, like other fathers, finds in Rahab a type of the church. When Jericho was taken, her family had to gather in her house to be saved. If they left it, they could not escape. To Cyprian the parallel is overwhelming: "Do you think a man can abandon the church, set up for himself another house and home, and yet stay alive?" (par. 8).

(4) The Passover. The Passover with its plain christological reference teaches the same lesson: "In one house shall it be eaten." It follows that "the faithful have no home but the one church." Psalm 68:6 adds the confirmation of the Spirit that God's people are to dwell in "this home, the house of unanimity" (par. 8).

(5) The Spirit. The association of home and Spirit suggests to Cyprian the biblical description of the Spirit as a dove, the bird which "loves human company and knows the fellowship of a single home," and which also lives with other doves in "the law of unanimity." The Spirit's presence rules out discord and division (par. 9).

## 5. The Schismatics and Their Arguments

*a. The Schismatics*

(1) Fierceness. In contrast to those taught by the Spirit, schismatics show a fierce and twisted mind which finds a place for neither peace nor unity. God permits this "out of respect for the freedom of the will" and in order that here and now there may be judgment in the church, the faithful being approved and the faithless detected (par. 10).

(2) Arrogance. Schismatic leaders presumptuously "make themselves prelates without any lawful ordination and call themselves bishops though no one gives them a bishopric" (par. 10). They are pseudo-bishops (Epistle 69.6). They invent false altars and illicit priesthoods. They are rebellious enemies (Epistle 69.1).

(3) Delusion. Like the false prophets of the Old Testament, schismatics suffer from delusion. They speak peace where there is no peace. "Although there can be no other than the one baptism . . . they fancy

they baptize. . . . Men are not washed there; they are defiled. . . . That birth makes sons for the devil, not for God." Having their origin in lying and perfidy, sects can give only the appearance and not the reality of faith and peace (par. 11).

### b. Their Arguments

(1) "Where two or three. . . ." Some schismatics claim Christ's presence on the basis of Matthew 18:20. Cyprian replies that the promise is given in the context of harmony: "If two of you shall agree on earth . . ." (v. 19). Unanimity and concord come first, and then Christ's presence. Hence "the Lord's words were spoken about his own church and addressed to members of the church" (par. 12).

(2) Martyrdom. Schismatics also appeal to the martyrdom of some of their members. Cyprian will have none of this. Suffering "cannot purge the grievous and inexpiable sin of discord." "You cannot be a martyr if you are not in the church." He who "refuses to be of one mind with the church cannot abide with God." He "may be killed, he cannot be crowned." 1 Corinthians 13:2–3 offers Cyprian a biblical basis for this rejoinder (par. 14).

(3) Prophecies and Miracles. Schismatics also produce prophecies and miracles in self-vindication. Again Cyprian is not impressed. The Lord will dismiss many who spoke and did mighty works in his name. Pointing to the first and great commandment, and the second which is like it, he requires unity and love. If a man does not keep to "the right and proper road," he may prophesy and work miracles "and yet not reach the heavenly kingdom" (pars. 14–15).

## 6. Exhortation

After describing some additional aspects of schism — the fact that it was foretold (pars. 16–17), examples in the Old Testament (par. 18), its greater heinousness than apostasy (par. 19), and its vain appeal to the support of confessors (pars. 20–22) — Cyprian summons schismatics to return to the church, since "whatever leaves the womb cannot live and breathe apart" (par. 23). He backs up his appeal with biblical exhortations to peace and examples of unanimity in apostolic days (par. 25), sadly noting how the original unity has declined as liberality and the vigor of faith have decayed (par. 26). He urges the brethren to "observe and fulfill the Lord's commands" so that they will not be surprised by his "sudden advent" but "reign with Christ in his kingdom" (par. 27).

## 7. Cyprian's Contribution

### a. Positive Factors

(1) Concern for Unity. We must always be grateful to Cyprian for

taking unity so seriously. In a pluralistic age when division is taken for granted or even regarded as meritorious his message has a particular timeliness. For Cyprian, disunity does not just have a scandalous aspect, weakening the impact of the gospel in the world. It also has a sinful aspect, signifying disobedience to the will of him who desires unity for his church.

(2) Reality of Unity. Cyprian will not accept unity merely as a goal or ideal, or as something that we must fashion. God himself has already established unity. In the ultimate sense it cannot be shattered by our disunities. It has a given and indestructible reality. Whether Cyprian sees this correctly or draws the right inferences may be left aside for the moment. What counts is that he does see it. He thus sets before us the proper basis and starting point of unity.

(3) Nature of Unity. Cyprian has two useful insights into the nature of unity. On the one hand, he will not let us be content with Docetic unity that finds no flesh and blood expression. Unity means one church in one place even if it has to comprise several congregations. It does not mean many separated and competing churches in one place even if these rival groups claim an indefinable unity in spite of their divisions. On the other hand, Cyprian holds no brief for the embodiment of unity in a centralized international organization. The universal church comes to embodiment in the local churches. These cannot be totally autonomous. They must be in communion and bear mutual responsibility. Nevertheless, Cyprian sees neither one church dominating the rest nor a federation establishing central control as the universal church. He does not divide the church from the churches but finds the church in the churches. Unity does not demand the nightmare of a vast dictatorial organization. Its specific embodiment is the local church in communion with all the other local churches.

(4) The Scriptural Basis of Unity. Cyprian does not theorize in the void. He turns at every point to scripture in support of what he says. At times his expositions may be a little fanciful, but the cumulative force of his biblical appeal should not be discounted. In this regard Cyprian offers an example of the loyalty to tradition for which he pleads. At the same time he makes it plain that any biblical theology must wrestle seriously with the problem of unity. The Bible itself demands it.

### b. Negative Factors

(1) Oversimplification. Oversimplification may be Cyprian's main fault. This can be seen especially in his equation of divinely established unity with the historical body centered on the properly authorized bishop. If he develops this understanding with logical and rhetorical skill, he hardly displays an equivalent theological discernment. He misses the tension between what God has established and the outworking of it by sinners in the practical complexities of life. He wants to say:

"We are what we are, and schismatics are not." He does not allow for the element of becoming what we are. His direct equation of what God sees us to be and what we are here and now leads to confusion and ultimate deception.

(2) The same oversimplification may be seen in Cyprian's discussion of the autonomy and yet also the mutual interdependence of the churches. Here history brings to light the possibilities of self-contradiction, whose origins lie, of course, in the oversimplification of direct equation. On Cyprian's view the churches with an ongoing ministerial succession have to be in agreement. When, however, there is disagreement with Rome over rebaptizing returning schismatics, Cyprian's logic fails him, for his theology will not let him agree with Rome nor will it let him rend the unity of the apostolic churches by a breach with Rome. Even if he appeals to Carthage's responsibility for orthodoxy at Rome, Rome can raise a counterclaim. Already the specter raises its ugly head; the churches themselves might be in schism while still claiming to be, and perhaps even being, the one church in the one place. Schism can arise at the corporate level as well as the local level. Cyprian's presentation, however, offers no solution to this difficulty. At the level of human fulfillment, unity can in fact be broken, unless the hopeless attempt is made to find the church only in the larger or smaller group which maintains its separate communion and recognizes no others.

### b. Debatable Inferences

(1) The basic oversimplifications lead Cyprian to debatable positions which his logic demands but neither theology nor history can accept. Thus he pursues the line that a pagan converted through schismatics, even though confessing Christ, holding the creed, using the means of grace, and living in discipleship, cannot be in the church and therefore can have no salvation. For all the importance of unity, or of the element of truth in the distinction of church and sect, few Christians across the centuries have been able to live with this reading of the situation. If Roman documents have sometimes argued that outside communion with the bishop of Rome there is no salvation — not quite what Cyprian had in mind — the Roman church can also speak of other sheep who are not (yet) of the one flock. If disunity is a scandal and a sin, it can hardly be an instrument of perdition for those who sincerely call on the name of the Lord.

(2) The invalidity of schismatic ministry offers another instance of logical but dubious inference due to basic oversimplification. Logic demands that tasks committed to the church cannot be carried out by the sect. Here, however, Cyprian is led again to an impossible extreme. Novatianists, in administering baptism, do all that scripture requires. Can one really say, then, that their baptisms are no baptisms simply

because they are given outside the historical body and its regular ministry? This makes so little sense that theology has introduced at this point important distinctions between regularity, validity, and efficacy. Cyprian no doubt would dismiss these as sophistries. Schismatic baptism, being irregular, can be neither valid nor efficacious. It is not baptism. Converts moving from schism to church must be baptized, not again, but for the first time. On Cyprian's simplistic understanding of unity he may well be right. The inference beings to light the oversimplification. It plunges him at once into the difficulty with Rome which threatens the whole structure of apostolic unity. It also raises the basic problem. Novatianists are schismatics and act irregularly, but can one say that they are not Christians and do not perform acts of Christian ministry at all? May it not even be that Cyprian, anticipating the judgment of God, is himself breaking, or at least endangering, the divinely established unity of the church which it is our duty to work out as best we may, not by shortcuts, but along the complex and perplexing paths of the mission and presence of sinful believers in a sinful world?

## C. AUGUSTINE OF HIPPO

The Diocletian persecution, which began in 303, added a new twist to the problem of unity. The edicts which launched the persecution demanded the handing over of sacred books and vessels, and not a few bishops and other clergy gave way here even while resisting full-scale apostasy. These traditors, along with apostates, came under disciplinary action, but some who came under suspicion, whether rightly or wrongly, remained in office, and many bishops were also officiating who had been ordained by deposed or suspected traditors. Hence a new rigorist group, the Donatists, arose to call for the expulsion of all suspects and also to challenge the validity of the ministrations of those who had received consecration at apostate hands.

The Donatist affinity to Cyprian's more extreme positions, which were rejected at Arles in 314, should not pass unnoticed. To be sure, Cyprian would not have approved of the Donatist schism nor regarded its ministrations as valid. He cannot, then, be associated with or made responsible for the Donatist conclusions or their attempted enforcement. Nevertheless, Cyprian and the Donatists share in common the linking of validity or invalidity to human factors: catholicism or sectarianism on the one side, loyalty or defection on the other. This affinity could be a contributory factor to the strength of Donatism in North Africa.

The Donatists failed to make their point in the church at large. When their continued activities brought disorder, they were put down, although not eliminated, by secular forces. Later in the fourth century, however, they again became an important factor on the North African scene. This explains why Augustine of Hippo, after his conversion and the commencement of his North African ministry, devoted a good deal of theological and pastoral effort to the Donatist problem. How Augustine made his points against Donatism at the expository as well as the more strictly doctrinal level may be seen in the scattered applications he makes in his *Homilies on the First Epistle of John*.

## 1. Features of Schism

### a. Self-Centeredness

Augustine finds the roots of schism in a focusing on the self: "Schisms arise when men say, we are righteous, we sanctify the unclean, we justify the wicked." The Donatist demand for purity in a minister, while reasonable from a disciplinary point of view, involves an exalting of the minister's importance as though God's work depended ultimately on him. This orientation reaches an intolerable limit when some ministers see themselves as righteous in distinction from others. Here, however, is the very essence of Donatism (1.8).

### b. Narrowness

By pretending to be the only true church, the Donatists fall into contradiction. Although Christ died for all, they claim that he is in them alone: "He who purchased the whole and possesses the whole is only in the part." They fail to see that if Christ is the propitiator "not only for our sins," then we have to include not just North African schismatics but "the church in all nations" (1.8). By restricting true Christianity to themselves they "refuse communion to the city that killed Christ" and "give Christ the strange honor of confinement to two languages, Latin and Punic" (2.3). The absurdity of these implications shows up the absurdity of the original position.

### c. Hatred

1 John teaches brotherly love, but these "true Christians" display hatred instead of love. Behind their intolerance lies a twisted and inconsistent view of things. "To brethren whom they slander they will not grant toleration for the sake of the peace of Jesus Christ," but for the sake of their own party they will grant it to other schismatics whom they condemn (1.13). Party interest outweighs authentic concern for either unity or truth.

## 2. The Basis of Unity

### a. Universality of Christ's Death

As noted, Augustine bases his case against Donatism on the universal sweep of Christ's atoning work. Since Christ died for all, no place is left for the idea that the church can have members only in a geographically confined area. Disciples must be found from every nation, as in the catholic church. With Christ's death as the focal point, unity and universality meet.

### b. Exclusiveness of Christ's Death

Like Paul, Augustine also sees that while Christ died for all, Christ alone died a vicarious death. Here lies the heart of unity. Factions naming Augustine or Donatus, Paul or Peter, are ruled out. We all meet in the one name of Christ "through which sins are forgiven" (2.4). We all have to recognize, then, all those who call on this Lord. We cannot deny them the name of brethren.

## 3. Donatist Claims

### a. They Confess Christ

It might seem that if Augustine shows that Donatists should accept others, by the same token others should accept Donatists. Do not they confess Christ? Augustine resists this conclusion, however, on the ground that their deeds belie their words. "Actions may deny as well as tongues" (3.8). Donatists maintain orthodoxy according to John's test. They agree that Christ has come in the flesh. But they reject this in their deeds, for they do not embody love and they disrupt unity (6.13). Hence Augustine will not number them among those who name the name of Christ.

### b. They Die for the Faith

Like Cyprian, Augustine has to face the roll of schismatic martyrs. As he observes, Donatist zeal led many extremists, the so-called Circumcellions, not only to take violent action in the churches but also to court death for their faith. Nevertheless, he cannot see here authentic Christian martyrdom. Why not? John argues the paramount importance of love. Without love, it is no good to be ready "to hurl oneself to destruction" (6.2).

### c. They Give the Sacraments

When Donatists claim that they, too, give the sacraments, Augustine does not follow Cyprian in declaring their baptisms invalid, for this would be to concede their own point that validity depends on the ministers. He adopts three different lines of approach.

(1) "The evil man as well as the good can have the name of Christ." He may also "have all the sacraments." But "to have charity and to be an evil man is not possible" (7.6).

(2) When Donatists baptize, they "post the title deeds of a greater owner." This owner recognizes the deeds. Hence, "when one comes into

the catholic church, there is . . . no erasing of the emperor's title." In itself, however, the act of posting is a usurped and empty one (7.11).

(3) Those outside the church — Augustine agrees with Cyprian here — cannot be really in it. The reverse may be true. "Many are within the church that are within in seeming only." But external schism always means exclusion. The best that Augustine can hope for is that some of those outside may be "predestinated to come within" (6.13).

### 4. The Test of Love

#### a. Love of Christ Is Love of the Brethren

John's equation of love of God and love of the brethren provides Augustine with his reason for the exclusion of Donatists. "None can love the Father unless he love the Son; and he that loves the Son loves also the sons of God; and he that loves them . . . becomes himself a member. . . . And thus the end will be one Christ, loving himself; for the love of the members for one another is the love of the body for itself" (10.3). "If you love the Head, you love the members." Donatists manifestly fail by this test.

#### b. Love's Universal Dimension

Taking up a previous point, Augustine avoids a possible objection — Donatists love Donatists — by insisting that love of Christian brethren cannot be set under a geographical restriction. If Donatists desire recognition as Christians through love for Christ, they are commanded: "Stretch out your love over all the world, for Christ's members are spread the world over." Love of a part alone means separation from the whole. "If your love is for a part only, you are sundered; if sundered, you are not in the body; if not in the body, you are not under the Head." Christ cannot be had without his body. "You may sever yourselves from the body, but he cannot be severed from it." "You cannot honor him above and trample him below" (10.8).

#### c. Love and Repression

Donatists, suffering under the church's repressive measures, found little evidence of the love of which Augustine spoke so eloquently. Augustine might have replied that the Donatists were not Christian brethren anyway, but he realized that the church's love must be love of enemies, too. Hence he advanced a different set of considerations.

(1) Donatists are the real persecutors, since it is they who "have divided the church" (10.9).

(2) Love has a stern as well as a gentle side. It is not "a careless indifference." Faced with error, it may have to take the form of discipline (7.8).

(3) Acts of discipline can look like acts of hatred, just as outwardly

God's handing over of Jesus resembles that of Judas. The difference lies at the level of "mind" or "intention" (7.7). "Love, and do what you will" comes into play here (7.8). The church's acts against the Donatists stand the test of love in terms of motivation, whereas the violent acts of the Donatists, similar though they may be externally, cannot meet this test. Nor, indeed, can the gentler words that the Donatists may utter. Love may reprove, denounce, and even prosecute while hatred speaks softly. We must "look for the spring, search out the root" (10.7).

## 5. Belief and Opinion

### a. Faith and Work

Augustine admits that Donatists agree with Peter in confessing that Jesus is the Christ. This faith, not Peter himself, is the rock on which the church is built. (Augustine suggests that the rock may be Peter, or Christ himself, in his *In Petr.* 1.21.) Nevertheless, if faith be genuine, it works by love. Hence it appertains only to Christians "who are such not in name only but in deed and in life" (10.1).

### b. The Gospel and the Donatist Story

Do Donatists really believe the gospel? Augustine questions this. Christ in the gospel spreads his church across the world and gives it the message of forgiveness. Donatists believe their own story of the traditors. "Christ is God, you are men. Which most deserves belief?" "You know well that if you believed Christ, you could have nothing to say about the traditors." But Donatists believe and preach their own account of the traditors. Hence their claim to faith has no substance. They will not "believe the promise of Christ" (10.10).

## 6. Assessment

### a. Advance

Augustine takes some positive steps in relation to unity and schism. He does not rely so heavily on formal criteria such as association with the bishop. He does not flatly invalidate schismatic baptism. Since Christ has instituted baptism and is the true minister, external authorization, though important, cannot be the crucial factor. Greater stress falls on the internal criteria of faith and love. Augustine appreciates the fact that the church consists of sinners under the forgiveness of God. Hence members are protected against the self-centeredness and self-righteousness which characterize schism. The divine as well as the human dimension of communion is sensed. Communion with the Father and the Son leads to communion with the brethren. Absence of communion with the brethren betrays absence of communion with God. The appeal for unity ceases to be merely an appeal for return to the church.

It becomes an appeal for the love of God and neighbor which stands at the heart of Christian faith, confession, life, and ministry.

### b. Problems

Yet difficulties remain in Augustine's treatment. First, he refuses to consider the possibility that schismatics might show love as well as the church. Donatists, of course, seem to have given him no reason to think this. Probably all splits, when they first take place, arouse such heated feelings that love recedes into the background. Nevertheless, in today's denominations which result from past divisions, mutual love can obviously exist, and love is not the monopoly of the group which can claim the strongest historical links with the primitive church. The supreme criterion set up by Augustine opens the door to conclusions which he himself did not consider and which drastically modify his teaching.

Second, Augustine's defense of the unloving acts of the church, namely, that they are authentically loving in intention, carries little conviction. A truth lies behind it. Intention or motivation must be considered as well as the external act. Yet a triple difficulty arises. When Augustine appeals to God and Judas, the area of similarity is very restricted: God does not sell Jesus for thirty pieces of silver. Action cannot be played down in such a way as to result in the patent self-contradiction that, so long as good is intended, cruelty, lying, or lechery can be good and not bad. Finally, God and not Augustine knows the intents of the hearts. Who is to say that all church members act out of love or that Donatists doing similar acts do not act out of love?

Third, Augustine has to agree with Cyprian that schismatic sacraments have no efficacy. Hence Donatists cannot be Christians. They go to perdition if they do not repent. Augustine makes this point with great clarity. The church may include purely outward believers, but sects cannot include inward believers. Can this be justified theologically? Does it help toward a solution of the vexatious problem of schism? May not Augustine, too, be guilty of a restriction of the gospel of forgiveness, of the universality of the atoning work of Christ? Is he not finally dominated by an equation of the divine reality and the human structure which, for all its value in resisting a purely nebulous and disembodied unity, inevitably forms a factor in the perpetuation of disunity?

These early ecumenists, tackling the first manifestations of disunity, do significant preparatory work in thinking out the theology of unity. If they fail, the main reason seems not to be that they do not quote scripture, but that they do not develop an adequate biblical theology of the church and its unity. (It is not at once apparent, of course, that ecumenism in any age has been all that much more successful in this regard.) Nevertheless, certain foundation stones are laid. The importance of unity comes out clearly. So does the need for its embodiment. Its link with universality, not under a highly centralized authority but in strong connection with the universality of Christ's work, is finely expressed. Unity, it is seen, must be in the confession of Christ and under the divine forgiveness. Not least of all, in all discussion of unity and any steps that are taken toward it, the climate will have to be that of the Christian love which is rooted in the love of God and love for him. This criterion must be a constituent of unity.

# CHAPTER V
## *An Incarnational Theologian: Athanasius*

From the very beginning the confession of Jesus as Lord caused theological problems for the church. Jewish Christians, with their strong doctrine of the oneness of God, which they were not, of course, expected to renounce, inevitably tended to think of Christ as subordinate to the Father and even, perhaps, as Son of God by adoption rather than nature or essence. Gentile Christians might have been tempted to solve the problem polytheistically, but the monotheistic core of the Christian message closed this path. Hence the only options seemed to be either a modal or a dynamic monarchianism. According to the former they could view Christ simply as an economic and temporary mode of the one God, while according to the latter they could see in Jesus a finite man in whom the eternal but impersonal Word found embodiment and who in virtue of this association could be acknowledged as the Son of God.

More specifically christological problems added to the difficulty. Docetists insisted on the full deity of the Son, but because the flesh seemed to be an unworthy or impossible vehicle for God they discounted the humanity as a mere semblance. Subordinationists, on the other hand, accepted the humanity but fell short of an authentic deity. Groups which maintained both deity and humanity found it hard to think of the two together, especially when inherited ideas of the immateriality and impassibility of God imposed prior limits on what God supposedly could and could not do.

One might wonder why early thinkers allowed such matters to trouble them so much. Was it so important that they work out tidy solutions to problems in which no full human understanding could be attained? Did not the discussion of these themes bring little profit, cause much futile and damaging dissension, and tie the confession unnecessarily and possibly harmfully to the metaphysical concepts and categories of the debaters?

Two factors weighed against these considerations. First, since the early Christians took the confession seriously, they could not avoid the theological task of working out its rationality both positively as a part of the renewal of the mind and negatively in answer to rationalistic objections. Second, they perceived very clearly that the divine humanity of Christ belongs essentially to the gospel of reconciliation. As we saw earlier, Ignatius, the writer to Diognetus, and Irenaeus all expressed this. Dismissal of the questions of the relationship of Father to Son or of Christ's deity to his humanity finally meant dismissal of the Christian message itself. For all the difficulties that might be caused and the haggling and squabbling that might unfortunately result, theology could not shirk its duty when no less than the essence of the gospel was at stake.

The trinitarian and christological debates, which had flared up off and on for two centuries, reached explosion point in Alexandria around 318. Alexander the bishop gave an address on the Trinity under the title of "Unity in Trinity." Arius, a presbyter, suspected the bishop of modalism. In response he taught an outrageous form of subordinationism which plainly denied Christ's essential deity: "There was when the Son was not"; "He had his essence from the non-existent"; "He is not equal, no, nor one in essence with the Father." This teaching launched a controversy which, in spite of the decision of Nicea in 325 ("one in essence with the Father"), could not be settled until the Council of Constantinople reestablished the Nicene confession in 381, and which for complexity, intrigue, and bitterness has seldom, if ever, been exceeded in the history of the church.

On the very eve of the Arian explosion there appeared in Alexandria a little work on the interrelated theme of incarnation and atonement (316–318). Athanasius, the youthful author of *The Incarnation of the Word,* would later play a key role in the opposition to the Arians. In spite of incredible pressures, he would stand firm when the tides of Arianism seemed to be flooding the churches: "Athanasius against the world." In more detailed works he would tackle the Arian arguments with astonishing theological insight and acumen. Nevertheless, it is perhaps from this early writing, composed in the main with an apologetic intent, that we can learn the dogmatic and evangelical concern which led Athanasius, at so great cost to himself, to resist what seemed to be a triumphant theological and ecclesiastical movement.

*The Incarnation of the Word* predates the Arian campaign. Hence it does not deal at all with the teaching of Arius. In a real sense, however, it undercuts this teaching in advance. It explores the point and purpose of the incarnation in relation to the destiny and fall of man and the reconciling and self-revealing work of God. In a simple but effective way it thus brings to light the essential issue in the detailed argumentations which were so soon to follow. At the same time it offers a brief but coherent account of the whole sweep of biblical teaching. Not without reason, then, this early essay of Athanasius has come to be regarded as one of the most significant of all contributions to incarnational theology.

## A. THE PROBLEM: THE FALL OF MAN

### 1. God's Creation

*a. Pagan Views*

In a previous treatise, *Against the Heathen,* Athanasius had depicted the error of idolatry. He finds it necessary, however, to summarize what had been said in order to lay out the problem which the incarnation solves. He begins, then, with a critical sketch of pagan views of the origin of things. Thus the Epicureans espouse individual self-organization, which Athanasius regards as absurd in the light of causality. Plato and others see God making "the world out of matter previously existing." In this view God is weak, "unable to produce anything . . . without the material," and acting simply as "a mechanic." The "sectaries" separate the true God and the artificer of all things. John 1:3 sufficiently refutes this.

*b. Christian Teaching*

In contrast, Christian faith believes that "out of nothing, and without its having previous existence, God made the universe to exist through the Word" (Gen 1:1; Heb 11:3). He did so out of goodness and out of generosity as its source. He showed "especial pity" to the race of men, for, perceiving their frailty, he gave them a further gift, making them after his image and giving them a portion of the power of his Word, thus enabling them "to abide ever in blessedness" (3.3).

### 2. Man's Fall

*a. Sin*

Why, then, should God become man? The fall of the race explains it. Men despised the contemplation of God and devised evil. God had promised incorruption for obedience and threatened death for disobedience. But they chose disobedience (par. 4).

*b. Corruption*

Sin immediately brought with it a return to the natural state of corruption. "As they have had their being out of nothing . . . they might look for corruption into nothing." Owing their being to the loving-kindness of the Word, "they were turned back by their sin to what was not (for what is evil is not, but what is good is)." By nature man is mortal. Only the divine image, a free gift by the grace of the Word, prevents corruption. Sin, however, brings back death in a vicious circle of increasing transgression and progressive corruption. Once man sins, he comes not only under the power of the devil but also "under the threat of the deity." That is, the threatened judgment of God comes into operation. The race becomes involved, then, in an apparently irreversible rush to lawlessness and perdition (5.1–2).

### 3. God's Dilemma

#### a. The Claim of Justice

In this situation God cannot appropriately ignore his own law or deny his own sentence by simply breaking the devil's hold over us. "It were monstrous for God, the Father of truth, to appear a liar for our profit and preservation." Repentance does not meet the situation. It neither guards the just claim of God, calls men back from what is their nature, nor deals with the corruption which results from transgression. It seems that the very pronouncement of God himself demands the dissolution of his handiwork (pars. 6–7).

#### b. The Claim of Goodness

Yet how can God allow this? "It were unseemly that creatures once made rational, and having partaken of the Word, should go to ruin." "It were not worthy of God's goodness that the things he had made should waste away." God cannot allow death and the devil to have the last word. "Neglect reveals weakness and not goodness." Better not make us at all than make us and lose us. To leave men "to the current of corruption" is unthinkable in God. It is unseemly and unworthy of his goodness. How, then, can the apparently divergent claims of justice and goodness both be met? (par. 6).

## B. THE INCARNATE WORD AS ANSWER: RECONCILIATION

### 1. The Work of the Word

#### a. Power

The seemingly hopeless situation can be met only by the Word of God, "which had also at the beginning made everything out of nothing." The Word has the power to do what has to be done. He can bring "the corruptible to incorruption" while maintaining the just claim of the Father. He can "of natural fitness" "recreate everything." He is also worthy both to suffer for all and to be ambassador for all (7.4–5).

### b. Condescension

So far as man is concerned, of course, the Word stands under no obligation to "come to our realm." Indeed, in a general way he does not need to come, since he is already present: "No part of creation is left void of him." Nevertheless, he does come in a special way. He does this "in condescension to show his loving-kindness to us." This pity involves a threefold act.

(1) "He takes a body of our kind," although "from a spotless and stainless virgin."

(2) Since all were under the penalty of death's corruption, he gave this body "over to death in the stead of all." This undid the law of human ruin, since all were held to have died in him.

(3) He rose again in the body. Thus by his appropriation of his body and the grace of his resurrection "he turned men back to incorruption and quickened them again" (par. 8).

### c. Incarnation

Athanasius feels that the reason for the incarnation requires fuller explanation. Since the Word is the Son of the Father, and as such immortal, he cannot suffer death in himself. On the other hand, no man is able either to die for all or to remain incorruptible. Hence the Word takes a body which as the body of the Word can be be offered as "an equivalent" for all and yet remain incorruptible. In the body, then, the Word did two things.

(1) "By offering his own temple . . . for all he satisfied the debt by his death."

(2) "Being conjoined with all by a like nature he naturally clothes all with incorruption by the promise of his resurrection" (par. 9).

## 2. God's Self-justification

### a. His Care

The coming of the Word makes it clear that God does not neglect his creation. The race does not deserve anything from God. It has allowed a usurper to beset it. Yet God avenges and reclaims it as his own work. He will not permit what he has made to perish. He cares for it even to the point of the vicarious death of his Son, the incarnate Word.

### b. His Purpose

In this way God fulfills his purpose in creating man and thereby vindicates himself and his work. Through the activity of the Word a new beginning of life has been made for us. "By the Word of God being made man has come the destruction of death and the resurrection of life." We still die physically, but no longer "as subject to condemnation." "As men who rise from the dead we await the general resurrection of all." While God remains true to his just sentence, he also saves his work from ruin (10.5). The apparent futility of his creation and of the failure of his work yields, therefore, an even more glorious fulfillment of his original purpose.

## C. THE INCARNATE WORD AS ANSWER: REVELATION

### 1. Ignorance

#### a. Primal Knowledge

Athanasius explores another dimension of the plight of man and the work of the Word. As created and material beings, men could not of their own nature know the uncreated and immaterial God. Yet God in grace and mercy did not leave them "destitute of the knowledge of himself" lest life should be meaningless and there should be no distinction between the human and animal realms. The creation of men makes sense only as God "wishes to be known by them." Hence "he gives them a share in his own image, our Lord Jesus Christ," in order that by "perceiving the image, that is, the Word of the Father, they may be able through him to get an idea of the Father, and, knowing their Maker, live the happy and truly blessed life." Athanasius, then, connects creation in the divine image with the gift of primal knowledge, which in turn results in the achievement of authentic humanity (11.1–3).

#### b. The Fall

With the fall, primal knowledge of God gave way to ignorance of God. Athanasius sees a fourfold movement here: (1) despising of grace; (2) rejection of grace; (3) forgetting of the idea of God; and (4) invention of false gods, whether creatures or demons. In consequence, "everything was full of irreligion and lawlessness," and God and his Word were not known (11.4–6).

### 2. Forms of Revelation

#### a. Nature

In spite of man's fall and ignorance, God did not hide himself, nor was he confined to a single mode of self-revelation. Again he had provided for human need, for if men would not learn about God from themselves, "they might be able through the works of creation to avoid ignorance of the Maker." Creation's harmony offered testimony to "its ruler, the Word of the Father, who by his own providence over all things makes known the Father of all" (11.7–12.1).

### b. The Law and the Prophets

God foresaw, too, that natural revelation would not be enough to halt man in his dizzy descent. He thus made the additional provision of human writings, a law and prophets, so that men might learn about divine things from other men. As Athanasius understands it, these were not meant for the Jews alone but for all the world, as "a holy school of the knowledge of God and the conduct of the soul." Unfortunately this remedy also proved unsuccessful against pleasures and demonic illusions (12.2–6). The plunge into irrational thought and conduct continued. Hence God had to consider whether to let ignorance prevail or to offer a new and effective self-revelation (par. 13).

### 3. The Revealing Work of the Word

### a. The Reason

Taking up the themes of paragraph 6, Athanasius explains that God neither could nor would abandon humanity to illusion and irrationality. To do so would be to accept the futility of his creative work. It would even be to toy with man. It were better for man never to have been made rational at all than to be allowed to slip back into a brutish state. It would be most unfitting and at odds with the divine glory for creatures whom God has made for himself to be left imagining that others are their makers, as though God would have made them for others. Not only out of mercy for his creatures, but also in justification of his purpose and in keeping with what is appropriate, God takes steps to renew what was once in his image, so that man might once more be able to know him and thereby to achieve his divinely ordained destiny (13.2–7).

### b. The Presence of the Image

How can the image be renewed? Athanasius argues that men cannot renew it themselves, "since they are but image after an image." Nor can angels do it, for they are not God's image. Only the coming of the Word "in his own person" will suffice. For the Word is the image of the Father. He, then, can "create afresh the man after the image." Might not the Word have come directly, however, and not by way of incarnation? No, for renewal could be effected only if death and corruption were vanquished, and for this purpose a mortal body was needed so that "while death might in it be once for all done away, men made after his image might once more be renewed." The presence of the Father's incarnate image was thus the answer to the problem of man's restoration in the image and the knowledge of God (13.7–9).

### c. The Nature of the Work

Having noted that neither man nor creation but only the Word can restore divine knowledge, Athanasius asks how the Word can do this. He replies that the Word, who knows all things, takes a body and gives instruction "from things of earth, that is, by the works of his body" (par. 14). A wise and considerate pedagogue is seen here. The Word acts like a "kind teacher" who, observing that some pupils cannot profit by higher subjects, "comes down to their level and teaches them ... by simpler courses." Fallen men look for God in creaturely things. In the Word, then, God shows them himself through creaturely things; he "meets the senses of men halfway." Men are thus taught the truth on all sides. If they look at creation they are confronted by God's handiwork. If they look at mankind they find the man who alone is Son of God. Even if they look at demons they see them expelled by the Word, while if they look at the dead they see the risen Word as Lord of death. The incarnate Word casts the works of all others in the shade, so that "in whatever direction the bias of men might be, there he might recall and teach them of his own true Father" (par. 15).

The incarnation plays a crucial role here. As men's senses center on the Word as man, they are brought to know him as God. The Word manifests himself everywhere, above and below, in the depth and the breadth. All things have been filled with the knowledge of God. He does not come into the world and immediately sacrifice himself. He first makes himself visible in his works. He thus accomplishes two things: reconciliation, "putting away death from us and receiving us again"; and revelation, "manifesting and making himself known by his works to be the Word of the Father and the ruler and king of the universe" (par. 16).

### d. The Ongoing Word

The thought of the Word's universal presence reminds the author that his presence in the body does not mean his absence elsewhere or the cessation of his providential working. Far from being contained, he contains all things. Present in creation, in being he is still distinct from it. He includes the whole without being included. At one and the same time he is in the body, though not bound to it, he is in all things, but external to the universe, and he abides in the Father only. Hence the incarnation means no change in the Word nor dulling of his glory. He sanctified the body. On earth the Word neither ceased to quicken and sustain all things nor suffered defilement. "On the contrary, being corruptible, he quickened and cleansed the body also" (par. 17).

### e. The Work of the Body

Athanasius insists, of course, on the reality of the bodily life of the Word. The Word was born, ate, suffered, and died. He had a body "in truth and not in seeming." Yet the body in which these things were done "belonged to none other but the Lord." He took the body in order that by its work he might make himself known to be God's Son. In this regard his mighty works are parallel to the works of creation. They offer visible manifestation of the invisible God (par. 18). Men are thus given another chance. Having "failed to perceive his Godhead shown in creation" they can "recover their sight and through him receive an idea of the knowledge of the Father." Indeed, he made creation itself "break silence," for with the earthquake and the darkness at the cross "all creation was confessing that he that was made manifest and suffered in the body was not man merely, but the Son of God and Saviour of all." Athanasius summed up his thinking on this whole matter in the simple statement: "Thus, then, God the Word showed himself to men by his works" (par. 19).

## D. THE CROSS

### 1. Significance

Before answering Jewish and Greek objections, Athanasius devotes a section (pars. 20–29) to closer discussion of the crucifixion. He begins by explaining that the debt owed by all — the debt of death — had to be paid, but that none of us could meet the payment except by perishing. Christ died, then, to make this payment "in the stead of all, to make men quit and free of their old trespass." Yet death had not only to be died for all. It had also to be abolished. Christ did this in the resurrection, "displaying his own body as incorruptible" (though able to die as a body) "by virtue of the union of the Word with it." At the cross, then, two marvels happened. First, "the death of all was accomplished in the Lord's body." Second, "death and corruption were wholly done away by reason of the Word united with it" (par. 20).

### 2. Results

For Christians this means that death takes on a new aspect. It is no longer a fulfillment of the divine condemnation. As God appoints, death still overtakes the mortal body. But this takes place within a new teleology. We die "that we may be able to gain a better resurrection." We are put into the earth like seeds. We shall rise again, since death has been brought to nought by the grace of the Savior (21.1–2). This changed meaning of death for Christians comes to expression in the elimination of the fear of death. Despising both death and also the present life, even young believers are prepared for martyrdom (par. 28).

### 3. Reasons

Granted that Christ had to die for all, why did he have to endure the ignominy and pain of the cross? Athanasius finds various reasons.

### a. A Death of Strength

Christ could hardly die of old age or sickness. His death had to be one of strength and not of weakness. On the other hand, he could not take his own life. Hence he had to suffer at the hands of others.

### b. The Necessity of Death

Is not any death a sign of weakness? Why then, if Christ is strong, should he die at all? He had come to do so in order both to pay the debt in our stead and also to defeat death in his resurrection. The whole rationale of the incarnation demands death (21.3–7).

### c. A Public Death

There must be no doubt as to the reality of his death and resurrection. Hence a public death such as that of execution is demanded. His power has also to be manifest. Had he devised a glorious death, this would have defeated its purpose. To make his power clear and incontestable he faced death in the worst form his enemies could inflict. So, then, "something surprising and startling has happened; for the death which they thought to inflict as a disgrace was actually a monument against death itself" (pars. 23–24).

### d. Fulfillment and Invitation

Two further reasons are added for the edification of Christians who inquire "not from love of debate but from love of learning." First, prophecy was fulfilled as Christ was made a curse by being hanged on a tree. Second, the outspreading of his arms on the cross constitutes an invitation. He calls all men to him as he is lifted up on the cross (25.1–4). Athanasius works out more fully the theme of prophetic fulfillment and the unity of the Testaments in his answer to objections from the Jews (pars. 33–40).

## 4. The Resurrection

In the light of what has been said already, the significance of the resurrection needs little further exposition. Athanasius himself simply offers a "demonstration." For this he does not adduce the resurrection narratives but points to the great things that Christ was still doing in the conversion of pagans, the arresting of their wickedness, and the exposure and expulsion of idols and idolatry. "This work is not that of one dead, but of one that lives, and especially of God." Indeed, the whole gospel, and not just the resurrection, finds confirmation in the ongoing Christian mission. "As . . . his works bear him witness day by day, it must be evident that the Saviour raised his own body and that he is the true Son of God . . . who took a body for the salvation of all, and taught the world concerning the Father, and brought death to nought, and brought incorruption upon all by the promise of the resurrection" (par. 31).

## E. OBSERVATIONS

### 1. Critical

*a. General*

At the general level, *The Incarnation of the Word* suffers from obvious defects. As the author admits, it is repetitive: "Do not be surprised if we frequently repeat the same words on the same subject" (20.3). At the same time, it tries to cover too much ground in too short a compass. Themes are lavishly introduced which cannot be adequately pondered or explored. The biblical basis also tends to be too slender, both in the sense that not enough scriptural support is offered and also in the sense that too many scriptural teachings are not even taken into account. Too often, Athanasius lapses into arguments which, while not without cogency on their own level, invite counterarguments that blunt the force of the general presentation. To be sure, Athanasius did not intend to write a biblical exposition or a theological treatise. The essay is an apology and an appeal for faith. As he himself says, the author offers "only a rudimentary sketch and outline." He acknowledges that this needs to be supplemented from the scriptures which were "spoken and written by God through men who spoke of God." Nevertheless, the nature of the work does not wholly explain or excuse the general weaknesses in its execution.

*b. Detailed*

(1) The Image of God. A good example of Athanasius' failure to work out some of his themes may be found in his reflections on the divine image. Lack of precision constitutes the main problem here. Is the image an added gift? Does man refuse the gift, lose it, or in some way retain and blur it? Does Christ's work bring restoration of the image, complete renewing, or possibly both? The hasty remarks of Athanasius on the subject leave many unanswered questions.

(2) Revelation in Creation. Athanasius has some interesting thoughts on natural revelation, but again his presentation lacks clarity. He seems to be saying that man was made to know God through the image but when this failed God had a backup system, that of revelation through creation. He also seems to associate this natural revelation with the further backup of revelation through the law and prophets in the Old Testament. Does this mean that natural revelation, like the Old Testament, was given only after the fall? Surely this makes little sense. But does it make much more sense to put the Old Testament revelation on the same plane as that of creation? Athanasius himself realizes well

enough that "the whole inspired scripture cries aloud" concerning the things of Christ. Hence the law and the prophets belong to the work of the Word in revelation and reconciliation (pars. 33–40). Does Athanasius mean, then, that the Old Testament has both a general function and also a more specific prophetic function? The general drift of his argument may be clear; the details demand more careful outworking.

(3) The Humanity of Christ. Athanasius sees and insists that the work of salvation requires an authentic incarnation. Nevertheless, he gives so strong an initiative to the eternal Word that the humanity, or at least the body, seems to be something that the Word merely takes and uses rather than becomes. Obviously, if the Word was made flesh and not flesh the Word, the Word constitutes the unity of the being of Jesus, as orthodox Christology affirms. Yet Athanasius works so totally "from above" that one may see in him at least an emphasis that would give impetus to Apollinarian and Monophysite thinking. He does not clearly espouse these views. Diminution of Christ's humanity would defeat Athanasius' understanding. But has he sufficiently considered the inferences that might be drawn from his less judicious statements?

## 2. Appreciative

### a. General

(1) Force. Even at the general level the weaker features of the work are more than counterbalanced by the strengths. Among these its sheer force must be mentioned first. Here is a writer who knows what he wants to say. He does not beat about the bush. He wastes no time in relation to either style or content. He speaks vigorously, effectively, and for the most part clearly. His sentences can be long; yet they are seldom wordy. He packs an enormous amount of material into small space. The whole essay can be read very quickly. It makes a stronger impact, however, than much writing that is of far greater length or offers a much more impressive show of erudition.

(2) Depth. Contributing to the force of the work is its depth. If Athanasius can be faulted for inadequate exploration, at least he offers us themes worth exploring. From first to last The Incarnation of the Word deals with the deep things of God. Simplicity characterizes its main thesis. Some of the supporting arguments may even be simplistic. Yet the work opens up for us those profound and exciting themes which belong to the heart of the gospel as the work of the reconciling and self-revealing Word. No theologian who knows his business can ignore them or ever feel that he has exhausted them.

### b. Detailed

(1) Christology and Soteriology. Like Irenaeus, Athanasius grasps clearly and firmly the soteriological significance of the incarna-

tion. Christology, then, can never be a purely speculative concern. It belongs intrinsically to the Christian message. The message cannot exist without it. The gospel of salvation through death and resurrection makes sense only if the death and resurrection are those, not of any man, but of the incarnate Word. Understanding Christology may not be easy, but a right Christology is essential. The task has to be undertaken. For the God-man cannot be taken out of the salvation story nor can confession of the incarnation be disjoined from saving faith.

(2) Salvation by the Cross and Resurrection. Athanasius avoids the tempting but facile conclusion that salvation comes by the mere association of the incarnate Word with our humanity. He recognizes, of course, that the incarnation means salvation. God became man that we might become divine. As his body, by union with the Word, enjoys incorruption, so our bodies, by union with his, may attain the same incorruption. Nevertheless, Athanasius does not short-circuit the cross and resurrection. The incarnation means the taking of a mortal body in order that the death of sin should be died therein for us. Incorruption becomes ours through the promise of the resurrection. Incarnation, crucifixion, and resurrection form an indissoluble whole. It has to be this man who dies and rises again. But this man has to die, and this man who dies has also to rise again, as he may in virtue of the fact that he is this man. Athanasius undoubtedly puts the incarnation at the center of the gospel, yet not in the place of or at the expense of the death and rising again, but rather in unbreakable relationship with them.

(3) Salvation and Creation. Like Irenaeus again, Athanasius firmly relates the completion of God's work to its commencement. If salvation means more than restoration, it means restoration, too. God's work of creation, apparently frustrated by the fall, achieves its goal with the coming of the Word. This basic insight has exciting implications for Athanasius. The image of God stands related first to Christ as image, and then to the image of Christ. Justice, grace, the divine purpose, and the divine self-vindication can all be given their due. The work of God has the twofold but related form of reconciliation and self-revelation. Overarching all, however, we see God's providential sovereignty. With supralapsarian wisdom God has provided for every contingency. Man's revolt does not catch God unprepared. Obstacles arise, but nothing can thwart God or stop him in the victorious fulfillment of his plan for us. He cannot be set at odds with himself. He does not have to resort to stopgaps. By the incarnate work of the Word the fall is reversed, justice is satisfied, ignorance is remedied, grace is manifested, and the destiny of those who were created in the image of the Word comes to even more glorious fulfillment as they are re-created in the same image.

## CHAPTER VI
# *Theologians of the Trinity*

The christological struggle initiated by Arius in about 318 arose out of the larger trinitarian problem. If Alexander incurred the suspicion of modalism (that is, of blurring or obliterating the distinctions of Father, Son, and Spirit), Arius did not offer the corrective of a distinction in unity. Instead, he cut the knot by denying true deity to the Son and the Spirit along subordinationist lines. He did this to the accompaniment of specific assertions about the Son which complicated and aggravated the issue. Thus the achievement of a balanced trinitarian formulation was impeded rather than promoted by the controversy, except to the degree that the crisis brought to the discussion of the problem a new urgency.

On the one hand, of course, no one wished to counter Arianism with Sabellianism. This was part of the problem with the "one substance" teaching of Nicea in 325. If it exposed Arianism, it could also have a modalist ring. Hilary points out in his *On the Trinity* that the phrase was suspected because of its implication "that he himself is the Father who is also the Son" (iv. 4). Indeed, Arian strategy demanded that modalism be attributed to the defenders of Nicea (v. 1). But the charge was stoutly resisted, as was Sabellianism itself.

On the other hand, the Arian solution plainly would not do. Denying to Christ not only consubstantiality with the Father but also immutability or true eternity, it reduced him to the rank of a creature and thereby disqualified him from his saving ministry. The gospel, which could at least be preserved in modalism, lost its core and basis in Arianism. If the modal confusion of Father, Son, and Spirit had to be avoided, the deity of the Son had also to be preserved.

How this can be done forms the theme of the book *On the Trinity* which Hilary of Poitiers wrote, probably in 356, when he was expelled to Phrygia for refusing to condemn Athanasius as Constantius the emperor demanded. In this lengthy work Hilary does not attempt a systematic study and exposition of the Trinity. He makes some basic affir-

81

mations concerning the one God who is Father, Son, and Holy Spirit but devotes much of the work to a confutation of Arian positions and arguments. The trinitarian teaching is developed in the context of the christological controversy. This explains, of course, why less attention is paid to the Holy Spirit.

Only when the Arian issue had been settled at Constantinople in 381 did the way open up for a more detached attempt to understand the Trinity independently of a specific polemical situation. Augustine's masterly work *On the Trinity*, composed c. 400–417, may be regarded as an attempt to fill this need. In distinction from Hilary's work, it is not intended to counter a particular christological error. It can deal more freely with the Spirit as well as the Son, the more so since the question of the Spirit had been more acutely raised in the latter part of the fourth century. The problems relating to the Trinity can be more broadly discussed. Resources can be sought which might help towards a better comprehension, or at least a beginning of comprehension, of the mystery of the divine being. In a sense, then, the theology of the Trinity goes through two further stages with these two theologians and their works. The christological controversy both clarifies the basic requirements and also sets in motion a more adequate development. A general attempt can then be made at more refined exposition and understanding.

## A. HILARY

### 1. Epistemology

*a. The Limits*

Hilary does not approach his task with any zeal for using the tools of philosophy in theological investigation. Instead he has a keen sense of the difficulties of the work which the Arian style of thinking has forced upon him. Earlier in life he had devoted much time to philosophical discussions of deity, but he had soon found that God is "far beyond the power of comprehension" (i.7). The need to answer Arianism means that he has to "violate the divine command," which orders him simply to preach the gospel. He is still aware, however, that three decisive difficulties encounter us as we try to "speak about such lofty and mysterious subjects" (ii.5).

(1) We cannot understand what we wish to say. "God is invisible, ineffable, infinite. The mind grows weary in trying to follow him; the understanding is limited in comprehending him" (ii.6).

(2) "All language is powerless to express what is to be said." God surpasses our powers of expression as well as comprehension. "Words do not portray the subject as it is" (ii.7).

(3) Analogies, while necessary, are inadequate. We have to "look for certain resemblances in inferior things," but in reality there is "no

comparison between earthly things and God." An analogy is "more useful to man than appropriate to God." It "hints at the meaning rather than explaining it fully" (i.19). Taken strictly, it will mislead instead of helping.

### b. The Basis

(1) Confession. Lacking any human means of understanding God, Hilary begins with the confession of Exodus 3:14: "I am who I am." The simple fact of revelation that "God is" forms the starting point both for a definition of God and also for all else that we may then know about him as Creator and Savior. By revelation the mind advances "beyond the knowledge of natural reason" to a faith which "rejects the captious and useless questions of philosophy" and grasps the "deeds of God" in Christ's incarnation, whereby he dies "both to obliterate our condemnation and also to secure for us eternal life" (i.13).

(2) Scripture. As Hilary derives the fundamental confession from scripture, so he turns to scripture for further instruction. In various times and places, scripture comes from one and the same "Prophetic Spirit" (v.38). To use it correctly, however, the reader must "look for the meaning of the words in the words themselves rather than reading his own meaning into them." In this way he will "take away more than he brought," not insisting that "the words signify what he presupposes before reading them" (i.18). Error arises when the heavenly words are understood "in an arbitrary way and not according to the evident meaning of the truth itself." "Heresy does not come from scripture but from the understanding of it; the fault is in the mind, not in the words" (ii.3).

(3) The Spirit. To find the meaning in the words themselves requires divine aid. In the prayer in i.38, therefore, Hilary asks God to "summon us to share in the prophetic and apostolic Spirit so that we may understand these words in no other sense than that in which they spoke them." When faith and a zeal for truth inspire us to read, "new faculties" are needed for the enlightenment of the conscience "by the gift that comes from heaven." In this way, when we go on to write about the things of God, we shall "concede to God the knowledge about himself and submit to his words with reverent awe" (i.18). Consulting holy scripture, we learn about God from God.

## 2. The Doctrine

### a. Presentation

(1) Baptismal Formula. For his basic statement about the Trinity Hilary uses the baptismal formula from Matthew 28:19: "Baptizing in the name of the Father and of the Son and of the Holy Spirit." He equates the Father with the Origin. "There is one source of all. God the Father is one from whom are all things." The Son is the Only-Begotten.

As such he is "one through whom are all things." Hilary describes the Holy Spirit as "the Gift." He, too, is one — "the Gift in all things." Hilary sums it up as follows: "There is one Power from whom are all things, one Offspring through whom are all things, and one Gift of perfect hope." Defining the relations within the Trinity, he offers the striking statement: "infinity in the Eternal, the form in the Image, and the use in the Gift" (ii.1).

(2) The Father. As the source of all things, the Father has his being in himself. "He possesses what he is from himself and in himself." He is infinite, for "he himself is not in anything and all things are in him." "He is unborn, eternal, and always possesses in himself what he is" (ii.6).

(3) The Son. The sonship of the eternal Son does not mean separation or division, "for he who has begotten is immutable." There is no adoption; he is the true Son of God (John 14:9). The fullness of the Father, not just a part of him, is in the Son. "He did not come into being as others do by a command. . . . he is from one and has life in himself" (John 5:26). He is "the perfect one from the perfect one." "He who has all has given all. That he has does not mean that he does not give; that he gives does not mean that he does not have" (ii.8). Yet the giving implies no division or dissection. "The nature of the Godhead does not differ in the one and the other, because both are one." "Nor are there two gods but one from one." "The life of the living one is in the living one" (ii.11). In an attempt at fuller understanding Hilary ironically invokes, not a learned philosopher, but "a poor fisherman . . . unknown, unlearned, a line in his hands." An exposition of John 1:1–4 follows (ii.13–21).

(4) The Spirit. The basic fact relating to the Spirit is that he has been received. "He is because he is given." The apostolic testimony supports this. The Spirit has to be joined with the Father and the Son in the confession. Hence he cannot be separated from them, for "the whole is incomplete if something is missing from it" (ii.29). To be sure, the Father is Spirit and the Son is Spirit and both are holy (ii.30); yet a distinction arises, for God the Spirit is to be worshiped in the Spirit, and if we read of the Lord who is Spirit we read also of the Spirit of the Lord (ii.31). The Holy Spirit inspires the patriarchs and prophets, fills John from his mother's womb, is given to believers "that they might understand the truth that had been bestowed upon them," and adds varied gifts to the one necessary Gift (ii.32–35). The Spirit receives from the Son and is sent by the Son, although he proceeds from the Father (viii.20). Hilary's primary concern here is to safeguard the deity of the Son. He thus equates receiving from the Son with receiving from the Father but does not commit himself to procession from the Son. The most that he will say is that the Spirit is from the Father through the Only-Begotten (xii.57). The deity of the Spirit remains unchallenged. As the final prayer puts it, "I know that thy Holy Spirit is from thee."

"There are no boundaries for the Spirit. . . . Shall I place his nature among those of creatures, and shall I . . . set limits for the beginning of his origin?" (xii.56).

### b. Arian Arguments

(1) Texts. Against the equality of Father, Son, and Spirit, the Arians brought many texts which it would be tedious to discuss in detail. In the New Testament the important passages are Mark 10:18, John 17:3; 5:19; 14:28, and Mark 13:32. These call God alone good, speak of the knowledge of the only true God, say that the Son can do nothing of himself, describe the Father as greater than the Son, and refer to the Son's ignorance regarding the last day. In the Old Testament, Proverbs 8:22 provided the Arians with their strongest support. Here Wisdom, generally equated with the Word, says of itself that "the Lord created me as the beginning of his ways."

(2) Logical Inference. While the Arians adduced texts, their strength lay in what they deduced from these rather than in direct exegesis. Texts served as a starting point for philosophical reflection. Hence the true challenge came, not from scripture, but from the adoption of a totally different source and style of theology, as Tertullian had observed in relation to the Gnostics. For this reason the Arian debate moves quickly from the field of biblical exposition to that of philosophical discussion.

(3) The Question of Generation. This comes out very clearly in the basic question: "What is meant when Christ is called the Only-Begotten of the Father?" Arius concludes from the use of the term "generation" that even if the Son is begotten before time, his begetting marks a logical break. He who begets is prior to him who is begotten. The father exists before generation; the son does not. The son, then, is given existence out of non-existence, whereas the most that can be said of the father is that from not being a father he becomes a father, that is, being a father is not intrinsic to the father's existence. In contrast, the son does not exist at all until he exists as a son. Hence it must be said that the son has a beginning of existence. Two conclusions may thus be drawn. First, the Son of God is not God as the Father is God. Second, the Son is in his own way created (vi.5; xii.16).

### c. Replies

(1) Texts. Hilary devotes much of *On the Trinity* to a consideration of the Arian texts. He deals with the New Testament group in Book ix and faces the Old Testament text — "the most powerful wave of their storm . . . the terrible billow of their swirling tempest" — in Book xii. His main endeavor is to set the sayings in both their immediate and their comprehensive biblical contexts so that Arian inferences are excluded. At the same time, Hilary has his own texts and passages

which he expounds at length in his work. These build up the general context in which the Arian verses are to be understood if the words are to be interpreted from the words themselves.

(2) Logical Inference. Hilary meets this in two ways. On the one hand he opposes the philosophical method in principle. If we follow it, "we teach what we do not understand." How can "we who are men improve the words of God?" Faith does not come "by the knowledge of the flesh but the gift of the Spirit" (x.64–65). On the other hand Hilary sees a need to defeat the logicians at their own game. He thus engages in patient analysis of their deductions and looks for flaws in their reasoning, while at the same time making deductions of his own from what he views as the plain meaning of the biblical and apostolic teaching.

(3) The Question of Generation. Hilary agrees with the Arians that in understanding the relation between God and Christ we must begin with the biblical terms "Father" and "Son." At the very outset, however, he points out that we cannot transfer directly to God what fatherhood and sonship mean in human experience. We have to learn from God himself what generation is in God. The distinctive nature of divine begetting thus constitutes both his central rebuttal of Arianism and also the key to his exposition of the Trinity.

Thus it might be argued from the analogy of human birth that if the Son is truly God, then the God who previously was is born anew as the Son. Hilary, however, points out that while the God who existed was not born, "God was born from the God who existed and preserves in himself the nature of his begetter in the birth of the nature" (vi.13). This can be understood only if it is realized that "God is not born from God after the manner of a human birth. . . . For this birth is . . . one from one. . . . It is the birth of a living nature from a living nature. It is God proceeding from God. . . . He does not begin to be out of nothing, but comes forth from him who remains, and to have come forth signifies birth and not beginning" (vi.35). What may be learned from human birth is that man is born of man. Similarly, God — one, living, and eternal — is born of God. "In God everything that lives is. God is life, and nothing can come from life except what is alive. . . . Thus . . . he possesses the birth and does not undergo any change, and he bestows an increase but does not lose his nature, and he follows the birth, which he has given by the likeness of an indistinguishable nature, and the birth, which is the living one from the living one, does not abandon its nature when it is born" (vii.28).

A fundamental point for Hilary is that whereas human nature and parenthood are not synonymous, God does not receive his fatherhood from anywhere else. He has the name of the Father because he is by nature Father (cf. i.6). Eternally God, he is eternally Father. Hilary sums it up in xii.23. "It is one thing to be born from him who has not been" (that is, a human parent), "and it is another to be born from him who always is." It is "proper for the Father to be always the Father" and so it is also "proper for the Son to be always the Son." This brings Hilary back to the confession with which he began: "God always is" (xii.24–25).

### 3. Hilary's Contribution

#### a. Defects

*On the Trinity* falls short in various ways. While written with rhetorical skill, it does not avoid repetitiveness, verbosity, and obscurity (although the corrupt state of the text may be largely responsible for the obscurity). If some points are handled with unnecessary fullness, others are treated too cursorily. Hilary might also have done better not to have ventured quite so far out of port. In his anxiety to do justice to Christ's deity, he has problems with the humanity (see x.27–35). The more casual discussion of the Holy Spirit weakens his total presentation. Fixation on the question of generation cuts short more general consideration of the relations of the one God and his modes of being as Father, Son, and Holy Spirit. In the setting of the time, Hilary may be excused for his polemical orientation. It must also be remembered that he was doing pioneering work in the West. He tells us elsewhere that he never heard the phrase "of one substance" until 355, and he had to coin even a term like incarnation. Nevertheless, the work promises more than it does in fact deliver.

#### b. Qualities

(1) Revelation. The main strength of *On the Trinity* lies not so much in its content as in the theological perception which its author displays. For he sees very clearly that knowledge of God can come only from God himself. "We should use the teachings of God to acquire the knowledge of God." "We must believe God when he speaks about himself." "We can have no other concept of him than that which he has revealed about himself" (iv.14). "We must learn from God what we are to think about God because he is the only source of information about himself" (v.21). Only by God's self-revelation can there be any objective knowledge of God as distinct from subjective ideas about him.

(2) Scripture. Hilary realizes that what God tells us about himself may be found only in scripture. Hence sound theology derives from scripture, not philosophy. Readers, however, can infuse their own concepts into scripture, so texts alone will not suffice. "All the attendant circumstances" must also be studied. "The understanding of the words is to be gathered from the reasons why they were spoken, because the words are subordinated to the event, not the event to the words" (iv.14). Again, "the meaning of words is to be learned either from those that precede or from those that follow" (ix.2). Unlike Tertullian, Hilary sees no need to jump from scripture to the rule of faith. He pleads instead for an

exposition of scripture in terms of itself and not in terms of philosophical presuppositions.

(3) Comparisons. Perhaps Hilary's most decisive insight is that while creaturely comparisons are necessary, one cannot learn about the Creator directly from the creature. Comparisons help, but only as they offer "partial illustration." No comparison "does adequate justice to the nature of God, since it is fitting and right to believe God when he testifies concerning himself" (vii.30). Hilary, then, avoids the trap in the so-called vestiges of the Trinity. He always remembers that what is said about God is indeed said about *God*. If generation be mentioned, it is divine generation. We cannot finally understand it; yet neither can we really understand our own generation (ii.9). Philosophy simply leads us astray when it subjects divine truth to creaturely logic. It may be very clear but it misses the point that while God expresses his revelation in human terms, the knowledge of God must come from God and must relate to God if it is in fact to be knowledge of God. Hilary grasps this point. Hence his work, while it is in no sense a final word, can at least be described as a valuable and authentic word.

### B. AUGUSTINE

Augustine wrote his work *On the Trinity* in the first two decades of the fifth century. By this time two steps had been taken. First, the trinitarian debates had died down, and the being of Christ as God and man had become a new focus of discussion. Hence Augustine could write with no particular polemical reference. Second, the main principles of the doctrine of the Trinity had also been worked out, more perhaps by the Cappadocians than by Hilary. Like Hilary, Basil and the Gregories believed that Father, Son, and Holy Spirit are equally God, the Godhead being one in substance and operation. Yet they found in Father, Son, and Holy Spirit not three names or three modes in a modalist sense, but three modes of being in the one God for which the terms "hypostases," "subsistences," or "persons" might be used. The problem of understanding what the formula of one substance and three subsistences implies forms the theme of Augustine's study.

### 1. The Trinity: Books I-VII

#### a. Divine Unity and Equality

Augustine begins by stating the truth about God as he has received it. He points out that his aim is not to prove this truth, but to understand it. The Father, Son, and Spirit are distinct, and yet they are a unity in the equality of the one substance. Any inferiority of the Son refers to his human nature or to the trinitarian order whereby he has received his equal being from the Father (bk. i). God may not be seen, but visible manifestations of the Son and Spirit occur in their historical missions (bks. ii–iii). The Son's mission culminates in the incarnation, the purpose of which is (1) to remedy pride, (2) to win restoration, and (3) to reunite. The Spirit's mission comes to a head at Pentecost (bk. iv).

### b. Metaphysical Formulation

God, being simple, cannot be differentiated from his attributes. How, then, can he be both begotten and unbegotten? These attributes denote relations, not substances (bk. v). Substantive terms, such as "wisdom," apply to the Godhead and hence to each person, although they may be appropriated specifically to one. The words used to denote distinction of person are, of course, inadequate, being substantive, not relational. Since we obviously cannot call the persons relations, persons will have to do. We have to see, however, that the terms bear a special sense in relation to God (bks. vi–vii).

## 2. Understanding What Is Believed: Book VIII

### a. Approach

In his effort to understand the Trinity, Augustine says that he will follow "a more inward method of approach" (viii.1). As will appear later, this rests on the creation of man in the image of God.

### b. Quantitative Thinking

A warning against thinking quantitatively is issued. The soul may be more or less good. God is simply the good. The good makes degrees of goodness possible (viii.5).

### c. Love and Faith

To cleave to the good we must love the good (that is, God). But love demands knowledge, and knowledge, faith. Love arises as response to the idea of goodness which the records convey as we believe them. To know the Trinity one must first "know the nature of love." Love is the willing of righteousness for self and others which finally rests on love of love, that is, love of God (viii.10).

### d. Love and the Trinity

Does the vision of love offer us a vision of the Trinity? In love we have "the lover, that which is loved, and love." Yet the analogy is far from perfect. A particular weakness for Augustine is that this relation obtains at the physical level, too. He thus concludes: "we have found, not the thing itself, but where it is to be sought" (vii.14).

### 3. Psychological Trinities: Books IX–XIII

#### a. Mind, Knowledge, and Love

A more weighty problem about love is that in one man, lover and loved are the same (ix.2). Love, however, presupposes self-knowledge. There arises, then, a trinity of mind, self-knowledge, and self-love (ix.5f.). These are one substance in a mutual coinherence in which "all are in all" (ix.7–8). Each is equal to the others. "Mind is no greater than its offspring, when its self-knowledge is equal to its being, nor than its love, when its self-love is equal to its knowledge and to its being" (ix.18).

#### b. Memory, Will, and Understanding

Augustine, however, is not yet satisfied. He probes more deeply into self-knowledge. Rejecting materialistic explanations of this (x.7–10), he turns to such self-evident realities as mind and will. "No one can possibly doubt that he lives and remembers, understands, wills, ..." (x.14, 15–18). Among these realities he can see a basic triad of memory, understanding, and will. Although these are "one essence," they nevertheless are "three inasmuch as they are related to one another," "not merely each to each but each to all ... the whole of each is equal to the whole of each, and ... to the whole of all together" (x.18).

#### c. Sensory Trinities

Thus far Augustine has achieved a formal trinity. But two problems remain. First, this trinity may apply to evil as well as to good. Second, the role of faith and its data is obscure. Augustine sees the two problems as one and moves toward a solution of both by investigating the relation of the mind to the material world, whether in the form of perception or of imagination.

Perception, too, offers a trinity, that of object, sense-perceptions, and attention, while imagination offers yet another, that of memory, inward vision, and the will which directs attention. Here, however, we have trinities of the outward man. Belonging to the material world, they offer no true image. All the same, there is a likeness, and if sense-knowledge belongs to the outward man, the inward man is involved, too (bk. xi).

#### d. Knowledge and Wisdom

Man shares sense-perception with the animals. He alone, however, enjoys rationality. This has both a temporal and an eternal function. Augustine finds the significance of the creation of man as male and female here. Since male and female are not a trinity, he does not see the image itself in the creation of man as male and female, and he dismisses the suggestion of father, mother, and child, since no child is mentioned in Genesis 1:27. Yet male and female are important in this connection, for they are thought to represent the eternal and temporal functions of rationality. Each is image, but the true image lies in the male (1 Cor 11:7). With the fall the temporal function broke free from the eternal, but there can still be movement from temporal things (knowledge) to eternal life (wisdom) (bk. xii).

With this added insight, Augustine picks up his earlier discussion. The image must be sought first in knowledge. Faith enters in here. It relates to the historical facts of salvation. Its trinity is that of memory, understanding, and will. It leaves us short of the divine Trinity, but it is a way we have to go. By giving us knowledge of Christ, it leads us to wisdom, for in him are all the treasures of wisdom. The movement, then, is through knowledge, the lower and temporal function of rationality, to wisdom, its higher and eternal function.

### 4. The Image in the Contemplation of God: Book XIV

*a. Definition of Wisdom*
Augustine equates wisdom with God himself (xiv.1–2). In man it is the knowledge of divine things in eternal contemplation.

*b. Definition of the Image*
The definition of wisdom yields a definition of the image in man. It is "the power to use reason and intellect for the understanding and beholding of God" (xiv.5). In it may be seen a unique trinity of mind in its integral self-remembering, self-understanding, and self-loving (xiv.11ff.). The uniqueness consists in its power "to remember, understand, and love its Maker" (xiv.15). By way of the knowledge achieved through sensory revelation the formal trinity thus attains to its true content.

*c. Obscuring and Restoring of the Image*
We have to go the way of sense-perception because in the fall the eternal function suffered through distraction to temporal things. Thus the image, although it remained, came to be "obscured and defaced." Through the grace of God, however, the mind has been reoriented. There is thus begun a renewing of the image (xiv.22–23) which will be completed only when we finally see God (xiv.23–25).

### 5. Image and Original: Book XV

*a. Limits*
Can one rise from the image to the original? Even if not, Augustine suggests, "the enquirer has found something if he succeeds in finding how far what he sought passes comprehension" (xv.2–3). Yet Augustine presses on. God's attributes, which belong to the one God and

also to each person of the Trinity (xv.7), may finally be reduced to wisdom. God is his own wisdom. But how is wisdom Trinity (xv.9)? Human analogies fail here. Augustine has to agree with Hilary that "no man can comprehend the wisdom by which God knows all things" (xv.13). As Paul puts it, we see "through a mirror, in an enigma" (1 Cor 13:12) (xv.14). Yet we do see.

### b. The Word

The concept of God's Word offers a clue. Augustine is reminded of the relationship between unspoken speech (thought) and the spoken word. As our word is made utterance, the divine Word is made flesh (xv.20). But whereas our word rests on scanty knowledge, God's knowledge is from himself, and the divine Word corresponds to it perfectly (xv.23). In contrast to the imperfection of our knowledge and utterance and their distinction from our being, the Father's begetting is his speaking of himself, and his being and knowledge are identical (xv.24).

### c. The Spirit

Again using the thought of love, Augustine now suggests that the Spirit is "the mutual love whereby the Father and the Son love one another" (xv.27). To be sure, the Father is love, the Son is love, the whole Trinity is love. Only Source, Word, and Gift are exclusive terms (xv.28–29). Nevertheless, if the love of Father to Son and Son to Father "displays . . . the communion of both, it is most fitting that the Spirit who is common to both should have the special name of love" (xv.37). One must not conclude, however, that Christ as the Son of God's love is the Son of the Spirit. He is Son of God's substance, just as, being Son by God's will, he is Son of God's nature (xv.37–38).

### d. Analogy of Memory, Understanding, and Will

Augustine now works in another thread. He sees his earlier comparison to have value to the extent that memory, understanding, and will are coinherent and inseparable. The element of unlikeness, of course, is that the three belong to "me": "What they do is done for me . . . or by me through their means." In contrast, "in the uncompounded simplicity of the supreme being which is God, though there is one God, there are yet three persons" (xv.42–43). Hence, as faith sees, the mind offers only an image. Even when we are finally like God a distinction will always remain: "Even when we see face to face, the being that owes its constancy to grace will not attain equality to the being which is essentially changeless" (xv.43–44).

### e. Begetting and Proceeding

Augustine has to admit that he cannot state the difference between the begetting of the Son and the procession of the Spirit. Indeed, even of the attempt to understand it he says: "I am aware of more endeavour than success." Both, however, are outside time, so that the deity of neither the Son nor the Spirit can be impugned (xv.47).

## 6. Conclusion

Wisely, Augustine does not ask that unbelievers should first understand the Trinity and then believe. They should begin by "believing what the holy books contain concerning the supreme Trinity that is God." Then "let them go on by prayer and inquiry and right living to the pursuit of understanding" (xv.49). As for himself, Augustine confesses: "I dare not claim to have said anything worthy of the ineffable greatness of the supreme Trinity" (xv.50). He thus follows Hilary by winding up his treatise with adoration and petition: "It were better to bring this book at last to an end, not with argument, but with prayer" (xv.50–51).

## 7. Remarks

### a. Qualities

To speak of evaluating a work such as Augustine's *On the Trinity* would be presumptuous. By any standards it must rank as one of the outstanding achievements of Christian theology. It has all the perspicacity and is written with all the grace and force for which Augustine is justly renowned. Choosing the path of psychological analysis, the author follows a difficult but well-conceived and not unrewarding course. Like a juggler, he has many balls in the air at the same time. Yet he handles them all with dexterity, manages to work them into a harmonious pattern, and brings them all down safely in a striking climax.

For all the intellectual brilliance of the work, Augustine never loses sight of two basic elements. First, he is not working up from man to God in the sense that a study of man will lead us by material or logical necessity to the Trinity. He starts with belief in the Trinity on the basis of divine self-revelation. He aims to understand the self-revealed God by a study of the mental structure of man. He realizes that even this is possible only by reason of the revealed creation of man in the image of the divine original.

Again, Augustine preserves the healthy sense of limitation which Hilary had so heavily underscored. Image and original differ. What can be said of man does not correspond exactly to what must be said of God. Human words and concepts take us so far, yet they always fall short when their object is the Triune God. The Creator cannot be made in the image of the creature even though the creature be made in the image of the Creator. Rightly, then, Augustine concludes with worship rather than explanation. Words about God must finally be addressed to God.

The overpowering reality of the Trinity replaces the attempt to explain and express it.

### b. Problems

For all its dazzling qualities, can *On the Trinity* be called a genuine success? At the mundane level it surely makes excessive demands on the ordinary reader. The juggler's balls are kept in the air, but they are hard to follow. Their interrelations as Augustine tosses them up may be clear in advance to the author; they are by no means evident to those who try to follow his juggling. While the apparently pointless digressions and abrupt transitions bear witness to the extraordinary fertility of Augustine's mind, they tend to obscure the main argument and inevitably engender an element of bewilderment and confusion.

At the material level, Augustine's case stands or falls with his equation of the divine image with the mind and its faculties. Unfortunately he offers little support for this identification. Since scripture itself gives no precise definition, the field is open. Augustine's understanding might thus be said to have as good a claim as any other. Has he a right, however, to make this presupposition the virtual key to his whole understanding of the Trinity?

The circular nature of the argument may be accepted. As noted, Augustine does not aim to arrive at the Trinity by way of psychological analysis. If he did, he would obviously be finding what he has put there. Beginning with faith in the Trinity, he looks about for structures which will help him to understand it. Since he knows what he is looking for, he of course finds it. Surely this is valid. One is left with the uneasy feeling, however, that there is still a good deal of manipulation in the whole procedure. Does what is found in the mind really have to be a trinity? If Augustine had been looking for one in two or one in four, could he not just as easily have adjusted his analysis to produce what was needed? Justin's discovery of the cross in the most unlikely places offers an obvious parallel.

The serious infiltration of philosophy into Augustine's discussion commends it in some circles, but does it not harm it as a piece of authentic theology? The handling of scripture provides us with a test. Certainly the whole treatise rests finally on the biblical witness. Again, many verses of scripture are quoted and sometimes they play an integral part in the discussion, as in the section on the renewal of the image. For long stretches, however, they occur infrequently or have only allegorical significance. If Augustine derives his faith from scripture, he does not seek his understanding of it in terms of biblical exegesis or an outworking of the rationality of biblical teaching. By taking the course he does, he gives help, perhaps, to the relatively few who share his philosophical background, but his extraneous and only thinly Christianized discussions do little for those who do not share or understand the background.

Seldom, perhaps, has so striking a work set so excellent a goal and then so dismally failed to achieve it.

### c. Insights

Nevertheless, *On the Trinity* contains insights which the author does not fully exploit but which may be even more theologically fruitful than his principal argument. Three may be mentioned briefly in the present context.

(1) Augustine makes an important point when he says that the distinction of persons in the Trinity is relational, not substantive. He does not, however, follow this up by a proper consideration of the possibility that the divine image should also be seen relationally, as seems to be hinted at in Genesis 1:27. His psychological concentration hampers him in this regard. Nevertheless, we are given a pointer here which modern theologians in particular have found it worthwhile to follow.

(2) Augustine firmly grasps the truth that we know God as Trinity only because he is and reveals himself to be so. Here his use of philosophy falls finally within an authentic theology. His analysis and analogies may carry little weight, and one might ask whether he has any ultimate confidence in them himself. He realizes that it is not the truth of God which depends on them but only our understanding of that truth. If they have merit, it derives from God's creation of man in his image. If they have not, we have failed to achieve the understanding sought, but the truth itself, and our faith in it, are not overthrown.

(3) Finally, Augustine leaves us with two analogies which many have found more helpful than he himself suspected. First, the analogy of speaking the Word in Book xv can be expanded, as in Barth's *Church Dogmatics* 1, to cover the three aspects of speaker, what is spoken, and speaking and also to apply to the three coinherent forms of the Word as revealed, written, and proclaimed. Hence the true analogy of the self-revealing God will be found in the structure of the self-revelation. Second, the analogy of love in Book viii, which Augustine shies away from because it either has physical associations or breaks down as self-love, sheds light both on the being of God as Trinity (that is, as lover, loved, and love), and also on the rationality of this being, since the Triune God can obviously be God who is love without either being imprisoned in self-centered love or needing an external object of love Even if Augustine himself does not step boldly through this door, at least he opens it for others to enter.

# CHAPTER VII

# *Sermons and Letters*

## A. WORD AND SACRAMENT IN THE WRITINGS OF JOHN CHRYSOSTOM

Not all the writings of the period after Nicea (325) consisted of weighty theological treatises. Throughout the successive trinitarian and christological crises, the church went about its ordinary business. Conversions and the catechetical instruction of converts continued. Monasticism began to flourish. Problems of church life and order were discussed and settled. The ministry engaged in its weekly round of pastoral care.

Among the activities which gave rise to literary production, preaching figures prominently. Indeed, the late fourth century produced one of the most eminent preachers of Christian history in John Chrysostom of Antioch. Ordained at Antioch after a period of strenuous asceticism, Chrysostom learned from the Antioch school of exegesis the art of predominantly historical exposition. His sermons, especially when they connect to form an expository series, have a solid biblical basis. At the same time, Chrysostom's extraordinary rhetorical gifts add charm, vitality, and force to what might otherwise be useful, but pedestrian, homilies.

Chrysostom's success as a presbyter at Antioch led to his ill-advised appointment as bishop of Constantinople (397). Here the very qualities which led him to the position — his simplicity and dedication as a pastor and his boldness and effectiveness as a speaker — brought about his undoing. Provoking the hostility of the empress Eudoxia, he was finally ousted and shamefully harried to death in itinerant exile (404). His voice survives, however, in the sermons which have come down to us in written form. We shall listen to that voice in some themes from the *Homilies on John*, which he preached at Antioch in 390.

### 1. New Sonship in Homily 10 on John 1:11–13

### a. God's Part in Salvation

Chrysostom states plainly that if we are to be sons of God there has to be a work of God. God draws us. Christ comes, not in the sense of being present where before he was absent, but in special manifestation. At baptism we are made golden instead of earthly, since then the Spirit "falls like fire on our souls." Baptism results in our experiencing a "mystical birth and purification."

### b. Man's Part in Salvation

Chrysostom sees no difficulty in stressing the human side. God draws "those who are willing to be drawn." Faith as well as the grace of the Spirit moulds us to the form of God. Grace does not come at random; it comes to those who want it and seek it. In this sense it is in our own power to become sons. If God's part is to give grace, man's is to receive faith. If baptism purifies us, to remain pure depends on our own will and effort. Hence Chrysostom issues a warning: "Let us not think that faith is enough for our salvation." We must also "give evidence of purity of life," which he construes as our wedding garment.

## 2. Old and New Grace in Homily 14 on John 1:16–17

### a. Fullness and Grace for Grace

Chrysostom quickly shows what it means to receive Christ's fullness. Christ is "the fountain and root of all virtues." We thus draw on him who pours forth the wealth of his blessings, while "after the outpouring still remaining full." "Grace for grace" he then interprets as "the new for the old." Just as there is an old justice and a new, an old faith and a new, and an old adoption, glory, law, worship, covenant, holiness, baptism, sacrifice, temple, and circumcision as well as a new, so also "there was grace before and there is grace now."

### b. The Relation of Old and New

Chrysostom thinks of the relationship between the old and the new in terms of type and reality. Hence "they retain the same name but not the same meaning." They are not the same, and yet we must not think "that they are altogether different either." For types, if less than the truth, are not divorced from the truth. Thus adoption in the Old Testament does not set aside the spirit of bondage, but it still points to adoption in the New Testament, which involves the reality of sonship "by the cleansing of regeneration and the renewing of the Holy Spirit."

### c. Similarities of Grace

As regards grace, certain things are shared. Thus the law is grace. So, too, were creation and the gift of the inner tribunal of conscience. "God always takes the initiative in the giving of benefits."

Pardon for the transgression of the law must also be described as grace, as the Psalmist testifies when speaking of God's "deeds of mercy and judgment."

### d. Differences of Grace

Three main differences are found in new grace. (1) It brings "much more splendid gifts" of justice, holiness, and adoption. (2) It makes us "dear to God, no longer merely as servants, but as sons and friends." (3) Whereas the law "was given," grace and truth "came," that is, the giver himself came as his gift. Pardon is declared through others in the Old Testament; it is pronounced directly by Jesus Christ in the New Testament.

### e. Old Testament Types

To clarify and conclude his exposition Chrysostom offers three examples of Old Testament typology, all of which point to Christ as their reality and fulfillment. (1) Christ is the truth behind the Passover lamb. The difference lies in the fact that "he himself becomes the offering, presenting himself to the Father as a sacrifice and oblation." (2) Christ is the truth typified by Moses when he prayed with arms propped up by Aaron and Hur. The difference lies in the fact that "Christ . . . himself held his hands outstretched on the cross by his own power." (3) Christ is the truth signified by the curse of those who "do not abide in the words of the law." The difference lies in the fact that Christ lifts the burden of the law and redeems us from its curse by becoming a curse for us.

## 3. The New Man in Homily 25 on John 3:5

### a. The New Birth and Faith

Chrysostom derives from the misunderstanding of Nicodemus the point that "nothing is worse than to relegate spiritual things to human reasoning." The new birth itself "opens for us the vaults above." "The weakness of human reasoning" has to be put aside here in order to "come to the sublimity of faith." Jesus has come "to bring a new method of procreation." "If someone asks: How of water? I in turn ask: How of earth?" Even our first creation "I cannot elucidate by reason but accept only by faith." How much more faith is needed in "things that are so mystical and spiritual."

### b. The First Man and the New Man

Important differences are seen between the first man and the new man. (1) At the first creation man came after other creatures, "but now quite the reverse; the new man is created before the new creation." (2) The first man "was made in the image of God," but the new man has been made "one with God himself." (3) The first man was given "life in paradise; now he has opened up heaven to us." (4) At first, man was "formed on the sixth day, . . . but now on the first day." In "this wonderful and strange bringing-forth," it is hardly possible that we can give any proof or explanation, since "Father, Son, and Holy Spirit do all." We walk, then, by faith, not sight.

### c. The Function of Water

Though we cannot understand how birth can take place "of water," the essential function of water comes out plainly in baptism as the fulfillment of the covenant. "Burial and death, and resurrection and life, all take place together." We are immersed and emerge, the old man is buried and the new man rises again. As the former is easy for us, "so it is easy for God to bury the old man and raise up the new." We do our part three times to indicate "that the power of the Father and the Son and the Holy Spirit does it all."

## 4. Holy Scripture in Homily 41 on John 5:39–40

### a. Reading Scripture

The *Homilies on John* often refer to the proper reading of scripture. In Homily 11 Chrysostom tells his hearers to read for themselves. They should take the selection and "read it frequently as they sit at home . . . and often ponder carefully the thoughts stored up in it." This must be a priority with which neither business nor pleasure should interfere. Lack of books is no excuse. The rich can easily buy them, the poor always have "the tools of the trade at which they work," and the very poor can come to "the reading continually carried on here."

### b. Reading and Christ

Chrysostom recognizes, however, that superficial reading does not suffice in relation to spiritual things. If the scriptures bear witness to Christ, then there is need for careful search and deep thought. "The meaning is not expressed superficially" or set forth in the literal sense, but "lies buried at a great depth." Chrysostom does not advocate allegorical exegesis here. He has in view apprehension of the spiritual realities conveyed by the words and a grasp of the total meaning of scripture in its christological reference. Hence he goes on to explain that Christ was foreshadowed in earlier times according to the needs of the period. Faith, as well as the reading of scripture, is required, then, if there is to be "significant and real profit," that is, really having eternal life and not just thinking we have it.

### c. Reading and the Spirit

Faith enables us to hear the voice of the Spirit above and beyond the voice of the human author. Chrysostom alludes to this already in

Homily 1. He exhorts the congregation: "Let us no longer listen as to the
fisherman ... but as to the One who knows the deep things of God, I
mean the Holy Spirit, as he strokes this lyre." Only as the Spirit speaks
are we granted the power to "perceive heavenly things." The Spirit does
not speak, of course, apart from the human author. John "has, speaking
within him, the Paraclete who is present everywhere." Nor is this just
an *ad hoc* arrangement. If hearers or readers fail to hear the Spirit
speak, it is because of their own inadequacy, not because the Spirit
withholds himself from the fisherman's words, which "are God-
inspired." The Spirit speaks through words that he himself has given. To
receive their truth, therefore, we must hear them as his words.

### 5. Feeding on Christ in Homily 47 on John 6:53–70

*a. The Spirit Gives Life*

Chrysostom takes up again the thought of Homily 41 when he
preaches on the discourse in John 6:53–70. We must listen to this
passage with the spiritual faculties. The words are to be taken in their
natural sense but this cannot yield a physical application, since the
words are themselves "divine and spiritual." Chrysostom refers to hearing with an earthly mind when he says that the flesh profits nothing. To
get to the authentic reality we must "penetrate beneath all mysteries
with inward eyes." In this way the Spirit gives life.

*b. The Flesh Gives Life*

As it turns out, the flesh does profit after all. This time, of course,
the flesh is not hearing with an earthly mind. It is the flesh of Christ
incarnate, crucified, and risen. This flesh is real flesh and it gives
eternal life. Nevertheless, eating the flesh of Christ cannot be understood in a fleshly way as though some sort of cannibalism were involved.
Eating Christ's flesh means being "closely united with him." In virtue of
this union we come to eternal life through him who was made flesh for
us. The homily closes with an appeal that we should not "pursue fleeting
things while fleeing from those that remain steadfast."

### 6. Comments

While Chrysostom does not attempt theology in the strict sense,
he give evidence of substantial theological acumen. This is least apparent, perhaps, in his handling of the relation of divine to human
action in salvation, or of faith to works. Even here, however, a preacher
to Christians might be expected to put special emphasis on human
response and effort. It must also be admitted that if man cannot come to
God in and of himself, he does not come under sheer compulsion.

In his sacramental teaching Chrysostom plainly takes a realistic view. When scripture says that we are born of water he accepts it at face value. God uses water in the new birth as, in a different way, he used earth at creation. Yet automatic efficacy is far from his mind. As we have seen, willingness on man's part is implied in the birth to divine sonship. Again, water itself can no more give the new life than earth can give the first life. God gives new life by water as God makes the first life from earth.

While Chrysostom does not treat the baptismal water as purely figurative, he has a keen awareness of the relation between outer and inner meaning. Immersion in water and emergence from it mean death and resurrection. The baptism of the early church brought this out with dramatic force. If the sign is used to effect what it signifies, its signification lies in the spiritual, not the material, sphere. Purification as well as death comes to expression in the rite. The cleansing water points us to the cleansing fire of the Spirit, which has only inward and not outward reality.

The Eucharist stands in the background of Chrysostom's exposition of John 6. A different problem arises here. We are not told that in baptism the water is the Spirit, but in the Eucharist Christ says that the bread is the body. A realistic view includes feeding through the bread, but does it include literal feeding on the body? Chrysostom does not think so. The words, spiritually understood, require a nonphysical interpretation of eating the flesh. The flesh saves, but nourishment by it refers to spiritual feeding. A realistic sacramental teaching need not mean that Christ's body is literally chewed, swallowed, and digested.

Chrysostom's approach to scripture is similar. Realism prevails to the extent that meanings are not to be read into the words. Yet the words may not always be meant literally and deeper meanings often lie beneath the surface. Three principles operate here. (1) The Spirit has inspired scripture. (2) Jesus Christ constitutes the true theme. (3) The Spirit's ministry is needed for true interpretation and application. Since the Holy Spirit will not teach what is not there, attention must be given to the true sense. The true sense, however, will not be grasped in its depth or fullness unless it is lit up by the Spirit. Chrysostom contends, therefore, for the interplay of sound scholarship and illumination by the Spirit which characterizes much of the early approach to scripture and which receives new emphasis in the age of the Reformation.


## B. DOCTRINE AND MINISTRY IN JEROME

If Chrysostom was the outstanding preacher of the late fourth century, Jerome was the outstanding scholar. Born c. 347, he, too, went through an ascetic period before ordination at Antioch in 377. After study in Constantinople he lived in Rome (382–385), where he started his monumental translation and revision of the Bible in Latin. Failing to succeed as bishop of Rome, he moved east and in 386 set up the monasteries in Bethlehem, where he spent the rest of his long life (d. 420).

Throughout the period from at least 375 Jerome engaged incessantly in study, writing, and controversy. His major literary achievement was the Vulgate translation. To do the Old Testament more accurately he learned Hebrew, although he also left translations of the Psalms and Job from the Greek. Commentaries form a great part of his literary output. At first he used an allegorical method, but later, breaking free from Origen's influence, he adopted a historical approach. He translated some of Origen's homilies on the biblical books, and his other translations include *On the Holy Spirit* by Didymus, the *Rule* of Pachomius, and a lost version of Origen's *Principles*. His controversial writings defend asceticism, refute the Luciferians and Pelagians, and attack Rufinus for his support of Origen. His historical writings comprise a translation of Eusebius, biographies, and some less dependable hermit stories.

Amid this frenzy of activity Jerome found time to write many important letters to various people on various themes. Apart from their historical value, these often have material theological significance too. In the present context we shall look at three which touch on doctrinal and pastoral subjects.

### 1. Doctrine

#### a. The Problem of Hypostasis

A trinitarian complication caused Jerome to write to Damasus of Rome c. 374 (Letter 15). The Christians in the East had come to refer to the Father, Son, and Holy Spirit as three hypostases. Those in the West equated hypostasis and ousia (substance) and thus feared tritheism at this point, as may be seen as early as the exchange between Dionysius of Rome and Dionysius of Alexandria in the middle of the third century. When Arianism came on the scene, Alexandria, too, insisted that there could be only one divine hypostasis, but others who stood for the deity of Christ suspected modalism in this, as they did also in the use of the term "homoousion" (of one substance). Thus an impasse was reached which blocked all progress until the semantic difficulty could be solved.

At the Council of Alexandria in 362 the separated orthodox groups drew together. The Alexandrians relaxed their opposition to the three hypostases; for while as the equivalent of ousia the term could refer only to the one God, when used for three subsistences it might carry a legitimate reference to Father, Son, and Spirit. Since this concession dispelled the fear of modalism, recognition of the homoousion could be offered in return. Unfortunately, however, a minority party in

Antioch held up the process of reconciliation by standing out against the new use of hypostasis.

### b. Jerome's Position

Jerome came into the act as a supporter of this minority view. He wrote his letter to Damasus ostensibly to ask for instructions on the use of hypostasis, but possibly to strengthen Damasus in his support for the Antioch group. After deploring the way in which the East with its feuds was "bit by bit tearing the seamless vest of the Lord," he made a plea for protection. An Arian group was trying to extract from him the "unheard of formula of three hypostases" "in spite of the definition of Nicea and the decree of Alexandria" in 362.

Jerome saw clearly enough that, in a certain sense, hypostasis could be valid. When defined as "three persons subsisting," it commanded his full material support. He was ready to anathematize those who refused to acknowledge three hypostases in the sense of "three things hypostatized, that is three persons subsisting." Yet he still would not accept the term hypostasis since in the sense of *ousia* it could refer only to the one substance: "In the three persons there is one hypostasis." He thus agreed with the teaching but would continue to resist the term unless Damasus, as the representative of the West, was prepared to let him speak of three hypostases.

### c. Jerome's Defense

Why was Jerome so stubborn about the term? He gave three reasons. (1) He feared it would be an umbrella for Arians, since they could still give it their own meaning. (2) He claimed that "in the whole range of secular learning hypostasis never means anything but ousia." (3) He found it "profane" for anyone to speak of three substances in the Godhead. "There is one nature of God and one only; and this, and this alone, truly is. ... Because his nature alone is uncreated, and in the three persons there subsists but one Godhead, there is only one nature which truly is. ... To say that in God are three hypostases, however, is to try to predicate three natures of God." To Jerome, the heretics were the ones "tenacious of a word." Why? Because deep down they still wanted to have a term which they could use in the old sense of three different and unequal substances.

### d. Conclusion

Jerome's fears may not have been groundless, but they were certainly exaggerated. In fact, "hypostases" proved to be as good a term as any for what the West no less ambiguously called "the three persons." Constantinople (381) endorsed it in the sense of three subsistences. The council thus ruled out modalism just as its ratification of homoousion had ruled out Arianism. Nevertheless, Jerome makes a useful contribution with his clear distinction between the two uses. If he errs by calling the use of "persons" a new one with no secular support, he helps by pinpointing the implications of that use should there be a confused equation with *ousia*. Out of the debates of the period it gradually became plain that *ousia* and *substantia* would refer to the one God, while hypostases and *personae* could be equivalents for the Father, Son, and Spirit. Once this was settled, the path was cleared for a measure of christological agreement at least in the trinitarian sphere.

### 2. Ministry

#### a. A Pastoral Rule

Around 394 Jerome received a series of requests that he should draw up a kind of rule for ministers. The requests came from a young man named Nepotian, nephew of Heliodorus, who, after a period of army service, had given away his savings and received ordination as a presbyter. Jerome finally gave his ideas on such a rule in an interesting letter to Nepotian (Letter 52).

The opening paragraph explains the reason for writing. Jerome then assures Nepotian that he will deal with the matter, not rhetorically, but with a simplicity nourished by concern for wisdom. Paradoxically, he makes this point with a lavish display of pagan learning and a highly fanciful exposition of David's relation to Abishag, which he construes as an embracing of wisdom in all its warmth and fullness (pars. 1–4).

(1) Avoidance of Worldly Gain. In a further conceit Jerome draws his first rule from the term "clergy" with its root in the Greek *kleros* (lot). The clergy are the lot of the Lord or have the Lord as their lot. Hence they must neither engage in business nor rise from poverty to wealth, nor indeed associate with clergy who do: "Welcome poor men and strangers to your homely board, that with them Christ may be your guest" (par. 5). Fishing for legacies comes in for special censure. "If heir there must be, the church has first claim. . . . Why do we thrust ourselves in between mother and children?" (par. 6).

(2) Avoidance of Women. Women should seldom have access to the minister's home except for relatives or older women in time of sickness. Nor should widows and virgins be visited except with solid companions. Confidences should be heard only in the presence of others. Jerome has no time for gifts, notes, or endearments. He delivers the solemn warning: "Always bear in mind that it was a woman who expelled the tiller of paradise from his heritage" (par. 5).

(3) Reading Scripture. Jerome recommends constant reading of the Bible. "Never, indeed, let the sacred volume be out of your hand." Practice, however, must conform to the lessons learned and taught. "He is a fine and dainty master who, with his stomach full, reads a homily on fasting" (par. 7).

(4) Spiritual Obedience. A filial attitude to the bishop marks a good presbyter. Love, not fear, must inform the obedience rendered. It should be met with respect, for "there should be but one ministry." Jerome sees no good reason for the custom whereby presbyters never preach in the bishop's presence: "A wise son is the glory of his father" (par. 7).

(5) Shunning Applause. True preaching brings groans, not applause. Profundity rates above garrulity. It is easy enough to sway the crowd with words. The uneducated "most admire what they fail to understand." The words of a good preacher, however, will be "seasoned by his reading of scripture" and his hearers' tears will be his glory (par. 8).

(6) Moderation. (a) Dress. Jerome warns against gaudy clothes. Yet, unless there is no money to buy better, he also condemns the opposite extreme. "Showiness and slovenliness are alike to be shunned" (par. 9).

(b) Church Furnishings. Costly adornment of churches and altars should not be a concern of the clergy. Instead their care should be for "the choice of Christ's ministers." Jerome will not accept the precedent of the temple unless we are also ready to accept all the laws of Old Testament worship. "Our Lord by his poverty has consecrated the poverty of his house. Let us therefore think of his cross and count riches to be but dirt." "Why do we cherish and love what it is Peter's boast not to possess?" (par. 10).

(7) Feasting and Dainty Fasting. Jerome cannot agree that clergy should give lavish feasts to important people. He dismisses the excuse that good influence can be exerted this way. "A secular magistrate will defer more to a clergyman who is self-denying." "If he will only listen to the clergy over a glass," it is better to go to Christ in prayer. Excessive use of wine must be avoided. Indeed, Jerome inclines to total abstinence: "I will readily forego the cup in which I cannot but suspect poison" (par. 11). With his ascetic bent he commends fasting for the clergy, but with moderation and simplicity. Ordinary foods should not be abandoned for "fancy decoctions" or "dainties" used to "seek a reputation for abstinence" (par. 12).

(8) Human and Divine Approval. The good pastor does not seek compliments or act ostentatiously to impress the people. Like Paul, he will aim at "God's approval rather than man's regard," neither elated by praise nor crushed by reproach. Winning popular acclaim may be doing despite to God (par. 13).

(9) Gossip. The clergyman must guard against "a blabbing tongue and itching ears." "Neither detract from others nor listen to their detractors." Detractors can be easily silenced by lack of response: "No one cares to speak to an unwilling listener" (par. 14). Since parishioners confide in their pastors, the latter must guard their secrets. "Do not let one house know what is going on in another." We have reason "to love the homes of

all Christians as though they were our own," but they should know us primarily as "comforters in sorrow rather than as guests in times of joy" (par. 15).

(10) Various Admonitions. Jerome winds up his rule with a collection of practical injunctions such as not to hunt for gifts, not to engage in matchmaking, and not to distribute alms to the poor for a commission, which "is to be more cruel than any robber." Best that a donor distribute his own gifts, but if the duty is undertaken on his behalf, the clergyman must remember that "he is the best almoner who keeps nothing for himself" (par. 16).

Anticipating criticism because of his opposition to common practice, Jerome finally offers three arguments in self-defense: (a) he writes only because he has been asked; (b) he applies all that he has written to himself first; and (c) he has not aimed at any individuals. If anyone is still angry, "he will have first to own that he himself suits my description" (par. 17).

### b. Presbyters and Deacons

(1) The Issue. In the fourth century, as church holdings and income increased in larger dioceses, the deacons, who with the bishop handled these material resources, achieved a higher status than the presbyters and even began to intrude into some presbyterial functions. This had already brought opposition from Ambrosiaster, who, in his *Commentaries on Paul's Epistles* and his *Questions,* pointed out that deacons exist to serve presbyters and bishops, both of whom, celebrating the Eucharist, are *sacerdotes.*

At some unknown date a layman Evangelus seems to have consulted Jerome on this matter. In reply Jerome wrote a letter (Letter 146) in which he accepts and develops the thesis of Ambrosiaster. Jerome's experiences with bishop John of Jerusalem and his own work on Titus both inclined him in this direction and provided him with the needed material. Both Ambrosiaster and Jerome appeal to Alexandrian practice, although on different counts.

(2) Presbyters and Bishops in Scripture. Jerome at once takes the offensive against the deacons. Their presumption rates as folly in view of the biblical witness to the equation of presbyters and bishops (Phil 1:1; Acts 20:28; Titus 1:5–7; 1 Tim 4:14; 1 Pet 5:1–2; 2 John 1; 3 John 1). "When the apostle clearly teaches that presbyters are the same as bishops, must not a mere server of tables and of widows be insane to set himself arrogantly above them?" Through their prayers presbyters "make the body and blood of Christ." How, then, can deacons claim precedence over them?

(3) Presbyters and Bishops in History. Jerome argues that when "subsequently" a single bishop "was chosen to preside over the rest," "this was done to remedy schism" (cf. Ignatius). For a long period, he

points out, the Alexandrian presbyters chose the bishop as deacons choose the archdeacon. The only right reserved for bishops alone was that of ordination. At this point Jerome has a rather unclear digression designed to show that no matter what the status or wealth of a diocese, the bishop's "dignity is the same and his priesthood is the same." There is no lower or higher bishop. "All alike are successors of the apostles."

(4) Diaconal Infringements. Jerome gives three instances of the arrogance of deacons at Rome in about 350: (a) they recommend men for ordination as presbyters; (b) they seat themselves among the presbyters; and (c) they give the blessing at social gatherings. Apparently, the lower number of deacons (seven) "makes them persons of greater consequence, while presbyters are less thought of owing to their great numbers" (forty-six).

(5) Presbyters and Deacons. Returning to the equation of presbyters and bishops, Jerome explains that two terms are used because they refer to different things, the one to age and the other to rank. That presbyters are higher than deacons is shown by the fact that the movement is from deacon to presbyter, not presbyter to deacon. This remains true even though deacons, in the typical fashion of administrators, are more highly paid. In conclusion Jerome considers the possibility that the apostles modeled the ministry on the Old Testament: "Bishops, presbyters, and the deacons occupy in the church the same positions as those which Aaron, his sons, and the Levites occupied in the temple." He seems not to notice that this does not fit in too well with his biblical and historical argument.

### 3. Observations

*a. The Rule*

Jerome's rule for the ministry speaks clearly enough for itself. If it errs a little on the side of severity, it is much more moderate than one might have expected. Indeed, common sense, rather than asceticism, characterizes most of the admonitions. Jerome realized only too well the temptations to which a celibate fourth-century pastor was exposed. Authentic ministering could only too easily be changed into self-serving. Excuses could so easily be found for dilution of the original goals and standards. Jerome rightly contends for an exercise of the pastorate which will stress its divine orientation and minimize the dangers of individual and vocational corruption. *Mutatis mutandis* the rule might well serve as a useful set of guidelines for clergy in any age, church, or society.

*b. The Question of Rank*

(1) Importance. Jerome's equation of presbyters and bishops in distinction from deacons has considerable historical and dogmatic im-

portance. Biblically his case is hard to refute, and no one has yet come up with a better historical explanation of the rise of monepiscopacy. Across the centuries, indeed, the essential oneness of episcopal and presbyterial functions has been recognized; no solid evidence has been adduced to show that from New Testament days presbyters exercised these functions only as the bishop's delegates. An exaggerated episcopalianism as well as an ill-founded papalism is thus resisted, and the validity of presbyterial as well as episcopal succession, or of the two together, is established. The ramifications of this have yet to be thought out and worked out in modern ecumenical relations and programs.

(2) Insights. As regards the relation between presbyters and deacons, Jerome makes some excellent points. (a) He rightly sees that primacy belongs to the ministry of the word and prayer. (b) He indicates that worldly ideas of importance and status have brought about the erroneous overrating of deacons. (c) He brings out the fact that administrators — church bureaucrats are perhaps the closest modern equivalents of deacons even though they may be in presbyterial orders — exist to serve and not to control or rule those who do the basic work of ministry. (d) While he personally has little financial concern, he perhaps hints that the administrative habit of awarding administrators more remuneration again betrays an unbiblical and untheological secularization in the understanding and practice of ministry.

(3) Criticisms. On the other hand, various faults may be found in Jerome's handling of the matter. (a) He inveighs far too violently against deacons. (b) He unduly downgrades their practical ministry, as in the example of relief for the poor. (c) He compartmentalizes the ministry too rigidly and views it too hierarchically in trying to exclude them from spiritual functions. (d) He hardly stays close to apostolic teaching or practice when he makes the offering of the Eucharist the supreme episcopal-presbyterial function. (e) He misses the point that a non-secular understanding of the ministry imposes a mutuality of service. If in their function deacons must serve presbyters, presbyters must likewise serve deacons in theirs. On either side, insistence on rights and prerogatives can only betray ministry and not uphold it.

# CHAPTER VIII
## *Augustine Again*

## A. THE ENCHIRIDION

### 1. The Work

Augustine of Hippo wrote so much on so many themes and with such great depth that few students or teachers can be expected to achieve a mastery of his thought or achievement. Fortunately, however, a certain Laurentius in 421 asked Augustine for a brief exposition of basic Christian teaching. Augustine, while recognizing the difficulty of the request, tried to fulfill it in his so-called *Enchiridion,* a handbook on faith, hope, and love in which, taking the Creed and the Lord's Prayer as his guides, he touched successively on the main heads of doctrine. In this work he has left us a mature and fairly comprehensive survey of his theology, from which even beginners can derive an authoritative if rudimentary acquaintance with it.

### 2. Introduction

In the early chapters of the *Enchiridion* Augustine explains the origin and nature of the work. Worship of God is the source of wisdom (chap. 2). Worshipping God in faith, hope, and love constitutes the Christian faith (chap. 3). The Creed and the Lord's Prayer can guide us in the interpretation of faith, hope, and love, for "faith believes, hope and love pray" (chap. 7).

### 3. Theology

The question of belief does not concern the nature of things, with which "physicists" deal. Christians may know little of such matters. Indeed, even students of them may know less than they think. The Creator of the natural order forms the theme of theology. As faith perceives, "nothing exists save God himself and what comes from him." This God, the Triune God, *is* (chap. 9).

### 4. Creation

"The Trinity, supremely and equally and immutably good,"made all things. He made them good, although not supremely and equally and immutably so (chap. 10). He overrules them, so that evil is allowed only because "in his omnipotence he can bring forth good out of evil" "so that [evil] does not exist any more" (chap. 11).

### 5. Evil

Defining evil as the privation of good, Augustine denies it authentic existence as a substance (chap. 11). Its possibility arises only because the good in a created thing is mutable and therefore "can be diminished or augmented," although it cannot be destroyed so long as the thing itself exists. Without the good and its privation there can be no evil (chap. 12). "Nothing evil exists in itself, but only as an evil aspect of some actual entity. Therefore there can be nothing evil except something good" (chap. 13). Along such lines the apparent contradiction of evil in a good world disappears, for "in these two contraries we call evil and good the rule of the logicians fails to apply," namely, the rule of the excluded middle whereby, for example, a drink cannot be sweet and sour at the same time and place. For, whereas good can exist without evil, "evil cannot exist without good," having "no mode in which to exist." One may thus say: "It is good to be a man . . . but evil to be wicked" (chap. 14).

### 6. The Fall

How does evil arise in man? Good comes from God, but "the cause of evil is the defection of the will of a being who is mutably good from the Good which is immutable" (chap. 23). From this "primal lapse" or "first privation of the good," all other evils flow: ignorance, "an appetite for noxious things," banishment, original sin, and damnation (chaps. 24–26). Yet even as "the whole mass of the human race stood condemned, . . . paying the fully deserved penalty for impious desertion," God's goodness did not cease to sustain the race, since in the divine mercy evil had been permitted only that good might be brought out of it, namely, "by pardoning some who were unworthy of it" (chap. 27).

### 7. Election, Bondage, and Grace

*a. Election*

The "some" referred to in Chapter 27 are defined in Chapter 29 as those whom God elected to replace fallen angels, or, as Augustine graphically puts it, "to fill up the loss which the diabolical disaster had caused in the angelic society."

### b. Bondage

Can the elect "be restored through the merit of their own works"? No, "for what good works could a lost soul do except as he had been rescued from his lostness?" Can he "do this by the determination of his free will"? No, "for it was in the evil use of his free will that man destroyed himself and his will at the same time" (chap. 30). Man retains a certain freedom. He freely does the will of his master, sin. "He who is slave to sin is free to sin." But this is the opposite of true freedom which is "the joy that comes in doing what is right." On his own, then, man does not have the freedom to do good works or to return to God (chap. 30).

### c. Grace

Grace alone can save man through faith. Faith, of course, is not to be understood here as a work, but "as a divine gift." By this gift authentic freedom is attained and the process of restoration and righteousness inaugurated. "We are then truly free when God orders our lives, that is, forms and creates us ... as good men, which he is now doing by his grace, that we may indeed be new creatures in Jesus Christ" (chap. 31). Works cannot merit salvation, nor can the will do works nor choose salvation. Yet works and the free will have a place. Grace fashions us for works. It also frees the will, for "it predisposes a man before he wills, to prompt his willing." Thus "the whole process is credited to God, who both prepares the will to receive divine aid and aids the will which he has thus prepared" (chap. 32).

## 8. The Mediator

### a. His Work

Neither faith nor the freed will alone could bring restoration, for not only was the human race bound, but it "was bound in a just doom and all men were children of wrath." To meet this situation "a mediator was required, that is to say, a reconciler, who by offering a unique sacrifice ... should allay that wrath." The true point of grace is that even prior to our liberation for faith and renewal "we are reconciled to God through the mediator and receive the Holy Spirit so that we may be changed from enemies into sons" (chap. 33).

### b. His Incarnation

In his mediatorial work, Jesus the reconciler was made flesh, and "in that assumption nothing was lacking that belongs to human nature," although, in keeping with the virgin birth, "his was a nature free from the bonds of all sin." Jesus Christ is both "God before all ages and man in this age of ours." "In the unity of his person a rational soul and body is joined to the Word." Becoming man, "he emptied himself, taking on the form of a servant, yet neither losing nor diminishing the form of God" (chap. 34). Grace is manifested supremely here, "for what had the human nature in the man Christ merited that it, and no other, should be assumed into the unity of the person of the only Son of God?" (chap. 36). By this same grace, "God's great and sole grace," we are justified from our sins.

### 9. The Spirit and the Incarnation

Conception by the Holy Spirit, who as Gift is equal to the Giver, "and therefore not inferior to Father or Son," implies again that Christ's birth according to his human nature was a work of grace (chap. 37). Naturally, the Spirit is not to be seen as the Father of Jesus in the same way as Mary is the mother. He might be called the Maker of the man Jesus, although only to the extent that the whole Trinity was involved in that action. But being born of the Spirit means more than being made by the Spirit (chap. 38). At the same time, being born of something does not have to mean being the son of something or vice versa. A louse is not the son of a louse, and one can be a son by adoption or destination (chap. 39). Hence Christ, although born of the Spirit, is Son of the Father. His being born of the Spirit denotes "the grace of God by which a certain human person, no merit whatever preceding, . . . was joined to the Word of God in such a unity of person that the selfsame one who is Son of Man should be Son of God" (chap. 40).

### 10. Baptism and Original Sin

The exchange in reconciliation comes out in Augustine's discussion of baptism. "The God to whom we are to be reconciled has made him the sacrifice for sin by which we may be reconciled. He himself is therefore sin as we ourselves are righteousness, not our own but God's, not in ourselves, but in him" (chap. 41). Baptism expresses this, for in it we die to sin and "are alive by being reborn in the baptismal font" (chap. 42). "Infants die to original sin only," adults to actual sins as well (chap. 43). Original sin comprises many sins, such as pride and disobedience, so that infants too have remission of sins (chap. 44). They also share in the actual sins of their forefathers at least as far back as two or three generations. But all prior sin of this kind is forgiven, the new birth having been instituted because the first birth was "tainted" (chaps. 46–47).

### 11. Atonement and Justification

Augustine now returns to Christ's work and views it from some new angles.

a. Radical condemnation through one man is set aside by the one mediator "who was born in such a way as not to need to be reborn" (chap. 48).

b. The new birth cannot be by John's preparatory baptism. It is by the birth which "is not with water alone but with the Holy Spirit as well. Thus, whoever believes in Christ is reborn by that same Spirit of whom Christ was also born, not needing to be reborn" (chap. 49).

c. In the atonement the devil is overcome justly, for Christ's unjust death releases us from our just death. "As the devil had most unjustly slain him who was in no way deserving of death, he also did most justly lose those whom he had justly held in bondage." Christ underwent his unjust death "through his own free act of showing mercy" and "as part of a definite plan" to take away the world's sin (chap. 49).

d. Since "the death of Christ crucified is nothing other than the likeness of forgiveness of sins," "in the very same sense in which the death is real, so also is the forgiveness of sins real." The reality of the resurrection implies similarly our authentic justification (chap. 52).

e. The things that happened to Christ on earth serve as a model for "the Christian life which we lead here on earth," that is, as a life of mortification and renewal (chap. 53).

### 12. The Church

#### a. *Its Two Parts*

For Augustine the church comprises "not just the part that journies here on earth" but also "that part which in heaven has always from creation held fast to God," that is, the church of the holy angels. Augustine wisely refuses to take up questions as to the nature and hierarchy of angels, although he will not disallow such discussion so long as one avoids the mistake "of those who think they know what they do not know" (chaps. 56–59).

#### b. *The Reconciling of the Parts*

Christ shed his blood for the part which, better known to us, wanders on earth. Yet the work of Christ also reconciles the two parts and thus repairs "the ruins left by the angelic apostasy." The restoration of heaven will be achieved when those "lost from the angelic apostasy are replaced from the ranks of mankind," while that of earth is achieved when those "predestined to eternal life are redeemed from the old state of corruption" (chap. 62).

*c. Forgiveness in the Church*

New guilt is incurred with post-baptismal sin but "forgiveness should never be despaired of in holy church for those who truly repent" (chaps. 64–65). Outside the church sins are not forgiven, for the church "alone has received the pledge of the Holy Spirit without whom is no forgiveness of sins" (chap. 65).

## 13. Faith and Works

*a. Antinomianism*

Augustine insists that "the faith that saves" is "the faith which works through love." Hence he cannot believe that there may be a salvation by fire for those who maintain a Christian confession but live persistently in sin (chaps. 67–68).

*b. Purgatory*

He thus questions (1) the concept of a purgatory in which such a life of sin may be made good, and (2) the application of 1 Corinthians 3:11–15 to this whole matter. On the other hand, he accepts the possibility that some of the faithful will be saved through a purgatorial fire, whether in this life or after it (chaps. 68–69). Since the intermediate state may be one of "rest or affliction" according to present achievement, he can see value in Eucharists and intercession for those whose life is "neither so good as not to need such helps after death nor so bad as not to gain benefit from them after death" (chaps. 109–110). But he refuses to be dogmatic in this sphere.

## 14. The Resurrection

Although aware of the difficult problem it raises, Augustine firmly confesses the resurrection of the body (chap. 84).

a. He equates body and flesh except insofar as flesh denotes corruption, as in 1 Corinthians 15:50. Yet resurrection is not resuscitation (chap. 89). The body will be a spiritual one in the sense of the removal of all encumbrances, so that there will be complete facility as well as complete felicity (chap. 91).

b. Augustine expects the resurrection of an aborted fetus, developed or even undeveloped, since "the perfection which time would have accomplished will not be lacking any more than blemishes wrought by time will still be present" (chap. 85). He confesses ignorance as to the time when life starts in the womb, but thinks it too rash to say of a dead fetus that it never lived at all, for there might be life "not yet apparent in the motions of a living thing." In such cases, then, hope of the resurrection may not be denied (chap. 86).

c. The wicked are raised to the second death in which the soul is not "compelled to leave its body," but instead "is not allowed to leave the body." While there might be degrees of punishment, Augustine holds out no hope of salvation. Sentimentality must not blind us to the facts (chaps. 111–112). The conditions of both saved and lost "will then be fixed and endless." The real loss, which can never be mitigated, will be "estrangement from the life of God." No torments can compare to this, and it will "abide for ever" (chaps. 112–113).

### 15. Predestination

#### a. God's Justice

Some might think it unjust that God condemns those on whom he will not show mercy. Augustine answers with Paul: "O man, who are you to reply to God?" If we do not understand, we can hardly talk back. If we do understand, we see that "the human race was condemned in its apostate state by a divine judgment so just that if not even a single member of the race were ever saved from it, no one could rail against God's justice." The divine justice is indeed set forth in the deserved damnation of the reprobate (chap. 98).

#### b. God's Will and Man's Will

The same act may be a fulfillment both of God's will and of man's will, but in different senses. Man can even will evil—what God does not will! — and still do God's sovereign will. Those who willed Christ's death did so with an evil will, whereas the Father willed the same death with a good will. It thus follows (1) that "the will of the Omnipotent is always undefeated" and (2) that this will can never be evil, for "even when it inflicts evils, it is still just, and obviously what is just is not evil" (chaps. 100–102).

#### c. God's Will to Save

Does not scripture say that God wills the salvation of all? Yet all are not saved. We have to ask, then, what the saying means. (1) It means that "no one is saved unless he wills it." (2) It means that he wills some to be saved from the different groups of humanity. In context, even kings can be saved, for "God has judged it good that through the prayers of the lowly he would deign to grant salvation to the exalted." (3) Augustine is ready to consider other interpretations "as long as we are not compelled to believe that the Omnipotent has willed anything to be done which was not done" (chap. 103).

#### d. True Freedom

Man was fittingly created so that he could will both good and evil. "In the future life he will not have the power to will evil, and yet this will not thereby restrict his free will. Indeed, his will will be much freer." The good of being able not to sin will yield to the higher good of not being able to sin. If man had willed not to sin, with divine aid God's will would have been done *by* him. Since he chose to sin, God's will has been done *concerning* him through the grace and work of the Mediator. Notwithstanding man's loss of the first freedom, the divinely willed destiny of true freedom has thus been achieved (chaps. 105–107).

### 16. Hope and Love

Augustine hardly achieved the desired brevity in his exposition (with the help of the creed) of faith. He allowed philosophical questions to intrude and went off into too many digressions. He did not even offer a full and balanced treatment of faith. We may be grateful for his thinking on such difficult matters as evil or freedom, even if he is not at his most biblical in these areas, but they left him little time for his discussion (with the guidance of the Lord's Prayer) of hope and love.

#### a. Hope

Turning at last to hope and love, he forged a transitional link by saying that out of faith "there is born the good hope of the faithful, accompanied by a holy love." The Lord's Prayer then serves as a guide to love. Hope must not be placed in man, but what we hope for should be sought from God (chap. 114). This explains the seven petitions of the Lord's Prayer, three for eternal goods and four for temporal goods, which are necessary for obtaining the eternal goods.

#### b. Love

Augustine brings the work to a fine conclusion with a brief account of love. Love is supreme. This comes out in the following points. (1) "He who loves aright believes and hopes aright." (2) Faith works through love, for if it does what the law commands, the law can be achieved only when love is shed abroad in the heart (chap. 117). (3) Four stages may be discerned in historical and individual life: pre-law, law, grace, and final peace. The turning point is reached with the third stage when "the mightier power of love" comes through Christ and the Spirit (chap. 118). (4) Love is the end of the commandment, so that "the imperatives are rightly obeyed only when they are measured by the standard of our love of God and our love of our neighbour in God." (5) Love reaches its fullness when we love God "at sight" and there is no more cupidity for it to restrain or overcome (chap. 121).

In a postscript Augustine cannot refrain from a final play of words on his triad. He has written the work because he believes and hopes good things for Lawrence and loves him greatly as a member of the body. In a combination of justifiable hope and self-criticism he then expresses his concluding wish: "May the book's usefulness match its prolixity."

## B. THE SPIRIT AND THE LETTER

### 1. The Setting

Pelagianism presented perhaps the greatest threat to the gospel in the days of Augustine's ministry. It began harmlessly enough. Pelagius, the "British monk," issued a stirring call for sanctification of the many nominal believers found at Rome at the beginning of the fifth century. His basic concerns — divine justice and human responsibility — could not in themselves be a reason for controversy. Unfortunately, however, Pelagius took express issue with the saying of Augustine: "Give what thou commandest and command what thou wilt" (*Confessions* 40). With his disciple Celestius he also began drawing from his pastoral principles the logical but hazardous inferences that perfection is possible, that infants are guilty of no sin, and that the fall is a following of Adam's example.

Pelagianism as it had developed by 412 can be summed up in three essential theses. a. "God has not willed to command anything impossible, for he is righteous; and he will not condemn a man for what he could not help, for he is holy" (Pel. *Epistle to Demetrias*, chap. 16). b. Of the three elements in conduct, namely, ability (*posse*), will (*velle*) and act (*esse*), the first "is properly ascribed to God, who conferred it on his creatures, while the other two . . . are to be referred to the human agent (Pel. *In Defense of Free Will*). c. "Everything good and everything evil . . . is done by us, not born with us" (Pel. *In Defense of Free Will*). Additional charges were brought against Celestius at the Council of Carthage in 412, including the charge that he believed Adam was created mortal and that the law as well as the gospel leads to the kingdom.

Augustine was not present at Carthage in 412, but already in 411 the imperial legate Marcellinus had written to him for guidance on the issues raised. In reply Augustine composed his *On the Deserts and Remissions of Sins*, in which he set forth his own conviction that Adam's fault infected the race and that even if sinlessness is theoretically possible because of God's power, there is in man a culpable unwillingness to do the right which only God's help, if it be given, can overcome. Marcellinus detected a contradiction between this unwillingness and the possibility of perfection. He thus requested a fuller explanation and Augustine answered with his work *On the Spirit and the Letter* in 412.

### 2. The Problem

Augustine begins by stating the difficulty as Marcellinus sees it. The possibility and the reality conflict. He points out, however, that often God can do certain things but does not do them. Man's righteousness falls into this category. While it is "man's business" it is also a "divine gift" and therefore a "divine work" (chap. 2). The reality is set before us by scripture. "No man in this life, though he be free to choose, is ever found without sin" (chap. 3).

### 3. The Error

Error arises, not when generosity would like to think there are exceptions, but when righteousness is seen merely as man's work and it is believed "that the power of the human will can of itself, without the help of God, either achieve perfection or advance steadily towards it" (chap. 4). Doing the right requires not merely the natural gift of freedom and the gift of instruction through the commandment but also the gift of the Holy Spirit imparting "the delight in and the love of God" (chap. 5).

### 4. Teaching as Letter

Without the life-giving Spirit, teaching remains a "letter that kills." What does this mean? Not just that if we take figurative sayings in a literal way we miss their "deeper significance" but also that the commandments, without the Spirit, kill us by increasing sinful desire (Romans 5–7). God's purpose here is so to show us our sinfulness that we see "our need for God, not only as teacher but as helper" (chaps. 6–9). When this is perceived, the right order of things is also perceived. "He extends his mercy, not because they know him, but in order that they may know him; he extends his righteousness, not because they are upright in heart, but that they may become upright in heart" (chap. 11). In all this Augustine's chief authority is Paul. He thus moves on to an exposition of Paul's doctrine of justification.

### 5. Paul's Doctrine of Grace

a. Paul "unhesitatingly preaches the gift of God by which alone salvation comes to the children of God" (chap. 12).

b. When he says that no one can be justified by law, he has more in view than "the law of ancient rites," for in the same context he speaks of the law which brings knowledge of sin (chap. 14).

c. Justification by faith does not mean justification by "our free choice of what the law commands."

d. Justification is (1) by God's righteousness, "not that by which God is righteous, but that wherewith he clothes man when he justifies the ungodly"; (2) by the gift of God through the help of the Spirit; (3) by faith, that is, "the faith whereby we believe in Christ" and not "that by which Christ believes"; and (4) by free grace, not "without our will," but by its restoration through grace for the fulfillment of the law (chap. 15).

### 6. The Use of the Law

a. While the law is not made for the righteous, it still may be rightly employed. The unrighteous can use it as a tutor to grace. The righteous can use it to "put the fear of it upon the unrighteous" so that "they may take refuge by faith with the grace that justifies" (chap. 16).

b. Misusing the law as a means of self-righteousness brings self-glorying, and this in turn leads to the dreadful situation of idolatry and immorality depicted in Romans 1 (chaps. 17–19).

c. In contrast to the law of works, that of faith eliminates self-glorying. Thus "what is enjoined with threatening under the law of works is granted to belief under the law of faith" (chap. 22).

d. This comes about by the gift of the Holy Spirit. "By the law of works God says, 'Do what I command,' by the law of faith we say, 'Give what thou commandest'." As God does this by the Spirit, we enjoy the power to do without self-glorying what the law commands (chap. 22).

### 7. Letter and Spirit

Tying in the theme of law and faith with that of letter and Spirit, Augustine now specifically equates the letter with the decalogue (chaps. 23–24). At most the decalogue might be fulfilled only through fear of penalty, "in a temper of servitude, not freedom." The Spirit alone gives the love, the freedom, the delight in the law, which make real fulfillment possible (chaps. 26–27). Here then is the way of authentic righteousness in the threefold sense: a. through the gift of the Spirit we work righteousness; b. we are clothed with the righteousness of faith; and c. we are God's righteousness, "not that by which he is righteous, but that by which we are made so by him" (chap. 31).

God, of course, gave the law. But as such the law is external. "Only when the lifegiving Spirit is present does he cause it to be written within and loved," not feared (chap. 32). Covenant renewal is thus achieved according to the prophecy in Jeremiah 31:31–34, which is shown to be true prophecy, not just prediction, in that "God promises that which he does himself: the promise is not his and the doing another's" (chap. 40). The distinction of covenants is not just that a spiritual understanding is now imparted. The law is written within, fear yields to delight, and the transgressor killed by the letter "is here made a lover by the Spirit that gives life" (chap. 42).

### 8. The Law and the Gentiles

A difficulty arises at this point. Romans 2:14–15 says that the law is already on the hearts of Gentiles by nature. How, then, "are the faithful of the new covenant distinguished from the Gentiles?" Do not the Gentiles have both "an advantage over the old Israel" and also temporal priority over the new? (chap. 43).

### a. Gentile Christians?

To see a reference to Gentile Christians offers a possible solution. It rules out any idea of justification apart from faith. Greek doers of the law either "are made righteous by him who justifies the ungodly" or "they are held or accounted just" by men (chap. 45). On this reading, "by nature" indicates a restoration of the true nature of man: "It is the work of the Spirit of grace to renew in us the image of God in which by nature we were made" (chap. 47).

### b. Pagans

If the Gentiles here be seen as pagans, Paul is speaking of the commendable acts which even those who do not know God can do because "the image of God has not been so obliterated . . . that no faint outlines of the original remain" (chap. 48). There thus persists "both a certain awareness of what is lawful and a certain power of doing it," but justification requires a renewing of what was not altogether effaced by "the Christian grace which is the mediator's intercession" (chap. 48).

### c. The Common Aim of Law

Either way the teleology of law does not change. Law rules out self-glorying and points to the only source of righteousness (chap. 50). It "is set forth to this end, that every man may recognize his own infirmity and so, . . . by winning faith through the favour of the Justifier, may attain and do and live in it." "For the work which if a man do he shall live in it is done only by one who is justified, and justification is granted to the prayer of faith" (chap. 51).

## 9. Grace, Freedom, and Faith

### a. Grace and Freedom

Does grace invalidate freedom of choice? No, it establishes it. "Grace heals the will whereby righteousness may freely be loved." Augustine finds a linked series here: law, knowledge of sin, faith, grace, healing, freedom of choice, love of righteousness, doing of the law. The mistake is either to boast of freedom when we are slaves of sin or, having been made free, to boast of it as though it were our own work (chap. 52).

### b. Freedom and Faith

Is faith our own choice? Is it in our own power? In answer to this question Augustine distinguishes between will (*voluntas*) and ability (*potestas*). These are not the same. We may will what we cannot do and we may not will what we can, yet we cannot do without willing. This is true even under compulsion, for, although forced, the will is still present. Power is "the union of will with the capacity to act. That is in a man's power which he does if he wills and does not if he wills not" (chap. 53). In the case of faith, one may say that it is in our power, for "everyone believes when he wills, and when he believes, believes willingly." Nevertheless, a distinction must be made, for while the will is "with us," the power is "from God" (chap. 54).

### c. The Nature of Faith

Augustine now makes a further distinction. Even those who are under the law believe in God. What, then, is justifying faith? It is the faith of filial love as distinct from that of servile fear. It is the faith "that believes in him who justifies the ungodly" and that "gains the bountiful outpouring of the Holy Spirit," so that it works through love (chap. 56).

### d. The Nature of Will

The nature of the will by which we believe must also be defined. Is it "the gift of God" or is it "exerted by the freedom of choice which is implanted in us by nature"? If we deny the former, do we not engage in self-glorying? If we deny the latter, do we not offer an excuse to unbelief? (chap. 57). A first answer is that freedom of choice is "a neutral power which can either be exerted to faith or sink into unbelief." "The act of faith whereby a man believes God . . . arises at God's call from the freedom of choice which he received in the way of nature at his creation. God wills all men to be saved . . . but not so as to deprive them of that freedom of choice for the good or evil use of which they are subject to the judgment of absolute justice" (chap. 58). Yet for the proper use of this freedom of choice more is needed than the ability given at creation. God also "works for our willing and believing through the inducements and impressions which we experience" both externally and internally. Without these "freedom of choice could produce no act of belief." Hence "it is God who brings about in a man the very will to believe," while "to consent to the calling of God or to refuse it . . . belongs to our own will" (chap. 60).

If it is asked why some consent and some do not, Augustine can only appeal to Romans 11.00 and Romans 0:11. No doubt God could bring all to faith, just as he could bring believers to sinlessness or indeed to incorruptibility. Scripture, however, shows that he does not do so, and "I am never so happy," says Augustine, "as when I have most ample support in the scripture" (chap. 63). The reality of things must be respected even if a mystery remains which men cannot explain and which they question only if "they bethink themselves too little that they are men." "There lies therefore a secret in the hidden depths of God's judgments" which shuts off all praise of self and permits only praise of God. "But that secret who can explore?" (chap. 66).

### 10. Survey

#### a. Answer to Pelagianism

In this work Augustine does not wade out so far as he did later into the deep waters of human bondage and divine predestination. One almost detects an Arminian note in some of his closing chapters. Nevertheless, he decisively checks the erroneous inferences of the Pelagians. Thus he makes it irrefutably clear that the predicament of the race cannot be resolved merely by the proper use of the will under the tutelage of moral instruction. The basic problem of alienation from God, which Pelagius meets simply at the level of ethical misconduct, can be overcome only by the justifying work of Christ, by faith in response to the call of the Father, and by the rekindling of an inward love of God through the gift of the Holy Spirit. Thus the commands of God can be fulfilled only as he gives what he commands. Will and act (*velle* and *esse*) cannot be achieved on the basis of the original ability (*posse*). The common fall of humanity leaves individuals incapable of doing the good. A new ability must be given. The granting of this new ability is the content of the gospel. God in his righteousness and grace has taken pity. Through the ministry of Christ and the Spirit he carries believers beyond the neutral freedom of choice to a more authentic freedom than Adam lost.

#### b. Exposition of the Gospel

As the heart of his reply to Pelagianism in *The Spirit and the Letter* Augustine offers as good an exposition of Paul's teaching in Romans as one will find anywhere in the fathers. It may be that he finally construes "to justify" as "to make righteous," thus giving rise to ambiguities which were finally to demand clarification and, unfortunately, to lead to division, at the time of the Reformation. Nevertheless, he lays his finger on all the basic points. No one can achieve salvation by servile fulfillment of the moral law. Success in this attempt defeats itself since it leads to self-glorying. The proper work of law is to bring to light the sin for which Christ's work alone provides the remedy. By Christ's work the sinner receives the gift of God's righteousness through the faith in Christ which is the faith of filial love. The divine gift means the imparting of inward love by which alone true fulfillment of the commands is possible. If this work takes place in some but not in all, Augustine refuses here to explain this either in terms of a limited number of vacancies or in terms of a decree of predestination and reprobation. The fact that our willing is involved implies a measure of human responsibility. The rest lies in the unfathomable secret of God.

#### c. Freedom and Freedom of Choice

An interesting feature of *The Spirit and the Letter* is that Augustine distinguishes between freedom of choice, which he calls neutral, and freedom to do the good, which he obviously does not concede to fallen man. Is there some confusion here, and if so, does it mean that at this early stage Augustine might have been open to agreement with the Pelagians?

As regards the first question, Augustine sees clearly enough that true freedom includes power as well as will. Hence freedom of choice may go hand in hand with inability to do what is chosen, just as choice may not be choice of that for which there is ability. Freedom of choice and lack of true freedom for the good may thus coexist.

As regards the second point, Augustine plainly rejects the Pelagian position that original ability suffices when helped by moral teaching. A new ability has to be given if true freedom is to be enjoyed. Now Pelagius might well have fallen in line with Augustine here. Preaching to confessing Christians, he might have urged them to use the new ability granted, to practice the love of God shed abroad in the heart, to fulfill the command precisely because what is commanded has in fact been given. In this way he could also have worked down to the root of the problem in those whose confession had no reality. Hence his pastoral goals could have been achieved without theological deviation and the whole church could have profited instead of being disrupted. For some reason, however, Pelagius took another path. He evolved a new theology out of his legitimate pastoral concern. In so doing he inevitably conflicted with Augustine. *The Spirit and the Letter* undoubtedly leaves the door open for Pelagian self-correction. In no sense, however, does it make a movement of compromise on the essential theological and evangelical issues.

# CHAPTER IX

# Two Cyrils

## A. CYRIL OF JERUSALEM: THE CATECHETICAL LECTURES

### 1. The Lectures

Catechetical instruction neither began nor ended in Alexandria. Notwithstanding the pressures of persecution, schism, and dogmatic controversy, the evangelistic ministry of the early church brought in a steady flow of converts whom the individual churches prepared for the impressive public baptisms at Easter and Pentecost. It need occasion no surprise, then, that among the works of the fathers there has come down to us a Lenten series of catechetical addresses. These formed the culminating instruction given immediately prior to baptism and after the longer introductory courses. They were delivered by Cyril of Jerusalem, probably for the first time when he became bishop in 349, and then in succeeding years. They were not originally meant for publication, but catechumens seem to have taken them down in shorthand and in this way they were preserved for wider use in the church.

Although not without interruptions due to theological and ecclesiastical troubles, Cyril supervised the Jerusalem church between 349 and 387. Having outlasted the persecuting emperors, the church was increasing rapidly during this period. It was still plagued, however, by the Arian controversy until a final settlement was reached at Constantinople in 381. Cyril himself, although unquestionably orthodox, had no enthusiasm for homoousion, but he was finally won over to it and played an important role at the second ecumenical council. Indeed, it is generally thought that the Jerusalem Creed, which he expounds in the Lectures, formed the basis of the definitive symbol adopted at Constantinople.

Nominalism was also raising its faceless head now that Christianity was establishing itself as the religion of the empire. Cyril undoubtedly had a keen awareness of its presence. In his Lectures, as we shall see, he delivers many warnings against insincerity. In terms of spiritual efficacy, the step of baptism will be a futile one unless it is undertaken with genuine faith and commitment.

### 2. Baptism and Sin

*a. Warnings*

It is in the Procatechesis that Cyril gives his most serious warnings against merely going through the external motions. Simon Magus is recalled. "He was dipped in the font but he was not enlightened" (par. 2). False motives are exposed. The insincere cannot finally be stopped, but "though the water will not refuse to receive you, you will get no welcome from the Spirit" (par. 4). Baptism takes place only once (par. 7). In the same way, "God requires of us only one thing, sincerity" (par. 8). Lecture 1 drives home the point. We are to "attain by faith the pledge of the Holy Spirit" (1.2). When the Lord "finds a secret hypocrisy, he rejects the man as unfit for true service" (1.3) "It rests with God to bestow grace, but with you to accept and cherish it. Do not despise the grace because it is freely given, but rather cherish it with reverence once you have received it" (1.4).

*b. Sin and Grace*

A brief description is next given of the situation which leads to baptism. The starting point is the "terrible thing" called sin. This is "an evil freely chosen, the product of the will." "Though the Creator, being good, created unto good works, the creature of its own free will turned aside to wickedness" (2.1). While "the accursed devil" is its source, sin is "an evil springing up within you" (2.2–3). Yet God's grace brings the answer to man's sin, for "God is a lover of man." "The sum of your sins does not surpass the magnitude of God's mercies" (2.6). "Even a whole people's sin does not defeat the mercy of God," as one sees from the incident of the golden calf (2.10). The worst of sinners can find a place of repentance. Several examples show "that there is salvation for the penitent" (2.10–20).

*c. Baptism*

The candidates are coming to baptism for cleansing and forgiveness. The water alone does not effect this; it is the Holy Spirit who implants a seal on the soul. "For as the water purifies the body, so the Spirit seals the soul." Thus in entering the water we are not to regard it as "mere water," but to look for its saving power by the efficacy of the Holy Spirit (3.3–4). Why does God give the grace through water? In answer Cyril points to the important role of water in the Old Testament (3.5), finds in baptism the points of division between the Old Testament and the New (3.6), and argues that "Jesus sanctified baptism when he himself was baptized" (3.11). Hence "if a man does not receive baptism he does not attain salvation, except only the martyrs" (3.10). Nevertheless, while baptism "can expiate" even the sin of crucifying Christ (3.15), the rite alone does not do it. Repentance, faith, and sincerity are required. "Upon you also, if you have sincere piety, the Holy Spirit will descend" (3.14).

### 3. True Religion and Faith

#### a. True Religion

What is meant by sincerity? Cyril equates it with true religion, which he defines as "pious doctrine and virtuous action"; neither is legitimate without the other (4.2). His primary concern in these Lectures is with the "knowledge of doctrines." He thus outlines in 4.4–36 the main doctrinal themes from God to holy scripture. As regards the latter, he stresses the unity of the Old and the New Testaments with Christ as the focal point. "God foretold in the Old Testament the Christ who appeared in the New" (4.33). The canon of scripture is to be learned from the church. Cyril warns, "Have nothing to do with the apocryphal writings" (4.35), and his canon does not contain Revelation (4.36). He calls for "earnest study," but only of "those books which we read openly in the church" (4.35). The teaching which catechumens hear "is that of the divinely inspired scriptures" (4.33).

#### b. Faith

Since true religion embraces pious doctrine, it obviously involves faith, and Cyril devotes Catechesis 5 to this. Since God is faithful, we are like God in being "the faithful" (5.1). As human ventures demand faith, much more so does the service of God (5.3–4). Abraham "was justified, not by works alone, but by faith," that is, by believing the divine promises, every deed of his being thus "perfected by faith" (5.5). When we believe the resurrection of Christ, "by the likeness of our faith . . . we become the adopted sons of Abraham . . . and like him receive the spiritual seal, being circumcised by the Holy Spirit through the laver of baptism" (5.6). "Faith has such power that . . . some have been saved through the faith of others," such as the man sick of the palsy or Lazarus (5.8–9). Cyril finds "a second kind of faith" in "the special gift" which enables us "to do things beyond human power" (5.11). Finally, faith also means what is believed. In this sense it is compared to God's opening of a deposit account in a bank of which he is the author; it is our task to keep the deposit for God and then to return it to him when the Lord returns (5.13). This aspect of faith forms a smooth transition to the fuller discussion of the articles of faith which constitutes the main body of the Lectures.

### 4. God the Father

#### a. *The Unity of God*

The Triune God is the one God. We are limited in our understanding of this. "We say about God not what is due . . . but as much as our nature grasps" (6.2). Yet in spite of the divine incomprehensibility we may lawfully speak. "Because I cannot take in all the sunlight, may I not take in what is sufficient for my wants?" (6.5). Only the Son and the Spirit can behold the Father perfectly (6.6). The God who is one, who is, who is eternal, who is ever the selfsame, "fathers the countless operations of the Godhead." Being perfect in all things and everywhere present, he fashions all things through Christ (6.9). In the light of his greatness and goodness, idol worship can only be regarded as nonsensical, and the various dualistic systems from that of Simon Magus to that of Mani abound in illogicalities and defilements (6.10–34).

#### b. *The Fatherhood of God*

In the most proper sense God is Father as the Father of the Only-Begotten. "The very mention of the name of Father suggests the thought of the Son" and vice versa (7.1–4). Improperly speaking, God is "Father of many things," but "in nature and in truth he is Father of One only" (7.5). He did not become Father; "He is eternally Father of the Only-Begotten. A perfect Father, he begot a perfect Son, delivering all things to him whom he begot" (7.5). Less strictly, God is the Father of believers. Christ points to the distinction here when he speaks of "my father and your father" (7.7). Christians are not children by nature but by adoption. "Having been translated from servitude to adoption as sons, by the grace of the Father, through the Son and Holy Spirit, we are privileged by his ineffable lovingkindness" to call God Father (7.7). God is also Father figuratively, as in his care for orphans or his creation of men (7.10–12). Perversely, however, men choose stocks and stones or even Satan as father. By the opposite choice, that is, by faith, we come into "holy sonship" by being made sons of God (7.13).

#### c. *The Omnipotence of God*

God is the almighty Lord of both souls and bodies (8.1 3). "He tolerates many things because he so wills," not "for lack of power." He makes use of evils "to carry out his own dispensation" (8.4). Since all things belong to God, we may use them all for him. "Never say that money is the devil's." If we are not to be the slaves of riches, we are also "not to regard as enemies the things that God has given to serve us" (8.7).

#### d. *The Creatorhood of God*

God may not be seen with bodily eyes, but since he created all things, "from his divine works we can get some impression of his power" (9.2). Heretics and pagans, however, "see with the eyes of flesh but the eyes of their understanding are darkened" (9.4). In themselves the works of God bear clear testimony to God's power (9.5–15). If some plead ignorance of natural science, Cyril replies: "Enter into yourself and gain knowledge of the Creator from your own nature" (9.15). By analogy from the greatness and beauty of created things we may have a concept of the Creator (9.16).

### 5. God the Son

#### a. The Titles of Christ

Faith in God the Father implies faith in God the Son. Discussion of the second article begins with a survey of the various names and titles of Jesus, such as Christ, Savior, Lord, Vine, Door, High Priest (10.1–6). The witnesses to Christ are also enumerated: the Father and Spirit as divine witnesses, Gabriel as an angelic witness, Mary and the rest as human witnesses, the devils as demonic witnesses, and the cross, tomb, trees, places, and sun as natural witnesses (10.19–20).

#### b. The Deity of Christ

In view of the current christological discussion, Cyril thought it necessary to give a careful account of Christ's sonship. This fine presentation cannot be adequately summarized, but the following points may be noted.

(1) Christ is the one Son of God by nature, the Only-Begotten without brothers. We call him Son of God, "not of ourselves, but because the Father himself named Christ his Son" (11.2).

(2) "He was begotten from all eternity by an inscrutable and incomprehensible generation, . . . begotten Son from the beginning, like in all things to his Genitor" (11.4).

(3) "That which he had not he received but that which he has he has eternally." As Son of David according to the flesh, "he is subject to time . . . and his descent can be reckoned; but in his Godhead he is subject to neither time nor place nor genealogical reckoning" (11.5).

(4) His generation is not to be viewed as human. No analogies help here (11.8–11). "The Father begot in a manner no man would understand but as he himself only knows. For we do not claim to declare how he begot him; we merely affirm that it was not in this way or that" (11.11).

(5) The Father "did not bring the Son from non-being into being, nor by adoption receive into sonship him who was not; but the Father, being eternal, eternally and ineffably begot one only Son" (11.14).

(6) The Father as true God begot the Son as true God (11.9). Since the begetting God is perfect (11.7), his begetting was perfect, and he who

was begotten was perfect; the begetting did not diminish the Father's perfection. "Perfect is he who begets and perfect that which was begotten; he who begot is God, God is he who was begotten" (11.18).

### c. The Incarnation of the Son

Christ is confessed as man, too. For if he is God "but did not assume manhood, then we are strangers to salvation" (12.1).

(1) The Purpose of the Incarnation

(a) He came to save us from "the grievous wound of mankind," as the prophets foretold (12.5–12).

(b) "Since we could not behold or enjoy him as he is, he became what we are" (12.13).

(c) "His body was made a bait to death, so that the dragon, hoping to devour it, might disgorge those whom he had already devoured" (12.15).

(d) The time, place, and manner of his coming may all be learned from the prophets (12.17–26).

(2) Defense of the Incarnation

Objections against the incarnation are answered by Cyril. They relate primarily to the association of deity and humanity and to the virgin birth.

(a) Regarding the former Cyril finds a simple answer. "If it is felt that taking humanity is unworthy of deity, the answer is clear: He is not ashamed to take flesh from such members when he formed these very members" (12.26).

(b) Regarding the virgin birth he points out that ordinary birth is a remarkable thing but still takes place. Even more so, the creation of man out of the dust of the earth might seem to be impossible, but it has still been accomplished by God. The same applies to the virgin birth. We learn the possible from the actual.

### d. The Atoning Work of Christ

(1) The Crucifixion. Cyril finds it necessary to insist on the reality of Christ's death. "He truly suffered for all men. . . . His death was not imaginary" (13.4). Yet "being in the flesh like other men, he was not crucified for the sins men commit" (13.5). He died willingly. "Do you know why this lover of men did not shun death? To prevent the whole world from perishing in its sins." Hence the cross is "his own peculiar glory" (13.6). The story of the passion is foretold by the prophets as well as recorded in the gospels: "All has been inscribed in the prophetic records . . . by the Holy Spirit" (13.8). We discover this when we read scripture properly, "not to engage in speculative exposition . . . but rather to be convinced of what we already believe" (13.9). Cyril also expresses amazement at the verisimilitude of the Old Testament types, such as Eden or the brazen serpent (13.19–20). How did Christ's death

achieve reconciliation? Cyril puts it succinctly. "We were enemies of God through sin and God had decreed the death of the sinner. One of two things, therefore, was necessary, either that God, in his truth, should destroy all men, or that, in his lovingkindness, he should remit the sentence. But mark the wisdom of God: he upheld the truth of his sentence and the exercise of his lovingkindness. Christ took our sins 'in his body on the tree.'" Christ's righteousness more than counterbalanced human sin. Hence the sentence was carried out in him and in this way the remission of our sins was graciously secured as well (13.33).

(2) The Resurrection. Cyril acknowledges that only in the light of the resurrection can one see the meaning of the cross and boldly confess it (13.4). Like the crucifixion, the resurrection events are not only recorded in the New Testament but also prophesied in the Old (14.2–20). He adduces as witnesses the women, the apostles, the angels, the moon, the grave, the linens he left behind, and those who like Tabitha have themselves been raised up in the name of the risen Lord (14.21–24).

### e. The Second Coming of Christ

While no place remains now for millennialism, Cyril states firmly that "we preach not only one coming of Christ but a second as well" which "will bring with it the crown of the kingdom of God" (15.1). This, too, the prophets foretell (15.2–3). Signs have also been given, and Cyril lists and discusses them. While indicating their fulfillment, he wisely admits that "we do not know whether all this will happen in our time." All the same, "it is good to be aware of events and to be on guard" (15.4–11). A more detailed equation is made between Daniel's fourth kingdom and the Roman empire (15.12–21). Christ's people will be raptured at his coming: "They will then ride upon chariots of clouds and be gathered together by the angels" (15.22–23). But solemn and searching judgment follows with eternal condemnation no less a possibility than eternal felicity. "The judgment will be terrible, the sentence a reason for dread. The kingdom of heaven lies before us, everlasting fire has been prepared" (15.26). A call is issued, then, for righteous works and good stewardship.

## 6. God the Holy Spirit

### a. The Biblical Doctrine of the Spirit

Spiritual grace is especially needed in speaking about the Holy Spirit (16.1). We can be safe "when we adduce the words of sacred scripture" (16.1), for "the Holy Spirit has authored the scriptures; he has himself spoken all that he wished or all that we can grasp" (16.2). There is one Spirit who inspired both the prophets and the apostles, so that we are not to "separate the Old from the New Testament and say that the Spirit is one in the Old and another in the New" (16.4). Though the

Spirit is one in nature, yet "by the will of God and in the name of the Son he brings about many virtuous effects"; the gifts of the spirit are mentioned here (16.12). The general use of the term "spirit" calls for discussion and differentiation (16.13). The Holy Spirit may be known by the fact that "his actions effect what is good and salutary" (16.16).

### b. The Works of the Spirit

Enlightenment enjoys high priority among the works of the Spirit. "He dispels ignorance and instills knowledge." "He enlightens the saints" (16.17–18). The Spirit also gives the power of exorcism (16.19). He comforts, intercedes, and teaches (16.20). He dispenses such gifts as chastity, almsgiving, and poverty (16.22). Gifts are a work of the whole Trinity: "The Father, through the Son, with the Holy Spirit, bestows all gifts" (16.24). Laying on of hands is connected with the giving of the Spirit himself in both the Old Testament and the New, and Cyril suggests that the grace will come similarly on the candidates (16.26). As we learn from the Old Testament, the works of the Spirit also include wisdom (16.27, 31) and a new heart and spirit (16.30).

### c. The Titles of the Spirit

Many titles are used for the Spirit. He is called the Advocate and the Sanctifier. He is also described as the Spirit of truth, grace, adoption, counsel, etc. (17.2–5). He is the Spirit of God, of the Father, of Christ, and of the Son (17.2, 4). Yet "though the titles are different, the Holy Spirit is one and the same . . . living, subsisting, ever present with the Father and Son . . . the author of the divine scriptures in the Old and the New Testaments" (17.5). After this clarification Cyril expands his presentation of the works of the Spirit by instances from the New Testament (17.8–33). He takes the tongues of Pentecost to be foreign languages which the Holy Spirit taught the apostles instantaneously in a reversal of "the first evil confusion at Babylon" (17.16–17). The enumeration concludes with a fresh warning against insincerity and an assurance that "if you draw near with faith, men will minister to you visibly, but the Holy Spirit will bestow on you what is not visible" (17.36). With remission of sins will come also, in measure, the ability to "accomplish deeds beyond the power of man" (17.37) and to all of us his bounty is imparted that we may "always exhibit the fruits of the Holy Spirit" (17.38).

## 7. The Church and the Resurrection of the Dead

### a. The Resurrection of the Dead

When he comes to the resurrection of the dead, Cyril makes a strange excursion into natural theology, even dragging in a hibernating toad and, as an unequivocal precedent of resurrection again after decay,

the fabled phoenix (18.2–14). These arguments, he says, are "for unbelievers." Believers, of course, will find support for their belief in scripture. He thus returns to his more usual theological style with a series of
Old and New Testament verses which "bear witness to the resurrection
of the dead" (18.16). From Paul he argues that while the body shall be
raised "the very same body . . . it will not abide in its present condition
but as an eternal body" (18.18).

### b. The Church

Since time was apparently running short, Cyril has only a brief
section on the church. The term "church" might in itself signify any
assembly; he thus finds the qualifying adjective "catholic" of supreme
importance (18.23–26). This describes the church's universality (18.23),
but it also serves to differentiate the true church from heretical gatherings (18.26). The catholic church, which we are to ask for when in a
strange town, is "the mother of us all and the spouse of our Lord Jesus
Christ" (18.26). Catholicity also distinguishes the "second church,"
which "alone has unlimited power throughout the whole world" (18.27),
from the first church, which was restricted to Judea and which was
rejected with its rejection of Jesus (18.25, 27). This sharp concept of two
churches was to have momentous theological and practical consequences, especially in the area of relations between Christians and
Jews.

### 8. Evaluation

As a course of basic Christian instruction, the Catechetical Lectures have few rivals in the history of theology. They display a wide
range of biblical knowledge. The heads of doctrine are treated with a
notable combination of comprehensiveness and depth. Felicity of style
goes hand in hand with mastery of the material on the one side and
spiritual fervor on the other. Occasional blemishes cannot be denied.
When Cyril resorts to philosophical argument or exposition, he runs into
obvious conflict with his predominantly biblical method and increases,
rather than decreases, his vulnerability. Again, his understanding of
scripture will not always command assent, and some of his theological
statements call out for emendation or rebuttal. As lectures, many of the
Catecheses are too long, as Cyril himself at times acknowledges (see
16.32). Nevertheless, the work stands out by reason of its overall quality, the solidity of its teaching, and its abundance of well-turned and
striking phrases.

The marked difference in quality is one of the strongest reasons
for doubting whether the Five Mystagogical Lectures, which have been
traditionally associated with the Catecheses, are really from the same
pen. The Mystagogical Lectures follow on naturally enough, since they

take the candidates through the rites of confession, baptism, anointing, and first Eucharist. Nor is it at all improbable that they came from the same place and period. Indeed, some commentators are prepared to think that Cyril had something to do with their original form. Apart from evident differences in style and quality, however, the Mystagogical Lectures seem to equate the gift of the Spirit more specifically with the anointing: "While your body is anointed with the visible oil, your soul is sanctified by the Holy Spirit" (ML 3.3). The Catecheses, in contrast, associate the baptism of the Spirit with the baptism in water, except perhaps in the enigmatic saying in 16.26 in which Cyril speaks of the coming grace in the context of the laying on of hands. A suggested solution to the general problem of authorship is that the Mystagogical Lectures were composed or possibly revised by Cyril's successor, John (387–417), although this solution raises difficulties of its own which need not be discussed here.

To those who wish to claim Cyril as an early proponent of the chrism-Spirit equation, it might be important to defend the Mystagogical Lectures as his work. Whether the issue mattered so much when baptism, confirmation, and first Eucharist formed a single complex is another question. The certain factor is that the Catechetical Lectures constitute a unity of their own and must be recognized both as a notable landmark in the church's instructional ministry and also as a theological contribution of a very high order.

## B. CYRIL OF ALEXANDRIA: THE THIRD DOGMATIC LETTER TO NESTORIUS

### 1. The Occasion

The churches were not to enjoy christological peace for long after the settlement of Constantinople (381). By 430 Constantinople itself had become a new center of controversy as Nestorius the bishop, with his insistence on the true humanity of Christ, came under the suspicion of undermining the unity of Christ's person. A careful consideration of what Nestorius actually said suggests that he did not really teach the heresy of two persons, but he was condemned at Ephesus in 431 when many of his contemporaries took this to be the drift of his teaching and especially of his refusal to describe Mary as *theotokos,* the God-bearer or mother of God. Among those who played a leading part in exposing, refuting, and prosecuting Nestorius was Cyril of Alexandria. It was in the course of the debate that in 430, in the name of the Synod of Egypt, Cyril wrote to Nestorius laying down the teaching he must accept and appending anathemas to which he must subscribe.

## 2. The Basic Truth

Cyril begins with a statement of truth which, he claims, the fathers confessed as they were taught by the Spirit. "The unique Word ... begotten of the very substance of the Father ... underwent a birth like ours ... not throwing off what he was but, even though he became man by the assumption of flesh, yet still remaining what he was, that is, God indeed in nature and truth." The flesh was not "changed into the nature of Godhead nor was the ineffable nature of the Word of God transformed into the nature of flesh." "Even when seen as a babe he filled all creation as God and was enthroned with him who begot him."

## 3. The Hypostatic Union

No division is seen, of course, between God and man. Concepts which fall short of authentic union are thus excluded. a. We cannot speak of a union only of "dignity and authority, for this would be an empty phrase and no more." b. Nor can we speak of two Christs, one the Word of God, the other born of a woman. c. Nor can we say "that the Word of God tabernacled in him who was begotten of the holy virgin as an ordinary man, lest Christ should be thought of as a Godbearing man." d. Nor are we to define the union in terms of association, for "this is not enough for a natural (or hypostatic) union." e. Nor is it accurate to speak of an acquired relation. f. Indeed, Cyril finds the term "conjunction" too weak in this whole context. In Christ, God the Word and his flesh are not conjoined but united in one hypostasis.

## 4. Unsatisfactory Phrase

With Nestorius in view, Cyril now lists three weak or even abhorrent phrases which cannot be accepted. a. We must not say: "I adore him who was born for the sake of him who bore him." b. Nor should we say: "I worship him who was seen for the sake of the invisible." c. Particularly objectionable is the statement: "He who is assumed is styled as God with him who assumed," for this posits two Christs and patently denies true and authentic union.

## 5. Necessary Points

a. In contrast, we are to confess of Christ that "he who was begotten from God the Father as Son and God only begotten, though being by his own nature impassible, suffered in the flesh for us." b. It thus follows that "he was in the crucified flesh impassibly making his own the sufferings of his own flesh." c. This leads to a further consideration: "He tasted death for everyone . . . although by nature he was life and was himself the resurrection." d. Cyril adds that by celebration of "the unbloody service in the churches . . . we are sanctified, becoming partakers of the holy flesh and honourable blood of Christ the Saviour of all of us."

### 6. The One Hypostasis

a. We cannot speak of "two hypostases or persons," for different entities are united into the "indivisible unity."

b. Since, "being God by nature, he became flesh, that is, man ensouled with a rational soul," we need not be embarrassed by recorded sayings of his which "befit humanity."

c. "All the terms used in the gospels are to be referred to one person, the one incarnate hypostasis of the Word."

d. The virgin may be called *theotokos,* since she "gave birth after the flesh to God who was united by hypostasis with the flesh," although, of course, the Word did not have "the beginning of its existence from flesh," nor did the Word "need human birth."

### 7. The Anathemas

As the price of peace Nestorius had to accept the teaching which Cyril had outlined and at the same time join in condemning twelve opinions, of which the following, perhaps, are the most important.

a. First there must be rejection of any denial that "the Word of God the Father was united by hypostasis to one flesh and is one Christ with his own flesh, that is, the same both God and man together."

b. Also to be rejected is any division of the hypostases after the union or any belief in their conjunction other than "in a union by nature."

c. The distribution of some sayings in the gospels to a man separated from the Word and of others to the Word alone must also be anathematized

d. So, too, must the failure to say of Christ that he is "by nature one Son." To this Nestorius replied that it is an error to say that "after the taking of manhood the Son of God is one by nature."

e. Cyril also calls for condemnation of the denial that "the Word of God suffered in the flesh, and was crucified in the flesh, and tasted death in the flesh . . . although he is as God life and lifegiving."

f. Finally, anathema must be pronounced on the idea that Christ "was glorified by the Spirit as making use of an alien power that worked through him."

### 8. Survey

*a. Gains*

Cyril's brief but well-packed theological statement makes it clear that the unity of Christ must be preserved at all costs. Insofar as inadequate explanations of the unity must inevitably bring about its dissolution, they are rightly brought under criticism. The credibility of the figure of Christ is at stake here, as is also the authenticity of his portrayal in scripture. Equally at stake is the message of salvation, for the atonement makes sense, not if the death on the cross is that of a man associated with God, but only if it is that of the lifegiving Son of God himself in his flesh. In carefully considered language Cyril provides safeguards against erosion at these essential points and in the process sketches the necessary features in a satisfactory understanding of the incarnate Word.

*b. Losses*

The gains are offset, however, by unfortunate losses which seem to be due mainly to Cyril's domineering temperament. His statement leaves little room for the discussion that might have cleared up misunderstandings. Not content to describe opposing phrases as inadequate, he categorically denounces them as erroneous. Apparently he does not even consider that his own exposition might also need clarification or modification. His call for anathematizing slams the door in a way little calculated to win over his real or fancied opponents. If it brings about a triumph of the truth, it no less effectively excludes agreement in the truth.

*c. Problems*

The letter, for all its essential soundness, also raises questions. On occasion Cyril unhappily equates hypostatic union, or union by hypostasis, with natural union, or union by nature. This undoubtedly prepares the way for Eutychianism and Monophysitism and their appeal to Cyril. What does he mean by it? Would he have accepted the counterbalance of Leo's Tome and the Chalcedonian Definition with their one hypostasis and two natures? The basic problem is that he does not finally make clear what he means by the one hypostasis and its relation to the humanity. Presumably the hypostasis is that of God the Son, one of the three hypostases in the one *ousia* of God. But again, as Cyril presents it, human nature seems to be threatened with complete absorption by the hypostatic union. At a later date Leontius of Byzantium would try to show that the one hypostasis does not have to imply one nature. In his *Three Books against the Nestorians and Eutychians* he argues that "if Godhead and manhood, when united in substance, do not retain, even in the union, the natural property of each, they are mixed together and there remains neither Godhead nor manhood." Hence, if the manhood has no autonomous center of being, this is not because it is completely anhypostasis (without center), but because it is enhypostasis (centered in the Word). No doubt this is what Cyril had in mind. Yet the clarification came too late to prevent the confusion of union by hypostasis with union by nature which occasioned the first decisive break in ecumenical unity.

# CHAPTER X
# *A Cappadocian and the Damascene*

## A. A CAPPADOCIAN: GREGORY OF NYSSA

### 1. The Cappadocian Fathers

During the later fourth century, Cappadocia made a notable contribution to the church's theology and mission. Three great leaders from the area helped to carry the Nicene faith to triumph at Constantinople in 381. They worked hard to clear up misunderstandings. They also set an excellent example in maintaining pastoral standards, improving Christian life, and promoting asceticism.

Basil of Caesarea undoubtedly played the chief part in the development of Cappadocian influence, for in addition to his gifts as theologian and pastor he had considerable administrative talents. His friend Gregory of Nazianzus gave him able support, although Basil's attempt to place him in the remote bishopric of Sasima proved to be a fiasco and caused a rift between the two. During a brief tenure of the see of Constantinople, Gregory presided at the ecumenical council of 381, and it was in Constantinople that he delivered most of the *Theological Orations* which won him the title of Theologos and which are his chief claim to theological distinction.

The third in the Cappadocian trio was Gregory of Nyssa (c. 334–395), a younger brother of Basil. After a period as a professor of rhetoric, Gregory retired with Basil and their sister Macrina into the monastic life. He emerged to become bishop of Nyssa in 372. Although far from successful on the political side of church life, Gregory made his mark at the Council of Constantinople. He left a sizable body of writings including works of exegesis, sermons, letters, brief theological treatises, and the important *Catechetical Oration*.

### 2. The Catechetical Oration

Written around 383, the *Catechetical Oration* seems to have been composed, not as an actual course of instruction, but as a manual for those charged with the task of teaching catechumens. It attempts to state the essential Christian doctrines in a form which will satisfy philosophical criteria and meet philosophical objections. It obviously exerted influence at a broader level than that of ordinary catechizing, for later theologians such as Theodoret refer to it. Covering the chief heads of Christian teaching in compact form, it yields insight both into Gregory's own theological understanding and also into that of the Eastern church of his time.

### 3. Introduction

Gregory opens his work with a discussion of the catechetical task. He describes teaching as "an essential duty" which serves to enlarge the church. Its aim never changes, but different approaches must be used in different cases. Two general categories may be discerned, monotheistic Jews on the one side and polytheistic or atheistic Greeks on the other. With the latter in mind, Gregory suggests that the first job must be either to use God's works to show to atheists the existence of God, or to lead polytheists "to the acknowledgment of a single deity." In order to achieve this goal he provides a brief philosophical argument.

### 4. The Doctrine of God

Monotheism now being presupposed, Gregory aims in the section on God to show both Jews and Greeks that "some distinction of persons (or hypostases)" exists within the unity. He arrives at the person of the Word analogically from the existence of reason, power, life, or wisdom in us. The Word in us, of course, is transitory since we are transitory beings. However, "The incorruptible and eternal nature has a speech which is eternal and substantial." This Word, having subsistence, can easily be shown to have life and will. While it is distinct by reason of its individual subsistence, yet "by manifesting in itself the attributes to be seen in God, it is identical in nature with him" (chap. 1). A similar process of thought leads to a similar conclusion in relation to the Holy Spirit (chap. 2). Gregory acknowledges that "we cannot, of course, express the ineffable depth of the mystery in words." Nevertheless, we can have some apprehension of the distinction of persons and unity of nature, so that the truths in both monadic monotheism and strict polytheism are preserved without the defects or aberrations of either (chap. 3). As is most fitting in Gregory's view, scripture is used to answer Jewish objections. He quotes and expounds "the divinely inspired" Psalm 33:6 in this connection.

## 5. The Creation, Fall, and Death of Man

### a. Creation

Starting with the rationality of the universe, Gregory presses home the point that the wisdom or Word of God lies behind it and indeed created it. "There is no other cause by which the different parts of the universe were created than the Word himself." In particular, the Word created man, "not driven by any necessity . . . but out of his abundant love" and so that no aspect of his nature "should lie idle with none to share or enjoy it." To be fit to share in this divine goodness, man had to be given "some element in his nature akin to what he was to share." He was thus "endowed with life, reason, wisdom," and immortality, or, in other words, he was created "in the image of God" (chap. 5).

### b. Fall

Does not man's present situation give the lie to this understanding? No, says Gregory, for "human life is at present in an unnatural condition." Man "was not made by his Creator in a state of evil." By creation he enjoyed "the gift of liberty and free will." Hence evil originated, not in the divine will, but in some way within, as a withdrawal from the good which enables its opposite, not created by God, to come into existence (chap. 5).

By why did man choose this course? In answer Gregory advances an intricate and labored argument.

(1) God produced in man a harmonious blend of the intelligible and the sensible.

(2) He set over the earth an angelic power "which took it amiss . . . that out of the nature subject to him there should be produced a being to resemble the transcendent dignity."

(3) This being, created and therefore mutable, fell into envy through closing its eyes to the good.

(4) He then misused his divinely given capacity for thought "to mingle evil with the free will of man." In this way he "in some measure quenched and obscured God's blessing," so that in us life, power, blessing, and candor came to be replaced by death, weakness, cursing, and shame (chap. 6).

Can God be good, however, if he foresaw this disaster and still created man? This question of the good God and an evil world, Gregory replies, has force only as good and evil are defined by reference to bodily pleasure or pain. In fact, "nothing is evil save wickedness." But wickedness "does not exist in its own right." God, then, did not create it: "He is not the author of what has no existence." Evil arises only as the privation of good. It is possible because God does not compel us to do his will. "If a man in broad daylight of his own free will chooses to close his eyes, the sun is not responsible for his failure to see" (chap. 7).

### c. Death

Is not the divine sentence of death the final evil? Not at all, says Gregory, for death makes possible a refashioning of man in his original state. The nature created for immortality was certainly clothed with mortality, but this brings only the dissolving of the sentient part and does not affect the divine image. Nor does dissolution mean destruction, which is passing into nonbeing. God dissolves the sentient part only to remold it, while at the same time he subjects the soul to healing judgments which, like surgical procedures, may be painful but by which he "restores his own creation to its original grace." A divine teleology may thus be discerned, and the final answer to the apparent riddle of God's goodness and our present situation appears. "Just as he saw man's perversion, so he perceived his restoration once more to the good" (chap. 8).

## 6. Incarnation and the Atonement

### a. Explanation

As God created man through the Word, to whom but to the Word did it belong "to restore him who was fallen"? But why should this involve the incarnation and the consequent humanity of the Word? Gregory advances in response the thesis that "no shame at all attaches to what is alien to evil," and surely the bodily life of Christ cannot be called evil (chap. 9). Yet can the infinite deity be contained in a finite body? Circumscription is not the point of incarnation. Even the human intellect can roam beyond the body in which it is set (chap. 10). We cannot understand the unity of soul and body and yet we accept the fact of it. Similarly "we are unable to detect how the divine is mingled with the human, yet we have no doubt ... that God underwent birth in human nature" (chap. 11).

### b. Miracles

God's activities make this plain, for as his very existence can be seen in his works, so "the wonders evident in his actions we regard as sufficient proof of the presence of the Godhead." Even in birth and death — the limits of life — divine power, and not human weakness, may be seen, that is, in the virgin birth and the resurrection. Incredulity, Gregory observes, implies acknowledgment "that the miracles transcend nature" (chap. 12).

### c. Purpose

"Why, then, did the divine stoop to such humiliation?" (chap. 14). The answer is plain once it is seen that "the love of man is the proper mark of the divine nature," for God came among us to save us from our "pitiful and wretched state" (chap. 15). Could he not have done this, however, by "a sovereign and divine act of authority" instead of taking the "tedious, circuitous route" of incarnation? To this Gregory has several answers.

(1) God enters human nature, not a state of evil, so that incarnation implies for him no self-contradiction.

(2) Similarly, he takes on the mutability of natural life, but this does not imply that he also adopts our weakness, since weakness has the moral sense of inclination to evil.

(3) By being united with both the intelligible and the sensible elements in our nature, after their separation in his death, through the resurrection "he united what was separated in an unbreakable union." He thus opposed to the principle of death in one person the principle of resurrection in another person, thereby restoring "man's primal grace," that is, eternal life (chap. 16).

(4) We should not question the divine method, since the sick must not prescribe to the doctor the manner of treatment (chap. 17).

(5) While the divine rationality will be clear only "when we see what we hope for," historical developments display the efficacy of the divine action, since idolatry is being overthrown and the divinely legislated practice of Judaism has been terminated with the destruction of Jerusalem and the temple (chap. 18).

### d. Union of the Divine Attributes

God's plan commends itself finally because in it there was no tendency "for one of his attributes to be present . . . while another was absent" (chap. 20). When we fell into the power of the adversary, deceived by the bait of good on the fishhook of evil, God "had to contrive a just and not a dictatorial method" to restore our freedom. He had to offer the master a better bargain as "the price of the slave" (chap. 22).

### e. The Ransom

The incarnate Christ was the bargain which offered the devil more than he held. God planned, however, to offer the Son under the veil of flesh in order that "the enemy might not be terrified at the approach of transcendent power" (chap. 23) but "like a greedy fish might swallow the Godhead like a fishhook along with the flesh which was the bait." The power as well as the justice of God comes to light here. It is the power which is so great that "it is not bounded by circumstances contrary to its nature." Thus God's condescension to our weak nature displays his power even more clearly than the work of creation does. "God can become man and not cease to be God" (chap. 24).

### f. Immanence and Incarnation

Gregory finds no fundamental incompatibility in God's assumption of our nature. We have our being in God so that he is not in any case external to us. He is generally united with us in his sustaining of existing things. He thus does nothing strange when he enters into a particular union with our nature "in order that by its union with the divine . . . it might become divine" (chap. 25).

### g. Deceit

Did God use deceit to defeat the enemy? Gregory thinks not. If justice means rendering to each his due, it is just that the deceiver should be himself deceived. Wisdom, however, combines this justice with the noble end of love. Thus what is evil in the deceiver, the deceit whereby he ruined our nature, is good in God, "who made use of a deceitful device to save the one who had been ruined" and even to benefit "the very one who had brought us to ruin." It is here that Gregory, following Origen, can hold out a universal hope which embraces the devil, too. For, as he sees it, death, darkness, and corruption fall into nonexistence when they come into contact with life, light, and incorruption. This separation will be effected, perhaps, only through a long and painful process. In the end, however, "all creation will join in united thanksgiving, both those whose purification has involved punishment and those who never needed purification at all" (chap. 26).

### h. Extent of the Incarnation

To effect a total cleansing God "shared all the marks of our nature." He also lived a human life from birth to death. Hence his power covers all that lies between. Since God transcends all creation, sharing our properties can be no more and no less unworthy of God than union with a heavenly body. Both unions fall short of his dignity, but coming to the aid of the needy befits his nature (chap. 27). Birth is not in itself a contradiction of his deity. "The only thing alien to the divine is evil. Nature is not evil" (chap. 28).

### i. Problems

(1) Why did God delay the incarnation? He did so in order that evil might first come to full manifestation (chap. 29).

(2) Can he really have destroyed evil, however, when obviously it is still around us? Yes, the serpent has received a mortal blow. If vestiges of evil still harass us, this is because even after the death of the head the tail "still remains pulsing with its own life" (chap. 30).

(3) Why do not all believe? God issues a general call to the race but out of regard for us has left us with the will, "a faculty which is free from bondage . . . and is grounded in the freedom of the mind." If the will were forced, we should lose the boon of intelligence, virtue would vanish, and life would lose its honor (chap. 30).

(4) Why did Christ go to the cross? Death forms the second limit of

human life. Hence "to experience all that belongs to our nature" Christ had also to die. Yet the death did not occur because of the birth. "The birth was accepted by him for the sake of the death," so that he by his death might "recall us from death to life" and exalt "the lump of our humanity along with the Godhead" (chap. 32). This death took place on the cross because by its shape the cross signifies the bringing of diverse natures of existing things into one accord. Thus the eyes of all creation focus on the incarnate and crucified Word as the center of creation and the basis of its harmony. Gregory sees no reason to discuss in detail the resurrection and ascension since they accord so plainly both with the positive side of our restoration and also with the sublime and transcendent power of God.

### 7. The Sacraments

#### a. Baptism

A second birth is needed to bring the mortal creature to immortal life. This is effected by prayer, invocation, water, and faith. If it be asked how external things can do this, Gregory makes the common appeal to the mystery of our first birth and finds the solution in both cases in God's power. The baptismal rite he explains in terms of its affinity to the work to which it owes its efficacy, namely, the death and resurrection of him in whom "life became a reality, so that by means of the flesh which he assumed and deified, salvation might come to all that was akin to it." Baptism, then, represents a beginning of regeneration which will finally end in the resurrection. To be sure, our nature will in any case reach the end of refashioning in accordance with the Creator's plan for it. But whereas the nature purified in baptism will enter into the fullness of life, "those who have not been initiated into this purification must necessarily be purified by fire" (chap. 35). Only faith and water — simple things — are needed, "but what a blessing springs from these things — no less than kinship with God himself" (chap. 36).

#### b. The Eucharist

Since man consists of soul and body, "those who come to salvation must be united with the author of their life by means of both." The bread and wine of communion make possible the bodily union. Gregory has a complicated explanation of this. Christ used bread and wine in nourishment. They thus became by assimilation his flesh and blood, and the body in which God dwelt was in a sense identical with them. This body, then, can serve to nourish believers as they take bread and wine consecrated by the Word. For, following out his plan to deify humanity by close relation with deity, God, by means of his flesh, which is constituted of bread and wine, implants himself in all believers through their partaking of bread and wine. "He unites himself with their bodies so that mankind too, by its union with what is immortal, may share in incorruptibility." The blessing forms the key, for through it God "changés the nature of the visible elements into that immortal body" (chap. 37).

### 8. Faith and Renewal

#### a. Faith
Gregory thinks it important that he who is born by spiritual rebirth should know "by whom he is born and what kind of creature he becomes." For in this birth a choice of parent can be made. The obvious choice is to be born of a nature which is immutably good, that is, of the Trinity, which was not created. Only as a man allies himself with the uncreated nature and not with the creation which is akin to him and shares his good can he be said to be born from above and to undergo a change for the better (chaps. 38–39).

#### b. Renewal
The fact must be faced that many "are born in appearance only and not in reality." Change cannot be present "when there is no noticeable alteration." Baptism "produces no essential change in human nature." The change must consist in a doing away of the "evil characteristics" of human nature. Without this, "the water is only water and the gift of the Spirit is nowhere evident in the action." "If you persist in displaying the marks of evil, it is useless to prattle to yourself about the birth from above." Life after baptism must show a moral difference from life before it. Thus a life of renewal, conformable to the divine nature and holding out the promise of blessing instead of punishment, has to be chosen (chap. 40).

### 9. Comments

#### a. Points of Interest
The *Catechetical Oration* has many points of interest. In it Gregory sees and states clearly the need to adapt instruction to the different ideas and backgrounds of the hearers. He manifests an obvious ability to deal with the problems which bothered cultured Gentiles as they confronted the gospel. He expounds the doctrine of the Trinity with no little skill and competence, admirably perceives the harmony of the divine attributes in the incarnation and atonement, and appreciates the soteriological purpose of the divine action. Along the familiar lines of his generation, he steers a careful course between dualism and the divine authorship of evil. He firmly insists on the place of the body in salvation and yet avoids the idea of sacramental efficacy merely through the performance of external actions. At some points Gregory gives evidence

of keen theological insight, as in his discernment that the divine power finds supreme manifestation as power in human weakness and in his emphasis that there can be no incongruity between God and his creation — only between God and the state of evil.

### b. Problems

For all its merits, the *Catechetical Oration* can hardly be described as a theological triumph. For one thing, it offers a type of catechetical instruction which is constantly merging into apologetics. This explains, but surely does not justify, the astonishing lack of explicit biblical basis. Instead of expounding the faith, Gregory entangles himself in philosophical discussions whose value is often debatable and whose upshot is to obscure rather than elucidate. If the basis were consistently scriptural, this might not matter so much. It could be seen simply as Gregory's attempt to express the gospel in the jargon of his age. But is it always the gospel that he is expressing? Gregory is guilty both of arbitrary omission on the one side and speculative expansion on the other. His early section on angelic envy and the origin of evil bodes no good for what is to follow. The universalism which makes of perdition a purgatory offers a more categorical, but no more solidly grounded, development of the tentative suggestions of Origen. The growing stress on salvation by incarnation and deification weakens the biblical concentration on the passion, while Gregory's doctrine of the atonement and his explanation of the cross fall lamentably and ludicrously short of what the rich presentation in holy scripture demands. Nor can the complex statement on Eucharistic nourishment be regarded as ultimately valid or valuable as an exposition or explanation of the biblical teaching.

### c. Summary

In the *Catechetical Oration* we find an early and instructive example of a theology of more pronounced philosophical style. If this opens up certain possibilities, it also brings to light inherent limitations of which, unfortunately, Gregory shows too little awareness. In the long run, no doubt, he uses philosophy to explicate the faith he already has. In this sense he still engages in true theology, and his work might be construed as an essay on the rationality of the divine being and action. Yet Gregory does not make this clear to the teachers whom he is ostensibly guiding, so that unless they have a prior understanding of their task, they might easily become involved in futile argumentation and controversy. Indeed, one wonders whether Gregory does not himself lose sight of his primary theological remit. Extraneous trains of thought completely replace the Bible's own account of itself. He grasps an illusory freedom in order to launch out into fancies with neither basis nor restraint. His good intentions of stating the faith for the Greeks do not counterbalance his failure to think through the theological task more clearly and to carry it out more cautiously and faithfully. In the long run, then, the *Catechetical Oration* has a predominantly negative value, not so much as an example of what not to do, but more as a warning that better understanding and greater restraint are needed if a translation of categories is to be done successfully in either theology in general or catechetical instruction in particular.

## B. THE DAMASCENE: JOHN

### 1. Introduction

*a. The Life of John*

Eastern theology reached its climax and culmination in the eighth century with *The Orthodox Faith* of John of Damascus. John was the grandson of an important Christian official of Damascus named Mansur. His father, Sergius, was also a civil servant under the Omayyad Caliph. At first John followed his father in government administration, but in about 715 he moved to St. Sabbas monastery (Mar Saba) near Jerusalem. When Leo the Isaurian published the iconoclastic edict in 726, John joined in the opposition to it and stated his case in *Three Apologetic Discourses.* Composed in about 730, these proved so successful that under the name of Mansur, John was anathematized posthumously in 753. He spent the whole of his life after 715 at Mar Saba and wrote several polemical, moral, dogmatic, and homiletical works, dying in about 749.

*b. The Orthodox Faith*

*The Orthodox Faith* forms the third part of the *Fount of Knowledge,* one of his last books, which he apparently wrote at the request of a friend, Cosmas of Maiuma. The first part of this work consists of the *Philosophical Chapters,* which are concerned in the main with the terms and concepts found in philosophical discussion, especially those that have acquired a technical theological sense. A section then follows called *Heresies in Epitome.* Here John gives a brief account of 103 heresies. In the case of the first 100 he does little more than edit existing material, but in dealing with the last three, the Ishmaelites, Mohammedans, and obscure Aposchistae, he breaks new ground. In a suitable transition to the dogmatic section John concludes the part on heresies with an expanded version of what "the Catholic Church . . . instructed by the Holy Spirit . . . teaches rightly and religiously." The full title of the third and final section is *The Exact Exposition of the Orthodox Faith.* Here in 100 chapters John expounds the main articles of doctrine in the Nicene Faith with a heavy concentration on the trinitarian and christological teaching.

## 2. The Doctrine of God

### a. The Knowledge of God

(1) By Revelation. John opens *The Orthodox Faith* by pointing out that "after the first blessed state of nature, no one has ever known God, unless God himself revealed it to him."

(2) General Revelation. A general revelation is not excluded, "for through nature the knowledge of the existence of God has been revealed by him to all men."

(3) Special Revelation. In special revelation, which extends through the Old Testament to Christ, "God has given us knowledge of himself according to our capacity" (i.1).

### b. The Limitations of Knowledge

(1) Matter. John candidly admits that God has withheld "that which we are not able to bear" (i.1).

(2) Expression. He also sees that "in what concerns theology" "not all things are capable of expression nor are they all knowable." We often "have to express in human terms things which transcend the human order" (i.2).

(3) Scripture. Having confessed the one God in three persons, and the incarnation of the Word by the good pleasure of the Father and with the cooperation of the Holy Spirit, John concludes that "it is impossible either to say or fully to understand anything about God beyond what has been divinely proclaimed to us . . . by the sacred declaration of the Old and New Testaments" (i.2).

### c. The Existence and Essence of God

(1) Existence. John believes that since mutable things are created, it follows that that there must be an immutable Creator. The harmony of the universe supports this (i.3).

(2) Essence. If, however, the existence of God is easily demonstrable, knowing his essence is another matter. Negative definitions, such as "God has no body" or "God is incorruptible," do not suffice. "God transcends all beings and being itself." Even divine qualities, such as goodness or wisdom, do not show the nature of God but only things relating to his nature (i.4).

### d. The Triune God

(1) Unity. John begins his exposition of God by using scripture to show the unity of God. For those who do not accept scripture, he offers some logical considerations arising out of the definition of God (i.5).

(2) Trinity. For God's being as Word and Spirit, John largely restates the argument of Gregory of Nyssa (i.6–7). Should the Jew object, some Old Testament references are added so that "the sacred scripture may refute him and reduce him to silence" (i.7).

### e. The Eternal Begetting and Procession

(1) Begetting. Summarizing the thinking of the past centuries, John insists that in God begetting cannot mark a change or a beginning. Yet one cannot "speak of God as naturally lacking the power of begetting." Begetting is not creation; it "means producing of the substance of the begetter an offspring like in substance to the begetter." Human begetting is "in quite another manner," and while other analogies help, such as those of light and fire, none can do justice to the unique divine interrelation (i.8).

(2) Procession. Like other church fathers, John admits that he can understand neither begetting, nor procession, nor the difference between them. He accepts the terms because they "were handed down to us from scripture." In the early and eastern tradition, John says of the Spirit that "he proceeds from the Father and is communicated through the Son." The three persons are "of one and the same substance." It is only in respect of "the three personal properties" of being unbegotten, being begotten, and proceeding "that the three divine persons differ from one another, being indivisibly divided by the distinctive note of each individual person" (i.8). "The three are united . . . without being confused . . . and they have their circumincession one in the other without any blending or mingling and without change or division in substance" (i.8, see also i.14).

### f. Anthropomorphisms

Scripture often says things of God as if he had a body. This is because "we are unable to think or speak of the divine . . . operations . . . unless we have recourse to images, types, and symbols corresponding to our own nature." A loftier meaning has thus to be sought in the symbols except when we have sayings relating to "the presence of the Word of God in the flesh" (i.11). Thus God is not in any place and yet "he is said to be in a place," that is, "where his operation is plainly visible." Ultimately, of course, he is "wholly in all things and wholly over the universe" (i.13).

### 3. God the Creator

### a. Of the Ages

As Creator, God "who exists before the ages made the ages." The world has seven measurable ages from creation to the resurrection. As there are lesser ages within these, so above and before them is "an age coextensive with eternal things." The eighth age, "that which is to come," will also be eternal. Time will not then be measured by days and nights but will be one day for the just, and deep and endless night for sinners. "God is the one maker of the ages . . . and exists before the ages" (ii.1).

### b. Of Angels

"God was not content to contemplate himself, but out of a superabundance of goodness saw fit that there should be certain things to benefit by and participate in his goodness." He thus created all things of nothing, "By thinking he creates, and, with the Word fulfilling and the Spirit perfecting, the object of his thought subsists" (ii.2). Angels came first (ii.3). But by a free choice one of these "turned from what was according to nature to what was against it" and carried with him "a numberless horde of others." No repentance is seen for angels after their fall (ii.4).

### c. Of Men

After the creation of heaven and earth, which John tediously and unprofitably relates to the natural science of his day (ii.6–11), man was created according to the image of God (intellect and free will) and the likeness of God (virtue), "a miniature world within the larger one." Living on earth, he was destined for divinization, not substantially but by participation in the divine illumination. He also had the tendency to sin, not by nature but in choice and by divine permission "because of the freedom of the will" (ii.12). John interposes here a lengthy psychological analysis (ii.13–29) which has its own interest but which has theological significance only because of the insistence that "some things done," especially in the moral sphere, "depend on us" (ii.26–29). Hence, while God foreknows all things "he does not predestine them all." For he only foreknows the things that depend on us, and he predestines as well as foreknows the things that do not. In virtue of his endowment with free will, man had to undergo a test to see whether he would move away from his material nature to God or turn away from God and tend toward matter. As Gregory of Nyssa explained, man failed this test through the envy and the deceitful promises of the devil, who, "having raised him up to his own heights of conceit, dragged him down to the same abyss of ruin" (ii.30).

## 4. The Incarnation

### a. Purpose

Having fallen under God's judgment, man came also under the divine mercy. Faced with the problem of the death of man and his bondage to the devil, God displayed his goodness, wisdom, and justice by taking up man's cause, giving the devil his due, and rescuing "like through like." John comments with satisfaction in this regard that as man was caught with the bait of a promised divinity, so the devil is caught with the bait of a proffered humanity. For the divine assumption of humanity constitutes the work of deliverance and atonement. The Son of God, "being perfect God, became perfect man and accomplished

. . . the only new thing under the sun, by which the infinite power of God was clearly shown." He thus "stands mediator between God and men," becoming "obedient to the Father by healing our disobedience . . . and becoming to us a model of that obedience without which it is impossible to attain salvation" (iii.1).

### b. Nature

John devotes the rest of Book iii to a lengthy and intricate discussion of the one person and two natures of Christ. He sums up here the conclusions of the long christological debate and of the early church's arguments against the various heretical speculations. Obviously the details of John's treatment are beyond the scope of the present analysis, but some of the basic points may be considered.

The uniqueness of Christ must be recognized: "There never was, nor is, nor will be another Christ." This Christ is to be confessed as "the one person of the Son of God incarnate in two natures that remain perfect." "The union is substantial." "The Word makes human things his own because what is proper to his sacred flesh belongs to him and the things which are his own he communicates to his flesh." He may thus be described as a "compound hypostasis" (iii.7). "He is wholly perfect God but not wholly God but also man. Similarly he is wholly perfect man but not wholly man because he is not only man but also God" (iii.7; it should be noted that in this sentence the term "wholly" has the sense, not of "fully," but of "exclusively"). "Although there is no nature without hypostasis," each nature does not have to be provided with its own subsistence, for "it was in the person of the Word that the flesh subsisted" (iii.9). In virtue of the union of the person one might speak of "one incarnate nature," as Cyril did, but in this case nature is not understood in the sense of person, since it is "the nature of the person." The incarnation means that "without suffering change the very person of the Word became the person of the body" (iii.11).

In the incarnation "three things took place at the same time: the assuming of the body, its coming into being, and its being made divine by the Word" (iii.12). As the hypostatic union does not obliterate the two distinct natures, neither does it exclude two wills and operations, while naturally holding them in concert (iii.14) in virtue of the fact that "the human will followed after his will" (iii.18). "He assumed the whole man and everything that is his, except sin — for this last is not natural . . . he assumed all that he might sanctify all" (iii.20). When Christ is said to be made a curse for us, this is not by a natural and substantial appropriation, like his being made flesh, but by an apparent and relative appropriation (iii.25). Christ the Word suffered, but his divine nature did not (iii.26). "Death gulps down the bait of the body and is pierced by the hook of the divinity . . . then gives up all those that it had formerly swallowed down." While the body and soul of Christ are separated in death, the one person of the Word is still the person of each, so that body and soul are still "hypostatically related . . . through the Word" (iii.27). With the resurrection, the incorruptible body of Christ grants incorruption to our bodies also (iii.28). In the risen life "he put aside all his passions . . . but did not put aside any of the elements of his nature, neither body, nor soul," and both the ascension and the coming again "are actions of a circumscribed body" (iv.1). We adore him in his humanity, too. "The flesh is not of its own nature adorable but in the incarnate Word of God it is so . . . because of the Word of God hypostatically united to it." We thus adore "the flesh of God, that is, God incarnate" (iv.3).

### 5. The Means of Grace

#### a. Baptism

For John, baptism is a figure of death. As such it has to be the one trinitarian baptism with three immersions signifying the three days of the Lord's burial (iv.9). Since man is twofold, body and soul, baptism is also twofold through water and the Spirit, "the water completing the figure . . . and the Spirit producing the guarantee of life." "We are baptized in the Holy Trinity because . . . the three persons cannot but be together . . . for the Holy Trinity is indivisible." "Should a candidate receive baptism fraudulently, he will be condemned instead of helped" (iv.9).

#### b. Faith

Baptism, then, presupposes faith. For John faith is twofold. (1) It is belief in the teaching of the Holy Spirit through hearing the sacred scriptures. This faith is perfected by the things which Christ has ordained. (2) It is hope for the things promised by God and the success of our petitions (iv.10). Without faith the word of the cross seems to be foolishness, "for all the things of God are above the natural order." Understanding comes when "one is guided by faith," which is "an assent devoid of curiosity" (iv.11). Faith opens up the meaning of the cross, by which "death has been laid low, the sin of our first parent destroyed, hell plundered, resurrection bestowed." Life is appropriately given by a tree as death came by a tree (iv.11).

#### c. The Eucharist

As Christ "gave us a second birth," so he provided nourishment for the new life. Again, as baptism was given both by water and by Spirit, the food is both the ordinary bread (and wine) and also the Bread of life. The bread and wine become the body and blood through invocation of the Holy Spirit, who "comes down and works these things which are beyond description and understanding." Four points are to be noted. (1)

Bread and wine are used because "God knows our human weakness" and "does through the ordinary things of nature those which surpass the natural order." (2) All that we can say about the change of bread and wine is that "it is done through the Holy Spirit" and the Word of God which is "true and effective and omnipotent." (3) The bread and wine are not a figure of the body and blood of Christ "but the actual deified body of the Lord." (4) While the sacrament is to remission and eternal life "for those who partake worthily thereof and with faith," "for those who receive unworthily and without faith it is to chastisement and punishment" (iv.13).

### d. Scripture

After extravagant chapters on the virgin (iv.14), relics (iv.15), and images (iv.16), John deals briefly with holy scripture. The one God is seen as author of both Testaments, with salvation as their common theme. The human authors "spoke through the Holy Spirit." A rhetorical passage follows on the value of reading and reflecting on holy scripture although, John observes, "to get some profit from other sources is not forbidden." In his canonical list John excludes the Apocrypha but oddly puts the Apostolic Canons among the New Testament books (iv.17). He returns to his central concern in iv.18 by classifying sayings relating to Christ in four general categories: before the incarnation, in the union, after the union, and after the resurrection. In Chapters 19 and 20 he takes up another important theme of his, explaining what is meant when scripture calls "God's permission his action." In Chapter 22 he discusses the role of the law in the Christian life. He finds alteration or spiritualizing in the substitution of the Lord's day for the sabbath, the exaltation of virginity over marriage, and the finding of the true point of circumcision in baptism (chaps. 23–25). In the discussion of the sabbath he adopts a spiritualizing hermeneutic. Christians are to release the beast of burden, that is, the body, from the servitude of sin and urge it on to "the fullest observance of the divine commandments" (iv.23). Similarly, since the number seven signifies all time, the choice of the seventh day teaches us "that the true Israel should devote itself to God at all times." Imagination of this type fills the vacuum left when scripture is not put to proper dogmatic use.

### 6. Eschatology

John concludes the work with two eschatological chapters. The events leading up to the end are first outlined: the worldwide preaching of the gospel, the rise of antichrist, the persecution and purification of the church, the mission of Elijah and Enoch to Israel, and then the second coming of Christ (iv.26). The resurrection of the dead follows.

John presents evidence for this from both the Old Testament and the New, explaining that it will not involve a change of form but "a change from corruption to incorruption." God wills this and "he has the power to correspond to his will." The universalism of Gregory of Nyssa finds no echo in John of Damascus. At the last judgment the wicked will be given over to everlasting fire, not material fire, but "a kind of fire known to God." In contrast, the good will enter into eternal life and enjoy endless felicity with Christ (iv.27).

### 7. Evaluation

*a. Merits*

By any standard John has produced a remarkable theological work in his *Orthodox Faith*. Writing with clarity and rhetorical skill, he pieces together the contributions of his predecessors with considerable acumen and force. Since he recognizes the limits of theology, his thought rests implicitly on a biblical foundation. His expositions of the Trinity and the incarnation can stand comparison with anything that the church has to offer in these fields whether in his own time or in any age. As a summary of orthodoxy the work fully lives up to its title in at least some of the principal heads of doctrine. Something from the Damascene will be found in all the great theological writings of later times, and his work constitutes indispensable reading for all who would attain any degree of mastery in dogmatic science.

*b. Defects*

The faults of the work are equally evident. It is marked by important omissions. Except in the context of the Trinity, the doctrine of the Holy Spirit is poorly developed. The understanding of faith is also weak, and one looks in vain for teaching on justification or the church. Significant intrusions and expansions may also be noted. Whole chapters of natural science and psychology could well have been omitted. Angels receive inordinate attention, and Mariology is already being blown up out of proportion. A lack of balance results which may be seen even more strikingly by comparing his poverty-stricken treatment of the atonement with the excessively lengthy handling of the incarnation. A stress on the latter needs no justification, for who the Mediator is belongs essentially to what he does. But what he does, as scripture itself bears witness, demands its own share of attention both in the presentation of the gospel and also in theological reflection on it.

*c. A General Problem*

In John, as in Gregory of Nyssa, the wholesale philosophizing of theology constitutes a general problem. Here again theology is uprooted from its native soil in scripture and transplanted into a not wholly congenial environment. John's purpose in doing this can claim some validity. He underestimates, however, the dangers and difficulties involved. Even when indisputably biblical, his finished product bears little obvious relation to a biblical theology. Far too often, indeed, material continuity with holy scripture is either severed or maintained only by the flimsiest of threads. John makes two mistakes: he takes his biblical basis for granted, and he attaches too high an importance to the philosophical mode of presentation without considering seriously enough its theological implications. These mistakes do not finally invalidate his work, but they do lessen its value as a positive theological contribution.

# PART II
## *Medieval and Reformation Theology*

# CHAPTER XI

# Conflicts at Corbie

## A. THE EUCHARISTIC CONTROVERSY

The barbarian incursions into the western Roman empire had damaging consequences for Christian scholarship. Yet they did not bring the total collapse which a title like "The Dark Ages" might suggest. Scholars as well as saints and evangelists are to be found in a continuous stream even after the death of Gregory I and not least in the Celtic world. By the time of Charlemagne, theology was already acquiring the renewed force which would later bring the great movement of medieval theology. The monasteries played an important part in the ongoing life of learning. Significantly, a house which enjoyed special prominence in the ninth century, that of Corbie, was founded in the age of Charlemagne. Indeed, the emperor's cousin Adalhard was its first abbot. If the contributions of Corbie were destined to take a polemical form, the presence of three such scholarly and independent thinkers as Radbert, Ratramn, and Gottschalk testifies to its intellectual vitality.

### 1. Radbert

*a. The Man*

Paschasius Radbert came to Corbie under its first abbot. He quickly gained recognition as a scholar, and when the headship became vacant in 844 he was elected the fourth abbot. He resigned, however, in 853 and devoted himself to learning until his death around 865. His works include expositions of Matthew and Lamentations, a treatise on the virgin birth, short pieces on the three theological virtues, and biographies of the first two abbots, Adalhard and his brother Wala. He wrote his Eucharistic treatise, *The Lord's Body and Blood,* in 831 and sent a revised edition as a Christmas gift to Charles the Bald about 844.

*b. The Issue*

From early times Christians had referred to the Eucharistic elements as the Lord's body and blood and used very bold language in speaking about the sacramental nourishment. In the East, as we have seen, theologians like Gregory of Nyśsa had tried to show that without any suggestion of cannibalism an authentic feeding on Christ does take place. Fears of Eucharistic docetism or dualism rule out all concepts of a spiritual feeding which is not also bodily. In the West, however, no very coherent account had yet been given of the relation between the elements and the Lord's body and blood. This was an issue which engaged the scholars of Corbie and, it would seem, a wider circle too, for Charles the Bald was asking for guidance in the matter.

### c. The Lord's Body and Blood

(1) The Power of God. Radbert opens his treatise by accepting the miracle that after consecration the elements "are nothing but Christ's flesh and blood ... nothing different from what was born of Mary, suffered on the cross, and rose again from the tomb." This may seem unbelievable, but "for God nothing is impossible." "God's will is power ... what he wills comes to be as he wills" (1.4). The reason why no visible change takes place in this miracle, as it does in others, is "that faith may be proved in spirit." The faith required for worthy reception is that God can and does effect the miracle even if the senses do not perceive it.

(2) The Need for Knowledge. If faith accepts the miracle, need the mystery be discussed? Radbert argues that we should not be "ignorant or unaware what in it pertains to faith and what to knowledge." For knowledge is needed to defend faith just as faith is needed to nurture knowledge. Understanding must accompany faith lest "what has been produced for our cure should end in ruin for those who receive it" (2.1–2). Christ "frees us from all ignorance," just as it is by his Word that "a thing capable of intelligible perception through the senses is divinely transformed into his flesh and blood" (2.2).

(3) The Sacraments. Sacraments pledge salvation. "What is visibly done accomplishes inwardly something far different." These actions are called sacraments or mysteries either because of the secrecy of the act or because the Holy Spirit "latently accomplishes" the real actions "under the cover of things visible" (3.1). Baptism and the Eucharist are the church's sacraments, but the incarnation is "the great sacrament because in the visible man the divine majesty inwardly ... worked invisibly those things which came into being secretly by his power." In this sacrament we are pardoned, in baptism "a door for entering into adoption is opened for believers" (3.2), and in the Eucharist we are "made one with Christ," "invigorated by tasting him ... and prepared for things immortal and eternal" (3.4). "In all these sacraments the Holy Spirit works" as "in the holy scriptures he illumines our hearts." The

Spirit by whom Christ was conceived regenerates us; from bread and wine he daily creates Christ's flesh and blood (3.4).

(4) Truth and Figure

(a) John 6. Radbert cites verses from John 6 to show that the body and blood are created in truth. He again sees an analogy to the incarnation. True flesh is created from the virgin by the Spirit; by the same Spirit the body and blood of Christ are "mystically consecrated" out of the substance of bread and wine (4.1).

(b) Old and New Testament Figures. In contrast to the figures of the Old Testament, which were shadows, the figure in the New Testament is truth. It is figure insofar as what is understood differs from "what is sensed." It is called truth because the body is "created by the power of the Spirit" (4.1). The incarnation is again cited, for in it the humanity is the figure of Christ's substance through which we are led to understand the divinity; yet as figure it is "wholly truth and no shadow" (4.2). A pedagogic purpose underlies the use of the figure.

(c) The Passover Lamb and Manna. Developing his distinction, Radbert discusses the lamb and the manna, in which the shadow of the body and the original were the same only in the prefiguration (or promise) of truth and not in its fulfillment. Now, however, the mystery of the fulfillment of truth has been created out of the resurrection (5.1). "This is my body" indicates this. We must not "ask about the order of nature here." "The method resides in Christ's virtue, the knowledge in faith, the cause in power, the effect in will" (4.3).

(d) Faith and Unbelief. All partake of the sacraments, "but one man spiritually eats the flesh of Christ, . . . another man does not." What does the latter receive? He cannot receive "flesh and blood of value to himself, but judgment." He does not "understand anything other than he feels with his lips." "The power of the sacrament is withdrawn from him." He is condemned for his presumption. "He eats judgment to himself because he makes a bad use of something good" (6.2). Radbert tells the cautionary tale of the Jew who meant to spit out the Lord's body but could not. He seems to be suggesting that the body is in fact received to judgment, but it is just possible that he means that without the discernment of faith only the figure is received, and not the truth (6.3).

(5) Comments. In the rest of the work Radbert discusses matters of less import which need not detain us. In his essential teaching he has much to offer. He shows no fear of miracle. He grasps the point that faith sees hidden verities which the senses cannot perceive. Worthy reception is clearly differentiated from unworthy. The role of the Word and Spirit is given due weight. Analogy to the incarnation, and the sacramental significance of the incarnation itself, are helpfully indicated. Yet Radbert manages to achieve a tantalizing obscurity in what seem to be simple statements. Is he claiming that Christ's incarnate body replaces

the elements, so that the senses deceive us when they see only the elements? Or does he mean that, as in the incarnation, faith sees something the senses do not see, the deity as well as the humanity, the body and blood as well as the bread and wine? If the latter view is correct, Radbert might be pointing us to a fruitful incarnational analogy. The problem remains, however, that he speaks of a change which, while inner and not outer, is in the elements, not the recipients. His thought, then, seems to be that we must believe the change has taken place even though we cannot see it, and that we shall find to our profit that it has. If, on the other hand, we do not believe, there can be receiving only to hurt. The unworthy receive Christ, but in their failure to discern him by faith they come under judgment. What Radbert does not explain is why it is only by faith that visible things like body and blood can be seen. Certainly Christ's deity cannot be sensorily perceived, since it is in itself invisible, but if the truth behind the figure in the Eucharist is the incarnational body, which lies in the sensory sphere, then why should the demand be made for faith in the change in order that it may be discerned? The incarnational analogy breaks down here, and while at points Radbert seems to solve the problem by saying that for unbelievers the sacraments are only a figure and not the truth, he leaves us with the general impression that the faith he asks for simply consists of believing what is known not to be true.

## 2. Ratramn

### a. Life

Little is known of Radbert's contemporary Ratramn except that he, too, was a monk at Corbie and was still there in 868. He opened his career as an author with a work *On the Nativity*. With his *On Predestination* he also contributed to the predestinarian controversy. His chief work is *Against the Objections of the Greeks,* a defense of the filioque and Western usages against the attacks of Photius. He composed his *Christ's Body and Blood* at the request of Charles the Bald and in fairly obvious, if not explicit or highly polemical, debate with Radbert. An interesting point is that whereas Radbert, in spite of a promise to offer more extensive patristic support, quotes only Gregory the Great, Ratramn appeals to specific passages in Ambrose, Augustine, Isidore, Jerome, and Fulgentius. He also deals more fully with the relevant biblical material.

### b. Introduction

(1) The Question. Ratramn opens his *Christ's Body and Blood* by trying to clarify the question. Some say that in a figure we have nothing but "a naked manifestation of truth." Others see the figure of a mystery, so that "it is one thing which appears to bodily sense and another which faith beholds" (2).

(2) Definitions. To obviate ambiguity Ratramn defines the two important terms "figure" and "truth." The former involves what he calls "an overshadowing that reveals its intent under some sort of veil." Sayings like "I am the vine" illustrate this. They "say one thing and hint at another" (7). Truth, in contrast, is "representation of clear facts . . . uttered in pure and open and . . . natural meanings." Thus in a statement like "Christ died on the cross," "nothing else may be understood than what is said." It should be noted that Radbert takes a very different view, at least in relation to the sacrament. For him truth is what faith perceives, that is, not what is said but what is hinted at. But the distinction is not a direct one, and it might be argued with some plausibility that Radbert and Ratramn, like many disputants in this area, are finally saying much the same thing in different ways.

### c. *Mystery and Faith*

(1) Mystery. As Ratramn sees it, to say there is no figure but naked truth is to eliminate the mystery, that is, the sacrament. Mystery arises because the bread "exhibits one thing to human sense and proclaims another thing inwardly to the minds of the faithful." The senses perceive bread. Christ's body is not seen or consumed, but it is known to "the gaze of the believing soul." Since externally we clearly have bread and wine, it follows that these are Christ's body and blood "in a figurative sense" (9–10).

(2) Faith. To say there is not figure but naked truth is also to eliminate faith. Faith is the perceiving of the invisible. If, however, "everything is visible in truth" and nothing spiritual takes place, faith becomes unnecessary. Sight makes faith redundant. One wonders, of course, whether Ratramn really has Radbert in view here, for Radbert does not say that we can see the body and blood, and he leaves an obvious place for the belief that God has worked the miracle. But perhaps there is the more indirect criticism that if we have truth and not a figure then we ought to be able to see Christ's body and faith should not have to be exercised in receiving it.

### d. *The Change*

(1) Its Nature. What, then, do the words of institution effect? Ratramn first defines different forms of change, such as from non-being to being or from one being to another. He then denies that any transition of this kind takes place, for according to truth the former appearance of the creature is seen to remain (12–13). "It is nothing but what it was before" even though "it is another thing because the bread is made the body of Christ" (13). If we say that "everything is simple truth," we pose an insoluble riddle, for change is asserted but "nothing is seen to have changed" (1–15). Ratramn can see only two ways out of this dilemma.

Either we must conclude that the elements are not Christ's body and blood at all, or we must say that they "have been changed in some respect other than a bodily one" (15). What change could this be? A spiritual and figurative one in which, under cover of the bodily bread and wine, we have "Christ's spiritual body and spiritual blood" (16).

(2) The Parallel in Baptism. Baptism, he thinks, helps us here. It is called the fountain of life. Yet water can cleanse only the body. The point, then, is that to water "is added the power of the Holy Spirit." We thus see two contraries: the contemptible element which washes outwardly and the power of the Spirit which washes inwardly. "In its own properties water is corruptible, but in the mystery it is healing power" (17–18).

(3) The Two Aspects. In the Lord's Supper, as in baptism, we have an outward and an inward aspect. Viewed outwardly as bread and wine, the body and blood are created and subject to change and corruption, but viewed inwardly they are life and grant immortality to those who receive them. "What are seen and what are believed are not the same." With respect to the former they feed the mortal body, with respect to the latter they feed the immortal soul (19). In the rest of the treatise, which is its main bulk, Ratramn illustrates this from the passages in 1 Corinthians 10 and John 6 which were later to play so significant a part in the Reformation debates (20–31). He then goes on to prove by definite quotations that those who "say that these things do not happen in a figure but in truth" are "out of harmony with the writings of the holy fathers" (32–96). He sums up his teaching in three propositions: (a) the elements are put on the altar "as a figure or memorial of the Lord's death"; (b) the Lord's body and blood are taken by believers "when faith receives what the eye does not see but what it believes"; (c) what we have is "spiritual food spiritually feeding the soul" (101).

### e. Conclusion

Ratramn achieves greater clarity than Radbert, whether this be a mark of superficiality or profundity. But what precisely is the difference between them? Are they divided materially or simply by definition? Certainly there is a large area of agreement. Both stress God's power. Both say that Christ's body and blood are present to give life. Both issue a call for faith. Both see the importance of the Holy Spirit and the Word (cf. Ratramn 17 and 22). Ratramn can even allow that there is one substance which has the appearance of bread and wine from one standpoint and is Christ's body and blood from another (16). The difference seems to lie, then, in three interrelated points.

First, Ratramn finds an ongoing figure — "the sacraments of the body and blood have assumed their names" (31) — whereas Radbert swallows up the figure in the reality. Second, Ratramn denies a bodily change and sees instead a spiritual change, whereas Radbert would seem to be thinking of some real but invisible transformation. As Rat-ramn understands it, what happens is that the elements of bread and wine are "spiritually made" and thus have power as mysteries of Christ's body and blood. For Radbert they actually are the body and blood, although faith alone discerns this. Third, Ratramn distinguishes between the incarnate and crucified body, "which did not appear one thing outwardly and conceal another inwardly," and the body and blood received by believers, which "are one thing in appearance and another in meaning" (69). Radbert, of course, tries to find a parallel to the humanity and divinity of the incarnation, but this falters because no change takes place here and, more especially, because in the humanity and the divinity we have, not two bodily realities, the one visible and the other invisible, but a bodily reality on the one side and a spiritual on the other. The analogy, therefore, seems in fact to work out better for Ratramn than it does for Radbert.

Why Radbert's more difficult and less supported doctrine carried the day against Ratramn's more lucid and more broadly argued presentation is hard to say, although once the distinction of substance and accidents both explained the unchanged appearance of bread and wine and also eliminated the crasser implications, Radbert's case was naturally strengthened. One still wonders, however, if Ratramn's view could not have been fitted just as easily into the medieval schema, for Ratramn could speak of one substance of the sacrament in analogy to the one hypostasis of Christ with the visible and the invisible natures. As it turned out, Berengarius supported the resistance to an offensive literalism in Radbert, and with his condemnation in 1058 the work of Ratramn came under a cloud from which it did not emerge until its rediscovery by the Swiss and Anglican reformers.

## B. THE PREDESTINARIAN CONTROVERSY

### 1. The Debate

As already noted, Ratramn contributed to the predestinarian debate which agitated Corbie and much of Europe in the middle of the ninth century. In the center of this storm was a Saxon monk named Gottschalk (b. 805), who came to Corbie from Fulda in about 830. Gottschalk did not stay long at Corbie but moved to Orbais, and follow-ing his ordination soon afterwards, he ministered in Italy. Already, however, he had engaged in the study of Augustine that led him to the strictest doctrine of predestination and reprobation, which he was ac-cused of preaching in his Italian ministry. Opposition led to his condem-nation at Mainz in 848 and then to his degradation, beating, and impris-onment by Hincmar of Rheims in 849. He found supporters in Ratramn,

Prudentius of Troyes, and Florus and Remigius of Lyons. When three letters were sent to Remigius by Hincmar, Pardulus of Laon, and Rabanus Maurus in an attempt to justify the harsh measures taken against Gottschalk, Remigius, in the name of the church of Lyons, wrote his famous *Reply to the Three Letters* in which he clarifies the issues, gives qualified approval to Gottschalk's views, and sharply criticizes his treatment. Written between 849 and 855, the *Reply* is often thought to be in fact the work of the scholar Florus, or at least to rest on materials prepared by him. Yet Remigius obviously had a concern for predestination, as is shown by his treatises *On the General Damnation of Mankind* and *On Steadfastly Holding the Truth of Scripture*. He undoubtedly inspired and sponsored the *Reply*, even if he did not personally compose it.

### 2. Gottschalk's Preaching

Somewhat oddly Gottschalk was accused of false preaching rather than of false teaching or writing. Hincmar complained that he had "assumed the name of preacher of his own volition and had offered himself as evangelist to barbarian and pagan peoples." His message included the theses (1) that God foreordained both to the kingdom and also to death those whom he willed, (2) that there is absolute certainty of salvation and perdition, (3) that God does not will the salvation of all, (4) that Christ did not die only for the elect, and (5) that fallen man has freedom only for evil. Answering Hincmar first, Remigius found this hard to credit. "It seems to us in part incredible that in preaching to peoples who do not know the Lord he should neglect to summon them first of all to repentance but set before them problems exceedingly difficult even for believers and scholars." If he had really done this he should be "utterly laughed at" instead of being made an object of prominence (1). At the same time the five propositions attributed to and defended by him should not have been condemned "in fear with precipitate and thoughtless haste" but only after thorough investigation "with all care for piety and most devout zeal for finding and preserving the truth" (1). To this end Remigius set out seven rules of faith, of which the most important is the eternity and immutability of God and, consequently, of his foreknowledge and foreordination. Nothing is "accidental to his divinity." If he creates new things, it is without newness of will. "He can apply to a new work, not a new, but an eternal plan." Various scriptures, especially from the prophets and epistles, are adduced in support of this basic principle (2ff.).

### 3. The Five Propositions

When tested by the theological principle of Remigius, only one of the five propositions of Gottschalk is to be rejected.

### a. Foreordination to Salvation and Perdition

Augustine, in *The City of God* and the *Enchiridion,* teaches predestination to both salvation and perdition. Remigius emphasizes that the predestination of the wicked is "not to guilt but to punishment." God foreordained no one to sin "but only to pay the penalty of sin." This foreordination, however, is not to be denied (8).

### b. Certainty of Salvation and Perdition

That none of the elect can perish and none of the reprobate be saved is proclaimed generally by the truth of scripture and the authority of the fathers. Gottschalk may have put the matter poorly, but "divine truth should not for that reason be denied." God defends the elect while the reprobate are kept from salvation by "the untamable and constant villainy of their own wickedness" (9).

### c. Non-Universality of Salvation

Scripture says that God wills all men to be saved. Remigius, however, backs Gottschalk's thesis that God wills only the elect to be saved. The paradox is resolved when the "all" of the biblical verse is referred to all who are in fact saved, that is, all the elect (11–13). Remigius is not dogmatic here, but he finds support for this interpretation in Augustine.

### d. Limited Atonement

Since only the elect are saved, it may be accepted that Christ did not come to save all and did not die on the cross for all. Hence Remigius defends Gottschalk on this score, too (14–15).

### e. Freedom for Evil Alone

The one doctrine of Gottschalk with which Remigius takes sharp issue is that after the fall, which is by free will, "no one of us can exercise free will for doing good but only for doing evil." Remigius finds it hard to credit that Gottschalk taught this. He can see that, with qualification, there is truth here. Man in general and without grace cannot use free will for good. Free volition was certainly enfeebled by Adam's sin. When man deserted God, it became corrupt and "lost the good it had." Nevertheless, man did not lose "his proper nature in which he has by nature the inherent volition of free will." He lost the goodness of nature. Hence free will "may be saved from its lost estate." It has been set free by Christ. One cannot say of believers, as those whose wills have been freed by Christ, that they can exercise free will only for doing evil and not for doing good. One rather suspects that Remigius is at this point defending what Gottschalk really had in mind.

### 4. Gottschalk's Treatment

*a. Procedure*

Remigius severely condemns the irregularity as well as the cruelty of what was done to Gottschalk. He was beaten even before proper trial (24), and "everyone shudders at the unheard of and conscienceless brutality by which the wretched man was slashed to ribbons with murderous floggings" (25).

*b. Confusion of Person and Truth*

No less serious for Remigius is the way in which the condemnation of Gottschalk's opinions, however justified, involves condemnation of the divine truth contained in his teaching. He grieves, then, that "ecclesiastical truth has been condemned, not a wretched monk." As he wisely concludes, "we ought not to be so provoked by the wickedness and impudence of any man that we despise, assail, or even dare to condemn divine truth and the venerable authority of our fathers" (25).

### 5. Replies to Pardulus and Rabanus

*a. Pardulus*

Having made his main statement in the reply to Hincmar, Remigius found little to say to Pardulus, who simply tried to justify the zeal shown in the investigation. Letters of support from Amalarius and John Scotus aroused the scorn of Remigius, for the former had been noted for his errors, and "the Irishman does not adhere to the words of scripture as hitherto understood." "He should either be pitied as a mad man or accursed as a heretic" (40).

*b. Rabanus*

(1) Rabanus made two points. First, God cannot be the author of sin. Remigius simply comments that on this all agree, so Rabanus is wasting his time on what no one denies. Second, Rabanus relates predestination only to the elect. Scripture and the fathers teach us that God is the source of salvation to many but not that he also ordains to eternal death (47). Only heretics espouse the latter view. Remigius' caustic comment here is that Rabanus should be careful "lest in the character of those whom he so easily calls heretics he be found to condemn the holy and venerable fathers" (46).

(2) Rabanus concluded his letter by listing seven perversions in Gottschalk's doctrine of predestination, and Remigius thought it necessary to refute each point separately.

(a) God is a bad God if he irrationally predestines his work to destruction. Remigius refutes this by quoting Psalm 18:25–26 and its exposition by Augustine. He also adds the thought that God predestines to destruction those whom he foreknew would be wicked.

(b) If there is predestination apart from good or evil deeds, then deceit is found in the promises and warnings of Christ. Remigius simply denies that evil deeds have no bearing on reprobation.

(c) God is unjust if rewards and punishments are not related to righteousness and sin. Again a simple refutation suffices. No one says that there is no such relation.

(d) Christ died in vain if he cannot help the non-elect who believe and hope in him. Remigius makes the obvious reply that the elect and those who believe are one and the same, while the reprobate could be helped but in their own wickedness will not be. Even then God could save them but does not, for he wills "by a just vengeance to condemn some for the purpose of showing the terror of his sternness."

(e) The good angels are envious for fear their number should not be restored. Remigius replies that no place for envy remains since the number of the elect will be exactly the same as that of the angelic vacancies.

(f) The devil wins when those whom God willed to save share in his lot of perdition. On the contrary, says Remigius, the devil loses when the elect are infallibly snatched from his dominion.

(g) Hostility to the human race is shown when it is argued that the reprobate cannot be saved by faith and baptism. Remigius again finds perverted logic in Rabanus' thinking. Predestination is coincident with salvation by faith and baptism. The reprobate are not harmed by God but fall into the abyss in just punishment for "their persistent and untamable wickedness."

## 6. Appeal

Remigius brings his *Reply* to a close with a brief appeal. The truth of God should be faithfully acknowledged and the authority of the fathers obeyed. Animosity and confidence in novelties should be set aside and the treasury of true faith kept intact. The professing of ungodly novelties of speech and the contradictions of pseudoscience can lead only to a forgetting of the faith.

## 7. Summary

The Gottschalk debate shows plainly that the issues raised in the Pelagian controversy had not been satisfactorily settled and probably never will be. Little that is new emerges in this renewal of the debate, and when all was said and done the views of neither party prevailed nor was any agreeable compromise achieved.

On the side of Gottschalk and Remigius certain things might be said. They showed a proper sense of the implications of God's eternity. In avoiding dualism, they saw, too, that God cannot be viewed as the author of evil. Like Augustine they found a place for freedom both at the fall and also in the Christian life. Faith and works have authentic significance for salvation, but only inside the divine predestination. The inferences of antagonists like Rabanus are so plainly exercises in abstract logic that their refutation hardly seems worth the effort.

Yet something must be said for Hincmar and his colleagues. If Gottschalk did in fact preach his five points as a missionary, the situation surely called, not for the treatment he received, but at least for dialogue and counsel. Again, while God's predestination is eternal, this must not be thought to imply the kind of immutability which rules out temporality in outworking, for which allowance is also made in scripture. Furthermore, behind the exaggerated logic of Rabanus a real problem of divine equity and human responsibility seems to lie. God can, of course, hand over some or all to perdition, but on Gottschalk's view God seems to make an arbitrary choice, which would be reprehensible in human affairs. Nor is it easy to see why the reprobate should be held accountable for their sins when fallen man has no freedom for God apart from God's gracious liberation. Remigius himself has to make a concession and speak of the foreordination of wicked works at this point.

The controversy, perhaps, has only negative lessons to teach, but they are lessons the church has always been slow to learn. First, it is unlikely that agreement can ever be reached on the exact understanding and formulation of election. Second, the method of taking biblical verses and developing logical or philosophical lines of thought from them can hardly replace an authentically theological approach which considers the totality of the biblical message. Finally, fruitful discussion of the matter cannot be achieved in a spirit of rancor, ill will, excitement, or bitterness. Humility, calmness, restraint, toleration, and an agreement to disagree (if need be) are minimal prerequisites to the helpful interchange which might at least produce some consensus on basic concerns. Unfortunately, as in Gottschalk's time, feelings have usually run so high in this area that these conditions of profitable conversation have almost always been ignored or excluded.

# CHAPTER XII

# Faith Seeking Understanding: Anselm of Canterbury

In the eleventh century, theological leadership in the West passed briefly to another monastery, that of Bec in Normandy. Founded only in 1034, this foundation owed its rapid rise in fame to Lanfranc of Pavia, an outstanding scholar, counselor, and ecclesiastic who became the first archbishop of Canterbury under Norman rule and who took the lead in the condemnation of Berengar of Tours. Anselm, born in Aosta in about 1033, came to Bec in 1056 after a quarrel with his father. He became a monk in 1060, succeeded Lanfranc as prior in 1063, and then rose to be abbot in 1078. After Lanfranc's death and a prolonged vacancy during which William Rufus plundered the estates, Anselm was nominated to Canterbury in 1093. Of his fifteen years as archbishop, however, no less than six were spent in exile, three from 1097 to 1100 after a dispute over the recognition of Urban II as pope, and three more from 1103 to 1106 over the question of lay investiture. He thus had little opportunity for constructive episcopal ministry but proved himself by his theological writings to be one of the most powerful of all the church's teachers.

The first important works of Anselm, his *Monologion* and *Proslogion,* belong to his monastic years. The work on the atonement, *Cur Deus Homo,* seems to have been begun in England and completed during his first exile in Italy. Other significant works of the same period include the *Letter on the Incarnation of the Word* to Urban and *The Virgin Conception and Original Sin.* All these writings are expressions of the basic principle of faith seeking understanding — a principle which he finely states in the letter to Urban.

## A. LETTER ON THE INCARNATION OF THE WORD

The *Proslogion,* which was written earlier, introduces the theme of faith seeking understanding, but for a particularly good exposition of it we turn to Part 1 of the *Letter on the Incarnation of the Word.* Essential to true knowledge, in Anselm's view, is that the eyes should first be enlightened "through keeping the Lord's commandments . . . and first we should become little children by humble obedience to the testimonies of God." For the more we are nourished in scripture "by the things that feed us through obedience, the more accurately we are carried along to the things that satisfy us through knowledge." Without belief there can be no understanding. The unbeliever cannot have the experience which "surpasses hearing about a thing." The moral is clear. We must avoid obscure questions of divinity until we first seek "wisdom and good conduct in faith." Questions of the sacred page are to be taken up very cautiously. For true understanding faith and its obedience are prerequisites. When we have these, no difficulty or impossibility of understanding can push us away from the truth to which we adhere by faith.


## B. PROSLOGION


### 1. Preface

Anselm begins the *Proslogion* by explaining its origin. The preceding *Monologion* had been composed as an example of meditation on the grounds of faith. It led Anselm to ask whether one self-contained argument might be found to show that God exists. Having found one, he thought it might please some readers, and he thus wrote the *Proslogion* to deal "with this and one or two other matters." He did so as one who was seeking to understand what he believed. The meditative prayer which constitutes the first chapter develops this point. It reaches its poignant conclusion in the cry: "I am not trying, O Lord, to penetrate thy loftiness . . . but I desire in some measure to understand thy truth, which my heart believes. For I do not seek to understand in order to believe, but I believe in order to understand. For this too I believe, that unless I believe, I shall not understand."


### 2. The Existence of God

*a. The Concept*

Three points should be noted as Anselm moves on at once to his argument. (1) He retains the meditative style, speaking in address to God: "And so, O Lord, since thou givest understanding to faith, give me to understand . . . that thou dost exist." (2) The section on God's existence is only part of a larger study and should not be taken out of its context or blown up out of due proportion. (3) The controlling definition, that God is "a being than which none greater can be thought," is itself an article of faith: "Now we believe that thou art a being than which none greater can be thought" (chap. 2).

### b. The Definition

The definition, of course, implies the rationality of the belief. Anselm has four reasons for this. (1) Everyone can understand the definition. (2) Those who deny that this being exists are in self-contradiction, for such a being in reality is greater than such a being in concept alone (chap. 2). (3) This being exists so truly that it cannot be thought of as not existing. If it could, a being which could not be thought of as not existing would be greater. (4) All creatures can be thought of as not existing, so that God, whom Anselm equates with this being ("For thou art this being, O God"), can be said not only to exist but also to have "being in the truest and highest sense" (chap. 3).

### c. The Fool's Denial

When the fool says there is no God he seems to entertain the impossible thought that God does not exist. Does not this create a problem? No, says Anselm, for the fool is using an empty term when he speaks of God. He does not understand what God is. If he did, he could not think that God does not exist. Anselm ends this part with the thanksgiving that he now understands by God's light what he formerly believed by his gift, so that if he now refused to believe in God's existence he could not fail to understand its truth.

## 3. The Nature of God

### a. Supreme and Self-Existent

As the supreme and self-existent being God is (1) the Creator of all else out of nothing and (2) all that it is better to be than not to be, such as just and truthful. Certain problems arise here, however, which Anselm goes on to discuss.

### b. Sensible and Incorporeal

It is better to be sensible than not, but can God be this when he is Spirit? He can, for sensation exists for knowledge. God has "the highest knowledge of all things" and he may thus be said to sense in some way (chap. 6).

### c. Almighty

Can God be truly almighty when he cannot do some things? Anselm answers that the things God cannot do (such as tell lies or suffer corruption) imply impotence, not power. Power to do what one ought not is powerlessness to do what one ought. God is more truly almighty because he can do nothing through impotence (chap. 7).

### d. Compassionate and Impassible

If God is impassible, can he also be compassionate? He is, Anselm thinks, in effect but not in emotion. He saves wretched sinners but is not "affected by any share in our wretchedness" (chap. 8).

### e. Just and Merciful

How can God be just if he gives eternal life to those who deserve eternal death? Anselm shows a fine appreciation of mercy in his famous apostrophe: "O mercy, from what abundant sweetness and sweet abundance dost thou flow." But how is he to understand the affirmation of faith that God is merciful because he is just? God is just when he punishes the wicked, but by his own nature, not ours, he is also just in saving those whom he might justly destroy, for in so doing he does what is fitting to him as the highest good. Yet the mystery of election arises here, for we do not understand why among the equally evil God saves some through his supreme goodness and condemns others through his supreme justice. Surprisingly, no mention is made of Christ's atoning work in this section (chaps. 9–11).

## 4. Further Aspects of God

### a. Attributes

In a very short chapter (chap. 12) Anselm makes the significant statement that God is, and does not merely have, his attributes: "Thou art the very life by which thou livest and the wisdom by which thou art wise . . . and so with all thine attributes."

### b. Distinction from Spirits

All spiritual beings are uncircumscribed and eternal, but God is uniquely so, for he alone is everywhere and always (chap. 13).

### c. Seen and Not Seen

While God is seen now by understanding as well as faith, he is still beyond what is seen, for the soul is both "obscured by its own littleness and overpowered by God's immensity" (chap. 14). Anselm thus develops a variation of his basic theme: God is greater than can be thought. But this variation is implicit in the theme (chap. 15).

### d. Inaccessible Light and Ineffable Beauty

Lying beyond human vision, God has a glory beyond the understanding and a beauty beyond the perception of the soul, which is "frozen and stupefied and blocked up by the ancient enfeeblement of sin" (chaps. 16–17).

### e. Unity

Despite the multiplicity of his attributes, God undergoes no division. "Life and wisdom and the rest are not parts of this but all are one and each of them is the whole that thou art" (chap. 18). The divine temporality and spatiality conform to the same rule. "Yesterday and today and tomorrow thou art." "Thou art not in place or time but all things are in thee" (chap. 19). "Thou art before and beyond all things" and "thou art present when they have not yet arrived" (chap. 20).

### f. Uniqueness
Anselm now reaches another important conclusion: "Thou alone art what thou art and thou art he who is, . . . who properly and simply is, . . . while all things need thee for their being and their wellbeing" (chap. 22).

### g. The Trinity
God as the supreme good is not the Father alone but also the Word and the Spirit. There can be nothing other, greater, or less in the Word, which is truth itself. Since God is simple, nothing which is not what the Father is can be born of him. The good is also the one love common to the Father and the Son and proceeding from both — the Holy Spirit. In the divine simplicity there can proceed only the being from which it proceeds (chap. 23).

### h. The Good and Goods
Since created things are good, how much more so is the good which is their source, creative life — the salvation that bestows salvation, the wisdom that created all things of nothing. Great goods, then, belong to those who enjoy the supreme good (chap. 24). Not the least of these is the loving joy which comes with rejoicing in the good of others and the good of God (chap. 25), so that the fullness of superabounding joy is achieved (chap. 26).

## 5. Comments

When the whole *Proslogion* is surveyed, it is seen to be a work of astonishing wealth and variety as well as acuteness of thought. The devotional form preserves it from aridity even in the most subtle sections. The obvious grounding in faith forbids us from construing it as an essay in abstraction. The success of the work does not depend on its ability to convince unbelievers that they are in fact fools (although Anselm certainly sees irrationality in unbelief), but rather in its demonstration that faith has its own rationality. Once God is known, the problems which arise in relation to his existence and nature permit of a satisfying solution even though by definition the being of God surpasses understanding.

Many debates have arisen about Anselm's thesis that God, as the being than which no greater can be thought, cannot be thought of as nonexistent. Gaunilo, in the fool's defense, parodied this line of thought. The island than which no more perfect can be thought must exist even though no one can find it. Anselm made short work of this objection, for he had stated already that all created things may be thought of as existent or nonexistent, and the most perfect island cannot be the being than which no greater can be thought. Yet the suspicion has remained that this "being" might simply be a projection from the world we know, with no necessary reality of its own. Anselm, of course, realizes that the fool, as an unbeliever, can use the term "God" without realizing who or what God is. Hence he does not pretend to be advancing a proof which will necessarily win over the fool. What he does claim is that when we know God by faith we also see that he is the being than which no greater can be thought, so that irrationality characterizes the denial of his existence. Unbelievers, however, will continue to find in Anselm more verbal and mental ingenuity than solidity of thought or factual reality.

Does Anselm build on philosophy rather than revelation? He might seem to do so. His definition can hardly be called a biblical one, and his thesis seems to depend on the universality of concepts and the correspondence between concepts and reality. Nevertheless, one should not forget that God's self-existence has a biblical basis, that many of Anselm's statements rest on biblical teachings, and that if faith moves on to understanding, understanding itself moves on also to love and joy in a genuinely biblical progression.

This final point reminds us again that injustice is done to Anselm if attention focuses on his "ontological proof" and ignores the rest of the treatise. The inquiry into the rationality of faith naturally begins with God's existence, but it relates predominantly to his nature. Here again Anselm draws primarily on the biblical data to show that in spite of apparent contradictions the divine attributes form a coherent totality. The point might be made that if God's existence be not shown, the rest of the study falls to the ground, while if it is, the problems which follow raise no fundamental difficulty. The former statement may be true, but it hardly means that God's existence can be the only and unending subject of discussion. The latter statement needs qualification, for it is precisely in the investigation of God's nature that theology finds its proper work.

Philosophical though it may be in form, the *Proslogion* is undoubtedly theological in substance. Its primary concern is the understanding of faith. It draws its material from revelation and aims to show the rationality of what is revealed and believed. It deals with God's nature instead of confining itself apologetically to the question of his existence. It offers some striking insights, such as the identity of God and his attributes, which are easily missed when the first section is allotted disproportionate attention. Finally, it is carried through in a spirit of devotion which is wholly appropriate to theology, whose theme is neither an abstraction nor an extraneous reality — "the god of the philosophers" — but the personal God of faith and love and hope, "the God of Abraham, Isaac and Jacob" (Pascal).

## C. CUR DEUS HOMO?

Having attempted to show in the *Proslogion* the rationality of the doctrine of God, Anselm follows the same method in relation to the incarnation and the atonement in his epoch-making *Cur Deus Homo*. As he himself tells us, he wants to answer objections (book i) and show man's purpose and destiny (book ii) "by necessary reasons (Christ being put out of sight, as if nothing had been known of him)." In doing this, Anselm himself is, of course, a man of faith. He believes, however, that rational discussion will show "that all things we believe concerning Christ must necessarily take place." This time Anselm does not address his work to God but engages in a dialogue with Boso (monk and later abbot of Bec). Boso poses the questions to which Anselm gives the answers which are the heart of the work.

### 1. Objections to the Incarnation

a. Anselm begins in Book i by tackling the objection that by speaking of the birth and humanity of the Word we do God "injury and insult," since such things "seem inappropriate to God" (i.3).

b. When Anselm replies that it is fitting that man's disobedience should be rectified by man's obedience, this is dismissed as a beautiful fiction and "not a real happening" (i.4).

c. When Anselm points out that God could hardly let his plan for humanity be "entirely wiped out," the further objection is raised that God might surely have used some other, not the incarnate Son, to fulfill this plan (i.5).

d. When Anselm answers that we should then become the servants of another, the deeper complaint arises (1) that the devil has no right or claim against God and (2) that God is impotent if he cannot save sinners without condemning the just, and unrighteous if he is able but unwilling to do so (i.6–7). Anselm disposes of these criticisms by showing that Christ died voluntarily and not by requirement. He died, however, because salvation could be achieved in no other way. This answer necessarily leads to a discussion of the basic problem, in which Anselm presents an important chain of considerations.

(1) Salvation necessarily entails the remission of sin (chap. 10).

(2) Sin might be defined as not rendering God his due (chap. 11).

(3) Every debt or dishonor toward God must be made good: "This is the satisfaction that every sinner ought to make to God" (chap. 12).

(4) Forgiveness by mercy alone and without payment means un-fitting irregularity in God's kingdom (chap. 12).

(5) Either the debt must be paid or punishment, in which God is honored, must follow (chaps. 13–14).

(6) God purposes to replace with men the angels who fell, and for these men satisfaction must be made so that they are equal to the good angels who never sinned (chaps. 16–19).

(7) Satisfaction must be according to the measure of the sin, but since all that man does is owed to God he can never count anything as "part of the debt he owes for sin" (chap. 20).

(8) Even if he could, sin is of such weight that "nothing can suffice as satisfaction for one small sin, for instance, for a single glance in opposition to the will of God" (chap. 21).

(9) Hence the dilemma arises that man owes infinite satisfaction to God: he cannot be saved as God desires unless he makes the repay-ment, and yet he cannot make the repayment (chaps. 22–23).

The answer to the dilemma is the answer to the final objection. Salvation has to be through Christ. But how do Christ and his work avail for man's salvation? Boso raises this question, and Anselm tries to answer it in detail in Book ii.

## 2. The Rationale of the Incarnation

*a. Presuppositions*

Anselm begins his reply with some basic assumptions about man's nature and destiny.

(1) Man's "rational nature was created just by God so that it might be blessed in enjoyment of him" (ii.1).

(2) He would not have died if he had not sinned, and he will be raised again in the body (ii.2–3).

(3) Since God does nothing in vain, he will "complete what he began with human nature" (ii.4).

(4) He does this in grace, for our sakes not his own, not under any constraint but only by the necessity of his unchanging honor (ii.5).

*b. Positive Argument*

Having explained that God purposes to save man, or at least certain men, Anselm goes on to show why only Christ the God-man can achieve this.

(1) The chief point is simple enough. It consists in the twofold thesis that "no one but God can make satisfaction" but that "man ought to make it." "It is thus necessary for a God-man to make it" (chap. 6).

(2) The God-man "must be both perfect God and perfect man," two complete natures meeting in one person (chap. 7).

(3) His humanity must be the same as ours, for only thus can

satisfaction be made for us and our dignity restored. As regards the virgin birth Anselm simply points out that God, having already used three ways of making man, directly, by man alone, and by man and woman, now uses the fourth, by woman alone (chap. 8).

(5) Why the Son should be incarnate and not the Father or the Spirit depends on congruity. It is not fitting that there should be a heavenly Son and a different earthly Son, but it is supremely fitting that pardon should be through Christ when the offense is specifically against him as the true likeness of God (chap. 9).

(6) Since sin against Christ's person "is incommensurate with every other conceivable sin," his death "outweighs all the sins of men" (chap. 14), including the sins even of those who put him to death (chap. 15).

(7) Christ's self-offering constitutes a payment to God, partly because it is an example of perfect obedience, but chiefly because in honoring the Trinity it merits a recompense (chap. 18).

(8) The great reason why man's salvation follows from Christ's death is that Christ, not needing the recompense, both can and does pass it on to those for whose salvation he became man, "his kinsmen and brethren" (chap. 19).

(9) An incidental question is whether or not Christ's work extends to angels. It could, but does not, for angels would need a God-angel, and since Anselm does not think they derive from one, they cannot be saved by one (chap. 21).

(10) In conclusion Anselm has Boso confess that what has been said proves what is contained in scripture, although Anselm himself states more modestly that he is open to correction and that "if what we think we have discovered by reason is confirmed by the testimony of the truth, we should ascribe this, not to ourselves, but to God, who is blessed forever. Amen" (chap. 22).

### 3. Observations

Anselm's contribution to an understanding of the atonement has been so thoroughly discussed and debated that little more can or need be said.

On the negative side Anselm suffers chiefly from his decision not to expound the biblical teaching directly. This has serious consequences. He frequently seems to get the biblical message out of focus. He concentrates on some aspects and ignores others. His use of contemporary concepts is not under adequate control, nor is there sufficient check on his speculative imagination. The logic in his arguments does not always bear the weight he places on it. Even when it does, the impression remains that he is after all stating a predetermined position, not engaging, as he likes to suggest, in an exercise in pure thought in which the data of revelation are temporarily set aside.

Nevertheless, the qualities of *Cur Deus Homo* plainly counterbalance its defects. In the classical tradition of theology, Anselm sees and states clearly the interrelation of incarnation and atonement. He also sees and states the relation of both to creation. The objective work of God in reconciliation receives convincing exposition. In principle, if not always in detail, the great themes of biblical soteriology are developed, and they gain as well as lose by being put in the form of contemporary thought-forms and issues. If it is objected that Anselm does not really work out his argument in a vacuum, this misses the point that he is not trying to construct his own autonomous view of man's nature and destiny but rather to show the rationality of the Christian message to which he adheres by faith. This he does with no little cogency and clarity. Some of his individual discussions, acute and fascinating as they may be, are no doubt more subtle than persuasive. Nevertheless, in his presentation of the larger rationale of the purpose and work of God in creation and salvation Anselm achieves a mastery which has seldom been excelled and which offers a model of enduring significance for the Christian dogmatician.

## D. ORIGINAL SIN

The merit of *Cur Deus Homo* has often led to neglect of Anselm's not unimportant work on *The Virgin Conception and Original Sin,* in which he deals more broadly with issues that had occupied him earlier. This neglect is a mistake, for Anselm's modification of Augustine's teaching on original sin proved more immediately influential than his book on the atonement. After initial resistance, and thanks to the mediating work of Albert the Great, the teaching of Anselm carried the day in Scholastic theology. A contribution of the first magnitude was thus made to theological understanding.

### 1. Original Sin and Personal Sin

*a. Original Sin*

Anselm begins by differentiating between original sin and personal sin. "Original" denotes that which comes with our origin, not the origin of the race, for our first parents were created just, but "the origin of each particular person." This does not mean that sin originates afresh with each person. Original sin is that which "each derives with his nature in his own origin, so that it might be called natural as well as original."

*b. Personal Sin*

In contrast, personal sin is that which "each himself commits after he has become a person distinct from other persons." It is called personal because "it is done with the fault of the person." Incidentally, Anselm notes that over against both original and personal sin stands original and personal righteousness — original by divine creation and personal by divine gift.

### 2. Corruption of Human Nature

Anselm traces original or natural sin to the weakening effect of the first sin on the human body and soul, not only in Adam and Eve, but also in their descendants, since all human nature was in that first couple. "After sin it (human nature) is propagated as it made itself by sinning." Faced with the obligation of righteousness, the fact of its own corruption, and the demand for satisfaction, it cannot make satisfaction nor can it recover or even understand righteousness. Even in infants, then, the state of human nature is one of sin.

### 3. Sin and the Rational Will

If there is original sin, then there also has to be a rational soul. Original sin is no less unrighteous than any other. Infants, even though they seem not to have a rational soul, fall within the condemnation because they belong to the race which alone among God's creatures is endowed with a rational soul.

### 4. Unrighteousness and the Will

Anselm will not locate unrighteousness in the will nor in natural desires. The will is neutral in itself; it may be either just or unjust. Similarly, desires are neutral. Thus the sex drive is righteous in marriage but unrighteous outside it. An action is called unjust on account of an unjust will. This, and not the members or senses, bears responsibility for sinful acts. In the last resort this alone is punished, for "no being that does not possess a will feels punished."

### 5. The Nothingness of Evil

Basically, unrighteousness is nothing, although the affections and acts of an unjust will are something. Evil is the absence of good. "The lack of a good which ought to be is not some kind of being." Pain may be something. Injustice, however, "is nothing but the absence of justice and has no essence."

### 6. Sin

#### a. Punishment

If sin is nothing, why does God punish it? In reply Anselm follows the same paths as in *Cur Deus Homo*. God punishes the unjust for something, not for nothing. "He exacts from them the due honor which they were unwilling to repay freely."

#### b. Conception in Sin

Anselm returns to the question of infants. If they have no rational soul, how can original sin be attributed to them? He rejects the idea of uncleanness in the seed. "There is no sin in them because they do not yet possess a will." The solution lies in the fact that God often says that a thing "is," knowing that it will be. In conception infants derive the necessity of having the uncleanness of sin. "Sin is said to be in them because they contract in the seed the necessity of sinning as soon as they are men."

#### c. Its Magnitude

While stressing the gravity of sin, which means that none can be saved except through Christ's satisfaction, Anselm sees lesser guilt where original sin alone is at issue. Infants will not be punished for Adam's sin "as if they themselves had each committed it personally."

### 7. Infants

#### a. Descent

Infants fall under sin because "they were in Adam when he sinned." In Adam "the person made the nature sinful." Now "the nature makes the persons of infants sinful." Hence the sin of infants is less than that of Adam. Nevertheless, none is saved without the universal satisfaction "whereby both great and small sins are remitted."

#### b. Individual Responsibility

The objection arises: Why should infants bear the sin of Adam and their forefathers? As regards Adam, his sin and that of infants are not the same, so infants do not bear Adam's sin but their own. They may be said to bear it, however, because Adam's sin was the cause of theirs.

#### c. Original Sin

In infants, original sin is equated directly with "what is in the infant as soon as it has a rational soul." What is added after this is personal sin. Original sin must be defined, then, as "that deprivation of due justice which . . . is the outcome of Adam's disobedience." It carries with it a lack of blessedness which can be remedied only by the saving work of Christ through baptism.

## 8. Evaluation

Original sin raises difficult problems. Anselm tackles them bravely but not always successfully. He does not really explain why infants should be brought to account for natural sin. If they should be, and Christ's satisfaction covers them, why might they still perish if others fail to have them baptized? Infant loss poses an even more intractable problem than the infant responsibility from which it derives.

Nevertheless, Anselm has some useful things to say. His distinction between natural sin and personal sin is a good one. So is his distinction between desire and sin. This enables him to break free from the idea that sin is imparted through the act of sex and that, consequently, sex is sinful in marriage too. Anselm is surely right in rejecting the inherent sinfulness of the seed. Whether original or personal, sin lies in the rational soul or will. As original sin it consists in the lack of rectitude which, in some way that Anselm cannot explain, has come by nature to all Adam's progeny, although it is no part of human nature as God made it. Only in virtue of this defect do human desires take the excessive form which leads to sin.

If Anselm cannot account for the universality of sin, three points may be made on his behalf. First, no one has ever done so. Second, his corporate view has more in its favor than a series of isolated but identical individual decisions. Third, the fact remains even if it defies ultimate understanding. Anselm, then, is facing reality, not engaging in abstractions.

Nor should it be overlooked that his basic thesis is not without merit. Anselm sees a continuity of species from first to last. No individual can make a completely fresh start. This applies not only to physical but also to rational and moral characteristics. At the fall Adam gave the rational nature a decisive orientation which his descendants cannot reverse. A person without sin would stand outside the continuity of humanity and would thus be a contradiction in terms.

Christ is the only exception, and to make this point is part of Anselm's purpose. Christ is indeed in Adam, but in a different way. He was "not made of him by nature and will." He was to come of Adam but not to "take being of him." He was in Adam "by divine power." Hence we do not find natural sin in Christ as we do in others. He came from outside, being made in the likeness of sinful flesh, but himself without sin either natural or personal, the head of a new humanity which in him receives the forgiveness of sins and is restored to the natural and personal righteousness of human nature as God originally created it.

# CHAPTER XIII
## *Two Peters*


## A. PETER ABELARD AND THE ATONEMENT

### 1. Introduction

*a. Background*

The earlier and middle parts of the twelfth century produced many theologians of importance. Anselm of Laon proved a worthy pupil of his namesake. The school of St. Victor, an abbey founded in 1110, numbered outstanding thinkers and teachers like the German Hugh and the Scottish Richard. Indeed, Peter Lombard seems to have spent some time there when he first left Italy in 1135. Bernard of Clairvaux also belonged to this exciting and influential period.

*b. Abelard*

Of all the theologians of the time, however, Peter Abelard of Brittany stands out the most sharply, not only by reason of his intellectual brilliance and force, but also on account of his scandalous love affair. Born in 1097, Abelard studied with Anselm of Laon, but quickly outgrew his teacher in learning and critical acumen. His probing spirit and teaching gifts attracted students, but his nonconformity in thought and conduct finally brought down on him the condemnation of St. Bernard and the church; he was fortunate, perhaps, to be able to spend his last days quietly at Cluny (d. 1142) instead of suffering a more drastic fate. Yet his rationalism, if more abrasive than that of Anselm of Canterbury, seems to have been exaggerated by his accusers. Basically, he had no wish to challenge the truth of revelation, nor did he lack the faith and devotion which are the marks of an authentic theologian.

*c. Soteriology*

Of all the contributions of Abelard, the most interesting has proved to be his approach to the atonement, which displays his critical

184

spirit and ultimate depth of faith in admirable combination. Its subjectivity is often thought to sit well with Abelard's nominalistic tendencies, but it seems strangely out of place in the work in which he presents it, *The Exposition of Romans.* In the second half of this commentary Abelard adds to his remarks on Romans 3:19–26 an appendix in which he poses a problem and offers a solution. His suggested restatement of the atonement may be found in this appendix.

### 2. The Doctrine of the Atonement

*a. The Text of Romans 3:19–26*

(1) No Justification by the Law. In his comments on the Romans passage Abelard first shows that the Jews in particular cannot be justified by the law. The law indicts the Gentiles too, but it censures especially those to whom it was given. Abelard understands "the works of the law" to mean the observance of the law. The Jews may indeed observe the law, but this will not justify them because, unlike humans, God does not "judge from outward and visible appearances." Fulfillment according to the spirit, and not just the letter, is required. By this standard justification cannot be achieved. "Through the law every mouth is stopped" and "sins have become more recognizable than less."

(2) Manifestation of the Righteousness of God. The Romans passage, while it sums up what precedes regarding human unrighteousness, has a predominantly positive thrust. A divine righteousness has been manifested apart from the external demands of the law but not apart from the witness of the law and the prophets. Abelard offers a definition of this righteousness. As the righteousness of God, it is "something which God approves." He also makes an equation. As the righteousness of God, it is love.

(3) Justification by Faith. How does faith come into this? Abelard works out his answer in three stages. (a) We are judged by the faith which we hold concerning Christ, either by believing him or believing in him. (b) Faith concerning Christ means the increase of love in us, righteousness being thus imparted to the soul, "where alone love can exist." (c) In this regard no distinction arises between Jews and Gentiles, as it does in relation to external works.

(4) Justification and Love. Justification is free. For Abelard this means that it comes, "not by any previous merits . . . but by the grace of God who first hath loved us." Our redemption is accomplished by Christ the propitiator, that is, by his blood. In all this God shows the force of his righteousness, or love, so as "to convince us how much we ought to love him." Abelard finds added support for his equation of righteousness and love in the phrase "in this time," which he takes to mean "in this time of grace, i.e., love." The phrase also intimates that God's righteousness is seen to be "a love which perfectly meets the needs of men of our time."

*a. A Question*

(1) The Threefold Problem. Looking more closely into the work of redemption through Christ's death, Abelard discerns a threefold problem. (a) Why did God have to assume human nature to redeem us? (b) From whom did he redeem us? (c) By what standard of justice did he redeem us?

(2) The Traditional Answer. Theologians had obviously dealt with these problems before. The traditional teaching had it that God redeemed us from Satan. Satan acquired dominion over the human race when the first man offered him voluntary obedience. A deliverer, also man yet strong enough to defeat Satan, had to come and win a decisive victory if this dominion was to be broken.

(3) Abelard's Criticism. Against the traditional view Abelard made a series of criticisms in the form of probing questions. (a) Can Satan have any right or power except "through the express permission or even the assignment of the Lord"? (b) Cannot the Lord simply bring back those who are now subject to the devil? (c) Should not Satan be regarded as more guilty than those seduced by him? (d) Is it not unjust that the seducer should have rights over the seduced? (e) Even if Satan has such rights, "does he not deserve to lose them"? (f) Is it not more reasonable that the seduced should have a claim to redress? (g) Even if the Lord granted Satan permission, can he not withdraw it? (h) Why, then, should Christ have to suffer and die for our redemption? (i) Does not this seem to lead to the worst sin of all, that of crucifying God's Son? (j) In what way does Christ's death make us more righteous than we were before? (k) To whom was the price of blood paid for our redemption? (l) Is it not cruel and wicked that anyone should demand the blood of an innocent person as the price for anything?

## 3. The Solution

*a. Divine and Human Love*

In a brief reply to his own question Abelard offers a fresh understanding of the atonement. The final obstacle to redemption does not lie either in Satan's dominion or in God's justice. It lies in the lack of love in us. Hence deliverance takes place when, "through the unique act of grace manifested to us" in the incarnation and life and death of the Son, God "has more fully bound us to himself by love," so that our own hearts are enkindled by this gift of divine grace. Looking forward in faith to this divine gift, the patriarchs were aroused to very great love of God. In Christians, however, the response of love can be even greater, for "a realized gift inspires greater love than one which is merely hoped for." God's all-surpassing love evokes love in us, and the main obstacle to reconciliation is thus removed.

### b. Human Love

Abelard offers two indications of the way in which this human love that is evoked by God's love works itself out in us. On the negative side it frees us from slavery to sin, and on the positive side "it wins for us the true liberty of the sons of God, so that we do all things out of love rather than fear." Abelard quotes John 15:13 to show the supreme nature of Christ's love, Luke 12:4–9 to show that he came expressly to spread this true liberty of love among men, and Romans 5:5f. to show that this liberating love is imparted by the love of God.

### 4. Survey

### a. Omissions

A striking point is that Abelard's answer is so much briefer than the question. He bombards the traditional view with criticisms but makes no effort to deal with possible answers or show how his own view solves or undercuts the problem. His questions have a purely destructive function; they are designed to prove that the orthodox position is untenable. Yet the counterquestion arises whether the orthodox position does not involve valid matters which Abelard can ignore only by a gross oversimplification. Does not sin against God entail guilt before him? Can God's justice be met simply by a rekindling of love in the sinner? Is the outpouring of divine love at the cross really necessary to bring about the requisite response of human love? Is there not something almost grotesque about this act of love unless some specific purpose is served by it other than a mere demonstration of love? Does not scripture present many other aspects which have to be considered in any adequate interpretation of God's reconciling work?

### b. Qualities

The strength of Abelard undoubtedly lies in his criticism of the traditional teaching. Difficulties had always been caused by the portrayal of the atonement as a ransoming back from the devil. Anselm had also set aside the time-honored view, more cautiously but no less firmly than Abelard, who tossed caution to the winds. Abelard riddled the traditional doctrine with devastating questions to which it could give no adequate answers. Yet Abelard's presentation has a certain positive strength, too. He fixes on one aspect of the atonement. Although in so doing he runs the risk of one-sidedness, the aspect as such is a true and valid one. How can reconciliation be achieved when the guilty party has no love and no power to engender it? Human response forms an essential part of the whole work, and scripture teaches clearly enough that only the grace of God can call forth this response and thus grant liberation for righteousness, obedience, and fellowship. In giving new and powerful emphasis to this neglected dimension of Christ's work Abelard rendered an even more valuable service than by finally destroying a confused and inadequate understanding.

### c. Defects

At the same time, Abelard's teaching offers difficulties of its own at which we have already hinted. The underlying exposition of Romans does not carry too much conviction, for surely Abelard is subjectivizing what is fairly plainly a more objective Pauline teaching. Can we really equate the righteousness and love of God in the way that Anselm does? Does the epistle really mean what Abelard seems to imply, namely, that we are accepted by God in virtue of imparted love or the love evoked by God's love? Does the showing of God's righteousness really mean the demonstration of love which convinces us that we must love God? The exegetical problems, however, are accompanied by no less serious theological problems. Surely Abelard cannot seriously believe that Christ's death has the significance merely of a demonstration — that nothing is accomplished by it apart from a subjective effect or that it is not ultimately in virtue of what is done for us that its loving and love-evoking power is demonstrable to us and operative in us? Surely he cannot seriously believe that the legal and sacrificial presentations in scripture can be reduced so simply to the formula that reconciliation is just the kindling or rekindling of love in sinners? Surely he cannot seriously think that the dimension which he so rightly and ably represents does not need to be supplemented and complemented by other dimensions such as that which Anselm so carefully expounded only a generation before?

Yet we must not pepper Abelard with questions in the way that he peppered the traditional teaching. No doubt he appreciated the fact that he was not offering the one comprehensive answer. No doubt he saw clearly that if the great Augustine had used the mousetrap metaphor he had also shown that the will can be liberated from bondage only by God's love shed abroad in the heart by the Holy Spirit. If Abelard errs, his primary error lies in the impatience which blinds him to the real truths the ancient interpretation is trying to express. We should not make the same mistake with Abelard's thesis. It presents a valid and valuable aspect of the divine work of reconciliation. For this we must be genuinely grateful to its author even if we must also turn to others for the necessary complementary aspects, unable to believe that all else is confusion or that the totality of God's work can be grasped in Abelard's understanding alone.

## B. PETER LOMBARD AND THE SACRAMENTS

### 1. Introduction

*a. Life*

Peter Abelard was known in the twelfth century for brilliance and originality. For more enduring influence, however, we must turn to another Peter, who is generally recognized not to have the flair of Abelard but who succeeded in writing the type of work which admirably met the needs of the developing theological schools. Born in Italy, Peter Lombard came to Paris about 1135 and spent some time at St. Victor. While in Paris he read and possibly heard Abelard and also became acquainted with the *Decretum* of the canonist Gratian. His *Commentary on the Epistles of Paul* belongs to this period, and it established his reputation as a scholar. During a visit to Rome from 1148 to 1150, he came to know the *Orthodox Faith* of John of Damascus in a new Latin translation. He returned to France in 1152 and spent his final year as archbishop of Paris (1159), where he died in 1160. It was during this last period in France that he completed his masterpiece, *Libri sententiarum,* which earned for him the title of Master of Sentences.

*b. The Sentences*

The *Sentences* of Peter Lombard could hardly be called an original contribution to theology. What the author attempts (and finely accomplishes) is to give a clear and well-organized statement of the basic theological themes. He does not waste time on subtle points of philosophy. Much of his content is taken from others. Differing opinions and authorities are honestly presented; yet a strict orthodoxy prevails throughout. With its orderly arrangement of material and its succinctness of statement, the work forms probably the best introduction to theology composed in the whole Scholastic period. Students could acquire the essentials from it in readily digestible form, while teachers could freely expand on the theses in their own lectures and writings. It need occasion no surprise, then, that even the magnificent *Summa* of Aquinas took many generations to oust the *Sentences* from a position of academic leadership in the initial stages of theological training. The Bible, of course, formed the ultimate textbook.

### 2. The Sacraments

*a. Four Questions*

Like Calvin after him, Lombard arrived at the sacraments in Book iv of his work. Unlike Calvin, however, he dealt with them under Distinction 1 of the book. He makes an indifferent start by allegorizing the parable of the Good Samaritan to show the main function of the sacraments. As the Samaritan poured oil and wine on the wounded man, so "God instituted the remedies of sacraments against the wounds of original and actual sin." In more sober style he then poses the four questions that must be discussed: What is a sacrament? Why was it instituted? Of what does it consist? What is the difference between the sacraments of the old and new law?

### b. Definition

In reply to the first question Lombard offers two simple definitions. A sacrament is (1) a sign of a sacred thing and (2) the visible form of an invisible grace. Under (1) it is noted that a sacrament may be a sacred secret or something sacred signified, but Lombard's present concern is with the sign. An additional point (3) is that the sign consists of more than the sensory impression it makes, "for it makes something else enter thought" (iv.1.3).

These definitions, while true, do not bring out the distinctively Christian aspect of the sacrament. Hence Lombard proceeds to make some important distinctions. (1) Signs may be either natural, like smoke, or given. (2) Given signs are not all sacraments. (3) A sacrament bears a likeness to the thing whose sign it is. (4) It also exists "as its own cause," so that it sanctifies as well as signifies. Hence the ceremonial observances of the old law are "signs only and not sacraments," for, although they might remove external defilement, they could not bring inner cleansing (iv.1.4).

### c. Purpose

Lombard suggests three reasons for the institution of sacraments. (1) They are a means to increase humility. Material things are beneath us by nature. By submitting to them in order to find salvation, not from but through them, we achieve more meritorious obedience to God. (2) They are also a means to instruct. Through "what is perceived from without in a visible form" the mind, which is too dulled by sin to grasp divine things directly, can "understand the invisible virtue which is inward. (3) Finally they are a means to spur us to action. They turn us away from empty and harmful occupations, so that we are not so easily captured by the tempter. Lombard acknowledges that God can give grace to man without the sacraments. He has not "bound his power to them." Yet he has instituted them for these three reasons (iv.1.5).

### d. Constitution

To the constitution of the sacraments Lombard directs only a single sentence: they consist of words and things. In baptism, for example, he sees the invocation of the Trinity as the word and water as the thing. For Lombard, the formula adequately represents the word and no preached or even written word is needed (iv.1.5).

### e. Distinction of the Old and New Testament Sacraments

(1) Augustine's Dictum. Lombard introduces this important discussion by quoting Augustine's saying that "while the former [sacraments] only promised and signified, the latter give salvation" (iv.1.6).

(2) Circumcision. It seems, however, that circumcision conferred "the same remedy against sin as baptism now does." Augustine and Bede are quoted to this effect. Nevertheless, circumcision is less comprehensive than baptism. Those who lived before it, and women, can also receive salvation by faith or sacrifices (iv.1.7–8). Circumcision is also less complete than baptism. In it sins are put away, but in baptism assisting grace is also given and virtues are increased. Performed on the eighth day, circumcision signifies the common resurrection when all corruption will be cut away from the elect by Christ. True circumcision will then be achieved through Christ's resurrection on the eighth day. Circumcision itself, however, accomplishes nothing inwardly (iv.1.9). Nevertheless, since it does accomplish remission of sins, uncircumcised boys are in the same plight as unbaptized infants: "It is certain that they perish." Bede, who associates John 3:5 with Genesis 17:14, is Lombard's authority here. Bede, by the way, recognized that the law of administration on the eighth day posed a problem here. He suggested that if death threatened it could perhaps have been given earlier without any sin, as in the church (iv.1.10).

### e. Sacraments of the New Law

(1) The Seven Sacraments. Turning to the New Testament sacraments in particular, Lombard offers a list which establishes the important concept of seven sacraments. Previously "sacrament" had been used in a more precise sense for baptism and the Eucharist and in an extended sense for almost anything that might have spiritual significance. Lombard steers a middle course, including more than the limited use would allow but also concentrating on the more important observances. The sacraments of the new law are baptism, confirmation, the bread of blessing (that is, the Eucharist), penance, extreme unction, orders, and marriage.

(2) Distinction of the Sacraments. Lombard realizes, of course, that these observances do not all have the same application or function. He thus classifies them according to their negative or positive purpose. Some sacraments, such as marriage, are simply a remedy against sin. Others, such as the Eucharist or orders, fortify with grace and power. In others like baptism we see both aspects. No rank is suggested, but some sacraments are obviously more necessary than others. Baptism, the Eucharist, and in most cases penance are essential, but one can live the Christian life without being ordained or married.

(3) The Problem of Date. Why did not God give the sacraments immediately after the fall? This type of question had troubled some fathers, to whom Christ seemed to have come so late in time. Lombard

connects the late giving of the sacraments with the late coming of Christ, for it is from Christ's death and passion that the sacraments receive their power. Christ, however, did not wish to come until man was convinced that neither the natural nor the written law could help him. The sacraments, too, would be accepted only when this was plain. Marriage, of course, was instituted even before the fall, but not until after the fall did it become "a remedy against the corrupting effects of carnal concupiscence" (iv.2.1).

(4) Detailed Points

(a) Confirmation. Lombard supports episcopal confirmation on the ground of apostolic succession. Since the apostles alone confirmed, only those who hold their places may now do so, and all other administrations are null and void. In relation to the power of confirmation, Lombard distinguishes between the Spirit's gift for remission (baptism) and his gift for strengthening (confirmation). The idea of a twofold work of the Spirit is thus present, although one should not forget that Lombard also sees a positive side to baptism.

(b) Penance. In explaining penance Lombard relies heavily on Jerome's concept of the second plank after a shipwreck. The first plank is baptism, whereby the old man is put off and the new man put on. "Penance is the second plank . . . whereby we raise ourselves again after a fall," the old garment being put off and the new resumed. Lombard also sees, however, that penance is a virtue of the mind and not just a sacrament. He speaks of "an internal penance and an external penance." Each is "a cause of health and sanctification" (iv.14.1).

### 3. Ecclesiastical Orders

*a. The Seven Orders*

Orders are also a sacrament, but they demand separate treatment, which Lombard gives them in iv.24. His first point here is that there are seven orders of spiritual functions, as one can deduce from the fathers and from the example of Christ, who combined all the functions in himself (iv.24.1). All ministry demands participation in the Spirit, but advancement in ministry confers fuller grace (iv.24.2). Ministers should enjoy this grace and also be those "whose doctrine and spirituality are transferred by grace to others" (iv.24.3). The seven orders are listed: doorkeeper, lector, exorcist, acolyte, subdeacon, deacon, and priest. All are called clergy, which Lombard takes to mean "chosen by lot" (*kleros*).

*b. Presbyters*

Lombard insists that only the diaconate and presbyterate are properly described as sacred states. He gives two reasons: (1) the primitive church had these alone, and (2) the apostles gave us a command about these two alone. The minor orders were set up by the church for itself as time went on (iv.24.12).

### c. Definition of an Order

Lombard defines an order as a sacred sign or something by which spiritual power and office are handed to the ordained. A spiritual "character" or stamp is called an order or grade. Orders are a sacrament "because in receiving them a sacred thing, grace, which the things that are done there figure, is conferred" (iv.24.13).

### d. Order and Office

Lombard's discussion leads to the rather surprising conclusion that the episcopate is not an order. This is why the bishop does not appear in the list of seven. It should also be noted that when Lombard differentiates deacons and presbyters, he bases the presbyterate on the apostolic appointment of bishops and presbyters in each city. In continuing the discussion, Lombard observes that we find other names, but these are of "dignities and offices," not orders. "Bishop" is the name of both a dignity and an office. It derives from the actual function of bishops, that is, "bearing the care of those below them" (iv.24.15, quoting Isidore). The bishop, watching over the habits and life of the people, is "the chief of priests, the path of those who follow," "the highest priest," who "makes priests and deacons and distributes all ecclesiastical orders" (iv.24.16, quoting Isidore).

## 4. Questions

Even in such a restricted sector, Lombard's work obviously raises many important questions. For example, we may agree that Lombard is right that the word "sacrament" can be used in different ways. His own way is, no doubt, as good as any other. Nevertheless, better criteria are surely needed if the term is to be applied to some essential and obligatory aspects of ministry. The sacred number does not in itself offer a sufficient reason for fixing on the signs that Lombard lists. In fact, their disparate nature seems to offer a valid cause for challenging the whole construction.

The quasi-automatic functioning of the sacraments calls for scrutiny, too. Lombard, it is true, avoids a purely causal understanding. In his more detailed discussion he shows that unbelief or insincerity can form a dam which checks the inflow of grace. Hence a call for response must normally be issued. The great exception of infant baptism, however, reduces the value of this safeguard; infants can put up no resistance, remission and grace are conferred on them by the administration of the sacrament alone, and conversion can have only a modified significance except where there is a fall from grace. If this seems to favor infants, it has a harsher side which is no less dubious. Infants cannot usually have the alternative baptisms of blood (martyrdom) or the Spirit (a pure conversion). Without water baptism, then, they have no hope of salvation. Yet they are totally dependent on others for this baptism. They may perish, then, by the default of their elders, by premature death, or by the sheer accident of being born in the wrong time and place.

The question of penance betrayed Lombard into difficulties which his successors were to find equally intractable. The plank metaphor not only lacks biblical support but is incompatible with the authentic biblical comparison of baptism to the ark. The penalties for which penance procures remission also need closer definition. The institution of penance can be based only on linguistic ambivalence. Lombard himself sees clearly enough that penance is primarily and properly penitence, not an outward act or rite. One is naturally tempted to find an outer sign for the inner thing that is signified, as in water and Spirit baptism, but the lack of any scriptural basis constitutes the crucial difference.

As regards ministry, one has to ask why Lombard, even though he is well aware of the difference between the biblical and the ecclesiastical orders, still lumps them together so easily. Is he determined in advance to end up with a sevenfold ministry? A sevenfold increase in grace raises a new set of problems. Happily, Lombard makes no attempt to relate specific gifts to specific orders. His institutionalizing of the charisms, however, represents a victory for the institution which caused untold difficulties in his own and later times and against which there is almost bound to be unfortunate charismatic exaggeration.

Problems of a different type emerge with his distinction of the episcopate, not as an order, but as a dignity and office. Various forces were working against a high episcopalianism in Lombard's day, nor had it ever been definitely settled that episcopacy is the order *par excellence* through which the presbyterate, too, derives its ministry. Yet in relation to confirmation Lombard can also suggest that the bishops are in a special way the apostles' successors. Presumably he means that they succeed to the office of the apostles, while presbyters share with them the same order. But what does this amount to? He obviously confuses office and function. He hardly remains within a biblical framework in speaking of dignity. He ultimately has to concede, it would seem, that the distinction is ecclesiastical rather than theological. His use of the term "chief [or highest] priest" postulates a primacy in equality. Could he then have accepted a final presbyterianism if some place were left for an ongoing head of the presbytery? He does not tell us, and speculation on the matter is useless. He certainly offers little support for a theologically grounded episcopal succession; yet at the same time his teaching on office connects episcopal ordination very firmly to ecclesiastical order. Perhaps he does not think with sufficient theological or biblical depth to see that there might be a final clash between the basic constitution of the ministry and its ecclesiastical regulation.

Lombard obviously does little theological exploration. His authoritative statements can even give the impression of a certain superficiality. He offers no searching analysis of past or present convictions in terms of the New Testament data. Nevertheless, appearances can be deceptive. Not all Lombard's statements fit into a neat traditionalist pattern; some open up questions which he himself may not investigate but which leave plenty of room for further thought and analysis. Even some of those that are traditional can lead us along lines of questioning or inference which are no less exciting than unexpected. What more could one ask of a textbook?

# CHAPTER XIV

# The Angelic Doctor

## A. PRELIMINARY CONSIDERATIONS

### 1. The Man

Born about 1225, Thomas belonged to the neighborhood of Aquinas in Italy. In early childhood his parents dedicated him to the Benedictine order, and he went to school at Monte Cassino from 1230 to 1239. In 1240 he matriculated at the new University of Naples and spent four years there. He then became a Dominican monk and as such studied at Paris under Albert the Great (1245–1248). When Albert moved to Cologne he went with him for another four years of study (1248–1252). He came back to Paris as a teacher and lectured first on the Bible for two years and then on the *Sentences* of Peter Lombard. He became Master of Theology in 1256 and spent his remaining years teaching in Paris and in various parts of Italy. His theological associations were all with the Dominicans rather than the Benedictines. His comparatively short life came to an end in 1274.

### 2. The Writings

Thomas was astonishingly productive as an author. Although not so well known in this field, he wrote commentaries on many Old Testament books and also on Matthew, John, and Paul. His extensive knowledge of Aristotle came to expression in commentaries on the most important books of the ancient philosopher. His dogmatic writings include not only the *Summa theologiae* but also the *Summa contra Gentiles*. He also wrote smaller works on specific questions at issue in his day. His contribution to angelology earned him the title "Angelic Doctor."

### 3. The Summa theologiae

The *Summa theologiae,* on which Thomas worked for many years, constitutes his main claim to theological eminence. It is a massive work in which he aims to cover all aspects of theology and to give solid orthodox answers to all the questions which arose in relation to them. The *Summa,* however, was never completed. When urged to finish it in his later years, he is said to have described all that he had written thus far as chaff and to have sought from God an end to his earthly life. His modesty is perhaps more fitting than the adulation often heaped on him, for, like all great theologians, he perceived that what is said about God must always fall far short of its subject.

## 4. Features of the Summa

### a. Structure

Thomas, like Lombard, follows in the *Summa* an orderly pattern of discussion both in general and in detail. In general he has successive treatises on the successive heads of theology. Within each treatise a series of questions is posed, each with a varying number of subquestions in the form of articles. When dealing with a subquestion Thomas first gives reasons for the answer he rejects. He then advances his own thesis, expands it in an answer, and then offers individual replies to the reasons for the other view.

### b. Authorities

A notable feature of the *Summa* is the large number of biblical quotations. Almost all the books of scripture are culled by Thomas in his search for authorities. Next to scripture Aristotle plays a dominant role, although he is closely followed by Augustine. The Greek fathers do not figure greatly in Thomas's presentation. Nor does he refer much to his immediate predecessors, who do not have for him the same weight as the ancients. Lombard and Bernard are occasionally mentioned. Uncritical and unmerited attention is paid to the *Celestial Hierarchy* and *Divine Names* of Dionysius.

## B. THE NATURE OF THEOLOGY

## 1. Theology and Philosophy

Very properly Thomas opens the *Summa* with an attempt to define theology. He first deals with the need for it. If we should not seek what is beyond reason, and if philosophy deals with all that is, including God, then theology seems to be superfluous. It has, however, a distinct purpose which is clearly stated in 2 Timothy 3:16. Scripture has a divine origin in contrast to the rational source of philosophy. The end of theology is God, who surpasses the comprehension of reason. "Things which

are beyond reason have to be made known through divine revelation."
Indeed, revelation is needed, too, in things which can be known by
reason but on which salvation depends, for "such truth about God as
could be discovered by reason would be known only by the few and that
after a long time and mixed with many errors." Through revelation,
salvation comes "the more fittingly and certainly." Things beyond reason can in any case be revealed by God, and philosophy and theology can
know the same things in different ways. A generic distinction is perceived between "the theology which depends on sacred scripture" and
"the theology which is a part of philosophy" (1.1.1).

### 2. Theology as a Science

#### a. Is Theology a Science?

Thomas sees two objections to classifying theology as a science.
(1) It depends on articles of faith, not self-evident principles. (2) It deals
with particulars. Nevertheless, Augustine authoritatively calls theology a science. As is true of many sciences, it depends on the principles of
a higher science — the science of God. It also deals with particulars,
Thomas suggests, by way of illustration (1.1.2).

#### b. Is Theology a Single Science?

Theology covers both Creator and creature and also different
kinds of creatures. It thus seems to break the rule that one science has
one subject. Formal unity, however, derives from the fact that all the
subjects are dealt with from the angle of revelation. Again, God and
creatures are not the subjects of theology in an equal way. It is "concerned with God fundamentally and with creatures insofar as they
relate to him as their being and end." Drawing its knowledge from God,
theology "is like an imprint of the divine knowledge which is one and
undivided" (1.1.3).

#### c. Is Theology a Practical Science?

Since theology aims at action, it would seem to be practical. It has
indeed a practical side, but for Thomas it is more speculative, being
more basically concerned with divine truths than human actions. The
latter are of interest only as they bring "the perfect knowledge of God in
which eternal happiness consists" (1.1.4).

#### d. Is God the Subject?

It might be argued that God is not, since (1) a subject must be
presupposed and one cannot presuppose God, and (2) scripture reaches
conclusions about many things other than God. According to Thomas,
however, the main theme of this science is God; this is why it is called
theology. The first objection fails because we can use God's effects in

nature or grace in place of a definition. The second fails because all the other things on which scripture reaches conclusions are comprehended in God or related to him (1.1.7).

### 3. Modes of Theology

*a. Argument*

Ambrose and Boethius rule against argument in theology, and Thomas allows that "there is no way of proving the articles of faith by argument" except by disposing of objections. Yet theology can still argue from the articles of faith to prove other things. An appeal to authority, which is grounded on revelation and not reason, may also be used in argument. Reason may also serve, "not indeed to prove the faith . . . but to clarify certain points of doctrine." Since grace does not supplant nature but perfects it, reason ought to be the servant of faith. Theology can even use the authority of philosophers when they have been able to know the truth through natural reason, but only as supporting or probable arguments, since canonical scripture is "the proper authority from which theology is bound to argue." What of the fathers? One may argue from them with propriety, yet only with probability (1.1.8).

*b. Metaphor*

It might seem that metaphor should not have any place in theology, for other sciences do not use it, truth is obscured by it, and metaphors from the lower creation, which has less likeness to God, hardly seem to be fitting. Quoting Hosea 12:10, however, Thomas shows that all knowledge "begins from sense," that God suitably arranges that we should "reach intelligible things through sensible things," and that veils are needed since we cannot look directly at the divine ray. The veils do not destroy the ray of revelation, for revelation will not let us stop at the image. But why are lower forms of creation used as metaphors? Three answers are given. (1) There is less risk of confusing them with the reality. (2) They more clearly show what God is not. (3) Divine things are better hidden from the unworthy in this way (1.1.9).

### 4. Multiple Exegesis

If the scriptures are the supreme authority, can we defend their fourfold exegesis? In spite of the risk of obscurity, Thomas thinks that we can on the basis of Gregory's famous dictum that "in one and the same word they record an event and proclaim a mystery." As Thomas sees it, the words signify events and then the events signify other things so that we have both a literal and also a spiritual meaning. The spiritual meaning subdivides into the allegorical (the signifying of the New Testament in the Old), the moral (the signifying of what we are to do), and the anagogical (the signifying of what belongs to eternal glory). Confusion need not arise, for (1) all interpretations rest on the literal, (2) we can argue only from the literal, and (3) "nothing essential is contained in the spiritual sense of one passage which is not clearly expressed in the literal sense of another" (1.1.10).

### 5. Conclusions

a. Thomas has a clear understanding of what theology is and neither confuses it with philosophy nor makes philosophy its basis. Theology necessarily rests on the divine self-revelation through holy scripture. Even where philosophy might cover some of the same ground, it is ultimately dispensable, of little value to the majority, severely restricted in scope, and of much less use as an authority.

b. Thomas could not be more explicit in stating that by definition God is the subject of theology. Man and the world have a place in it only as they stand related to God. The focus on God gives theology its necessary unity. It cannot be a confused mixture of sciences nor can it be transformed into anthropology or cosmology.

c. Thomas shows a healthy respect for the limits of argument in divine things. As a theologian he naturally believes that the themes of theology should be set out in logical and orderly fashion. Nevertheless, he sees the impossibility of trying to prove first principles and the futility of trying to win over by argument those who totally reject revelation. Argument has its rightful place, but revelation is the necessary starting point of faith.

d. Thomas, for all the intellectualism of his presentation, accepts the fact of metaphor in revelation and also grasps the twofold noetic reason for it: (1) the sensory basis of all knowledge and (2) the opening of knowledge of God to the simple as well as the learned. He displays, too, an appreciation of the twofold operation of the veiling and the unveiling of divine truth in sensory images: (1) truth is unveiled for believers even as it is veiled; (2) truth is veiled for unbelievers even as it is unveiled.

In the light of these conclusions some common interpretations of Thomas demand careful reconsideration. It is not apparent that he subsumes theology under philosophy. Nor is it apparent that he makes philosophy the source, basis, or even the starting point of faith. Nor does he seem at all to pursue an essentially rationalistic or apologetical theology.

## C. THE DOCTRINE OF GOD

### 1. Existence

a. Under question 2 Thomas tackles three subquestions. The first concerns the self-evident nature of God's existence. Thomas allows an innate sense of God but finds it confused in most people. Unlike Anselm, he does not think that all people will equate God with that than which nothing greater can be thought; nor will those who deny God concede that that than which nothing greater can be thought exists in reality (1.2.1).

b. Turning to the demonstration of God's existence, Thomas begins with Romans 1:20: God can be demonstrated from his effects. This does not rule out faith, for natural reason affirms only the preambles to the articles of faith, and in any case this demonstration is not essential. While the effects are not proportionate to the cause, they show that the cause exists (1.2.2).

c. In the third subquestion Thomas asks directly whether God exists. The presence of evil and the possibility of other explanations of the world tell against his existence. The decisive point, however, is God's own statement in Exodus 3:14: "I am that I am." For some reason, Thomas then develops his famous five ways of proof from motion; efficient cause; the nature of possibility and necessity; the relative degrees and the supreme degree of truth, goodness, and nobility; and the intelligent governance of things (1.2.3).

## 2. Simplicity

In defining the manner of God's existence, Thomas takes the negative approach by showing what God is from what he is not. In successive articles he claims that God has no body, is not compounded (for example, of form and matter or essence and existence), and is not in composition with other things. The absolute simplicity of God results from this analysis (1.3.1–8).

## 3. Perfection

Under this heading Thomas makes three points. God is perfect (1.4.1). His perfection is a comprehensive one which embraces the perfection of all things (1.4.2). The creature can be like God by creation in the divine likeness and by new creation in the likeness of Christ (1.4.3). In discussing likeness Thomas makes an important distinction between imperfect or analogical likeness and equal and perfect likeness. It is in this context that he makes his famous statement about the analogy of being: "In so far as creatures are beings, they are like the first and universal principle of all being." Yet Thomas sees a qualitative unlikeness due to the lack of community of either specific nature or genus. He stresses, too, the element of irreversibility: a creature is like God, but God is not like a creature (1.4.3). Hence the analogy of being does not rule out an infinitely qualitative distinction.

At a later point (1.12.12) Thomas asks again about the knowledge of God through natural reason. What he said about knowledge of the preambles to the articles of faith and the inferred principle that faith presupposes natural knowledge seemed to favor a natural knowledge of God, notwithstanding the reservations in Question 1. Thomas clarifies the matter by stressing the limits of this knowledge. It begins from sense, and while it can teach us that God exists, it cannot lead us to see his essence.

He also takes up again the question of analogical knowledge in Q. 13, Art. 5. The same perfections can be ascribed to God and man but not univocally, for the perfections are separate in man and separate from his essence, but they are comprehensive in God and inseparable from his essence. On the other hand, the same perfections are not ascribed to God and man equivocally, as though human perfections could tell us nothing about the same perfections in God. They are ascribed to God and man by way of analogy, since they signify different relations to one and the same thing.

### 4. Justice and Mercy

After discussing God's love in Question 20, Thomas tackles the divine justice and mercy in Question 21. God's justice is the distribution of what is due, that is, not of what God owes but of what he has ordained (1.21.1). It is also the condescension of his goodness, as in the justification of the wicked. Mercy does not clash with justice but exceeds it in free giving (1.21.3). All God's works manifest both his justice and his mercy. All that God does is just, and justice "invariably presupposes a work of divine mercy as its foundation, since no one has any rights except by the goodness of God in creation" (1.21.4).

### 5. Providence

Thomas has four theses on providence in Question 22. a. It is properly ascribed to God (1.22.1). b. It embraces all things (1.22.2). c. It is direct in purpose if often indirect in execution (1.22.3). d. It imposes necessity on some things but not on all things, since contingent causes are provided for some effects as necessary ones are for others (1.22.4). Like Origen, Thomas finds no conflict between divine sovereignty and human freedom, since what God provides "happens in the manner in which God provides it, whether through contingency or necessity" (1.22.4).

### 6. Predestination

Thomas relates predestination very closely to providence. He derives it from Romans 8:30 and equates it with God's bringing the rational creature to an end it could not reach on its own, as an arrow is directed to its mark by an archer (1.23.1–2). Although it might be argued that God loves all men, that he will not cause any to perish, and that no fault can be alleged if no choice is left, Thomas argues for reprobation as well as election in the sense, not that the rejected are ordained to perdition, but that they are permitted to fail to attain the end of life. God wills good for all, but not every good for all. Reception of grace is *conditionally* impossible for the reprobate, since it lies with their will that they fall into one sin or another (1.23.3). Predestination presupposes election, which itself presupposes love. Love arises because God wills the good of eternal life, election because he wills it for some and not others (1.23.4). Election is free; God does not elect some because he finds good in them. Foreknown merits, then, are not the cause of predestination. Even if there is something in us which ordains us to salvation, it is wholly included in the effect of predestination. The election of some and the rejection of others rests solely on God's will, who displays his goodness by mercifully sparing some and justly punishing others. Why this is so rests with God's will, but Thomas argues that preparing unequal things for those who are not unequal is not unfair in this instance, since salvation is given, not owed. So long as what is due is not withheld, no one can complain if things are given gratuitously to some and not to others (1.23.5). Predestination infallibly achieves its effect, even if contingently and not by necessity, for God is immutable (1.23.6). The number of the elect is certain, not by reason of angelic vacancies, but because the elect are principals in the universe whose number is materially foreordained as well as foreknown by God (1.23.7). As regards the practical question whether prayer can further predestination, Thomas sees a need for distinction. In relation to predestination as cause it cannot help, but in relation to predestination as effect it does. For secondary causes are not suppressed but achieve their effect by subordination to predestination. Prayer does not help God in the sense of giving him extra power, but it helps him in the execution of his commands. Secondary causes cannot hinder predestination, but they do implement it (1.23.8).

### 7. Questions

a. When Thomas says that faith presupposes natural knowledge, so that rational knowledge of God is a knowledge of the preambles to the articles of faith, how does this relate to his earlier discussion of theology and philosophy and the serious limitation of the latter in divine things? In Thomistic interpretation undue stress has often been laid on Q. 2, Art. 2, but it should be considered (1) that here he is answering objections to proof of God's existence and (2) that he is contending only

for the possibility of proving a divine cause. The serious question is
whether faith can proceed without this natural knowledge. Q. 1, Art. 1
would seem to imply that it can, although the knowledge of certain
things by philosophy is not thereby invalidated.

b. What does Thomas mean by the analogy of being? This phrase
has been contested on the ground that it seems to assume a final
something — being — common to both God and man. Thomas, however,
guards against this by equating being and God. God does not have being;
he *is* being, and by creation he gives man a share in it. Thomas also
deals with the analogy of being in a context in which the unlikeness of
God and man is much to the fore. Affirming the divine likeness on the
basis of Genesis 1:26, Thomas has some difficulty in seeing how there
can be this likeness. He resorts to the term "analogy" as a weaker one
which is consistent also with the irreversibility of the image, namely,
that God makes man in his likeness, not man God. Perhaps Thomas is
mistaken in finding the likeness in being, for does not this apply to all
creatures? Nevertheless, one can hardly fault him for thereby reducing
God and man to a common denominator.

c. Is Thomas right to deal with predestination as a special instance of providence? Barth deals with this point very forcefully in
*Church Dogmatics* 2.2, and he makes a good case against Thomas in this
regard. In particular, Thomas manages to carry through his discussion
with no reference whatever to Christ and with no clear integration of
the doctrine into the divine acts in creation and history. For all the texts
quoted, then, the treatment is astonishingly non-biblical and abstract.
The most that can be said for Thomas is that, no matter what approach
be taken, the relationship of divine and human freedom will always
arise in both providence and predestination, so that here, at least, an
overlap occurs. It is another matter, however, whether either providence
or predestination should have its theological center in this aspect of the
matter.

## D. SIN, GRACE, AND FAITH

### 1. Sin

#### a. Original Sin

Thomas believes in original sin in the sense of a disordered
disposition due to the loss of the harmony of original uprightness
(2.1.82.2). It is in all people equally as a lack of original uprightness
with a common source (2.1.82.4). Actual sins, which are distinguished
from original sin, vary from person to person in both nature and extent
(2.1.82.2).

### b. Effects of Sin

Various problems crop up when the effects of sin are considered. With the loss of original good the constitution of human nature is not changed, but the natural inclination to virtue is diminished. Good itself cannot be totally destroyed, for "evil exists only in what is good" (Augustine *Enchiridion* 13f.) (2.1.85.1–2). Both original sin and actual sins cause weakness and ignorance, all the powers of the soul being "left to some extent destitute of their proper order" (2.1.82.3–4). Sin also results in death. Death is not, in the view of Thomas, natural to man. We have a corruptible body but God has adapted it to our form, the rational soul, and our end, eternal felicity (2.1.82.5–6).

## 2. Grace

### a. The Need for Grace

In his treatment of grace (2.1.109–113) Thomas asks first whether man can know any truth or do any good without grace. Some truths may indeed be known, if not without divine help, at least without the special light of grace, which must be added to natural light "only in such things as transcend natural knowledge," that is, the truths of faith (2.1.109.1). On the other hand, while good deeds might have been done by unfallen Adam with divine help alone, fallen man "cannot by his own power fulfill the whole good that pertains to his nature." Thomas concludes that "nature is impaired by sin more in the desire for good than in the knowledge of truth" (2.1.109.2).

What is it in detail that we cannot do without grace? We cannot love God above all things. We cannot fulfill the commandments either outwardly or inwardly. We cannot rise from sin or become righteous or return from a state of guilt to one of uprightness. We cannot merit eternal life or even prepare ourselves for grace. Indeed, when we have received grace we cannot do good or avoid sin without further grace. Nor can we dispense with grace in order to persevere. "Even a man in grace needs that perseverance be given him by God" (2.1.109.3–10). Like Augustine, Thomas takes a strict line on the absolute indispensability of grace to salvation.

### b. The Nature of Grace

The problems inherent in Thomas's dogmatic method come out very plainly in his short section on the essence of grace (Q. 110). Since he does not ask biblical questions, he has difficulty finding biblical answers. Linguistic or exegetical inquiry would have given his discussion a basis which his philosophical examination does not. To ask whether grace is something in the soul, whether it is a quality, or whether it differs from infused virtue, holds out little promise of a successful outcome.

Nevertheless, Thomas does achieve some useful insights. He distinguishes helpfully between grace as love, grace as gift, and grace as thanksgiving (2.1.110.1). He points out that grace as gift may be the effect of love as well as love itself, and in this sense one might speak of it as being within us. Yet Thomas retains a strong awareness that God's grace means his eternal love, as when we speak of the grace of predestination. He also realizes that regeneration is through grace (2.1.110.3). Grace is thus in the soul as subject, not object, and as such it is the source of meritorious works (2.1.110.4).

### c. The Divisions of Grace

(1) Free Grace and Sanctifying Grace. The emphasis on grace as gift leads Thomas to an acute, if biblically dubious, categorizing of grace. It falls basically into two types, sanctifying and free. Sanctifying grace is also free, but it is free in a different way, and all grace does not sanctify. Thomas defines sanctifying grace as "grace through which a man is himself united to God," while free grace is "grace whereby one man cooperates with another to lead him to God" (2.1.111.1).

(2) Sanctifying Grace. This grace may be subdivided into operative and cooperative grace. All God's works are grace, but "he perfects within us by cooperation what he initiates by operation" (quoting Augustine *On Grace and Free Will* 17) (2.1.111.2). Another subdivision consists of prevenient and subsequent grace. Five effects of grace are seen. It heals the soul, desires the good, performs the good, perseveres in good, and obtains glory. As the cause of the first effect, grace is prevenient in relation to the second, while as a cause of the second it is subsequent in relation to the first. Eternally grace is always prevenient, but in time and effects it may be both prevenient and subsequent (2.1.111.3).

(3) Free Grace. Free grace takes the form of charisms (1 Corinthians 12) and may be subdivided in accordance with three charismatic groupings. If we are to cooperate in leading others to God, we need three things: knowledge, the ability to verify revelation, and the ability to communicate. Hence the first grouping relates to knowledge and includes the charisms of faith, the word of wisdom, and the word of understanding. The second relates to demonstration and includes the charisms of healing, miracles, and predictive prophecy, means "peculiar to the divine power" which are needed to prove "divine revelations which transcend reason." The third relates to communication and includes the charisms of tongues (the idioms) and interpretation (the sense) (2.1.111.4). While free grace might seem to be higher than sanctifying grace, Thomas cannot accept this, chiefly because he groups love (1 Corinthians 13) with sanctifying grace, but also because free grace simply prepares man for his final end, while sanctifying grace relates him directly to it (2.1.111.5).

(4) Justification. The effect of operative grace is the justification of the wicked, which Thomas equates with the remission of sins (2.1.113.1). This comes about by grace but also includes a movement of the will in repentance and faith (except in the case of infants, maniacs, or morons) (2.1.113.3–5). Since all is grace, justification may properly be seen as instantaneous, and the infusion of grace comes first in order (2.1.113.7). In view of what it achieves, justification may be regarded as God's greatest work (2.1.113.9). It can also be called a miracle with respect to the agent and sometimes to the sequence, as in sudden conversions, but it is not a miracle in the sense of being beyond natural capacity, the soul being capable of God in virtue of its creation in God's image (2.1.113.10). Merit does not arise in the sphere of justification, for it is an effect of cooperative, not operative grace. Thomas can state categorically that no one, not even in the state of unfallen nature, can merit eternal life without grace (2.1.114).

### 3. Faith

#### a. The Object

Thomas rightly opens his discussion of faith by considering the object. While faith relates to human and earthly things, its true object is the first truth, or God (2.2.1.1). It assents to other things only on the ground of revelation and only as these things relate to God in some way. In itself the object of faith is simple, but to believers it is complex. It has, therefore, the form of propositions, although these are formulated only so as to know the reality by means of them (2.2.1.2). Can the things of faith be known scientifically? Oddly, it might seem, Thomas follows Gregory and says that there cannot be faith in what is known scientifically, that is, by sight (2.2.1.5). Yet he qualifies this significantly. (1) Certain things may be known by some scientifically, by others only through faith. (2) Faith includes things which can be known by demonstration. (3) The same person might know one thing, such as God's unity, scientifically, and another, such as the Trinity, by faith. A place is reserved, then, for scientific knowledge, but only for some things and some people (2.2.1.5).

#### b. The Act

As regards the act of faith, Thomas accepts its definition as "thinking with assent" (2.2.2.1). He explains, however, (1) that faith uses reason, not to prove what it believes, but to study the evidence by which a person is induced to believe; and (2) that the believer's intellect is determined by the will, not by reason (2.2.2.1). Nor should we neglect the distinction between believing there is a God, believing God, and believing in God — all constitute one and the same act in different relations to the object (2.2.2.2). In Art. 4 Thomas returns once more to the question of what can be proved by natural reason. Is it necessary to believe such things? Yes, for faith is a quicker way to knowledge of these things, makes this knowledge more widely accessible, and gives a certainty which rational demonstration cannot give. In Art. 5 Thomas defends the concept of implicit faith, but he demands explicit belief in the incarnation, passion, and resurrection of Christ, and also in the Holy Trinity, without which one cannot believe in the incarnation (2.2.2.7–8). Confession of faith, being specifically commanded by scripture, forms the outward act of faith (2.2.3.1). Thomas concludes from Romans 10:10 that in some circumstances confession is necessary to salvation (2.2.3.2).

### 4. Impressions

a. In view of the alleged semi-Pelagianism of Scholasticism, one cannot but be struck by the strong doctrine of predestination and grace in the *Summa*. If a place is found for merit, it is only within the process of salvation which first and last owes everything to God. Problems arise mainly through the compartmentalizing of grace and the sacramentalizing of its operation.

b. Thomas is often depicted as a double-deck theologian who builds revealed truth on rational truth. In fact, however, he gives rational demonstration a minimal, dispensable role. Things that can be known rationally may be presuppositions of things that are known by faith, but few can know them in this way; the way is laborious and uncertain, and apart from faith it cannot in any case lead to salvation. For apologetic reasons Thomas gives a certain prominence to this natural possibility, but to say that for him rational demonstration is the first deck and faith the second is surely stretching things. In its totality, is not his theology a theology of revelation alone, and not of reason and revelation?

c. Basically Thomas shows no negligible understanding of justification and faith. He neither confuses the former with sanctification nor reduces the latter to purely intellectual belief. Here again his main problem may well be that of the oversacramentalizing which can lead to the conclusion that justification takes place in baptism and sanctification is the only practical concern. His theses, however, do not obscure, if they do not fully elucidate, the biblical teaching. As regards implicit faith, his view that every believer does not have to understand all the details of dogma in order to be saved is not unreasonable so long as explicit faith in Christ is required. It can, of course, be misused as an excuse for failing to fulfill the church's instructional ministry.

d. The form of Thomas's presentation, while not unimpressive in itself, may well be his greatest handicap, so alien is it to the biblical form. Because of it, teaching which has a biblical basis tends to be lost or covered over in the inappropriate dress. Thomas, in fact, conducts an important experiment. Can one express the biblical message in words, concepts, and methods of argumentation derived from Aristotelianism? This is, of course, only one aspect of the wider question whether the biblical message can be properly put in the alien forms of any other age or culture. In other words, it is an acute form of the challenge which is thrown down to all preachers and theologians, since presenting the biblical message in contemporary terms is surely their task. We cannot fault Thomas for making the effort. Indeed, we must say that in the last analysis he demonstrates the possibility. Yet we must say that he also demonstrates the difficulty, since the losses are not inconsiderable when the gospel is forced into the Aristotelian straitjacket. The problem lies not so much in the use of new terms as in the imposing of an alien methodology in which biblical answers are sought for non-biblical questions and the answers are then developed in terms of the questions. The most astonishing thing, perhaps, is that the Christian message still comes through as clearly and forcefully as it does. Here the piety of Thomas — his essential faith — is manifested no less powerfully than his genius.

## CHAPTER XV
# *The Reformers and the Word of God*


## A. LUTHER

### 1. Introduction

In marked contrast to Scholastic theology, Reformation theology showed from the very first a strong concern for the Word of God. The implications of this concern had to be worked out with the advance of the Reformation itself. The facets and interrelations could not be perceived or expressed all at once. Nevertheless, the new turn in biblical exegesis and the fresh dedication to biblical Christianity gave centrality to the Word even before the indulgence crisis precipitated reform and decision. From the outset, then, the theology of the reformers would be not only a theology of justification but also a theology of the Word.

As events unfolded, Luther was to find himself increasingly driven back to the Word and engaged in the effort to expound and promote it. For a full understanding of his concept of the Word we should certainly have to explore the great mass of his writings. Some of his crucial ideas, however, are stated already in his early lectures, and for an introduction to the theology of the Word which he would later work out in thought and practice we may turn with full confidence to the scattered but varied and pregnant utterances in the Romans series of 1515.

These lectures were not printed by Luther. The manuscript survived, however, and after being lost for many years was tracked down and published by J. Ficker, first in a preliminary edition in 1908, then in the definitive edition of 1938 (Vol. 56 of the Weimar edition of Luther's works). Ficker also published (Vol. 57) some student notebooks in which the lectures are preserved as they were delivered in the classroom. On the basis of the Weimar edition two English translations were published, that of W. Pauck in *The Library of Christian Classics* (Vol. 15), which has an excellent introduction, and that of W. G. Tillmanns and J. A. D. Preus in *Luther's Works* (Vol. 25), which offers the full interlinear and marginal glosses as well as the scholia, and which will be used in the following discussion.

## 2. The Word and the Fool

A decisive insight for Luther is that God's Word always meets with resistance from self-opinionated sinners. Romans 3:7 gives him the chance to develop this thought. The proud will not acknowledge their sinfulness. They dismiss God as a fool when he diagnoses their sickness and prescribes the remedy. Their scorn, of course, is not directly for God himself, but for God in his Word. Thus a conflict arises between what the Word says and what we proudly think.

Foolish though the Word may seem, the way of real folly is to refuse to listen to it. This refusal cannot invalidate its truth (LW 25, p. 208). God is justified in his words. The proud do not even hear the Word in the true sense. Only the humble hear and receive it.

Part of the office of the Word is to prick the proud and foolish bubble of self-righteousness. The self-righteous have to "become" sinners, that is, win through to an awareness of their sin and falsehood, if they are to achieve the true righteousness which is God's gift of grace through faith (p. 215). It is unusual and difficult to "become" a sinner, for it means contradicting one's whole way of thought and adopting a new one. This new mode of thought comes from God. All the scriptures and all of God's acts aim at this change. When it happens, then the folly which led the proud to reject the Word as folly yields to the wisdom whereby they accept it and rejoice in it as divine wisdom and truth.

## 3. The Word Cut Short

The enigmatic quotation in Romans 9:28 leads Luther into a remarkable discussion of the cutting short of the Word. The reference, he thinks, is to the distinction of Spirit and letter. The Word of righteousness and faith is cut short in the sense that "it cannot be extended to the flesh . . . nor be captured by it." Carnal people will be offended by it and "cut off from it" (p. 396).

In this regard the New Testament Word differs from that of the Old Testament, which "spoke in figures about things that could be perceived by the senses." Hence the Word is now "cut off from all figures and signs and symbols" and also from "all those who adhered to those signs and symbols."

In a further development Luther sees a cutting off of the Word "from all things visible." Being perfect, it cannot declare what is imperfect. The visible is imperfect, for it does not satisfy the whole man. Completing and cutting short are related. The one carries a positive reference to the Spirit, the other a negative reference to the flesh.

Luther sums it up thus: "As the word of the law was a carnally understood word, imperfect and extended,˙or prolonged, so the word of the
Spirit, that is, of the law spiritually understood, is a finished and abbreviated word" (p. 397).

Yet there is more to it than that, for the imperfect Word merely
signifies, but the perfect Word "bestows what it signifies, namely, grace."
This ties in with justification. The abbreviated Word provides, through
faith, righteousness "for those to whom it is abbreviated." Faith, then, is
the finishing and shortening, for faith cuts off from the visible world and
it is a "brief conviction of things not seen."

A final point is that the abbreviated Word, like a blanket with the
end cut off, cannot cover both the old man and the new. The new man is
wonderfully completed, the old man is cut off. In the consummation
those who are wholly carnal are cut off. Thus God's promise can be
fulfilled and diminished at the same time. Cut short for many, it over-
flows "for [those to] whom it has been fulfilled" (p. 400).

## 4. The Word and Work

In relation to Romans 10:6 Luther finds it a mark of the folly of
carnal wisdom "to regard the work as more important than the word and
therefore to weigh the latter by the former": a humble work, a humble
Word. Spiritual wisdom, in contrast, looks to the Word and not the work
and makes the former the measure of the latter. The example of Eve
offers a warning here. She disobeyed God because the required work
seemed to be so little, and therefore she despised the Word. We must
always heed and follow the Word whether it "commands us to do something foolish or base or great or small," for the work is to be measured by
the Word (pp. 407–408).

## 5. The Word and Complacency

The Word of God invades a sinner's life with shattering force. It
runs contrary to his thinking and willing. Displeasure with self is "an
infallible sign that one really has the word." Complacency, or self-
grounded assurance, points in the opposite direction. Pleasure in self
and one's own words, thoughts, acts, and emotions is "the clearest sign
that the word of God is not in a person." This person does not really hear.
He hears what he wants to hear. He judges the Word by adapting it to
what he himself thinks. His thinking stands unchanged and his will
unbroken. Plainly, then, the Word does not come to him at all (p. 415).

## 6. The Word and Hearers

When the Word is resisted, its message is seen as a bad one

against which there is bitter complaint. Hence a subjective distinction arises when the Word is proclaimed. For some it is good and for others bad. The distinction is not in the Word itself but in its recipients. The Word is always good but it is treated in different ways. Thus it is "a good thing to good men and an evil thing to evil men." This differentiation takes place only when the Word is preached and heard (p. 420). Luther's thinking here seems to be much the same as in his famous statement that what we believe to be a god is a god to us.

### 7. The Word and Philosophy

With his concentration on God's Word, Luther finds himself in almost unavoidable antithesis to philosophy. This comes out most clearly in relation to Romans 8:19. Here Paul's theological or eschatological view of creation contrasts sharply with the philosophical or metaphysical view. Problems of essence, accident, activity, and motion have no importance for Paul. What counts is the expectation of creation and, even more so, what it expects (pp. 360–361).

On this basis Luther feels constrained to speak out against philosophy and to turn us to scripture. Having spent time in philosophical studies, he has come to regard them as "the study of vanity and perdition." If we must engage in them, our concern should be "to treat them as we do when we learn worthless skills to destroy them and study errors to refute them." At most they can help us to learn how to speak with those who are trained in them. But "it is high time that we undertake new studies and learn Jesus Christ and him crucified" (p. 361).

Philosophy deals with the "mechanics" of creation and not its goal. The supreme folly of philosophy is to extol the knowledge of that very creation which is sad about itself. Only a fool laughs at one who is crying and says that he sees him happy. This is precisely what philosophers do. "With a marvelous display of power" they "derive a happy science out of a sad creation." One can only conclude that "whoever searches into the essence and action of creation rather than its groaning and expectation is without doubt a fool and a blind man." Theologians of the Word will take another path, for they realize, as philosophers do not, that "creatures are also a creation of God" (p. 362).

## B. ZWINGLI

### 1. The Clarity and Certainty of the Word of God

For Zwingli, as for Luther, the Word of God played a dominant theological role. Through his own intensive study of the New Testament at Einsiedeln in 1516, Zwingli achieved a fresh grasp of the gospel. When he came as people's pastor to Zurich, he made it his aim as a preacher to expound God's Word in order, beginning with the gospels. His work as a reformer rested also on the principle, adopted by the city fathers, that all disputed matters must be decided by the Word of God. Zwingli always attempted to base his actions on biblical teaching and to meet opponents, whether Roman Catholic, Lutheran, or Anabaptist, with biblical arguments. No less than Luther, he wanted a theology and a church of the Word.

What does Zwingli regard as so significant about the Word? One answer may be found in his important work on *The Clarity and Certainty of the Word of God*. The material of this pamphlet first took shape when Zwingli, as secular priest, preached on the theme in the Oetenbach Convent in 1522. Winning the orders over to the Reformation proved to be one of the hardest tasks in Zurich or, for that matter, anywhere. Yet partly with the help of these sermons, he had some success at the Oetenbach, which was dissolved in 1524. Meanwhile he had revised and expanded the preached version and in this edited form it was published shortly after its delivery in 1522.

## 2. Introduction

Before taking up his true theme, Zwingli has a long preface in which he relates the Word of God to the divine image. The image consists, not in bodily likeness nor merely in faculties of the soul, but in that looking to God and his Word which is at least a sign of "the divine relationship, image, and similitude within us" (*Library of Christian Classics* 24, p. 61). The desire for God is a universal experience and is present within us by nature, that is, nature as God created it. This does not open the door to natural theology, or to a works-righteousness, for (a) the image is that of God, not man himself, (b) man as God created him has decayed and needs to be restored, (c) only God's grace can effect this restoration, and (d) only God's Word can meet the inner desire and give true light to the inward man (p. 67). Zwingli concludes, then, that "from the fact that we are the image of God we may see that there is nothing that can give greater joy or assurance or comfort to the soul than the word of its creator and maker" (p. 68).

## 3. The Certainty of the Word

Rather oddly, Zwingli reverses the order of the title and deals first and more briefly with what he calls "the certainty or power" (or infallibility) of the Word. He means by this the certainty that the Word will do what it says. "The word of God is so sure and strong that if God wills things are done the moment that he speaks his word." Illustrations are given from the Old Testament, such as creation, the cursing of the ground, the flood, and the birth of Isaac. To these are added examples from the New Testament, such as the cleansing of the leper, the healing of the centurion's servant, and the multiplying of the loaves and fishes. Sometimes, of course, an interval elapses between word and deed. But this has no significance for God. "With God there is no such thing as past or future," and "what seems long to us is not long to God, but eternally present." What God says will always take place as and when he wills. The whole message of the gospel offers a firm demonstration that what God has promised or promises will infallibly be performed (pp. 71–72).

### 4. The Clarity of the Word

#### a. Riddles and Parables

It is often objected that riddles and parables make the Bible an obscure book. Zwingli replies that parables form a gentle introduction to divine truth (pp. 72–75). To be sure, they also conceal the message, but only to him "who comes to the scriptures with his own speech and interpretation," not to him "who has a mind to learn from the word of God." Obscurity lies, then, in the hearer, not in the Word.

#### b. The Light of the Word

On the positive side, the Word enlightens the understanding so that it "confesses the word and knows the certainty of it." Zwingli calls this the concurrent or prevenient clarity of the Word. In the Old Testament, for example, the Word "brought its own enlightenment to Noah." Similarly, in commanding Abraham to offer up Isaac, God "enlightened him to see in it the true word of God." Moses, Jacob, Micaiah, Jeremiah, and Elijah were equally enlightened when they heard God's voice. They did not just understand the Word; they also perceived it to be in truth God's Word (pp. 75–78). Various New Testament passages support this, although Zwingli does not arrange these so well, and they merge into the general discussion. First quoting John 1:6, Zwingli then adduces John the Baptist's claim that what he has received is from above. In John 4 the Samaritan woman is given the insight to say that Christ will tell us all things. John 6:41–51 speaks of all being taught by God. Matthew 11:25–30 refers to revelation by the Father. Other passages from John 6, 1 Corinthians 2, Acts 9, and 1 John 2 show that the Word is clear, not just because it is easy to understand, but because it brings with it its own clarity to those who are open to its message (pp. 78ff.).

#### c. The Nature of the Clarity

This brings us to Zwingli's main thesis. The Word, as light, is intrinsically clear. Hence it has no need of official interpreters. The true teacher is not the doctor, father, pope, or council, but the Father of Jesus

Christ (p. 79), who teaches well with all clarity and conviction. But the proud, including arrogant ecclesiastics, are not the ones to learn this lesson. "How should the poor carpenter entrust himself to such princes?" He does not have to do so. "God reveals himself by his own Spirit. He will enlighten all who seek with humility" (p. 82).

### d. Causes of Difficulty

Zwingli realizes, of course, that many people in his day, his hearers included, do not see the truth of scripture when they read or hear it. But he finds external reasons for this. Monasticism obscures the gospel by claiming that this or that order offers the best chance of salvation. The papacy offers itself as a source of forgiveness and twists the Word of God to back up its claims. Scholasticism, dragging in secular philosophy, befuddles people by turning into a series of intellectual puzzles that which is inherently clear and simple. Difficulty arises, not because the Word itself offers difficulty, but because the whole apparatus of the institutional church has combined to make it difficult.

### e. The Recovery of Clarity

How, then, is the clarity of scripture to be restored? Zwingli advances the following proposals. First, we must go directly to scripture as Zwingli himself did (with the Greek) at Einsiedeln. Second, we must do so in humility, not trusting our own judgment any more than we trust human exegetes, but ready to be taught by the Word itself. Third, we must "ask God for light," for it is his will "that he alone should be our teacher" (pp. 91–92). Fourth, we must not presume to be judges of scripture, for it is God-breathed (2 Timothy 3:16). Fifth, we must trust God's Word as we trust no other word, for "it will never leave us in darkness, . . . it irradiates the soul of man with full salvation and grace, . . . it gives the soul sure comfort in God."

### f. Final Exhortation

By way of practical conclusion Zwingli gives "some instruction in the way to come to a true understanding of the Word of God and to a personal experience of the fact that you are taught of God." We are first to pray for the killing off of the old man, for divine infilling, and for God's confirming of what he has done. We are then to be confident that God's Word is for all people but specifically that it is for the poor and humble. We are finally to recognize that God's Word is achieved when it is seen (1) that it seeks God's revelation to man, (2) that it brings renewal and "assurance of the grace of God and eternal salvation," (3) that it destroys us and magnifies God, and (4) that fear of God gives joy, not sorrow. When these things result from reading God's Word, "it is a sure working of the Word and Spirit of God" (p. 95).

### 5. Comments

Zwingli is not offering us here a systematic doctrine of scripture. He is dealing with a situation in which its authority is accepted but its message is obscured and its power unknown. He does not specifically commend the tools of scholarship, although he himself uses them, for by and large his hearers and readers cannot delve into the originals. He makes a plea, then, for simple and unprejudiced reading by which the essential biblical message will come through so long as prayer is sincerely made for illumination by the Word itself and by the Holy Spirit. Zwingli does not suggest, of course, that the human mind can grasp and receive divine truth and salvation on its own, without God's help. Hence the role of the Spirit, or the Father, is a crucial one. God alone can light up the written word and enlighten the mind to perceive and believe its message. A scholar might achieve a good exegesis of the human words but the divine Word of revelation and grace has another dimension, so that God must make himself known through the human word. Scripture is clear when the Spirit makes it clear. If this offends the scholar, it gives hope to the unlearned. They, too, can see and know God's saving grace through scripture as God graciously discloses it to them. To this end prayer and openness are essential prerequisites. While clear in itself, the Word can be obscure when pride or prejudice afflicts the hearer. To prayerful humility God will respond in clarifying power, so that what is hidden from the wise is revealed to babes. For apprehension of the Word, the essentials are a teachable spirit on the one side and the teacher Spirit on the other.

Is this at root a theology of experience or subjectivity? Not at all. Zwingli believes, of course, that what he says will work out in practice. Confidence will be gained when it does. On the other hand, the work itself is not our work; it is that of the Word and Spirit. It is outside us even as it is done in us. Moreover, what is experienced by us corresponds to what scripture teaches us to seek. Our understanding is not true because it is ours. One might object, of course, that Zwingli does not face the possibility that others might follow his instructions and come to a different interpretation. If he were appealing to experience he would have to do so; but because he relies, not on his own experience, but on the clarity and certainty of the Word, and the unity of Father, Son, and Spirit, he cannot envisage any essential divergence in practical out-working, except insofar as total humility and openness are not readily achieved.

### C. BULLINGER

#### 1. The *Decades*

After Zwingli's untimely death at Cappel in 1531, Heinrich Bullinger took over the spiritual and theological guidance of the church in Zurich. Less original and forceful than his predecessor, he had compensating qualities which brought to Zurich a long period of peaceful and fruitful development. Good relations were maintained or established with sister churches, confessions were elaborated, exiles were entertained, and a busy program of preaching was carried through. In all these activities Bullinger played a leading part. He also engaged in an extensive writing ministry which included not only the publication of sermons but also commentaries, doctrinal studies, controversial works, and a history of the Reformation.

For a comprehensive summary of Bullinger's theology one can hardly do better than turn to the five books of his *Decades*. The *Decades* were fifty sermons which Bullinger preached in five groups of ten each on the main heads of Christian doctrine. He published the first two books in one volume in 1549, the third and fourth in a second volume in 1550, and the fifth in the third and final volume in 1551. Translations were quickly made into English, Dutch, and French. In England, where Bullinger was held in high esteem by Elizabethans who had enjoyed the hospitality of Zurich during the Marian exile, three successive editions came out in 1577, 1584, and 1587. Under Whitgift orders were drawn up, and probably approved by Convocation, that all unlicensed clergy should read a sermon of the *Decades* each week and summarize the contents in a notebook, which authorized preachers were to inspect (1586). The *Decades* thus enjoyed something of the status of an officially appointed textbook of theology.

When publishing the *Decades*, Bullinger introduced them with an account of the first four ecumenical councils and copies of various ancient creeds of both East and West. He did this in order to show that Reformed doctrine agrees fully with the teaching of the early ecumenical church as well as that of apostolic scripture.

### 2. The Word of God: Its Source and Manner of Revelation

*a. Role*

Adopting an arrangement that has often been followed in confessions and theologies, Bullinger devotes his first three sermons to the Word of God. The first sermon deals with the source of the Word and how and by whom it is revealed. Bullinger justifies his procedure by pointing to the authoritative role of the Word. "All the decrees of the Christian faith . . . have always been fetched out of it" and cannot be "drawn, taught, or last of all soundly confirmed from elsewhere" (Parker Society Edition, 1.1, p. 36).

*b. Definition*

Defining the Word, Bullinger finds a threefold reference to the

Word of God as (1) the Son of God, (2) the speech of God in "a lively expressed voice," and (3) the speech of God "registered in writings." He comments that since the speaker is true, what is spoken is also true (p. 37).

### c. Source
Bullinger backs up this comment by pointing out that the cause or beginning or certainty of the Word is to be found in God, who, although having no mouth, uses human speech in his self-revelation. He does this either directly, as at Sinai, or through angels, or through the prophets, or through Christ, or, after the sending of the Spirit, through the apostles. In all cases, however, the Word proceeds from God.

### d. Manner of Revelation
Discussing the different modes of revelation, Bullinger makes a historical survey. Spoken words were first used. Handed down orally, these already contained the substance of the gospel. They were then put in writing by Moses. A man of native ability and excellent training, Moses also enjoyed the aid of the Spirit, who "was wholly in the mind of Moses" and "directed his head as he writ" (p. 46). His works are thus "authentical" and in them, "although the word of God be revealed, spoken, and written by men, yet doth it not therefore cease to be that which indeed it is" (p. 48). As regards matter, sense, and meaning, Bullinger sees no difference between the spoken and the written Word.

After Moses, the prophets left "a breviary of true divinity and a most absolute sum of the word of God contained in writing" (p. 49). These works, too, have always been of great authority. For they did not come "from the prophets themselves as chief authors, but were inspired from God out of heaven by the Holy Spirit; for it is God which, dwelling by his Spirit in the minds of the prophets, speaketh to us by their mouths" (p. 50). The governance of so many "commonweals and congregations" by the prophets confirms this (p. 50).

Next came the Son, in whom God set forth his Word "most clearly, simply, and abundantly to all the world." To spread abroad his doctrine and benefits Christ himself chose the apostles, who, empowered by the Spirit, spoke and wrote God's Word to the nations (p. 52). Their teaching, first taught "by a lively expressed voice," then "set down in writing with pen and ink, is the doctrine of God and the very true word of God" (p. 54).

Bullinger concludes the historical account with the assurance that "by the vigilant care and unspeakable goodness of God" the scriptures have been preserved from destruction or corruption (p. 55). They all came from the same Spirit and they all teach us "how to live well and holily" (p. 56). We are thus to believe them, for "the Lord himself, which is the very living and eternal God, doth speak to us by the scriptures" (p. 57).

### 3. The Word of God: Its Recipients, Sufficiency, and Proper Hearing

#### a. Recipients

In the second sermon Bullinger follows up the theme that the Word is for all people. Even God's specific revelation to Israel did not mean that he was "altogether careless of the Gentiles." Nor were the biblical books written only to the first recipients. "The scriptures of the old and new Testaments ought to be received of us," for Christ and the apostles refer to both Moses and the prophets (1.2, p. 58). In the Old Testament Bullinger distinguishes between "some things which are for ever to be observed and some things which are ceremonial and suffered only till time of amendment" (p. 59). The New Testament shows us what is abrogated or changed. Even this is to be studied, for from it "we must preach Christ, forgiveness of sins, and repentance" (p. 60). The scripture which publishes it is not itself "taken away or . . . made void by Christ" (p. 59).

#### b. Sufficiency

Being given for salvation and sanctification, scripture provides all that is needed for this end, being "absolutely perfect in all points" (p. 61). Jesus might have taught many things not recorded in scripture, but this does not spoil its absolute perfection, for the Spirit led the apostles into all truth (p. 62). If we also have many things by oral tradition, this makes no difference; the oral and written traditions are one and the same. The apostles "left not unto us one thing in writing, and taught another thing by word of mouth." God's Word in scripture "teacheth abundantly all things that belong to true godliness" (p. 64).

#### c. Proper Hearing

Bullinger offers some simple but comprehensive requirements for true hearing. First, we are to read or hear "with great reverence." Second, we are to do so attentively and prayerfully. Third, sobriety is enjoined. Fourth, true faith, which includes obedience, is needed. Fifth, worldly affairs must be set aside. Sixth, overcurious questions must also be set aside. Finally, there is constant need to invoke the Spirit. "For what will it avail to hear the word of God . . . without the Holy Spirit of God to work or stir inwardly in our hearts?" Bullinger echoes Zwingli here. Received in the Spirit and in faith, the Word has "a mighty force and wonderful effect in us," converting, enlightening, instructing, feeding, strengthening, confirming, comforting, regenerating, cleansing, gladdening, and uniting to God, in sum, obtaining "all things for us at God's hands" (pp. 64–67).

## 4. The Word of God: Its Exposition

### a. The Question

The question of interpretation had some urgency in Bullinger's day. Some argued that scripture is "so dark that it cannot be read with any profit at all." Others claimed that "every man may lawfully invent or choose to himself" whatever meaning he fancies (1.3, p. 70). Bullinger's aim in the third sermon, then, will be to show that scripture can in fact understood but that sound principles of exposition must be adopted to arrive at the true sense.

### b. Simplicity of Scripture

As regards the simplicity or clarity of scripture, Bullinger points out that God "used a most common kind of speech wherewithal even the very idiots [the uneducated] were acquainted." Proverbs, parables, comparisons and stories abound, all adapted to "move and plainly teach the common sorts of wits among mortal men" (p. 71). Harder forms of expressions may be found, too, but these yield to study, diligence, faith, and exegetical skill. Furthermore, "uncertain, doubtful, and obscure things are made manifest by those things that are more certain, sure, and evident" (p. 72). Final obscurity will prevail only among the unbelieving and corrupt.

### c. Exposition

While scripture is simple, "godly and holy" exposition is needed. God himself used it through Moses and Ezra. Our Lord also expounded scripture. So did the apostles. The need of application arises in the same context. Refusal to expound and apply scripture "to places, times, states, and persons" means seeking "somewhat else than the honour due unto God" (p. 74). We are always in danger of following our own affections and corrupting scripture by wrong interpretation. A need arises, then, for sound hermeneutical principles and practice.

### d. Two Principles

Bullinger closes his sermon with some principles and rules of interpretation. He first states two basic principles. knowledge of the languages is requisite in a good interpreter; and plain things are to be taken "according to the mind and meaning" of the authors, the true sense being taken out of the scriptures, not "forcibly thrust" upon them (p. 75).

### e. Various Rules

"A few certain rules" are then added to the general principles. (1) First is the analogy of faith, which implies inner consistency in scripture. Nothing is to be brought in or admitted "against the received articles of our faith" (p. 76). Thus, if the Father is said to be greater than the Son, this cannot be taken in the sense of inequality. (2) The rule of love corresponds to the analogy of faith. Our interpretation must "not tend to the overthrow of charity, but to the furtherance and commendation of it to all men" (p. 77). Matthew 5:10, for example, must not be interpreted so as to give license to robbers. (3) More specifically we must "mark on what occasion everything is spoken, what goeth before, what followeth after, at what season, in what order, and of what person anything is spoken" (p. 78). Contextual exegesis has a great deal to do with proper application. Some sayings do not apply to all people everywhere, but we must be careful lest no sayings apply beyond the immediate hearers. (4) Scripture is to be compared with scripture, so that the darker passages are explained by the clearer and "the fewer by the more in number" (p. 79). The unity of scripture is here presupposed. (5) Selectivity is to be avoided. We cannot pick and choose, fixing on some things and "not having respect to the rest." Individual statements in particular must not be set in opposition to the general drift. (6) The sixth rule "and the most effectual of all" is "an heart that loveth God and his glory." We cannot be perfect in exposition, but no harm will result where there is true love of God. Better expositors will not condemn the less able, nor will the less able refuse correction by the better. A consuming zeal "to advance virtue" will bring commitment to the exegetical task in a positive and receptive spirit. For all the difficulties, it will be seen that "scripture doth admit of a godly and religious interpretation," which is indeed required if scripture is to function as a norm "for all men and ages to lead their lives by" (pp. 79–80).

### f. The Holy Spirit

A heart that loves God will pray continually for the Holy Spirit as exposition is attempted. This is supremely important to Bullinger. The best expositor of any book is its author. The human authors of scripture are dead. The divine author is not. He can be appealed to, then, in the exposition of his work. He will not solve the ordinary hermeneutical problems. He does not absolve us from exegetical work. He does not overrule the rules of understanding. Nevertheless, he can and will grant illumination. This is so significant for Bullinger that in the last paragraph of this final sermon he puts it twice in almost identical words: "As by the Holy Spirit the scripture was revealed and inspired, so also by the same Spirit it may be expounded to the glory of God" (p. 79). "As by the Spirit of God the scripture was revealed, so by the same Spirit it is requisite to expound it" (p. 80).

## D. CALVIN

Calvin wrote so much, and so much about God's Word, that full treatment of his teaching on this theme cannot be attempted here. We shall focus, then, on three aspects in his *Institutes of the Christian Religion*: the ground of confidence in scripture, the relation of Word and Spirit, and the unity of scripture.

## 1. Ground of Confidence in Scripture

Traditionally scripture had been accepted on the authority of the church. With the Reformation, however, this authority was challenged by scripture itself, so that to make scripture's authority depend on that of the church would no longer do. But what alternative remained? How can one even know what scripture is apart from the church? For that matter, how did the early church know? Why should we entrust ourselves to these particular writings as an authoritative norm for our beliefs and conduct?

(1) The Spirit's Witness. In tackling this question in Book i.7–8, Calvin recognizes at once that a human word can have authority as God's Word only if God himself, as its true author, is the source of this authority. The scriptures have full authority only "when men regard them as having sprung from heaven, as if there the living words of God were heard" (i.7.1). No human source of authority, whether reason or experience, can be substituted for the church. But the church is ruled out, being itself founded on the writings of the prophets and the preaching of the apostles (i.7.2). We have to go back, then, to God himself.

Even if it be granted, however, that God must be the source of the authority of scripture, how can we be sure that this is so? Credibility is not established "until we are persuaded beyond doubt that God is its author." No human reasons, judgments, or opinions, however, can bring the confidence that is needed. Calvin does not reject argument as totally useless. He even thinks that, though he does not excel "either in great dexterity or eloquence," he could refute the cavils "of those who despise scripture" and "shatter the boasts they mutter in their lurking places." Yet taking this course is "doing things backwards." It is not a "useful labor." For arguments will not imprint on the heart "that certainty which piety requires." He thus turns instead to "the secret testimony of the Spirit" (i.7.4)

If Calvin does not clearly define this testimony, he shows plainly why it is so central. It is more excellent than all reason. It is linked with the giving of scripture: "As God alone is a fit witness to himself in his word, so also the word will not find acceptance in men's hearts before it is sealed by the inward testimony of the Spirit." "This conviction requires no reasons." The mind reposes more confidently in it than in any reasons. It is a feeling "that can be born only of a heavenly revelation" (i.7.5).

Does this mean that the authority of God's Word rests finally on our experience of it as such? Some phrases in Calvin suggest this. "I speak of nothing other than what each believer experiences in himself" (i.7.5). Nevertheless, Calvin is not saying that the basis of the authority, or even of our assurance of it, is the fact that we experience it. The testimony of the Spirit forms the basis of the authority and grants the assurance. This is an inner testimony, for it takes place within. Yet it is outward, too, for the Spirit is outside us and the giving of his testimony is an action from without. The Spirit's testimony is not one and the same thing as our experience of it.

Being secret, does this testimony have a mystical character? Calvin admits that he is at a loss for words to describe it. All the same, he does not use the term "mystical." The mystery of the inner witness is (a) that it is God's work and (b) that it is the Spirit's work. No divine work can be pinned down in definitions and explanations. This is particularly true of the Spirit's work as a work in the subjective sphere to bring about repentance, faith, illumination, assurance, and understanding. Calvin, then, finds it hard to describe the inner testimony, but mysticism is precluded by the fact that it is a personal work of God and has a relational character.

(2) Scripture's Self-authentication. A final reason why the Spirit's testimony cannot be subjectivistic or mystical is that in and with the Spirit's ministry, scripture authenticates itself as God's Word and is thus a basis of its own authority. Calvin is not referring, of course, to a magical quality inherent in the book which convinces readers of its divine truth. Scripture authenticates itself because it has in fact sprung from God. The divine authorship gives it the ring of divine truth. The divine authorship and authority are just as axiomatic as that white is white or sweet is sweet (i.7.2). "The highest proof of scripture," then, is that "God in person speaks in it" (i.7.4).

This self-authentication cannot be isolated from the Spirit's testimony. Divine authorship grants the power of self-authentication, just as Calvin's authorship authenticates a work as his; nevertheless, the present ministry of the Spirit — the sealing of scripture on the heart — is needed if it is seriously to affect us and full certainty is to be attained. Bullinger's slogan may be recalled: "The same Spirit who wrote scripture must also expound it." Calvin has authentication in view, not exposition, but the principle holds good here, too. Scripture is from God. It authenticates itself as God's Word. But God is alive, not dead. He works along with his Word and speaks through it. He establishes its authority with a testimony which surpasses all that human testimony could ever offer.

If scripture's self-authentication were abstracted from the Spirit's testimony in a kind of soteriological deism, it could hardly impart final certainty. On the other hand, if the Spirit's testimony were isolated from scripture's self-authentication in a kind of noetic docetism, it could hardly escape the charge of subjectivism. Calvin, perhaps, does not sufficiently differentiate the two, so that some ambivalence arises. Nevertheless, the inadequate differentiation emphasizes the indissoluble unity so that all in all the gain outweighs the loss.

(3) Human Reasons. As noted, Calvin thought that good human reasons might also be found for scripture's authority. Even if arguments are futile without "the higher certainty," they can still "become very useful aids." In Chapter 7.1–13 Calvin refers especially to the superiority of scripture, its content, its antiquity, its truthfulness, miracles, prophecy, the providential transmission of the law and the prophets, the simplicity and authority of the New Testament, the consent of the church, and the fidelity of the martyrs. These considerations "brilliantly vindicate" scripture against disparagers. "Yet of themselves they are not strong enough to provide a firm faith until our heavenly Father lifts reverence for scripture beyond the realm of controversy." They are secondary aids but they cannot bring people to the faith whose certainty is founded only on the persuasion of the Spirit.

## 2. Word and Spirit

(1) The Issue. Calvin pursues the theme of the link between the testifying Spirit and the self-authenticating Word in Chapter 9. He is replying here to "giddy men" who are adding new revelations at the expense of scripture, which they "dare despise as childish and mean." Calvin's own theme is that the Spirit "has not the task of inventing new and unheard of revelations but of sealing our minds with that very doctrine which is commended by the gospel" (i.9.1).

(2) The Agreement of Spirit and Scripture. It follows, then, that scripture must be studied if "we want to receive any gain and benefit from the Spirit of God." Does this demean the Spirit? No, for "it is no ignominy for the Spirit to be in conformity with himself." If the Spirit were tied to human authorities, the question would have merit. In the case of scripture, however, this is not so. The Spirit "would have us recognize him in his own image which he has stamped upon the scriptures." The Spirit is their author; he cannot differ from himself (i.9.2).

(3) Inseparability of Word and Scripture. But is not the scripture letter? Only when divorced from the Spirit. If, however, it is branded on the heart by the Spirit and shows forth Christ, it is life. Three important theses follow. (a) The Holy Spirit so inheres in his truth expressed in scripture that only when proper dignity is given to scripture does "the Holy Spirit show forth his power." (b) God has joined the certainty of his Word and Spirit "by a kind of mutual bond." (c) It is through the Word that "the Lord dispenses the illumination of his Spirit to believers" (i.9.3). The inseparability of Word and Spirit is of crucial significance. It rules out barren biblicism on the one side and an uncontrolled appeal to

the Spirit on the other. It also undercuts many of the interesting but unprofitable debates which have arisen out of and in relation to the individual aspects of Calvin's doctrine of scripture.

### 3. The Unity of Scripture

(1) Unity and Distinction. As some groups separated Spirit and Word, others divided the Testaments and degraded the Old in favor of the New. Calvin, however, believed that all who come into the company of God's people are "covenanted by the same law and by the bond of the same doctrine." Hence a unity of scripture arises. At the same time differences between the Testaments obviously exist. He thus devotes two chapters of the *Institutes* to a discussion of the unity in difference (ii.10–11).

(2) Similarities. As regards the similarities, Calvin expands his basic concept of the one covenant. The covenant with the patriarchs "is so much like ours in substance and reality that the two are actually one and the same except in the mode of dispensation" (ii.10.2). This conclusion rests on three main points. (a) Material prosperity did not constitute the goal in the Old Testament. The promises, of which the gospel is the fulfillment, aspire to eternal life. (b) The first covenant rested on God's mercy, not on merits (see iii.15–18). (c) The Old Testament saints knew Christ as the Mediator through whom they were joined to God and were to share in his promises. In a forceful challenge Calvin asks: "Who dares to separate the Jews from Christ?" "The Old Testament always had its end in Christ and in eternal life" (ii.10.4).

The same covenant is accompanied by similar symbols. The signs of the old covenant are not just carnal; they meet more than just material needs. The apostles themselves teach us this. They show the deeper significance of the Red Sea crossing or the manna, especially in terms of the reference to Christ (ii.10.5–6).

Calvin takes up in more detail the thesis that eternal life is also the goal of the patriarchal covenant. Embracing God's Word, the patriarchs had "a real participation in God which cannot be without the blessing of eternal life" (sec. 7). The covenant formula of Leviticus 26:12 makes this clear (sec. 8). Even when there is estrangement and death, God's promise can overcome this, as is shown by the extension of mercy to a thousand generations (sec. 9). Material prosperity was not the covenant blessing in the Old Testament, as innumerable examples show (secs. 10–11). Indeed, in contrast to the wicked, who "by their pleasant felicity gradually slip into the whirlpool of death," the saints are buffeted about, but know that "their final end is to be life and salvation" (sec. 18). Calvin concludes, then, that in essentials the Testaments agree. The promise and goal of both is spiritual and eternal life. Christ is the common pledge of this; all trust of future blessedness reposes in him (sec. 23).

(3) Differences. While insisting on the unity, Calvin does not cover over the differences; indeed, scripture itself brings them to our attention. They can be summed up under five main heads.

(a) In the Old Testament the earthly benefits serve as a mirror to display the future heavenly inheritance. A pedagogic purpose is served here. Old Testament believers were not yet mature enough to enter the inheritance, and so the spiritual promises were foreshadowed in earthly ones. The physical benefits and punishments represent typologically spiritual felicity and final judgment (ii.11.1–3).

(b) Truth is also conveyed in the Old Testament by signs and ceremonies which typify Christ. The truth is the same, but in the New Testament substance replaces shadow. Hebrews can even speak of two covenants in this regard. The covenant was first "wrapped up in the shadowy and ineffectual observance of ceremonies." It attained its truth only "when sealed by Christ's blood" (pars. 4–6).

(c) Another difference lies between the literal and the spiritual. The reference is to the law, once put in writing but now engraved on the heart. The ministry of condemnation and death has yielded to that of righteousness and life. The image of things absent is replaced by the present reality (secs. 7–8).

(d) The covenant which was formerly one of bondage is now one of freedom. Old Testament believers knew freedom, too. But they were "still subject to the bonds and burdens of ceremonial observances." These imposed a servitude from which release came only with the non-legal covenant (sec. 9). Calvin notes, however, that the Old Testament is not to be equated with law, since it also contains gospel. Thus the differences noted thus far do not imply total disjunction but the distinction between "the clarity of the gospel and the obscurer dispensation of the word that had preceded it" (sec. 10).

(e) The final difference needs little elaboration. The Old Testament was predominantly for the one nation of Israel and the New Testament is for all nations. "The wall is torn down in Christ" (sec. 11) and "the Gentiles are now called" in a fulfillment of the promises which still seemed to be new and startling to those who first received and implemented the worldwide commission of the risen Lord (sec. 12).

Does God display mutability in dispensing the covenant in different ways? Calvin advances a doctrine of accommodation in his reply to this question. God "accommodated diverse forms to different ages" (sec. 13). The situation also demanded change. One sign was needed "to represent Christ absent and to proclaim him about to come," but it was fitting that another should be chosen when he was revealed. In any case we must accept the fact that "God has done everything wisely and justly" (sec. 14). Above all, God's constancy may be seen in the ongoing teaching of the same doctrine and requirement of the same worship (sec. 13).

The differences in mode do not affect the unity in substance. It is on the unity that Calvin puts the stress. This has for his whole theology, not least where it differs from Romanism on the one side and Anabaptism on the other, implications whose significance it is hardly possible to overestimate.

## CHAPTER XVI
# *New Thinking on Justification*

## A. LUTHER

### 1. The Righteousness of God

Fundamental to Luther's theology is his realization of what is meant by the righteousness of God. His decisive insight comes to expression already in the Romans lecture in which he discusses Romans 1:17. The gospel stands in contrast with human teaching. This displays the righteousness of man, who is or becomes righteous before himself and others. The gospel, however, reveals the righteousness of God, who is or becomes righteous before God. God's righteousness is "the cause of salvation." How? Because "by the righteousness of God we must not understand the righteousness by which he is righteous in himself but the righteousness by which we are made righteous by God" (*LW* 25, p. 151). Resuming the contrast, Luther points out that whereas human righteousness follows upon and originates in actions, God's righteousness precedes works; only righteous people can do righteous works. As a righteousness by which he makes us righteous, God's righteousness may be compared to his wisdom as the wisdom by which he makes us wise (p. 249 on 3:26).

Another aspect of God's righteousness is that God himself is shown to be righteous in his saving work (p. 210 on 3:4). In this sense God can even be said to be justified by us when we accept his righteousness and truth. This is what Luther calls God's passive righteousness. This passive righteousness, however, is "our active justification by God," for he regards the words which justify his words as righteousness (p. 211). The principle may thus be stated that God "is justified when he justifies, and when he justifies he is justified." God's passive righteousness is also active righteousness, and as such it is the same as faith in him, for the fact that we declare him righteous is his gift, and by the same gift he regards us as righteous.

## 2. Faith

Throughout his Romans lectures Luther insists that it is faith alone which justifies. Yet the exclusiveness of faith is only on the human side. On the divine side Christ is no less essential than faith. As Luther points out, the apostle usefully "joins together these two expressions 'through Christ' and 'by faith.'" We cannot use the slogan "by faith alone" "to approach God without Christ." "Both are necessary, namely, to have faith and to have Christ." Naturally we must not lean so heavily on Christ that faith seems not to be needed, but in the last resort "it is only through Christ that we are made worthy to approach God" (pp. 286–287 on 5:2).

Faith cannot count as a good work. Luther states this graphically in a comment on Romans 4:7: "All our good is outside us, and that good is Christ" (p. 267). Faith comes in because this good, that is, righteousness apart from works, is imputed only to believers (p. 36 on 4:5–9). "None of these things is in us except through faith" (p. 267). Luther keeps in excellent balance what might now be called the objective and the subjective aspects. A subjective movement cannot justify, but neither is justification accomplished by Christ's objective work apart from the God-given response of faith.

## 3. The Law

The exclusion of good works from justifying brings the law into dynamic tension with the gospel. The law's demands seem to imply that their fulfillment can bring salvation, but the gospel offers the righteousness of God as the cause of salvation. Yet by its very nature as demand the law can serve the gospel, for it shows plainly the impossibility of fulfillment. Luther has this in mind in his sharp contrast of the old and new law in the scholia on 7:5–6. First, "the law commands us to have love and Jesus Christ, but the gospel offers and presents them both to us." Second, "the law destroys the presumptuous, but the gospel comforts the humble." "The old law says to those who are proud in their own righteousness: 'You must have Christ and his Spirit,' the new law says to those who humbly admit their spiritual poverty: 'Behold, here is Christ and his Spirit'" (pp. 326–327). As the promise of the gospel, of course, the law can be gospel, too, when it preaches Christ, and the gospel can also be law. Its proper function, however, is to bring sin to light. Sin is not recognized until man learns to know and perceive the law. "He who has the law without faith and grace will assuredly see that he is a sinner and worthy of wrath" (p. 281).

Even in believers the law continues its work of accusation. This is connected with Luther's famous dictum that the saints "are at the same time both righteous and unrighteous . . . they are sinners in fact (*in re*) but righteous in hope (*in spe*)." In themselves they are sinners. This is disclosed by the fact that they still do not fulfill the law. They are righteous, however, "by the imputation of a merciful God" (p. 258 on 4:7).

Oddly, Luther can also see unbelievers as both righteous and unrighteous, but with two decisive distinctions. Unbelievers "are righteous in their own sight and thus they are always unrighteous outwardly," that is, in God's reckoning, whereas the saints "are always unrighteous in their own sight and therefore always justified outwardly" (p. 257). Secondly, unbelievers, as both righteous and unrighteous, are moving toward the transgression of the law, whereas believers, as both unrighteous and righteous, are moving toward its fulfillment (p. 260).

### 4. Works

#### a. Works of the Law

Vital to Luther's understanding of salvation is his distinction between works of the law and works of faith. By works of the law he does not mean works of the law in general, but "those which take place outside faith and grace and are done at the urging of the law," either through fear or the promise of reward (p. 234 on 3:20). Such works cannot justify. They are, in fact, an obstacle to justification for three reasons. (1) "They do not permit a man to see himself as unrighteous and in need of justification" (p. 234). (2) "The principle of works of necessity puffs up and makes for glorying" (p. 251 on 3:27). (3) These works give a false impression of righteousness even though they are in fact purely external — a layman is not a priest because he performs a priestly function, nor is an ape a man because it imitates human acts (p. 235).

#### b. Works of Faith

Luther obviously does not mean that no good works can be done in fulfillment of the law. His point is that such good works can be done only as works of faith "done out of the spirit of liberty and solely for the love of God" (p. 234). It is through faith in Christ that we are "made righteous for the performance of works of righteousness." As Luther puts it, God does not accent the person because of the works but the works because of the person (p. 256). We have to be righteous in order to do righteousness. When we are righteous, however, we will do righteousness. In this sense faith does not justify without its own works. Justification demands, not the works of the law, "but a living faith which produces its own works" (p. 235).

#### c. Preparatory Works

Not all works, however, can be called either works of the law or works of faith. There are works which are preparatory to acquiring righteousness. Those who do them are in a sense righteous because they have a will to be righteous. They do not trust in their works but are "preparing for justification in which they trust alone for their future righteousness." Works done in a pretended fulfillment of the law, in boasting, out of no true love of God, with an unwilling and hostile will, do not avail for righteousness. Preparatory works, however, are different. They do not justify any more than the works that follow faith. We are "not made righteous by doing righteous works, but rather we do righteous works by being righteous" (p. 242 on 3:20). Nevertheless, preparatory works are good, for although they do not constitute righteousness they are a prayer for it in accordance with the principle of faith, not "Do what I command," but "Give what you command" (pp. 251ff. on 3:27).

## B. CRANMER

### 1. On Salvation

As the Anglican Articles point out, the doctrine of justification is more broadly expounded in the Homily of Salvation in the First Book of Homilies. The author of this threefold homily cannot be identified for certain, but he is usually thought to have been archbishop Thomas Cranmer, who had promoted justification by faith in the early period of reform under Henry VIII, who pressed ahead with comprehensive liturgical and doctrinal reconstruction under Edward VI, and who played a major part in drafting the first version of the Articles in which the reference to the homily occurs. Whether or not Cranmer was the author, it certainly represents the teaching on justification which he held and which the Church of England, under his leadership, officially adopted.

#### a. Free Justification
In the first homily Cranmer begins by establishing the freedom of justification. He points out, however, that although it is "free to us, yet it cometh not so freely to us, that there is no ransom paid therefor at all." Can it still be called free when a price is paid? Yes, for "God provided the ransom for us, the most precious body and blood of his own most dear and best beloved Son Jesus Christ." Justification, then, is free to us but not to God.

#### b. Three Elements
In justification Cranmer perceives three concurrent factors: (1) grace on God's part; (2) the work of atonement on Christ's; and (3) a "true and lively faith" on man's. Faith, he notes, "is the gift of God and not man's only work without God."

#### c. Faith Alone and Not Alone
Faith, of course, does not stand in isolation. It "doth not exclude

repentance, hope, love, dread, and the fear of God." These things, however, are excluded "from the office of justifying." "All are present in the justified, yet they justify not altogether."

### d. Good Works

Good works are not excluded either. The justified "are most bounden to serve God in doing good deeds." But these good works are "imperfect and not able to deserve our justification," which comes freely by the mercy of God.

### e. The Office of God

For a proper understanding of justification, the offices of God and man must be differentiated. Only when the biblical and patristic doctrine of justification by faith is followed can this differentiation be achieved. The temptation is to think that man can justify himself. In fact, however, justification is the office of God, not man. We do not render it to God but receive it from him. Faith itself does not merit justification. At root we are justified by Christ alone. Faith plays a crucial role only as the means whereby we receive the justification which it has been God's office to provide.

### f. The Office of Man

What, then, is man's office? Cranmer states it negatively. Since we owe so great a debt to God for "his great mercy and goodness," "our office is not to pass the time of this present life unfruitfully and idly" or "to live contrary to our profession." In this regard Cranmer issues the common Reformation warning that the faith which does not produce good works "is not a right, pure, and lively faith, but a dead, devilish, counterfeit, and feigned faith." Authentic faith, as "a pure trust and confidence in God's merciful promises," is followed by "a loving heart to obey his commandments."

## 2. On Faith

### a. Dead Faith

Cranmer develops his understanding of faith in the second homily. He begins by noting that scripture takes faith in two ways. Of these he discusses first the dead faith which is "idle, barren, and unfruitful." He does not just equate this with external profession but with the mere belief that "all that is spoken in the bible is true." This belief can be called "a faith and belief to words of God," but it is not in itself "the faith and trust in God whereby we may look for grace, mercy, and eternal life at his hand." It is not "that sure and substantial faith which saveth sinners."

### b. Living Faith

In contrast, living faith, the faith which works by love, embraces "the common belief of the articles of our faith" but is also "a sure trust and confidence of the mercy of God through our Lord Jesus Christ, and a steadfast hope of all good things to be received at God's hands." It does not consist in outward confession alone; "it liveth and striveth inwardly in the heart."

### c. Faith and Works

As is no doubt proper in a homiletical context and at a time when the new view of justification was accused of undermining morality, Cranmer worked hard to show that true faith is not without works. If acceptable works cannot be done without faith, so "faith is lively and fruitful in showing forth good works." It "cannot long be idle" but in a response of grateful love of God is full of good works. Hebrews 11 offers Cranmer an excellent series of illustrations of faith at work. Readers are invited, then, to consider the reality of their own faith in the light of obedience or disobedience to God's commands.

### d. Works as a Manifestation of Faith

Cranmer pursues the theme of self-examination in the final part of the homily. We easily deceive ourselves. The test is "a very godly and christian life." James comes in here. "Shew me thy faith by thy deeds." "Thy deeds and works must be an open testimony of thy faith." Without them it is "a phantasy of faith and not the christian faith." To rely on this phantasy is a dangerous thing. We are not to "flatter ourselves, but look upon our works, and judge of our faith what it is."

## 3. On Good Works

### a. Necessity of Faith to Works

While true faith must manifest itself in works, the other side of the coin must never be overlooked. "Without faith can no good work be done acceptable and pleasant to God." Faith is to be tested by works, but works do not take precedence of faith. Faith is the root, works are the fruit. This order cannot be reversed.

### b. Dead Works

As in the case of faith, a distinction thus arises between different kinds of works. There can be dead works as well as a dead faith. If a dead faith does not issue in works, dead works do not issue from faith. Works without faith are dead shadows, for faith alone "giveth life to the soul." Works without faith may seem to be impressive, but they are like a sculpture or picture — a lifeless representation, not the living thing itself. A man has to be nourished by good works, but first he must have

by faith the life to nourish. Faith can save without works, as in the case
of the dying thief, but "works by themselves never justified any man."
"Neither faith is without works (having opportunity thereto), nor can
works avail to eternal life without faith."

### c. *Living Works*

Cranmer concludes his series by portraying the good works
"which spring out of true faith." From Christ's own teaching he argues
that fulfilling religious and ecclesiastical observances must not be confused with observance of God's laws. The monastic way comes under
particular attack. The chief vows of poverty, chastity, and obedience are
not wrong in themselves, but they are perverted in practice, monastic
works being substituted for authentic works. Cranmer offers instead "a
brief rehearsal of God's commandments." It might seem, perhaps, that
in his final exhortation Cranmer is reintroducing a righteousness of
works when he promises life to "those who travail continually in the
obedience of the commandments of God." But the phrase "wrought in
faith" safeguards the basic emphasis of the homilies and serves as an
excellent reminder that while true works do not precede or replace faith,
they do issue from it as its natural and necessary fruit.

## C. CALVIN

In his exposition of justification Calvin follows closely the established lines of Reformation teaching. A detailed examination, then,
would be superfluous in the present context. At the same time, however,
Calvin makes some distinctive contributions of his own to the doctrine.
These may be briefly noted.

### 1. Double Justification

Within the narrower discussion of justification in Book iii of his
*Institutes,* Calvin offers a fine definition: "We explain justification simply
as the acceptance with which God receives us into his favour as righ
teous men" (iii.11.2). Like Cranmer, however, Calvin wishes to keep a
proper place for works and thereby to show the underlying harmony of
Paul and James instead of playing off the one against the other. He
agrees with Cranmer that justification by faith is "the beginning, foundation, cause, proof and substance of works righteousness" (iii.17.9). But
he goes further in relation to James, finding in James 2 a secondary
sense of the word "justification." Justification by works refers to "the
declaration, not the imputation, of righteousness" (iii.17.12). Basically
the thought is the same as Cranmer's, or, for that matter, Luther's. True
faith manifests itself in good works. Absence of the latter denotes ab-

sence of the former. "An empty show of faith does not justify." There is, then, what Calvin elsewhere calls a "double justification." Primarily, justification is acceptance before God through the imputation of righteousness. This comes by faith alone. Secondarily and in consequence, however, justification is the declaration or manifestation before men of the righteousness of faith. This is justification by works.

## 2. Faith and the Holy Spirit

All the reformers fight against a false understanding of faith as a human work. They unanimously describe it as a gift of God. They also relate it to the working of God's Word and Spirit. Nowhere, however, is this relation to the Word and Spirit developed more clearly or thoroughly than in the works of Calvin. Since the subject is too vast for proper presentation here, a few quotations will perhaps indicate how profoundly and comprehensively Calvin examines this aspect of faith and why he might not unjustly be described, not as the theologian of election, but rather as the theologian of the Holy Spirit.

Calvin opens the first chapter of Book iii with a discussion of the way in which we receive the grace of Christ. He describes the Holy Spirit as "the bond by which Christ effectually unites us to himself." In this act of union, "faith is the principal work of the Holy Spirit," the Spirit being "the inner teacher by whose effort the promise of salvation penetrates into our minds." To put it in another way, Christ is the "inner schoolmaster who by his Spirit draws to himself those who are given him by the Father" (iii.1.4). The Word, of course, enters in, too: "Take away the word and no faith will then remain" (iii.2.6). Yet "without the illumination of the Spirit, the word can do nothing." Nor is it enough "for the mind to be illumined by the Spirit of God unless the heart is also strengthened by his power" (iii.2.33). Man does not initiate his own faith; it is "founded upon the might of the Spirit." "Christ illumines us into faith by the power of his Spirit" (sec. 35). Faith is a matter of the heart as well as of the mind. Indeed, "the heart's distrust is greater than the mind's blindness. It is harder for the heart to be furnished with assurance than for the mind to be endowed with thought." Nevertheless, whether it be in mind or heart, faith is implanted by the Spirit. If the Spirit illumines the mind, then "in the confirmation of the heart his power is much more clearly manifested" (sec. 36). Hence we "do injury to the Holy Spirit if we separate faith, which is his peculiar work, from him" (sec. 39). The faith which justifies is not a human possibility. Its role in justification in no sense preserves a sphere wherein man's work may also justify him before God. As faith does not look to itself but to Christ as its object (iii.2.1), so it does not derive from itself, but from the Spirit as its author (iii.2.33).

## 3. Causes of Justification

To speak of justification by faith alone can be misleading if the inference is drawn that justification depends exclusively on faith. As we have seen in both Luther and Cranmer, all the reformers try in different ways to block this inference. Calvin himself offers different safeguards, one of which is his interesting analysis of the causes of justification. He is already thinking along parallel lines when in answer to Osiander he says that God alone justifies, that Christ also justifies because he was given to us for righteousness (iii.11.6), and that faith justifies as a kind of empty vessel which receives the grace of Christ (par. 7). When he comes to the Scholastic thesis that works may also be a cause of holiness, Calvin deliberately adopts in reply the philosophical framework of a fourfold cause. Applying this to salvation he finds the efficient cause in the mercy and free love of the heavenly Father, the material cause in the reconciling work of Christ, the formal or instrumental cause in faith, which is a work of the Spirit, and the final cause in the demonstration of God's justice and the praise of his goodness. Obviously, no dispute can arise about the first cause or the last cause. As regards the second and third, Calvin thinks his opponents give works "half the place along with faith and Christ's righteousness." Scripture, however, "cries out against this," showing us "that Christ is for us both righteousness and life and that this benefit of righteousness is possessed by faith alone" (iii.14.17). In the last analysis justification is exclusively the work of the Triune God. Faith acquires its significance only as a means of appropriation, and even as such it is itself caused by the Holy Spirit.

## 4. Justification and Sanctification

Perhaps Calvin's most important contribution to the understanding of justification is his reuniting of two things which for purposes of clarity had in a sense been divided, namely, justification and sanctification. Now obviously neither Luther nor Cranmer nor others meant to keep the two apart. Their anxiety to relate faith to works bears ample testimony to this. On the other hand, the reformers in general can hardly be said to have presented a comprehensive view of Christian salvation and the Christian life in a way which brings out the full relationship of justification and sanctification. This was to be the great achievement of Calvin.

First, he brought sanctification and justification together in Book iii under the common head of the way of receiving Christ and its benefits and effects. This book begins with faith and ends with election and the resurrection. Significantly, it also includes a discussion of freedom and an exposition of the Lord's Prayer. It thus constitutes a discussion of the Christian life in its totality, not in its isolated constituents.

Second, Calvin related justification and sanctification directly. We are justified by faith, for by faith "we grasp Christ's righteousness, by which alone we are reconciled to God." But we cannot grasp this righteousness "without grasping sanctification also." "Christ justifies no one whom he does not at the same time sanctify." We may distinguish justification and sanctification, but "Christ contains both of them inseparably in himself." "You cannot possess Christ without being made partaker in his sanctification" (iii.16.1). Even when refuting Osiander's idea of essential righteousness, Calvin agrees that God does not leave in their vices those whom he justifies. "As Christ cannot be torn into two parts, so these two which be perceived in him together and conjointly are inseparable, namely, righteousness and sanctification" (iii.11.6). "Being partakers of Christ we grasp a double grace" (iii.11.1).

Third, Calvin integrates justification into sanctification, not the reverse. This does not weaken the significance of justification; he calls it "the main hinge on which religion turns" (iii.11.1). Yet it is not the totality of salvation. If justification is not to be swallowed up in sanctification or confused with it, sanctification is not to be reduced to justification or replaced by it. Thus in Book iii Calvin begins with faith and then moves on to repentance, self-denial, cross-bearing, meditation on the future life and the proper use of the present life. Only then does he introduce his very full treatment of justification. Then he resumes the theme of the Christian life with chapters on freedom, prayer, election and the resurrection, the culmination being reached with the eternal felicity which surpasses our present comprehension.

Fourth, Calvin agrees with other reformers that justification provides the motive force in sanctification. The final power of sanctification lies, of course, in Christ, who sanctifies as well as justifies (iii.16.1). Nevertheless, no sharper spur to uprightness exists than "the thought that our salvation stands upon no merit of ours but solely upon God's mercy" (iii.16.3). We are reminded here of the concept of double justification. True faith manifests itself in works and carries with it regeneration in the sense of renewal. Actual holiness of life is not separated from free imputation of righteousness. The impulse to sanctification is provided both by free justification — God's grace evoking gratitude — and also by justifying faith, which is oriented to God in trust and obedience. Justification may thus be seen as an actual step in sanctification.

Along these lines Calvin avoids the overemphasis on justification which Romanists oppose and Anabaptists suspect. There were grounds for this overemphasis at a time when justification was misinterpreted and even sanctification itself was poorly understood and practiced. Yet one extreme does not properly correct another. It is a testimony to the theological insight of Calvin that in arrangement and substance alike he holds the balance when so many others either perpetuate the extremes or offer only partial and not wholly adequate corrections. As he himself so finely puts it, "in our sharing in Christ, which justifies us, sanctification is just as much included as righteousness" (iii.16.1).

# CHAPTER XVII

# Law and Gospel, Covenant and Election

## A. MELANCHTHON ON LAW AND GOSPEL

### 1. The Law

*a. Definition*

In his *Loci Communes* (1521) Melanchthon, the young theologian who supported Luther in Wittenberg, took up the matter of the law immediately following his treatment of sin. In his view, the power and nature of sin are better revealed in this way, for "the law is said to be the knowledge of sin." As a general definition of law the thesis is advanced that it is "a judgment by which the good is commanded and the bad forbidden" (*Library of Christian Classics* 19, p. 49).

*b. Distinctions of Law*

Melanchthon differentiates three different kinds of law.

(1) Natural law. This enshrines "a common judgment to which all men give the same consent." Scripture teaches us that it has been impressed on our minds by God. It thus consists in "concreated attitudes" (p. 50).

(2) Divine law. This can be subdivided into moral law (pp. 53ff.), which embraces the so-called counsels and is of perpetual validity; judicial law, the laws which were given to the Hebrews but of which "the New Testament knows nothing"; and ceremonial law, which foreshadows the mysteries of the gospel and has found fulfillment in it (p. 61).

(3) Human law. This consists of laws established by men. Some are civil, and their validity can be accepted in principle. Others are pontifical or priestly and these lack any true authority (pp. 62–70). Even when they seem to be wise, "that very appearance, that rouge used by wicked, disgraceful Jezebel, is the thing that does the damage" (p. 70).

## 2. The Gospel

### a. Law and Gospel in Scripture

Melanchthon sets the law in contrast to the gospel. "The law shows sin, the gospel grace. The law indicates the disease, the gospel points out the remedy." Yet we must not equate the law with the Old Testament and the gospel with the New. Both law and gospel are "scattered in all the books of both the Old and New Testaments." "Every age is a time of law and a time of gospel." As God's promise of mercy or grace the gospel may be seen already in Genesis 3:15; 12:3; Deuteronomy 18:18–19; Exodus 34:6–7 ("try to find a more evangelical passage in the whole New Testament"); and even Deuteronomy 5:10 ("the etiology of the first [second] commandment"). All scripture, then, is in some parts law, in others gospel (p. 70).

### b. Law and Gospel in Christ

Christ, too, preaches both law and gospel, for "grace cannot be preached without law" (p. 75). To be sure, he changed certain things in the law. His primary prophetic office was not to "establish the law but to bestow grace." Nevertheless, he preached law, for without it "sin cannot be recognized, and unless we experience sin, we shall not understand the power and fulness of grace" (p. 76).

## 3. The Power of the Law and the Power of the Gospel

### a. Of the Law

Melanchthon devotes two sections to the power of the law and of the gospel. As regards the power of the law, scripture differs from human reason by seeing it as a power of wrath, not correction. The law's work is "to kill and to damn, to reveal the root of our sin" (p. 79). It unmasks sin of all kinds, inward as well as outward. "Nature per se cannot even recognize the filth of sin." Hence the sinner has first to be convinced of sin and moved to hate it. The Holy Spirit brings this about through the law. So, then, "Christian doctrine must begin with the function of the law" (p. 83).

### b. Of the Gospel

In contrast, the power of the gospel is to lift up the conscience-stricken with the promise of God's grace and mercy. "The law demands the impossible, and the conscience, convicted of sin, is assailed from all directions" (p. 84). No power of will or works or restitution can help. But then comes the power of the gospel to give new life to those who put their trust in the promise of grace in Christ.

### 4. Christ

For Melanchthon, Christ is, of course, the pledge and fulfillment of the gospel. All the promises of scripture relate to him. In the Old Testament the gospel was in a sense only intimated, just as Christ was "dimly revealed." The Old Testament has the quality of prophecy, the New Testament that of witness. "The apostles . . . testify of the revealed Christ whom the ancients had merely foretold" (p. 74). Yet either way Christ stands at the heart of the gospel, bringing the consolation which is its power instead of the terror which is the power of the law.

### 5. The Decalogue

In a later discussion Melanchthon takes up again the relation of the Old and New Testaments. In this analysis he describes the former as "a promise of material things linked up with the demands of the law" (p. 120). In the latter, however, good things are promised unconditionally. "It is a veritable prodigality of divine mercy" (p. 121). From this standpoint even the moral law is abrogated. Christian freedom also means freedom from the decalogue in the twofold sense that (a) it cannot condemn those who are in Christ, and (b) those who are in Christ are led by the Spirit to obey it, having a desire to do so, so that they would do what the law demands even if there were no law (p. 124). The will of God expressed in the law remains the same; but the Spirit is the living will of God, so that regenerated by him "we now will spontaneously that very thing which the law used to demand." Abrogation does not mean a change in God's will. It means the end of obligation and its replacement by spontaneity (p. 123).

## B. LUTHER ON ELECTION

### 1. Introduction

For a full, if polemical, exposition of Luther's doctrine of election one must go to his *Bondage of the Will*. Already in his Romans lectures, however, he plainly indicates his understanding of the matter. He also shows beyond question that a strong doctrine of election does not arise arbitrarily or fortuitously. As in Augustine's *Spirit and Letter*, predestination stands in the closest relation to justification.

### 2. General Considerations

*a. Difficulty of the Doctrine*

Like most of those who deal with election, Luther has a section on its difficulty. If we are not to "fall into the abyss of horror and hopelessness" when thinking about it, we must first "purge the eyes of the heart." Luther himself deals with the subject only because "the order of the lection and necessity" compel him. It is "very strong wine and the most complete meal" and it belongs, not in the first book as in Lombard's *Sentences*, but in the last book (*LW* 25, p. 389).

### b. Appearance and Reality

Part of the problem is that in the things of God we cannot see the reality. While "we understand our own work before it is done, we do not understand the work of God until it is done" (p. 367). Thus many things have the appearance of contingency, but with God there is no contingency; "it is only in our eyes" (p. 373). To be contingent is "to be a creature and not God" (p. 372).

### c. Carnal Wisdom

Basically, however, the difficulty lies in the foolish wisdom of the flesh. Until we learn to submit our questions to God's will, we will constantly find problems, not being able to see why God wills this or does that. Carnal wisdom "places itself above God" and thus views predestination as an insoluble riddle which it can only reject. The wisdom of the flesh must be replaced by that of the Spirit if one is to "delight in this subject with an ineffable pleasure." Understanding it, however, is an exercise for mature believers alone (p. 389).

## 3. Election and Justification

Starting out from Romans 8:28 Luther sees a vital connection between salvation, calling, and purpose. Assurance finds its ground in the fact that salvation is not by chance; if it depended on our will and works, then "it would depend upon chance." We could have no certainty of overcoming the foes listed at the end of Romans 8. God exposes his elect to these enemies in order to show that we are saved, "not by our own merits, but purely by his own election and immutable will," which is the same as "his immutable love" (p. 371). Election cuts off self-righteousness. In so doing it "strangles" carnal wisdom, which vigorously resists the truth that salvation comes, not from "something working in itself, but only from outside itself, namely, from God, who elects" (pp. 376–377).

## 4. Proofs of Election

### a. Words of God

To support the doctrine Luther aims "to collect the proofs of an immutable predestination." He does this first from the words of God in scripture. In this regard he has six main arguments: (1) the word "purpose" in Romans 8:28; (2) the stories of Isaac/Ishmael and Jacob/ Esau in Romans 9; (3) Romans 9:15, 17–18; (4) John 10:29; (5) John 13:18 and 6:44; and (6) Psalm 115:3 and 2 Timothy 2:19. Election, he says, is plainly taught in these passages (pp. 373–375).

### b. Works of God

God's acts back up his words. Luther limits himself to three examples: (1) the divine dealings recorded in Romans 9; (2) God's subjection of his saints to many evils and their deliverance from them; and (3) the passing over of the good and learned and the conversion of the wicked. In all these actions "God demonstrates his election" (pp. 374–375).

## 5. Objections

### a. Free Will

Carnal wisdom has four objections to the doctrine. The first is that "man has been given a free will by which he either merits or fails to merit something." Luther does not totally deny freedom. He contends, however, that without grace, which frees it for salvation, the will "has absolutely no power to achieve righteousness." "It is captive to sin" and cannot choose what is good before God. The first objection is thus dismissed as "the least important" (p. 375).

### b. God's Will to Save

The second objection is that God wills the salvation of all, that he created all for eternal life and sent his Son for all. Luther's reply is that when scripture speaks of "all" in this way it means all the elect. In the absolute sense Christ did not die for all but "for you" and "for many." Thus the argument has no validity (pp. 375–376).

### c. Responsibility

The third objection is that there can be condemnation only for responsible, not for necessary sin. Luther answers that there is a distinction between necessity and constraint. If sinners sin necessarily they also do so voluntarily. They like to sin. Hence reprobation and responsibility are not to be treated as antithetical or incompatible (p. 376).

### d. God: The Author of Sin?

The final objection is that God seems to be the author of sin if he wills sin and hardens sinners. For Luther this is "the strongest and primary objection." Only God's sovereign purpose can be adduced in answer to it. God wills sin in order that he might show both justice and mercy. If carnal wisdom complains, this simply shows its centeredness on self rather than on God. "At the end of the day God is to be glorified; to recognize this is salvation" (p. 376).

## 6. Three Degrees of the Elect

A strange and interesting passage concludes Luther's handling of Romans 8:28. In it he points out that despair of self leads to trust in Christ. Thus fear of non-election can be a comforting sign of election, for in this life only the elect and not the reprobate fear God's judgment. In this connection Luther discerns three classes or degrees of the elect.

### a. Contentment

In the first class are the elect who are content with the will of God which elects them.

### b. Acceptance

At a deeper level are those who accept the will of God even though God should want to consider them among the reprobate.

### c. Resignation

At the deepest or highest level are the elect who in effect resign themselves to hell should God so will. In this group Luther sees a full cleansing from self-will and a full understanding of the saying that love is stronger than death. For the elect God's love takes the form of cross and passion without which the soul grows lazy and neglects to love God. The true love which God is developing in us is "sweet toward its object but bitter to its subject." Readiness to accept the ultimate evil for others' good, as exemplified by Paul in Romans 9:1–5, characterizes this third and supreme rank of the elect, among whom the last of all considerations is an anxious, dominating, and stultifying concern for their own election (pp. 376–378).

## C. HOFMANN ON THE COVENANT

## 1. Baptism

In *The Ordinance of God,* which he wrote in Holland in 1530, the Anabaptist Melchior Hofmann expresses the tremendous significance of baptism for those who followed the Anabaptist way. Baptism is the epiphany of Christ. It is a putting on of Christ through faith, a laying aside of the old Adam and a putting on of the new (*LCC* 25, pp. 184ff.). It is a betrothal of the bride to the heavenly Bridegroom (pp. 193–194).

## 2. The Baptismal Covenant

The concept of a marriage is connected in Hofmann's thinking with that of a covenant. Baptism as he sees it is a sign of the covenant of God which was instituted for the mature and the rational (p. 192). The bride covenants herself with the Lord under the sign of the covenant (p. 196). This new covenant is rather fancifully equated with the third day of 2 Esdras 5:4, the third lunar festival or spiritual feast of tabernacles in the spiritual wilderness (p. 189). The substance of the covenant is that those who persevere will attain to the election. Since Christ died for all, it is possible that all should be elected by God if they struggle and conquer (p. 192). A strong emphasis on freedom may be seen in this understanding. Those are to be baptized who accept "the word and preachment of the crucified Christ Jesus and give themselves over to him of their own free will" (p. 193).

## D. HUBMAIER ON FREE WILL

### 1. The Three Wills

Already in 1527 another Anabaptist, Balthasar Hubmaier, had written a little work *On Free Will* in which he presented an alternative to Luther's strong teaching on the bondage of the will and predestination. As Hubmaier saw it, there are three wills, that of the flesh, the soul, and the spirit (*LCC* 25, p. 117). Prior to the fall all were good and "capable of carrying to completion a free choice of good and evil" (p. 119). With the fall, however, the freedom of the flesh was forfeited and the soul was "so maimed in will and wounded . . . that it can of itself not even choose good or reject evil" (pp. 120–121). The spirit, however, remained "utterly upright and intact before, during, and after the fall" (p. 120). Although "imprisoned," it "would gladly will and do," but owing to the fall of the flesh and the maiming of the soul it can only cry out to God or "give inward testimony to godliness against sin" (p. 123). In the restoration, however, while the flesh is resistant, the soul, awakened by the Word and enlightened by the Spirit, recovers its lost freedom and "can now freely and willingly be obedient to the spirit, . . . will and choose the good, . . . and reject and flee from evil" (p. 124). It can, of course, follow the flesh, too, so that conflict arises in the Christian life (p. 125).

### 2. The Ability to Respond

From some angles it might seem that Hubmaier teaches a bondage of the will prior to the saving work of God in Christ. The flesh is worthless, the soul wounded, and the spirit imprisoned. Yet Hubmaier also insists on the ongoing integrity of the spirit so that there is already in man something to respond to the gospel, and once the soul is free again it follows the spirit's willing of the good. Either way, however, Hubmaier asserts firmly that salvation depends on the choice of faith. The flesh is judged, the spirit is intact, and the soul has to decide. "If I will, I can be saved, by the grace of God. If I will not, I shall be damned — and that by my own fault" (p. 127). "God gives power and capacity to all men in so far as they themselves desire it" (p. 129). Once God restores the power of knowing, willing, and doing, man can again elect good and flee from evil (pp. 128–129). The wound of ignorance is healed by the wine of the law which teaches us what is good, while the wound of inability is healed by the oil of the gospel which deprives sins of "their venomous and destructive power." Henceforward rejection of the good cannot be attributed to Adam but to the soul itself, which "must bear its own sin" (pp. 130–131).

### 3. The Absolute and Revealed Will of God

In a second treatise *On Free Will,* also written in 1527, Hubmaier deals with God's will in relation to election. According to his absolute will God can save or damn as he chooses. According to his revealed will, however, he wills the salvation of all (p. 132). Now the two wills are, of course, one. "We know that although God is omnipotent and can do all things, yet he will not act toward us poor human beings according to his omnipotence but according to his mercy" (p. 133). By his secret will God might consign Peter to hell and raise Judas to heaven. From his revealed will, however, we know that "he does not want to drive away any struggling Jacob without a blessing . . ." and "must have pity on David, who cries out to him . . ." (pp. 133–134). We are not, then, to investigate the secret will but to "lay hold of the revealed will" (p. 134). This will be an attracting will to all who choose him, for he wills all to be saved and draws all to him by the offer of grace and mercy. It will be a repelling will, however, to those who do not receive him. Mercy may be seen in God's attracting will and justice in his repelling will. Yet his will is one. The difference lies in our will, not in God's. If we accept his offer we know his will as it truly is, the will to save. If, however, we reject the offer, we know it as a repelling will. He wills and draws all to salvation, "yet choice is still left to man." If we fall under the repelling will of God's justice and punishment, "we — not God — we, with our sins, are guilty before it" (p. 135).

## E. DIETRICH PHILIPS ON THE COVENANT

### 1. The Embracing Covenant

In his work *The Church of God,* published about 1560, Dietrich

Philips, the younger brother of the Anabaptist leader Obbe Philips, advanced an interesting version of covenant theology. God first made a covenant with Noah (*LCC* 25, p. 231). He then renewed it with Abraham as a covenant of promise which came down through his descendants to the time of Christ (p. 232). In virtue of this covenant "the congregation of God existed from the beginning in Christ, by whom all things are renewed" (p. 233). With Christ's coming, the covenant promise of blessing for all nations was fulfilled and "the congregation was extended . . . throughout the whole world by the true messengers (emissaries) of the Lord" (p. 233).

### 2. The Word as Law and Gospel

Extension of the church is by regeneration, which is itself the work of God's Word. The Word, however, has two forms. As law "it condemns the uncleanness of nature" and "teaches the knowledge of sin" (pp. 235–236). As gospel it is the word of grace, comfort, and invitation. When we are induced by the law to repent, we are born anew in the power of the Spirit, the law is silenced, and there "shines a clearer light of the gospel . . . into believing hearts" (p. 237). This is the new birth by the Word.

### 3. Figure and Reality

While Philips accepted the unity of the covenant, he made a distinction between figure and reality which was connected with his rejection of infant baptism. With Christ's coming, "figures had an end" and "the true realities came into being" (p. 233). Philips did not develop the thought but offered the example of Aaron and his sons as a figure pointing to the reality, namely, Christ and the congregation of God. What he seems to have had in mind is that Old Testament Israel prefigures the new and true Israel of the New Testament. Along the lines of this spiritualizing, baptism might be regarded as a covenant sign like circumcision. Circumcision is given to those who belong by natural birth to physical Israel which is the figure. Baptism, in contrast, is given to those who belong by supernatural birth to spiritual Israel, which is the reality.

## F. CALVIN ON ELECTION

### 1. The Covenant

Calvin's essential theology of the covenant has been summarized already in the chapter on the Word of God. A brief recapitulation will thus suffice in the present context. a. We learn even from the old covenant that there is no faith in the gracious God apart from the Mediator (ii.6.2). b. All are elect in Abraham, but Christ was properly the seed in whom all nations were to be blessed (par. 2). This means (1) that Christ alone has always been the hope of the godly and (2) that faith in God is faith in Christ. It is in him that "the freely given covenant, whereby God has adopted his elect, stands fast" (par. 4). c. The old and new covenants are basically one and the same, for (1) eternal blessings are the goal in each (ii.10.3); (2) the grace or mercy of God is the common basis (ii.10.4); (3) the signs are the same (ii.10.5); and (4) Christ is the common Mediator (ii.10.2). d. Fellowship with God is the covenant gift for Old Testament believers too (see Leviticus 26:12). e. The old covenant, like the new, carries with it eternal life, for God, "whose beneficence is not hindered by death, does not withdraw the fruit of his mercy from the dead" (ii.10.9).

Two important points stand out in this treatment. a. Calvin is less concerned than Luther or Melanchthon to distinguish law and gospel. Law is not the substance of the old covenant. It has its place, but it is set in teleological tension with the covenant of grace which precedes it and which it serves. The ultimate theme of both Old Testament and New is gospel. Stress falls, then, on the unity of law and gospel more than on their distinction.

b. Calvin resists the tendency to see merely a material covenant in the Old Testament and a spiritual one in the New. He sees, of course, that earthly symbols are used in the Old Testament. He also has to reckon with the flat statement in Hebrews that a new and better covenant has replaced the old one. Calvin, however, relates the earthly figures to the mode, not the reality, of the old covenant. While these may be called the covenant, as in the sacramental equation of sign and thing signified, they are only "accidental properties or additions and appendages, and in common parlance accessories of it" (ii.11.5). Thus Calvin might agree with Dietrich Philips that figures were abolished when Christ came, but not in the sense that only then did the true reality come. This has a more extensive bearing than one might suspect, for ultimately it affects the whole understanding of church and sacraments.

## 2. Free Will

### a. Sin Unnatural

With his consistent emphasis on God's gracious work in salvation, it is not surprising that Calvin should agree with Luther in resisting the idea of human freedom. He realizes, however, that sin is not natural to man but is a "degeneration from our original condition" (ii.1.10). Yet it has now become natural. "Man is corrupted through a natural vitiation, but a vitiation that did not flow from nature" (ii.1.11).

### b. The Enslaved Will

This being so, no freedom of the will for good can be claimed. The will itself remains, for even though man has no power to do the good, it is "by will, not by compulsion" that he acts wickedly (ii.2.7). The situation, then, is that of a bound will, not a destroyed will. The will has fallen into slavery to sin (ii.2.8).

### c. Spheres of the Understanding

To prevent misconceptions, Calvin here devotes several sections to the power of the human understanding in spheres outside the knowledge and service of God. He is no philistine; his doctrine of ignorance and depravity does not mean that humanity achieves nothing of worth. Social orders are set up and the arts and sciences flourish. The "light of truth" shining in secular writers shows that "the mind of man, though fallen and perverted from its wholeness, is nevertheless clothed and ornamented with God's excellent gifts" (secs. 13–15). Man's natural endowment is not to be scorned. The Spirit of God is at work in communicating all that is most excellent in human life (sec. 16). The gifts of this "general grace of God," which can take the form of special graces in individuals, are not to be neglected (secs. 16–17). Aptitudes exist which men still have some freedom to express.

### d. The Sphere of Corruption

Nevertheless, in understanding no less than will, man has no competence in divine things. In relation to God and his fatherly favor, "the greatest geniuses are blinder than moles" unless enlightened by the Spirit. In matters of the will man's plight is no less desperate. By its very nature the will is subject to depravity (ii.3.1–2). It can find no way to break free from evil. God in his goodness restrains the worst outworkings of sin. He even grants to some the special graces which make a measure of integrity possible. Even so, what appears praiseworthy to us "must be considered worthless" before God (secs. 3–4). For the enslaved will no achievement of virtue is possible.

### e. Responsibility

Since, however, the will does not lie under coercion, Calvin does not think that it can escape responsibility. God is in a sense under the necessity of doing good, but this does not mean that when he does good it is not an act of his will. "Who shall say that man therefore sins less willingly because he is under the necessity of sinning?" (sec. 5). Bernard is quoted here: "Neither does necessity avail to excuse the will, nor does the will . . . avail to exclude necessity." "The soul is at the same time enslaved and free: enslaved because of necessity, free because of will."

### f. Freedom and Grace

While Calvin lays heavy stress on the bondage of the will, we should not forget that its freedom is his chief concern. Freedom means liberation, and to claim freedom is to be blind to the need for liberation. The gospel teaches the bondage of the will in order to make clear this need for liberation and then to declare it in and through God's work of grace. "Divine grace corrects and cures the corruption of nature," not by helping a weak will but by its conversion, its total transformation and renewal (secs. 6–8). As Augustine so aptly put it, "the human will does not obtain grace by freedom but obtains freedom by grace." The will remains, but "except through grace it can neither be converted to God nor abide in God, and whatever it can do it is able to do only through grace" (sec. 14).

### 3. Election

#### a. Its Place

The doctrine of election has often been seen as Calvin's central doctrine. If so, it is odd that he never seemed sure where to put it in the *Institutes.* He located it differently in different editions. In the final edition of 1559 he did not relate it directly to the covenant, or providence, or even the bondage of the will, but put it rather awkwardly between prayer (iii.20) and the resurrection (iii.25). Perhaps, like Luther, he noted that in Romans it comes only after the treatment of sin, justification, and sanctification. Perhaps he perceived a natural transition from election and reprobation to the last judgment. Nonetheless, the crucial role of the doctrine is not at all suggested by its location.

#### b. Reservations

Calvin, too, approaches the theme with some timidity. He stresses the usefulness of the doctrine. It promotes God's glory, beats down human pride, and gives the believer confidence. All the same, curiosity raises the possibility of danger and confusion. Predestination lies within the sacred precincts of divine wisdom, which can be a labyrinth to those who break in with "carefree assurance." The only safe course is to stay with scripture. When this is done, there is no need for silence, and discussion need not have the dangerous consequences that are often feared (iii.21.1–4).

#### c. Definition

Election and reprobation form the two aspects of predestination, which is defined as "God's eternal decree by which he determined with himself what he willed to become of each man. ... Eternal life is ordained for some, eternal damnation for others." In a general way this can apply to nations, too. Israel is elect as distinct from the Gentiles (sec. 5). But even in Israel some are elect and others not (sec. 6). In the strictest sense, then, election applies to individuals. While election is revocable in relation to Israel it is irrevocable in relation to individuals, who "are never cut from salvation" (sec. 7). The divine decree of predestination has the following marks. It is more than foreknowledge. It is completely free. It implies an incomprehensible but just and irreprehensible decision. It is sealed by the calling and justifying of the elect and the "shutting off" of the reprobate (sec. 7). It is not on the basis of foreseen merits or holiness (iii.22.2–3).

### d. Christ and Election

In four ways Calvin relates election, the positive side of predestination, to Christ.

(1) The Mirror of Free Election. In his humanity Christ exemplifies the freedom of election. Why was Jesus of Nazareth chosen as Son of God and Savior? Not because of foreseen righteousness but by free divine decision (iii.22.1).

(2) Election in Christ. In our case the same freedom of election may be seen in the fact that we are not elect in ourselves. Worthiness is not the ground of the divine choice. "In us the Father found nothing worthy of election." He thus "turned his eyes upon his anointed to choose from that body as members those whom he was to take into the fellowship of life" (sec. 1).

(3) The Author of Election. Nor does Christ merely have an executive role in election. "He claims for himself, in common with the Father, the right to choose." He thus "makes himself the author of election" (sec. 7).

(4) The Mirror of Our Election. To know our own election, Calvin advises us to do as the Father himself does and "turn our eyes to Christ." God has not chosen us in ourselves but in Christ. Hence we can find assurance of election only in the Son. "Christ is the mirror wherein we must, and without self-deception may, contemplate our own election." In him "we have a sufficiently clear and firm testimony that we are inscribed in the book of life" (iii.24.5). He bears witness that the Father "will count as his sons all those who have received him in faith." We are safe forever "because we have been made his once and for all" (sec. 6).

### e. Election and Calling

As noted, calling seals election. Yet calling must be differentiated, for while a general call goes out for repentance and faith, "the spirit of repentance and faith is not given to all" (23.8). We thus have two calls, the general call of universal invitation and a special call to believers only or to some who have a temporary illumination of the Spirit (iii.24.8). The time of special calling lies in God's hands (23.10).

### f. Election and Faith

As the response to special calling, faith obviously plays a significant role in election. Yet in this field faith is not to be overestimated.

God does not just give us the ability to believe, so that we are elected when we exercise this ability. God gives us faith itself because he has elected us. Again, faith does not confirm election in the sense of making it sure and effectual. It confirms it only in the sense of verifying what was not previously known. Fundamentally faith is the work of election, not election of faith (iii.24.3). Election is "the mother of faith" (iii.22.10).

### g. Election and the Word

The Word has obvious importance in relation to election. (1) The doctrine is to be sought in the written word. If we exceed its bounds, "our course is outside the pathway and in darkness" (iii.21.2). (2) The Word is the means of calling. In the special calling of the elect the Holy Spirit "causes the preached word to dwell in their hearts" (iii.24.8). (3) The Word is not, however, the basis of election. Indeed, God sends it "to many whose blindness he intends to increase." Its teaching is "wrapped in enigmas" apart from divine illumination. It can convict the wicked as well as bring the elect to faith (iii.24.13).

### h. Reprobation

Calvin does not see how election could stand "except as set over against reprobation" (iii.23.1). Yet he accepts a distinction. God actively elects the saved; he "passes over" the lost. The reason for the divine choice is inscrutable, but the choice is not arbitrary, for God is not "a law unto himself" but "the law of all laws" (sec. 2). In condemning the wicked he simply exercises justice on the wicked, who deserve condemnation (secs. 2–3).

Yet did not God predestine the fall? Yes, and it is in this connection that Calvin makes his famous remark that "the decree is dreadful indeed, I confess" (sec. 7). He insists, however, that "it has its own equity, unknown . . . to us but very sure" (sec. 9). The wicked are condemned, of course, for their own malice and depravity. Yet he will countenance no "evasions." Man does not sin merely by God's permissive will (sec. 8), and so he is not condemned merely because he does wrong. He does wrong. This is why his judgment is just. But it must also be said that the wicked "have been raised up by the just but inscrutable judgment of God to show forth his glory in their condemnation" (iii.24.14). The "all" whose salvation God wills refers to all classes or orders of men (iii.24.16). If it seems that responsibility is eroded by reprobation, Calvin replies that the perdition of the wicked depends on reprobation "in such a way that the cause and occasion of it are found in themselves." "Man falls according as God's providence ordains, but he falls by his own fault" (iii.23.8).

# CHAPTER XVIII

# The Reformation and the Church

## A. THE AUGSBURG CONFESSION

### 1. Definition

Rather oddly, Melanchthon did not include the church among his *Loci*. The rudiments of a Lutheran understanding of the church were finely stated, however, in the Augsburg Confession of 1530. This advanced the famous definition which so powerfully influenced the thinking of all later reformers and Reformation confessions. The church is first described as "the one holy church which remains for ever," so that at least two of the original "notes" of the church — its unity and catholicity — are retained, and the promise of its preservation is recalled. This church is then identified as the communion of the saints. Hence no distinction is made here between the visible and the invisible church, although the German texts speak of the congregation of believers and the 1540 edition refers to the intermingling of evildoers and hypocrites in the congregation. Two things serve as distinguishing marks of this communion of the saints. First, the gospel is "rightly taught," or, as the German has it, "purely taught." Second, the sacraments are rightly administered, "rightly" in this case meaning "according to the gospel." Article 8 makes it clear that the worthiness or unworthiness of ministers does not determine whether the condition indicated by "rightly" is met. It is plainly recognized that in this life the unworthy are intermingled in the church and will continue to be until the day of judgment. The attempt to establish a pure church of true believers is seen as neither possible nor desirable.

### 2. Unity

The distinguishing marks of the church constitute the criterion of its unity. If there is unity of belief concerning the teaching of the gospel and the administration of the sacraments, no obstacle to unity exists. Uniformity of tradition and ceremonial is not required. In such matters no single course has been prescribed by scripture. The churches may ordain their own rites. Traditional rites "are to be preserved which can be preserved without sin and which are for tranquility and good order in the church." The gospel and the teaching of faith, however, serve as a razor in relation to traditions. Those which are "devised for the production of grace and satisfaction for sins" cannot be tolerated. They break the essential unity of belief.

From this standpoint unity with unreformed Rome lies outside the bounds of possibility. A substantial unity of belief exists with Rome, but Rome allows and even enforces practices which are at variance with it. In so doing it is itself the body that breaks the unity of the church. The widest diversity is compatible with unity, but when this diversity collides with the unity of belief, unity is shattered.

At root, the church's unity is confessional. For its preservation the purity of the gospel must be upheld and all individual practices tested, not so much by detailed biblical precepts, but by the general standard of the gospel. What gospel belief is forms, of course, another problem, Marburg had already illustrated the difficulty in 1529. Wide possibilities of disunion were obviously opened up by this criterion quite apart from the obvious incongruence of certain doctrines and practices with the essential message of salvation.

## B. DIETRICH PHILIPS

### 1. Members of the Church

Reference has already been made to *The Church of God* by Dietrich Philips. In defining the church Philips took a comprehensive view. It is "a congregation of holy beings . . . namely, of angels in heaven and of the believing reborn men on earth . . . all united together in Jesus Christ" (*Library of Christian Classics* 25, p. 229) Originally the church in heaven consisted of angels, but the wicked angels fell away from it in a first apostasy (pp. 229–230). Adam and Eve belonged to the church, too, but they were deceived by the serpent and fell away in a second apostasy (p. 230). God, however, began the restoration of man and "the reconstruction of the ruined church" with the promise of Genesis 3:15, which Christ was later to fulfill. The Israelites, all who truly confess God among the Gentiles, and finally believers from all nations are members of the reconstituted congregation along with the holy angels (pp. 231–233).

## 2. Entry into the Church

Now that Christ has come fulfilling the covenant promise and substituting the reality for the figure (p. 233), entry into the divine congregation is by new birth and enlightenment with the knowledge of God and his will. New birth comes inwardly with repentance and trust (pp. 234–235). The related knowledge of God is knowledge of the Triune God and his saving work in and through the incarnate Word and the Holy Spirit. When with this knowledge there is new birth in true faith, Jesus Christ gathers "such reborn people and new creatures" into his congregation (p. 240).

## 3. Seven Ordinances of the Church

For the church, as Philips sees it, seven ordinances have been set up which are possibly related to the seven gifts of the Spirit and set in antithesis to the seven sacraments. First the church must have "pure and unfalsified doctrine" and "correct ministers" (pp. 240–241). Second, there must be a scriptural use of the two dominical sacraments, which are visible symbols of God's grace and covenant and which admonish us "to a godly walk, to mortification of the flesh, to a burial of sin, to a resurrection into the new life" (pp. 242–243). Footwashing constitutes the third ordinance, reminding us of the need for inner cleansing and providing us with an exercise in mutual humbling (pp. 244-246). Then comes evangelical separation to prevent contamination and to induce penitence in offending brethren (pp. 246–248). The fifth ordinance is the commandment of love displayed both spiritually and materially (pp. 248–250). The sixth is the keeping of all the commandments, which is "the heavenly philosophy" and "the counsel and will of God" (pp. 250–251). The seventh and last is suffering and persecution, which true Christians must undergo for truth and righteousness, but which they are not to inflict (pp. 251–252), since "no congregation of the Lord may exercise dominion over the consciences of men with the outward sword" (p. 253). Dietrich states in conclusion that pseudo-congregations may be known by their failure to keep the ordinances. These serve as "evidences of true Christianity" (pp. 254-255), so that where their opposite is found it will be seen that there is no real church.

## 4. Twelve Notes of the Church

In addition to the seven ordinances which the Lord has laid on the church, Dietrich discerns twelve descriptions by which it may be known. First and fundamentally, the church is a. the holy city marked by common polity, laws, and statutes (p. 255). As such it is b. the new Jerusalem, renewed in the peace which Christ has given (pp. 255–256).

c. It comes down from heaven, for its members are born from above (p. 256). d. It is prepared as a bride adorned for her husband, "espoused and wedded" to Jesus Christ by faith (p. 256). e. It has the glory of God, for it is enlightened by Christ's appearing and walks in the light of his Word. f. It has a precious foundation, that of the apostles and prophets, with Christ as the chief cornerstone, and is walled about by the Spirit's gifts (p. 257). g. It has twelve gates, the apostles and their teaching of Christ, through which alone the city can be entered. h. It is of pure gold, its members being purified by tribulation, and it needs no temple, for the church itself is God's temple. i. The gates are never closed, for the door of grace is always open to penitents and believers (p. 258). j. It has within it a living stream, the Holy Spirit (pp. 258–259). k. The glory and honor of the nations are brought into it as thousands of Gentiles are added to the congregation (p. 259). l. Finally, the servants of God within it serve the Most High, have his name, see his face, and shall reign forever. These servants are the true Christians who have committed themselves to the service of righteousness (pp. 259–260).

Philips realizes, of course, that only in eternity will the church achieve the fullness of its true being as the holy city. He is not in the strict sense a perfectionist. Nevertheless, he believes that a beginning of this being has already been made in the Spirit. Where "this may be seen and found, there is the true congregation of the Lord" (p. 260).

## C. MENNO SIMONS

### 1. The Ban

It has been seen that separation, or church discipline, formed one of the ordinances of the church for Philips. The practice of discipline, or the ban, became an important issue in the Anabaptist congregations, for only by its proper exercise could the purity which was sought by adult baptism be maintained. Difficulties arose, however, about the severity of separation, especially when it was to be applied within a family. Some groups took a milder view, while others, including Philips, pressed for full strictness. Menno Simons tried to keep the peace with a modified rigorism, as may be seen in his work *On the Ban* (1550). Unfortunately he was unable to prevent a schism over the matter in 1555.

### 2. Basis of the Ban

Simons, like Philips, regards separation as a definite divine command and not a mere counsel, although he insists that even if it were a counsel it ought still to be followed (Q. 1). Since the ban is commanded, believers who do not observe it are guilty of disobedience, contempt for God's Word, and rebellion, no matter how pious they may be in other matters. The strict commanding of the ban by our Lord and the apostles means that we should either practice it or ourselves be "shunned and avoided by the congregation" (Q. 2).

### 3. Practice of the Ban

#### a. The Family
Although it might seem hard that the ban should be enforced on a family, Simons does not back down. Four rules are to be observed. (1) There can be no exceptions. (2) A husband or wife must vote with the church to ban an erring spouse. (3) The positive goal of amendment must be especially sought within the family. (4) Yet the possibility of more corruption is greater in the family; consequently Christ must be loved more than husband, wife, parent, or child. Simons recognizes, however, that "this is a delicate matter." Individuals may have difficulty in carrying it out. He thus advises that "you press no one farther than he is taught of God in his heart and that he in his conscience can bear," for scripture everywhere teaches "that we should bear with the weak" (Q. 3).

#### b. Greetings
Simons takes it that the ban excludes social dealings. He does not agree with absolute rigorists, however, that the courtesy of common greetings should be withheld. Such austerity hampers the reforming work of the ban. After all, "the ban is not given to destroy, but to build up" (Q. 4).

#### c. Works of Mercy
Works of mercy may be performed on behalf of the banned. Christians are to be kind to all men, even their enemies. The banned cannot be excluded. We owe them temporal help with our goods and spiritual help with the Word. The ban itself must be seen as "a mark of divine love." Christ's own example shows that we are not to be "cruel, unmerciful Christians." The only danger is that "by any necessary service, charity, love and mercy" "my soul should be led into corruption" (Q. 5).

#### d. Trade and Table Fellowship
The ban ruled out all *commercium* with the banned. Much of the dissension focused on the meaning of this term. Philips, for example, took it to include works of mercy and Simons, as we have seen, could not follow him in this. In relation to buying and selling, however, it was generally agreed that this should be stopped unless it involved only a very casual relationship: "It is manifest that a pious, God-fearing Christian could have no apostate as a regular buyer or seller" (Q. 6). The same

applies to table fellowship. Obviously a believer might happen to be
seated next to a banned person when traveling. This cannot be avoided
and need not involve *commercium*. Eating together at a tavern, however, is another matter. Simons advises, begs, and admonishes every
pious Christian "not to eat by or with him." Yet some right of conscience
remains, for Simons also warns that "if perchance some pious God-
fearing brother might do so, then let everyone beware lest he sin against
his brother by an unscriptural judgment" (Q. 7).

### 4. Offenses

Simons offers a short list of those who should come under the ban.
It embraces people who reject the church's judgment, who live in open
sin, who are disorderly, and who cause division. Every effort should first
be made to "regain" them "in all love and reasonableness." If they are
obstinate, however, they are to be "reluctantly but unanimously separated from the church of Christ and shunned in all divine obedience
until they repent." Simons believes that a true church can be preserved
only if the ban is used firmly. At the same time he wants to check any
tendency toward overuse. He also works hard to keep its loving character and positive function to the fore. Unhappily, disagreement about the
ban became itself a reason for banning, and the restoration of the pure
church faltered with the multiplication of "pure" but mutually separated churches (Q. 8).

### D. BULLINGER

#### 1. The Holy Catholic Church

*a. Definition*

Bullinger opens the fifth and final decade of his doctrinal sermons
with two sermons on the church (Parker Society Edition, 5.1–2). The
first of these, entitled "The Holy Catholic Church," begins with a definition. After considering the various terms for "church" — "*ecclesia*,"
"synagogue," and "*kuriake*" — he describes the church as "the whole
company and multitude of the faithful . . . in heaven and . . . upon earth,
where it doth agree plainly in unity of faith or true doctrine, and in the
lawful partaking of the sacraments . . . joined and united together as it
were in one house and fellowship" (p. 5). It is called catholic or universal
because it embraces believers "in all places and times" (including the
Old Testament saints), with no distinction of "region, nation, or
kindred," of "condition, age, sex, or kind" (p. 5). "All the faithful are
citizens and members of this church."

*b. Parts*

The church consists of two parts.

(1) Triumphant. The church triumphant is "that great company of holy spirits in heaven . . . triumphing truly through the blood of Jesus Christ" (pp. 5–6). To this fellowship we belong, "for we are companions and fellow-heirs with the saints from Adam unto the end of all worlds" — a very sweet thought for Bullinger.

(2) Militant. Between the church triumphant and the church on earth Bullinger sees no church expectant, for the Reformation doctrine of justification leaves no place for purgatory. Hence the second part of the church is the church militant, "a congregation of men upon earth, professing the name and religion of Christ, continually fighting in the world" (p. 7) in a spiritual warfare.

*c. Divisions*

(1) Invisible. The militant church may be seen in two ways. Strictly it consists of those who are "in very deed the church, the faithful and elect of God, lively members." In this sense the church is inward and invisible, "only known to God." It is believed by us as "the company of all those saints that are, have been, and shall be . . . who enjoy all good things in common granted to them by God." This church is the spouse of Christ (pp. 7–8).

(2) Visible. More broadly the church includes all who "do acknowledge and profess true religion." Here is "the outward and visible church." It, too, may be subdivided.

(a) General. Considered generally, the visible church denotes all believers and confessors. This church will abide and is dispersed across the world. In spite of opposition and persecution God will always sanctify some to himself to be "his flock and holy house," thus fulfilling the prophecy that "the church is perpetual" (Psalm 89; 132; see also Matthew 16).

(b) Particular. The visible church takes particular form in the individual churches. Bullinger equates these with the parishes, which take their names from the places where they are located. He does not pursue the question of the relation of the church to the churches nor that of the interrelationships of the local churches. For Bullinger the particular churches serve the ends of edification and discipline — ends which could hardly be attained ecumenically but which can be achieved through individual pastoral oversight.

*d. The Counterfeit*

Christ's church finds a counterpart in the counterfeit church of the wicked, the devil's church, "the incorporate body of all who are under Satan." Pagans, heretics, and schismatics make up this wicked church (pp. 10–11). Hypocrites also belongs to it. Self-righteous hypocrites who resist the gospel belong only to this church. Dissembling hypocrites may also belong to the visible church. Some do so only for a time, but others, while inwardly being of the wicked church, do so all their lives (p. 12). If they keep up appearances, "not yet putting off their visors," they obviously cannot be expelled. Nevertheless, while they are in the church, they are not of it. God, who knows the heart, sees this. From the double membership of hypocrites Bullinger returns to his basic distinction between the church as God sees it, the inward and invisible church, and the church as we see it, the outward and visible (pp. 15–16).

### e. Marks

(1) Outward. What are the marks of the visible church? Bullinger breaks no new ground here. With Calvin he accepts the two principal marks of sincere preaching of God's Word and lawful partaking of the sacraments (p. 17). It is through these that "Christ makes to himself a church." If hypocrites do not profit from the Word and sacraments, this does not affect the purity of the Word and sacraments or the consequent validity of the church. Indeed, even hypocrites are "truly sanctified visibly," that is, "counted among holy men." For their lack of spiritual purity no blame attaches to God or the ministry, only to themselves (pp. 17–18). In contrast, true believers who on occasion may be deprived of the Word or sacraments are for all that "true and lively members of Christ and the catholic church" (pp. 19–20). In this case the mark is that they are "joined together in one spirit and one faith with all the true members of the church." Thus the Word and sacrament are not exclusive marks. By "pure preaching" Bullinger means that which follows true biblical exegesis (p. 21). The sacraments are rightly administered when they agree with "the order in which the Lord himself instituted them" (pp. 12-22).

(2) Inward. Bullinger lists also some inward marks "belonging only to the godly." These are (a) the fellowship of God's Spirit, (b) sincere faith, and (c) double charity, that is, love of God and neighbor. Without them "no man is partaker of this spiritual body" (pp. 23-26).

### f. Planting and Preservation

The church does not have its source in human decrees or doctrines. "Her original is heavenly." The church is also built up only by the Word of God (p. 26). "She is founded, planted, gathered together, and builded only by the Word of Christ." The same Word preserves it, lest it be seduced or slip or perish (p. 27). In this light, episcopal succession, while not without weight, is nothing without the Word. For its upbuilding and preservation the church is given pastors and doctors (*doctores*), not leaders (*ductores*) and captains who practice war and deceit (p. 33). "The apostolical sword is the word of God" (p. 34).

### g. Inerrancy

Can the church err? The church triumphant "can never err." The church militant both does and does not. It errs in conduct; if we will acknowledge only a church without blemish, we can acknowledge none at all. Yet "by the benefit of imputation" it does not err (pp. 35–36). It errs in doctrine but "not wholly and altogether." "Remnants" are reserved "by whom the truth may flourish again." Churches built on human decrees can claim no inerrancy, but in the sense that the apostolic faith will never be completely abandoned "the church does not err." Even if many err, "it followeth not that none at all is free from error" (p. 37).

### h. Authority

Bullinger begins the discussion of authority with a sharp criticism of the medieval idea of the sixfold authority of consecration, keys, jurisdiction, preaching, judicial correction, and support. He then defines authority as both right and ability. God alone has both except insofar as he confers them on the apostles. Bullinger then distinguishes between absolute power, which belongs to God, and limited power, which is given to the church. This limited or ministerial power may do "what the absolute power or greater authority doth suffer to be done" (p. 42). It derives from God and serves the purpose of God, namely, the profit of the church. If it breaks free from its limit and goal, it becomes a devilish tyranny and not lawful ecclesiastical power derived from God.

Bullinger lists four main spheres of the church's operation: the appointment (and, if necessary, the deposition) of ministers, the teaching of received doctrine, the orderly and charitable judgment of doctrines according to the sentence of the Holy Spirit and the rule of holy scripture, and the ordering of ecclesiastical matters and administration of discipline. The church's limit in all these things is "the rule of the word and of love." In sum, Bullinger's view of authority in the church consists of three main theses: (1) Christ holds and exercises full or absolute power in the church; (2) he has given ministerial power to the church; (3) the church is to execute this religiously according to the rule of God's Word and Spirit.

## 2. The Unity of the Church

### a. One Church

Sensitive to the charge of schism and troubled also by separatist developments, Bullinger devotes a second sermon to the theme of the church's unity. He begins by referring to the texts used by Cyprian in his *Unity* and also by quoting from Cyprian himself. The church militant is marked by diversity. It is scattered across the world. It even includes evil men and hypocrites. Yet "of particular churches is gathered and compacted together the catholic and universal church." "There is but one only church of God ... whereof the only monarch is Jesus Christ" (5.2, pp. 49ff.).

### b. No Salvation outside the One Church

Bullinger finds no difficulty in agreeing with Cyprian that outside this one church is no true salvation, light, or truth. "Without the pale of God's church are no wholesome pastures found." Cyprian's famous passage is quoted: "He cannot now have God his father who hath not the church his mother." Jesus himself tells us that "out of the sheepfold life is not found" (pp. 51–52).

### c. False Grounds of Schism

(1) Doctrinal. Bullinger allows that schism may be justified when the sacraments are totally corrupted and "pure doctrine altogether adulterated." If, however, the simple essentials of the faith are maintained, scripture is expounded and applied, and all is done to edification, detailed differences of teaching, exposition, or skill do not provide "just occasion to depart from the church." Even when a church expositor makes a serious blunder, the proper course is to try to correct him. Only the arrogant, who will accept only their own interpretation and not rest with what is "common and simple," will proceed to make a schism.

(2) Moral. Many ministers fall short in life and conduct. Nevertheless, if they faithfully teach and lawfully administer the sacraments, "no man hath just occasion to forsake the church." We are to flee from false prophets, but, as Bullinger sees it, "not an evil life but false doctrine maketh a false prophet." The call for holiness of life remains, as does the demand for discipline when there is open sin. Schism, however, should not be decided on such grounds. The same applies in the case of unworthy members (pp. 58ff.).

(3) Ceremonial. Church observances always vary. But so long as nothing is done contrary to faith and good manners, variety constitutes no reason for breaking the bond of unity. Sensible Christians will follow the practices of whatever churches they attend (pp. 56-58).

### d. Schism and Rome

The Roman church naturally argued that the reformers themselves were guilty of unjustifiable schism. In answer Bullinger maintained that "we never departed from the catholic church of Christ" (pp. 62–63). Indeed, they never departed from "the ancient and apostolic church of Rome." Rome itself had ceased to be the true church. It had neither the inward nor the outward marks of the church (p. 66). It lacked faith and love, subjected scripture to itself, joined the pope to Christ as head, and corrupted the sacraments, so that leaving it could not be regarded as schism. Bullinger was still confident that God would "reserve to himself a mighty church even under the papism." If purity of doctrine was profaned, it was not wholly abolished (p. 73). The possibility of reformation was still open. Nevertheless, departure from Rome should not be reckoned as schism but as return to the true catholic church (p. 76).

### e. Figures of the Church

(1) House. As a house the church is built on the foundation of Christ, and its walls are believers (p. 79).

(2) Kingdom. The church may be equated with the kingdom, for Christ is its king, governing it by his Spirit and Word. Since he is himself present with it he needs no vicar. This excludes the kingship of the bishop of Rome (pp. 84ff.).

(3) Sheepfold. The church may be described also as Christ's sheepfold. Christ is the head shepherd and he appoints ministers as shepherds under him. These pastors "are all equal; Christ our Lord is the universal pastor and chief and Lord of pastors." No pastors are to be heads over others or princes (pp. 88–89).

(4) Vine. As the one vine the church has various branches, some fruitful and some not. It is Christ who "by his spiritual and lively juice makes the good fruitful in good works." Hypocrites, as dead branches, will in due time be cut off (pp. 83–84).

(5) Spouse. As Christ's spouse the church enjoys mutual participation with him. "He became ours in all things and we are also members of the same body." Justification, sanctification, and life are in Christ the husband, and he communicates these to his bride, "that in him we might be just and holy and might live through him" (p. 90).

(6) Mother. As Mother the church begets believers by preaching the Word and nourishes them with milk and later with meat. The Roman church cannot claim to be the holy mother church, since it has not kept faith and integrity with her husband. The true church, our holy mother, is a chaste matron, an undefiled virgin, "hearing only the voice or doctrine of her well-beloved husband, placing all the means of life and salvation in him alone" (pp. 90–92).

## E. CALVIN

### 1. Necessity of the Church

In discussing the church at the beginning of Book iv of the *Institutes,* Calvin first points out that the need for the church arises in connection with the means of grace. God has provided aids to generate and nurture faith, and "he has deposited this treasure in the church." Since, then, God's children are gathered into the bosom of the church, Calvin accepts the thesis that "for those to whom he is father the church may also be mother" (iv.1.1).

### 2. The True Church

We believe the church, not in the sense that we trust in it as we do in God, but because we cannot finally distinguish between God's children and the ungodly. "We must leave to God alone the knowledge of his church, whose foundation is his secret election" (iv.1.2). This church is universal and it is "united in Christ." It cannot waver or fall. Its unity is to be believed even though we do not see it. "We are not bidden to distinguish between the reprobate and the elect" (sec. 3).

### 3. The Visible Church

The communion of saints expresses the mutual sharing of believers in and with heavenly gifts. It suggests also the outward character of the church (sec. 3). Calvin, then, devotes the rest of his discussion to this outward or visible church. Three initial statements are made about it: it is "the mother through whom alone we enter into life"; we cannot be "dismissed from her school until we have been pupils all our lives"; and "away from her bosom one cannot hope for any forgiveness of sins or any salvation" (sec. 4).

### 4. The Church's Ministers

#### a. Divine Appointment

The ministry belongs essentially to the church: "The preaching of the heavenly doctrine has been enjoined upon the pastors." Men are chosen for this work both to test obedience and also to accommodate the message to us. The fallibility of the human instrumentality should not be a reason for deposing ministers or for setting up a rival and schismatic ministry (sec. 5).

#### b. Meaning and Limits

In relation to the ministry two things must be kept in balance. (1) God is the author of preaching, and so ministers are co-workers with God insofar as God joins his Spirit to their word and promises that it shall be beneficial. (2) God "leaves nothing to ministers by themselves." He himself does the work of illumination and renewal. Hence it is "sacrilege for man to claim any part of either for himself" (sec. 6).

## 5. The Distinction of the Visible and Invisible Church

### a. The Invisible Church

Before proceeding, Calvin summarizes his teaching on the invisible and visible church. The invisible church, consisting of "the children of God by grace of adoption," includes "all the elect from the beginning of the world" (sec. 7).

### b. The Visible Church

Scripture also uses the term "church" for all who "profess to worship one God and Christ." These include both the elect and also many "who have of Christ but the name and outward appearance." Communion is to be kept with this church (sec. 7).

### c. The Distinction

While disciplinary steps should be taken to expel notorious and obstinate offenders, Calvin sees no possibility of achieving a pure church, that is, an equation of the invisible church and the visible. "God's eyes alone see the ones who are unfeignedly holy." For us he has ordained "a certain charitable judgment whereby we recognize as members of the church those who by confession of faith, by example of life, and by partaking of the sacraments, profess the same God and Christ" (sec. 8).

## 6. Marks of the Church

Following the Lutheran tradition, Calvin refers to two marks that distinguish the face of the church: the pure preaching and hearing of God's Word, and the administering of the sacraments as Christ instituted them. Although discipline is important to Calvin, he does not add it as a third mark of the church. Even those who seem to be unworthy members may be accepted "because of the common agreement . . . by which they are borne and tolerated in the body of Christ." Churches may be recognized if they have and honor the ministry of the Word and the administration of the sacraments (sec. 9).

## 7. Avoidance of Schism

Like Bullinger, Calvin does not think there is any justification for leaving a church that "cherishes the true ministry of Word and sacrament." Unwarranted separation is indeed castigated as "the denial of God and Christ." Disagreement on non-essential doctrines provides no excuse. We all suffer from some measure of ignorance, and so we must "condone delusion on those matters which can go unknown without harm to the sum of religion and without loss of salvation" (sec. 12). Similarly, imperfection of life is no reason for schism. If discipline should be exercised, we should not neglect kindness where the Lord requires it (sec. 13). The Corinthians were guilty of many offenses, but the church abode among them because the ministry of Word and sacrament was not repudiated (sec. 14). "If we are not willing to admit a church unless it be perfect in every respect, we leave no church at all" (sec. 17). Forgiveness does not end with entry into the church. God has called us to eternal salvation, and so "sins have been and are daily pardoned to us" through God's generosity mediated by Christ's merit and the sanctification of the Spirit (sec. 21).

### 8. Delinquent Churches

Even when churches are filled with heinous sins, they are not "debarred from the Lord's mercy," for the covenant of God "remains and shall ever remain inviolable" (sec. 27). If, however, the sum of necessary doctrines is overturned and the use of the sacraments destroyed, the death of the church follows (iv.2.1). Insofar as this has happened in the Roman church, separation from it is not schism (iv.2.2–5). Nevertheless, Rome is not completely dead. Traces of the true church survive among the papists (sec. 11). If they cannot be given the title of the church, "we do not for this reason impugn the existence of churches among them." In these churches "Christ lies hidden." "The Lord wonderfully preserves in them a remnant of his people." "Some marks of the church remain" even if congregations and the whole body "lack the lawful form of the church" (sec. 12).

Whether or not the papal churches can be restored Calvin does not say. In view of the inviolability of the covenant and the reforming of so many churches in his own time, he would seem to accept this possibility. Nevertheless, the Roman primacy would have to go, since in Calvin's view it substituted a false headship for the true headship of Christ. Furthermore, although the churches under Roman headship might be renewed and reformed, the church of Rome could hardly be coextensive with the worldwide church. In this respect reformation would have to mean complete reversal. Authentic ministry of Word and sacrament is a wholly adequate mark of the churches. The church as a whole, however, must have its foundation in the apostolic word (iv.2.4) and its unity in the headship of Christ (iv.2.6). Papal overlordship and a centralized Roman communion are thus ruled out in principle.

# CHAPTER XIX
# *Baptism and Anabaptism*

## A. LUTHER AND BAPTISM

### 1. Introduction

From the very first Luther was engaged in thinking out the relation of salvation to baptism. Medieval theology had understood the justification of infants to be by baptism. The problems of the Christian life arise with postbaptismal sin. But how does this tie in with justification by faith in the remission of sins through Christ and his atoning work? An early insight of Luther is that baptism, with its demand for repentance and faith and its promise of forgiveness and renewal, has to have significance for the whole life of the Christian. An accompanying insight is that it has to be constantly and consistently related to the vicarious work of Christ. These are the concerns which dominate his discussions of baptism in the early Roman lectures and the powerful treatise on baptism in 1519.

### 2. The Roman Lectures

*a. Baptism and Christ*

In the Romans lectures Luther has occasion to discuss baptism in the scholia on Romans 6. With its statement that we are baptized into Christ's death, the text posits a close relation between baptism and Christ. Augustine is quoted approvingly in this regard: "For our twofold death the Savior pays with his single death, and in order to achieve a twofold resurrection he has set before us and offered us his own single resurrection. This is a sacrament and example, . . . for in this flesh he became a sacrament for the inner man and an example for the outward man" (*De trin*. 4.3). Paul is understood "to be speaking of the death and resurrection of Christ insofar as they refer to the sacrament" (*LW* 25, pp. 309–310).

### b. Baptism and Death

Analyzing death, Luther perceives two kinds, natural (or temporal) death and eternal death. He defines the temporal death as the separation of soul and body but observes that it is "only a figure and symbol" compared to eternal or spiritual death.

Eternal death is a good death in the sense that it is the death of death and the death of sin, that is, the separation of the soul and body from sin and corruption. This death is definitive. Sin and the sinner die for good and all through the one death of Christ. The devil brought in sin and death. God himself brought in the death of death and the sin of sin to remove what was brought in by the devil.

Eternal death can also be very terrible when it is the death of the damned; sin and the sinner do not die while man is saved, but rather, "man dies while sin lives on and continues for ever" (p. 311). In this death, then, there is no death of death, which is life, nor sin of sin, which is transgression of the law of sin, that is, righteousness. There is no escape from death by entry into a life without death.

### c. Baptism and Life

By death and burial with Christ the believer withdraws from worldly things and is dead to them. But this is not achieved all at once. As Luther notes, we are baptized "into death." At baptism we begin to live in such a way as to pursue this kind of death. Life as the goal is not fully possessed. Under the direction of baptism we have to go to death and move through this death to life (p. 312).

### d. Three Responses to Baptism

Luther traces three different responses to the baptismal direction. (1) Some people refuse to die. (2) Some endure it but only with great difficulty and complaint. (3) Some enter upon this death with joy, as Christ himself did (p. 312).

### e. Baptism and Repentance

Since the movement through death to life continues throughout the Christian life, baptism works itself out in terms of ongoing repentance. For Luther, repentance is the movement from unrighteousness (the *terminus a quo*) to righteousness (the *terminus ad quem*). Always repentant, we are still always sinners — but justified sinners. We are in part sinners and in part righteous, that is, penitents. The ungodly, too, are in part righteous and in part sinners, but they are moving the other way. "No one is so good that he does not become better, and no one so evil that he does not become worse, until at last we come to our final state," "which will be either heaven or hell" (pp. 434–435).

### 3. The Holy and Blessed Sacrament of Baptism

*a. Word and Definition*

In his treatise on baptism, "The Holy and Blessed Sacrament of Baptism," Luther recognizes that the word *baptismos* means plunging in water. Immersion, then, is the proper mode of baptism. It expresses most vividly the drowning of the old man. Baptism is defined as "an external sign and token" marking off Christians from others as "a people of Christ, our Leader, under whose banner of the holy cross we continually fight against sin" (*LW* 35, par. 2).

*b. Three Aspects to Be Considered*

(1) Sign. The sign consists of thrusting into and drawing out of the water in the Triune name. "The sign must thus have both its parts, the putting in and the drawing out" (par. 2).

(2) Signification. Dying to sin and rising again in God's grace are the meaning of baptism. The thought of washing accompanies that of death to sin, and the thought of the new birth accompanies that of resurrection. "Sins are drowned in baptism, and in place of sin, righteousness comes forth." Yet the death "is not fulfilled completely in this life." Completion will come only with physical death. The Christian life, then, is a spiritual baptism, an ongoing death to the sinful nature with all its sin, "the beginning of a blessed death." Similarly the resurrection begins in baptism but comes to completion only with the resurrection of the dead and the life everlasting. In the last day "we shall be truly lifted up out of baptism and completely reborn, the angels raising us up then as our sponsors receive us now" (pars. 4-5).

(3) Type. As in the flood the wicked world was drowned, so in baptism are our sins; as Noah and his family were saved in the ark, so are we through baptism. In contrast to the flood of judgment, however, baptism is a flood of grace. Those drowned in this flood are saved through it (par. 6).

*c. The Last Day*

From one angle, baptism denotes purity and freedom from sin. From another, sin continues, for the flesh is "by nature wicked and sinful" and will remain so until "God thrusts us into the earth again by death and makes us over at the last day." How is this to be explained? Luther finds in baptism a sign of final death and resurrection. Thus in our baptism we are already dead and raised again in sign and signification, but "the work of the sacrament has not yet been fully done, which is to say that death and the resurrection at the last day are still before us" (par. 7).

*d. Benefit*

Is baptism any help? Yes, for "in it God allies himself with you and becomes one with you in a gracious covenant of comfort." Baptism represents a desire for death and renewal. God accepts this, and from baptism "begins to make you a new person." Again, baptism is a pledge to continue in that desire and God accepts this, too, subjecting his people to tests and sufferings in order to free them from sin and make them new in a fulfillment of their baptism (par. 9).

### e. Justification

If the pledge of mortification is fulfilled by us, God "pledges himself not to impute the sins which remain in our nature after baptism" (par. 10). Apart from this covenant the smallest sin would condemn us. Baptism brings us under a judgment of mercy which does not condemn our sins but drives them out. When evil desires come, they can be a gracious admonition to remember our baptism, to call on God's mercy, to strive against sin, and even "to welcome death in order that we may be rid of sin" (p. 11).

### f. Faith

Faith means firmly believing that baptism not only signifies death and resurrection but "assuredly begins to achieve this," setting up a covenant in which we fight and slay sin and God deals graciously with us. The baptized person can be called pure because "he has started to become pure and has a sign and covenant of this purity . . . and God will not count his impurity against him." This faith is "the ground of all comfort." Even though we sin, we can set our baptism "high against all sins and terrors of conscience." "I am baptized" can be our confident reply to the admission: "I cannot do a single thing that is pure." For through baptism God "has bound himself in a covenant with me. He will not count my sin against me, but will slay it and blot it out" (par. 12).

### g. False Confidence

In contrast to faith we must avoid the false confidence that baptism makes us wholly pure, for this will lead to persistence in sin and the nullifying of baptism (par. 13). To be avoided, too, is the false confidence that satisfaction can be made for postbaptismal sin. This disregards baptism, misses its ongoing force, and leads to uncertainty how we stand with God. When sin is committed, true faith recalls and relies on the baptismal covenant and rejoices in the mercy of God (par. 14). When faith is strong, the hindrance which sin poses to the operation of baptism is removed. Lack of faith, however, cancels the operation of baptism. "Thus everything depends on faith."

### h. Operation

The operation of baptism covers forgiveness first, through God's promised non-imputation. It then covers the putting to death of sin.

This takes place through our own fight against sin but also through suffering and death (par. 15). Baptism makes these "profitable and helpful." They serve baptism in the doing of its work, the slaying of sin. "Sin does not like to die." Hence death is bitter and horrible. But God in his mercy and power drives out sin by its own work, that is, death. There is no other way. An easy life brings love of this life and horror of eternal life. Through suffering, the work of baptism, one learns "to die with gladness, to get rid of sin, and to live in harmony with baptism" (par. 16). External works may be done so long as they achieve the end of baptism (par. 17). All vows are subordinate to the supreme vow of baptism, so that the estate should be followed, celibate or married, which can best fulfill baptism (par. 18). Always the work of baptism is the norm and meaning of the Christian life for all Christians.

### i. False Security

Luther closes with another warning. Faith in the baptismal covenant brings joy and certainty instead of uncertainty and false comfort (par. 19). Nevertheless, there can be false security as well as false confidence. This shows itself in the idea that one can sin lightly or postpone the putting to death of sin until later in life. If God is mocked in this way the final trial may be so great that faith can no longer stand. Walking with fear must go hand in hand with a firm faith if the riches of God's grace are to be held secure (par. 20).

### j. Observations

The whole essay on baptism is marked by the originality and force which characterize Luther at his best. The relating of baptism to the covenant should be noted; it offers a basis for the later Reformed presentation. The emphasis on baptism's lifelong significance, and its connection with sanctification and suffering, call for attention too; Luther sounds a note here that the Anabaptists will echo and intensify. The ethical and eschatological implications of baptism give coherence to the whole understanding, while the theme of mortification constitutes a solid foundation for the theology of suffering and death and the associated pastoral practice. Justification, which might seem to be menaced by infant baptism, fits appropriately into Luther's interpretation by reason of the extension of baptism to the whole life of the Christian. This also corrects the aberrations of later medieval belief and its accompanying round of religious duties. Two omissions are surprising. Luther does not here relate baptism too well to the victorious death and resurrection of Christ. Neither does he have a very adequate section on renewal to correspond to the fine handling of mortification. Nevertheless, the points he makes are valid and he makes them well. One can only regret that the pedobaptist controversy was so quickly to dominate and even distort baptismal thinking when so promising a beginning had been made of a new, profound, and constructive understanding.

## B. THE ANABAPTISTS AND BAPTISM

### 1. Blaurock

#### a. The Negative Side

Anabaptism has a negative side which tends to claim attention first. It involves the rejection of infant baptism. Blaurock, in his *Beginnings of the Anabaptist Reformation,* gives two basic reasons for this. (1) It does not derive from scripture (*Library of Christian Classics* 25, pp. 41–42). (2) It is an invention of the papacy. It ought thus to be discontinued in the same way as the mass or all the practices associated with purgatory.

#### b. The Positive Side

Like all his colleagues, however, Blaurock was more concerned about the positive aspects of Anabaptism. Luther and Zwingli, he thought, had begun well. They had failed by clinging to pedobaptism. But "God wished to have his own people, separated from all peoples" (p. 42). To this end he brought in "the right true morning star of his truth to shine in fullness in the final age of this world." He did it in the form of the Swiss awakening centered on Grebel, Mantz, and Blaurock himself. Essential to this movement were four things: (1) a true faith manifested in love; (2) service of God in all godliness; (3) steadfastness in tribulation; and (4) "true Christian baptism on the basis of recognized and confessed faith" (p. 43). From the very outset, the restoration of baptism formed an integral part of the separation of God's people and the reconstitution of the church.

### 2. Grebel

#### a. Meaning of Baptism

Grebel, an early supporter of Zwingli in Zurich, worked out the significance of baptism in his famous letter to the peasant leader Thomas Müntzer, dated September 5, 1524. Why baptism is so important may be seen from the way in which its meaning covers the essential elements in Anabaptist faith and discipleship. (It might be noted in passing how closely the meaning discerned agrees with Luther's exposition in the little treatise on baptism.)

Grebel concentrates on four aspects. (1) Baptism signifies the washing away of sin by faith and Christ's blood. (2) It denotes a change of mind to faith. (3) It signifies death to sin. (4) It signifies that a man "walks in newness of life and spirit and that he shall certainly be saved if . . . by inner baptism he lives in faith" (*LCC* 25, p. 80).

#### b. Limitations of Baptism

For Grebel, baptism has no independent efficacy. (1) It does not "confirm or increase faith." (2) It does not give great comfort, nor is it "a final refuge on the deathbed" (p. 80). (3) It certainly does not save. Belief that it does dishonors "faith and the suffering of Christ in the case of the old and adult" and dishonors "the suffering of Christ in the case of the unbaptized infants" (p. 81). Outward baptism has significatory value only. What finally counts is the inner baptism signified by it.

### c. Infant Salvation

Infants cannot have the inner baptism which is by faith. Thus infant baptism is "a senseless, blasphemous abomination" which even under the papacy, Grebel thinks, was not practiced for the first six centuries. If, however, infants are by their age excluded from inner baptism, does this mean that they cannot be saved? Grebel believes not. Since "they have not yet come to the discernment of the knowledge of good and evil . . . they are surely saved by the suffering of Christ, the new Adam . . . unless, indeed, it can be proved that Christ did not suffer for children" (p. 81). But is not faith necessary to salvation? In adults, yes, but "we exclude children from this and hold that they are saved without faith" (p. 81). What happens when infants grow to maturity Grebel does not say. At some point they presumably lose their infant salvation and then have to come to faith in order to be saved as adults.

### 3. Simons

#### a. The Baptismal Command

Of the many works in which Menno Simons argued against infant baptism, his *Foundations of Christian Doctrine* might be taken as a typical example. The starting point here, as so often, is the wording of the great commission, which puts preaching or teaching before baptism. Since one cannot preach to infants or teach them, logic demands that they should not be baptized. The chronology of the institution had for Anabaptists the same kind of importance as "this is my body" had in another sphere for Luther.

#### b. Baptism and Circumcision

Against the appeal to circumcision Simons makes two points. First, Jesus was circumcised as an infant but was then baptized as an adult, not as an infant. Second, circumcision, in contrast to baptism, is limited to boys. Simons adds that even if the children of believers were to be baptized, this would put an end to wholesale baptisms, since true as distinct from nominal believers are few in number.

#### c. Baptism, Death, and Resurrection

From the meaning of baptism Simons deduces its unsuitability for children. In baptism we are to die to sin and be buried with Christ. Infants cannot do this, for sin is not in them. Regeneration follows, but this is an inner work which outward washing does not accomplish and which requires the hearing of the word and faith. Inner baptism, which infants cannot have, must always precede outward baptism. The latter serves as evidence of the obedience which comes with faith. None of this makes any sense in the case of infants.

### d. Baptism and Grace

Simons naturally does not believe that baptism confers grace. He goes further, however, and denies that it is a sign of grace. Christ alone, prefigured in the Old Testament, is a sign of grace. Baptism signifies what takes place in us, or even what we do. It is a sign of obedience. When we believe, we show this by obeying the baptismal command. We thereby pledge ourselves to discipleship. The work in us, not the work for us, constitutes the thing signified in baptism. Since this work does not take place in infants, baptism does not apply to them.

### e. Baptism and Faith

Simons, like Grebel, accepts the salvation of infants. He bases this on their membership in the covenant of grace. He denies, however, that they are saved by faith. Infants cannot have faith. Nor can baptism be given them with a view to their future instruction in the faith. To Luther's argument that consciousness is not necessary to faith, since adults do not lose it when they fall asleep, he gives the witty answer that we do not baptize adults when they are asleep. This does not affect, however, the deeper issues whether infants are saved in some other way than by faith and whether baptism is primarily a sign of faith. Simons for his part affirms both that infants are saved without faith and also that baptism is a sign of faith. He thus rejects infant baptism as erroneous and meaningless.

### f. Infant Baptism

How, then, did infant baptism arise? Simons presses the point that no command to baptize infants can be found in scripture. More cautiously than Grebel, he also finds no precedent for it in the first four (rather than six) centuries of Christian history. As he reads the situation, infant baptism, like so many evils, was introduced by the papacy, the culprit being Pope Innocent in 407. As a human invention, infant baptism ought to be ended along with other corruptions. Its discontinuation is part of the necessary reformation of the church. As such it is also part of the restoration or reconstitution of the separated and suffering church of the New Testament and the pre-Constantinian period.

## C. ZWINGLI AND BAPTISM

### 1. Introduction

Anabaptist pressures forced Zwingli into a thorough examination of baptism. At first he was inclined to agree that since justification is by faith, baptism has meaning only when it signifies the faith professed by adults. Yet the ecclesiological implications of this view, and to some extent the practical consequences, restrained him from full commitment to it. Then a fuller investigation of both Old and New Testament scripture yielded some important insights which made him a staunch theological and ecclesiastical opponent of his former friends and supporters who adopted Anabaptism. These insights find expression in his popular work *Of Baptism,* written in 1525.

### 2. Role of the Sacraments

Zwingli begins this work with three general points. a. Outward things cannot accomplish inward results: "Only Jesus Christ and no external thing can take away sins" (*Library of Christian Classics* 24, (p. 131). b. Sacraments are a concession to our frailty. c. The sacraments of the Old Testament (circumcision and the Passover) correspond to those of the New (baptism and the Lord's Supper), the reason for the change being that after Christ's blood was shed once and for all, the prophetically bloody signs were appropriately replaced by apostolically unbloody ones.

### 3. The Covenant

An important aspect of the sacrament for Zwingli is that it is a covenant sign. He does not develop this for the moment. He will do so in later writings. He insists, however, that the sacrament is a covenant pledge, seen here more from the standpoint of commitment than of promise. The baptized person is pledged to Jesus Christ. The sign testifies that he is "resolved to hear what God says to him, to learn the divine precepts, and to live his life in accordance with them" (p. 131). Baptism also testifies to the historical realities of Christ's death and resurrection in which this commitment is grounded. Zwingli brings this out in his later *Exposition of the Faith.* For the moment, however, his stress is on the pledge, as when he says that circumcision is "a covenant sign between God and the seed of Abraham" (p. 138).

An interesting point is that in *Of Baptism* Zwingli agrees with Grebel that baptism does not even confirm faith. He categorically calls this idea a mistake. "It is not possible for an external thing to confirm faith" (p. 138). Yet he seems almost at once to realize that this is overstated, for he concedes that miracles can be given to confirm faith (p. 139). He finally shifts his position in *Exposition of the Faith,* where the sixth note of the sacraments is that they "augment faith and are an aid to it," or that they "support and strengthen faith" by bringing the senses under its obedience. Even here, however, he thinks that this applies more particularly to the Lord's Supper than to baptism (*LCC* 24, p. 263).

The pledge aspect ties in closely with Luther's concept of the significance of baptism for the Christian life. As Zwingli puts it, immersion in the water signifies death, "that as Christ was dead and buried, so we too die to the world." Re-emergence from the water then denotes Christ's resurrection, that "as he rose again to die no more, we too have a new life in Christ" (p. 151). Our outward baptism, Paul says, shows us that we have died to the old man and now walk in newness of life. A "friendly exhortation is thus given to the Christian life." The rooting of mortification and renewal in Christ's death and resurrection comes out very clearly here. The covenant as pledge rests ultimately on the covenant as promise.

### 4. Threefold Baptism

#### a. The Three Senses

More significant even than the covenant reference is Zwingli's analysis of the concept of baptism in biblical usage. He first attempts a fourfold distinction, but in practice his fourth sense is a general one which combines the others. Thus three senses are in fact discerned. Baptism in its full signification covers all three, but the word may also be used for any one, or for a combination of two senses.

#### b. Water Baptism

The word "baptism" first denotes "the immersion in water whereby we are pledged individually to the Christian life." John's baptizing in Aenon offers a clear biblical example of this use (p. 133).

#### c. Spirit Baptism

The term can also denote "inward enlightenment and calling when we know God and cleave to him — that is, the baptism of the Spirit." The saying of Christ in Acts 1 speaks of this baptism. Only God can give it. Hence it lies outside the pedobaptist dispute, which is a dispute only "about water baptism and [external] teaching" (p. 133).

#### d. Teaching Baptism

The term can denote finally the external teaching of salvation which accompanies water baptism. The facts themselves make this plain, for John teaches when he baptizes. Indeed, when Christ asks whether John's baptism is from heaven or men, the whole ministry of John is in view, his teaching more so, perhaps, than his baptizing in water.

### e. Implications

Basic to Zwingli's understanding are two points. (1) The three baptisms can be given separately, water baptism without teaching or the Spirit, teaching baptism without water or the Spirit, Spirit baptism without water or teaching (p. 135). Full baptism, of course, embraces all three, but they will not always be, and do not have to be, concurrent. The penitent thief has Spirit baptism, perhaps teaching, but not water. The Jews in Acts 18 have teaching but not water or Spirit. The order varies. Spirit baptism can come first or last. Water and teaching baptism do not have to be given in a fixed sequence.

(2) The baptism that finally counts is that of the Spirit. No salvation lies in external baptism, whether of water or of teaching. To cover himself, Zwingli allows that Spirit baptism has an outward side too, the gift of tongues, but this "is given infrequently and only to a few," nor is it necessary to salvation. The inner baptism of the Spirit, which is the work of inner teaching and calling, is the baptism which alone can save, because it alone confers faith. "This baptism none can give save God alone" (p. 137).

## 5. Conclusions

Zwingli draws from his analysis six conclusions. (a) Water baptism signifies initiation to the life of faith and discipleship (p. 141). (b) It carries with it, either before or after, the baptism of teaching, of instruction in the new life to which the baptized are pledged (pp. 141–148). (c) Since the apostles as well as the Baptist can give only the baptism of water and external teaching, their baptism is one and the same (pp. 149–150). (d) The Baptist and the apostles cannot suspend their baptism on the inner baptism of the Spirit, for "none but God alone can baptize inwardly" (p. 149). (e) God may baptize inwardly either before, during, or after baptism of water or of teaching, so that the baptisms do not have to be concurrent. (f) It cannot be ruled out that infants, too, can have the inner baptism of the Spirit, so that water baptism can be given and teaching baptism will follow in due course if the infant grows to a suitable age. If objection is raised to this, Zwingli replies: "For my part, I allow God to work how and when he wills" (p.149).

## 6. Omissions

Two surprising omissions may be noted in Zwingli's treatment. (a) He makes no clear provision for the functioning of external baptism, whether of water or even teaching, as a means of inner grace. The sign seems to be disjoined from the thing signified even if it is rightly perceived that baptism in the full sense embraces both. (b) More particularly, Zwingli does not seem to do justice here to the work of the Word, which one would have expected him to relate to external teaching. The Word inwardly understood and believed (p. 154) plays an important role, but again in disjunction from the outer form. The underlying problem seems to be the extreme spiritualizing in which the external and the internal are almost fully separated, even though both are integral to baptism in its full New Testament sense.

Zwingli, of course, made good these omissions, to some extent at least, in his later *Exposition of the Faith*. Here sacraments are said to be signs representing the things signified and thereby mobilizing the senses in the service of faith (pp. 262–265). They can even give historical faith, although the Spirit alone can give the faith which is trust in God (p. 260). The Word comes through reading scripture, but this gives inner instruction only as the Spirit enables us to understand it. Baptism as external teaching need not predate the inner work of the Spirit, but neither can it be divorced from it except in the case of those who die in infancy. Zwingli seems to be feeling his way almost to a baptismal perichoresis of water, teaching, and Spirit, although necessarily without the equality of the three members which marks the trinitarian perichoresis.

## D. CALVIN AND INFANT BAPTISM

### 1. Introduction

In baptismal doctrine Calvin makes no very distinctive contribution. More or less all that he says is also said by others. Yet here as elsewhere he elaborates certain points, achieves a notable comprehensiveness, and adds the touch of elegance which distinguishes all his work. With some truth, then, he may be said to have made the definitive Reformation statement. This is especially true in relation to the baptism of infants. It is to *Institutes* iv.16, then, that we finally turn for an impressive discussion of this aspect of the doctrine.

### 2. Meaning of Baptism

Calvin opens the chapter by recalling the twofold significance of baptism. First, it denotes "the cleansing of our sins, which we obtain from Christ's blood," and second, it denotes "the mortification of our flesh, which rests upon participation in his death." A subsidiary point is that baptism is "a symbol for bearing witness to our religion before men" (sec. 2).

### 3. Baptism and Circumcision

Calvin finds an "anagogic relationship" between the Old Testament sign of circumcision and the New Testament sign of baptism. The obvious differences are in externals only. Materially the signs are one and the same; they are one in promise (God's fatherly favor), in the thing represented (forgiveness), and in foundation (sec. 4). The giving of circumcision to children shows plainly that the covenant promises pertain no less to them than to their parents. Since the covenant does not change (only the outer observance has changed) it obviously applies to Christian children, too. "Why then," asks Calvin, "shall they be debarred from the sign?" (secs. 5–6).

### 4. Christ and Infants

The inclusion of infants in the covenant blessing is supported by Christ's embracing and blessing of infants. He does not baptize them, but he asks that they be brought to him, says that the kingdom belongs to them, and "commends them with his prayer and blessing to his Father." In Christ's estimation they thus enjoy what baptism signifies, and to Calvin it makes no sense that they should be denied the sign (sec. 7). Even if scripture does not specifically record an infant baptism, this carries no more weight than does the lack of any reference to a woman taking communion. The rule of faith which shows that women should partake of the supper shows also that infants should be baptized, for the purpose for which baptism was instituted applies no less to infants than to older persons. The suggestion that the early church did not baptize infants arouses the scorn of Calvin, who can think of "no author, however ancient, who does not regard its origin in the apostolic age as a certainty" (sec. 8).

### 5. Blessings of Infant Baptism

In a brief section Calvin lists three blessings of infant baptism. a. The parents receive from it assurance of the promise that God's mercy extends to their children, too. b. It commends the children to the other members of the church. c. Later it spurs them to an earnest zeal for God. As Calvin sees it, the sign itself also carries with it a warning of divine judgment on those who refuse the proffered grace by despising the sign (sec. 9).

### 6. Anabaptists and the Covenant

In reply to Anabaptist arguments against the covenant thesis Calvin repeats many of the points already made in relation to the unity and distinction of the Testaments. He insists that the meaning of the covenant does not change with the new dispensation (sec. 10). He cannot agree that the promises of the Old Testament are essentially material and not spiritual (sec. 11). Nor can he accept a clear-cut distinction between God's physical children under the old order and his spiritual children under the new order (sec. 12). Abraham is in fact the father of all believers, whether in circumcision or in uncircumcision (sec. 13). He points out that in Paul's teaching, while not all Israelites are true children of Abraham, "the covenant which God had made with the descendants of Abraham could not be made void." "For the sake of the gospel God's blessing still rests among them" (sec. 14). The promise to Israel is not fulfilled allegorically but is still to be fulfilled literally. It is thus erroneous to look for a spiritualizing in which a carnal promise becomes a spiritual promise and physical infants symbolize newborn babes in Christ (sec. 15).

### 7. Infants and Faith

Responding to the argument that infants cannot have faith, Calvin develops a series of related theses. Infants cannot be viewed simply as children of Adam, for "in Adam we can but die." Even if we cannot understand it, we have to say that "those infants who are to be saved . . . are previously regenerated by the Lord and justified" (sec. 17). The examples of John the Baptist, and especially of our Lord himself, show that the work of the Holy Spirit can commence with the very inception of human life (secs. 17–18). While preaching is indeed the ordinary means of grace, God also gives "true knowledge of himself by inward means, that is, by the illumination of the Spirit apart from the medium of preaching" (sec. 19). Infants are certainly incapable of repentance and faith. Yet circumcision is a sign of repentance and a seal of the righteousness of faith and by the command of God it is given to infants. The seed of repentance and faith lies in infants "by the secret working of the Spirit," and they are "baptized into future repentance and faith" when these are formed in them (sec. 20). Elect children who die in infancy God "renews by the power incomprehensible to us, of his Spirit," while those who grow up will grow into the fulfillment of what their baptism signifies (sec. 21). Circumcision shows us clearly how mistaken it is to think that what is signified ought always to precede the sign in order of time (sec. 21). The point of the sign is indeed to give assurance of the thing signified, so that if the hope of God's mercy extends to children, it is against all sense to deny them the sign (sec. 22). Since salvation is by the thing signified, not the sign, unbaptized children must not be regarded as consigned to eternal death. Although baptism is not to be despised, for Christ commanded it, in no sense is it to be thought of as absolutely necessary (sec. 26).

### 8. Infants and the Lord's Supper

The objection that infants should no more be given baptism than the bread and wine of communion elicits three replies from Calvin. (a) The sign of new birth is proper for infants, in contrast to that of solid sustenance. (b) Self-examination is specifically required for participation in the supper. (c) Circumcision is for infants but the Passover is for those "old enough to be able to inquire into its meaning"; so, too, with baptism and the supper (sec. 30).

### 9. Answers to Servetus

Calvin concludes his discussion with answers to twenty detailed objections of Servetus. These need not detain us, but two points emerge with clarity from the debate. (a) Calvin consistently views baptism as a sacrament of grace and promise, so that he can speak of infants as those "whom God consecrates to himself by free adoption" (sec. 31, objection 7), or as those "whom he vouchsafed to embrace" (sec. 31, objection 9). (b) God himself is for Calvin the one who effects regeneration and brings us to faith, repentance, and renewal. Those to whom the gospel first comes in adulthood will be regenerated by the gospel (see sec. 24 on Abraham), but "when we are not old enough to be taught" (see sec. 24 on Isaac) "God keeps his own timetable of regeneration" (sec. 31, objection 16). Calvin's final note, then, is appropriately that of the sweet assurance of knowing that God cares for our children and of the strong stimulus to give evangelical instruction stemming from our grateful recognition that "immediately from birth God takes and acknowledges them as his children" (sec. 32).

# CHAPTER XX
# *Eucharistic Debates*

## A. MEDIEVAL AND TRIDENTINE TEACHING

### 1. Early Developments

The Corbie debate on Christ's presence in the elements resulted eventually in a victory for Radbert's more realistic understanding. Berengarius of Tours attempted in the eleventh century a restatement of the teaching of Erigena and Ratramn, but under attack from Lanfranc he was forced to assert in 1059 that the bread and wine are "the true body and blood of our Lord Jesus Christ and that these are sensibly handled and broken by the hands of the priests and crushed by the teeth of the faithful." A second admission in 1079 did not go so far but still referred to a substantial change. Lombard favored this, even though he saw the problems and rejected the concept of Christ's body being broken with the breaking of the bread. The Fourth Lateran Council of 1215 summed up developments up to this point with its decree that "the body and blood are truly contained in the sacrament of the altar under the species of bread and wine, the bread being transubstantiated into the body and the wine into the blood by the power of God."

### 2. Aquinas

With the new tool of Aristotelian philosophy, Aquinas gave greater precision to the teaching of Lateran IV. He raised many questions which might seem to be pettifogging but which helped to formulate the doctrine resisted by the reformers and adopted as definitive at Trent. Under Part 3, Q. 75, Art. 2 of the *Summa* he asks whether the substance of bread and wine remains after consecration and replies that since the body and blood of Christ can be present only by conversion, it does not. If it is then asked, however, whether the substance of bread and wine is annihilated (Art. 3), the reply is that this would rule out conversion and is thus impossible. Whether this type of conversion can take place (Art. 4) is decided by divine omnipotence. This conversion differs from all others. It is supernatural and is effected "only by the power of God." The conversion applies to the substance but not to the so-called accidents, that is, the sensory properties. Good reasons are seen for this. Conversion of the accidents would make partaking abhorrent, rouse the scorn of infidels, and make no demand for faith (Art. 5). Aquinas resists the notion that Christ is locally in the sacrament, since he is present by way of substance, not of spatial dimension (Art. 6). Since the old accidents are not appropriate to the new substance, they remain with no subject, being kept by God's infinite power (Q. 77, Art. 1). Their spatial dimension, being divinely given the power to exist in itself, can be the subject of other accidents.

### 3. Trent

#### a. Opposition

Through the later Middle Ages various groups resisted the official Eucharistic dogma. Thus Wycliffe in 1382 was accused of teaching that the material substance of bread remains and that Christ's body is not in the sacrament essentially or really. The Lollard Conclusions of 1394 refer scathingly to "the pretended miracle of the altar" and describe the service of Corpus Christi as "not true but fictitious and full of false miracles." Discontent came to a head at once with the beginning of the Reformation. The reformers achieved no unanimity in their own understanding, but they all agreed that the medieval view of the presence was mistaken, and they also joined forces in attacking the associated idea of a propitiatory mass, that is, the mass offered as a repetition of Christ's sacrifice in which propitiation is made for the temporal penalties of postbaptismal sin on behalf of both the living and the dead.

#### b. Transubstantiation

In response to these developments the Council of Trent issued two fresh definitions of Eucharistic dogma. The first relates to transubstantiation. At Session 13 in October 1551, four propositions were advanced. (1) Christ stated that under the appearance of bread he offered his body. (2) For this reason the church has always held and the synod declares anew "that through consecration of the bread and wine there comes about a conversion of the whole substance of the bread (and the wine) into the substance of the body (and blood) of our Lord." (3) This conversion is "conveniently and properly called transubstantiation." (4) In virtue of it, the faithful may offer the sacrament "the full worship of adoration" which is due to God.

#### c. Eucharistic Sacrifice

Not until Session 22 in September 1562 did Trent issue its new definition of the Eucharistic sacrifice. Considerable care went into the drafting of this statement. Its contentions are as follows. (1) The same Christ is contained in this bloodless sacrifice as he who "on the altar of the cross once offered himself with the shedding of blood." (2) On this ground the sacrifice is truly propitiatory. (3) To profit from it, we must come with true hearts, right faith, and fear and reverence. (4) If we do, God, propitiated by it, will grant grace, penitence, and remission. (5) The fruits of the primary oblation are perceived most fully through the bloodless oblation. (6) It is offered for the sins, penances, satisfactions, and other necessities of both the faithful living and also the faithful dead in purgatory whose purification is not yet completed. It should be noted that this offering does not replace the cross as a sacrifice for the remission of eternal guilt or salvation from eternal perdition. Furthermore, it has power only as the offering of the same Christ who made the one sacrifice for sins forever. The Tridentine fathers wisely refrain from speaking of the mode of immolation, unlike some contemporary polemicists who equate it with the consuming of the bread and wine by the priest.

## B. ZWINGLI'S POSITION

### 1. Introduction

Unlike Luther, Zwingli moved rapidly away not only from transubstantiation but also from a literal interpretation of "This is my body." Incipient doubts seem to have been reinforced by his reading of early liturgies and canons and his fresh study of scripture and the fathers. In 1524 he gave a brief exposition of his view in his *Commentary on True and False Religion*. He was campaigning at this time for replacement of the mass by a simple thanksgiving service. He published two Latin treatises on the question in 1525. Running into bitter opposition, he decided to appeal to a wider public with a popular exposition in German. Published at speed, it came out early in March 1526 with the simple title *On the Lord's Supper*. This was by no means the end of the matter, for controversy with the Lutherans dragged on until it came to an unseemly head at Marburg in 1529. Much of Zwingli's later appeal to the king of France in *Exposition of the Faith* (1531) is devoted to an attempted clarification and commendation of his Eucharistic doctrine.

### 2. On the Lord's Supper

*a. Outline*

After a brief statement of purpose Zwingli shows clearly what his procedure will be. The work will consist of four articles. The first will discuss misinterpretations of the saying "This is my body." The second will show from scripture and the creed that it cannot bear these interpretations. The third will establish the true sense. The fourth will answer objections.

### b. First Article: Misinterpretations

Zwingli discerns three misinterpretations of the word of institution.

(1) It is taken to imply that we eat Christ's incarnate and crucified body in virtue of transubstantiation.

(2) It is taken to mean that Christ's body is eaten under the bread as in Luther's teaching.

(3) It is taken to mean that by transubstantiation the resurrection body of Christ is eaten.

The problem in each case is threefold.

(1) If an appeal is made to God's power, the saying, spoken by the priest, is not a divine command: "Bread, be thou my body" (*Library of Christian Classics* 24, pp. 189–190).

(2) The senses do not see any change as they do when God really commands and does things (pp. 190–191).

(3) The saying cannot grammatically produce transubstantiation (p. 191).

Canon law apparently recognizes the problem, too, for after giving the recantation of Berengarius, it oddly quotes the saying of Augustine: "What need of teeth and stomach? Believe and thou hast eaten. . . . He who believes in him feeds on him" (p. 197).

### c. Second Article: Scriptural and Creedal Proof

Zwingli now summons the two witnesses of scripture and the creed to show that the saying "This is my body" is not to be taken literally.

(1) Scripture. The chief contribution of scripture is to tell us that Christ has spiritual nourishment in mind. John 6 serves as the main text in this respect (pp. 199ff.). From the discourse here we learn that Christ is received as the bread of life through the Spirit and by faith. Faith is not belief that the bread is the body but the saving faith that Jesus is the Christ, the Savior, the Son of God (pp. 206–207). Augustine, as quoted in canon law, supports this interpretation: "You do not eat the body which you see, . . . I have given you a sacrament which spiritually understood will give you life. . . . His grace is not given by eating" (pp. 208–209). 1 Corinthians 10 provides Zwingli with a second basic text. The point here is that the wilderness generation "partook of the same Christ as we do" (Augustine). Since they obviously did not receive Christ's literal body and blood, their eating was "believing in the one who was to give his flesh and blood to death on their behalf." Similarly, "our eating is believing in the one who has already given his flesh and blood" (pp. 211–212).

(2) Creed. On a biblical basis the creed states plainly that between his ascension and coming again Christ in the body is seated at God's right hand (pp. 212–215). Zwingli, of course, does not dispute Christ's omnipresence according to his divine nature. It is as man, however, that he is incarnate, ascends, and returns. As man, therefore, he is not literally present and eaten in the sacrament. Even at the very moment when Christ says he is with his disciples always, he leaves them. His presence remains, but not in the bodily and perceptible mode in which it will be again at the last day (Acts 1). The argument that the resurrection body enjoys potential ubiquity does not impress Zwingli. The body is where God wills it, namely, at God's right hand. Potentiality and reality are not the same (pp. 217–218). It is indeed the resurrection body that ascends, so that omnipresence is not ascribed to it (p. 219). Moreover, the saying "This is my body" plainly refers to the crucified body. Nor does scripture speak of the resurrection body being in many places at the same time. We must abide, then, by the creedal statement that between the ascension and the coming again Christ is seated at God's right hand.

### d. Third Article: The True Sense

Zwingli now addresses the positive task of giving the proper interpretation of "This is my body" (pp. 222ff.). He first points to the common use of tropes or figures of speech in scripture, such as "the lamb of God." He then tries to show that "This is my body" can be taken in this way. The Passover saying "This is the Lord's passover" supports this view, for "This is my body" was spoken in a Passover context (pp. 225–227). Additional support is provided by the reference to the next drinking of the fruit of the vine (p. 227), the calm reaction of the disciples, and the absence of transubstantiation from their teachings (pp. 227–228). The equation of the cup and the testament in Luke and Paul can hardly be given any but a metaphorical significance (p. 229). Three fathers are quoted by Zwingli to back up his understanding. Jerome says that Jesus "represented and signified the reality of his body and blood" (p. 231). Ambrose speaks to the same effect: "We represent the things which are offered up for us" (pp. 231–233). Augustine points out no less plainly that in the last supper Christ "gave his disciples and bade them observe a representation or sign of his body and blood" (p. 233).

### e. Fourth Article: Reply to Objections.

Zwingli makes short shrift of the argument that those who take his view express themselves differently (pp. 235–236). The saying in 1 Corinthians 10: "The cup of blessing which we bless . . . ," occupies him a little longer. He points out (1) that strictly "to bless" means "to give thanks" or "to praise" and (2) that "communion" means "community." Thus Paul is not saying that we partake of Christ's body and blood but that in offering thanks and taking bread and wine we are the community of Christ's body and blood, the company which "in this sacrament confesses its faith in the Lord Jesus Christ, who gave his body and blood on our behalf" (pp. 236–237). Sayings from the canons favor this exposition (p. 236). At this point Zwingli states abruptly that other objections have no basis in God's Word. He thus brings his work to a rapid conclusion with the affirmation that "either the creed must be shattered, or our teaching is true." He appends the rhyming question of a layperson: "Tell me, if thou know'st, How Father, Son, and Holy Ghost, And bread and wine, and flesh and blood, Can all together be one God?" (p. 238).

### 3. Exposition of the Faith

#### a. The Sacraments

In his *Exposition of the Faith* Zwingli defines the sacraments as "signs and symbols of holy things, but not . . . the things of which they are the signs" (p. 247). They are signs of real things, representing and recalling things which once took place literally and naturally. By the bread and wine "Christ is himself as it were set before our eyes, so that not merely with the ear, but with eye and palate we see and taste that Christ whom the soul bears within itself and in whom it rejoices" (p. 248).

#### b. The Presence

In a special section on the presence Zwingli first repeats that Christ's body "is not eaten naturally and literally, since it is in heaven" (pp. 254–258). He then distinguishes the natures of Christ. By the union the whole Christ is born and laid in the manger, yet the divine nature is obviously not born of the virgin but begotten of the Father. Similarly, the whole Christ both ascends and is present always, but his ascension involved the human nature and his presence involves the divine. Since the human nature has ascended, Christ's body is not eaten naturally and literally, much less quantitatively. It is eaten sacramentally and spiritually (p. 257). To eat spiritually is to trust "with heart and soul upon the mercy and goodness of God through Christ," while to eat sacramentally is "to eat . . . with heart and mind in conjunction with the sacrament." Those who eat without faith may be said improperly to eat sacramentally, but in no sense do they eat spiritually (pp. 259–260).

#### c. The Virtue of the Sacraments

Zwingli adds another section to stress his positive evaluation of the sacraments. The supper has value because it was instituted by Christ, testifies to historical facts, has the name of what it signifies, represents a high thing, and stands in analogy to the thing signified — Christ, our food, and ourselves, the one fellowship (pp. 262–263). It also augments faith (pp. 263–264) even though it cannot give it (p. 260). It does this by claiming the four most important senses, indeed, all of them, for the obedience of faith. We hear, see, taste, touch, and smell in it the goodness of Christ, and as we do so the soul "tastes the sweet savor of heavenly hope." Finally, the sacrament as a pledge binds us together as "one body by the sacramental partaking of his body, for we are one body with him." The saying "This is my body" must be taken as a metonymy, meaning "This is the sacrament of my body," or "This is my sacramental or mystical body — the sacramental and representative symbol of the body which I really assumed and yielded over to death" (p. 265).

## C. THE TEACHING OF LUTHER

### 1. The Early Writings

In his *Blessed Sacrament of the True Body and Blood of Christ* (1519), Luther still seems to accept transubstantiation and the Eucharistic sacrifice, although he appeals strongly for the communion in both kinds forbidden under medieval law. A year later, in his *Treatise on the New Testament*, he plainly rejects the sacrifice and no longer states his view of the presence in terms of transubstantiation. *The Babylonian Captivity,* also published in 1520, goes even further, calling transubstantiation no more than a human opinion. By 1525, however, Luther shows more concern about the teachings of Carlstadt and Zwingli. He opposes the former in *Against the Heavenly Prophets* II (1525) and after a series of minor writings sums up his position against Zwingli in two works, *This is my Body* in 1527 and *Confession Concerning Christ's Supper* in 1528.

### 2. This Is My Body

In the first of these two works Luther deals essentially with the words of institution as the title suggests. His main argument is that (a) the onus of proof rests on those who want a figurative interpretation and (b) this involves considerable grammatical difficulties. He does not think that Christ's presence in heaven poses any problem, for God is not restricted to a local mode of presence. John 6:63, when it says that the flesh profits nothing, is referring to a fleshly mind, not to the body of Christ. Similarly, the spiritual is what is done by the Spirit, whether in relation to mind or body. The Swiss appeal to the fathers is rejected on the ground that the fathers believed the bread is in fact Christ's body, nourishing the body as well as the soul of the believer to eternal life.

*This is My Body* is forcefully and cleverly written. It raises important issues and testifies to Luther's concern for scripture and the gospel. The power and significance of God's word are also stressed, and a place is found for discussion of the benefits of the supper. The work is marred, however, by Luther's coarse and vituperative style. Doubt also remains whether his supposed literal exegesis can stand. Surely for him the proper form of the saying should be: "Under (or with) this is my body." His grammatical analysis creates difficulties for others; it does not finally establish his own view.

### 3. Confessions Concerning Christ's Supper

*a. Occasion and Purpose*

A reply to *This Is My Body* reached Wittenberg in 1527. Luther immediately undertook a counterreply and had it in press by February 1528. He had three purposes in view. (1) He wanted to warn his readers of the inadequacy of the Swiss arguments. (2) He planned to give a fresh analysis of the crucial passages. (3) He desired to give a brief confession of all the articles of his faith. The three divisions of the work correspond to the three purposes.

*b. Warning*

(1) Zwingli. Much of Luther's warning is against the various errors which he discerns in Zwingli.

(a) Interpretation. While defending his own "under" (or "in") as legitimate exposition, Luther rejects the inconsistent figurative views of his opponents (*LW* 37, pp. 164ff.). His main point is that a metaphor involves a new use of terms, not a change in the meaning of "is" to "represents" (pp. 170ff.). He rejects Zwingli's distinction between words of promise or command and narrative words of action because a command follows the word of institution (pp. 180ff.). Zwingli's category of alloeosis (the reference to one nature in terms of another) does not help, for it is unprovable and in view of God's power to accomplish a literal fulfillment it is in fact unnecessary (pp. 206ff.).

(b) Presence in Heaven. Much of Zwingli's case rests, as we have seen, on Christ's presence in heaven according to scripture and the creeds. For Luther, however, this has no cogency. To be present, Christ does not have to be visibly present (pp. 178–179). He is not in heaven at the first supper, and this cannot be distinguished from later ones (pp. 190–192). Christ died once, but forgiveness is constantly distributed by participation in his body (pp. 192–193). God's right hand is not itself local but omnipresent (pp. 206ff.). Christ's body is not present in the same mode as during the incarnation; the resurrection appearances show that even bodily he can be truly present in other modes (pp. 196–197).

(c) Christology. By introducing alloeosis Zwingli is betrayed into a confusing Nestorianism. This destroys the atonement, for it means that when we read that they crucified the Lord of glory, they simply put the man Jesus to death. Deity cannot perish; yet deity did in fact die when the man Jesus died, not by alloeosis, but by hypostatic union. Jesus died, "but this person is truly God, and therefore it is correct to say: the Son of God suffers" (p. 210). Alloeosis does not harmonize with the one person and two natures. It implies two persons (pp. 212–213).

(d) Modes of Presence. Zwingli errs by positing only a single mode of presence. Luther accepts a local mode, a definitive and uncircumscribed mode, and a repletive mode, as in the case of God's ubiquity. Christ can be present locally. He can also be present definitively, as after the resurrection. His deity means that he is also present repletively, and, since he is one person, this applies to Christ as man as well as to Christ as God. This may be hard to understand, but only by faith can we understand his resurrection presence. Similarly, faith must remain and "reason vanish in the case of the heavenly supernatural mode" (p. 221). This distinction of modes, by the way, opens the door to rapprochement, for once it is appreciated that Luther does not teach a pre-resurrection or even a pre-ascension mode, common ground may be sought in a presence according to the mode of the Spirit, as in Calvin.

(e) The Flesh. Zwingli argues from John 6:63 that Christ's body is of no avail, but Luther insists that what does not profit is a fleshly mind (pp. 236–237). Christ's body does profit when taken with faith, but not so when taken without faith (p. 238). Christ himself describes his flesh as food. The unprofitable flesh is that "which is not spirit and has no spirit but is opposed to spirit" (p. 250). Christ wants spiritual disciples. Fleshly disciples will not hear. The Spirit, or the word and teaching of the Spirit, gives life. The flesh, or the word and teaching of the flesh, is of no avail (p. 249).

(2) Oecolampadius

(a) Figure. According to Oecolampadius of Basel, the saying "This is my body" is figurative in the sense of "This is the sign of my body." Luther treats this as a gratuitous assumption. The figure would also be "an inverted, awkward" one, "making of the true substance a likeness or sign" (pp. 252–254). It fails to take into account that if one says "This is a rose," rose is meant literally even though in a carved rose wood is present as well as rose.

(b) Visible Presence. Like Zwingli, Oecolampadius argues that since Christ was visibly present at the first supper "This is my body" can be taken literally only if he is visibly present at every supper. Luther does not see the logic of this. The words "God created heaven and earth" are literal even though no one was there to see it happen. The matter may be hard to grasp, but the word is not on that account obscure (p. 272). Nor does the word have to be sacramental because the supper is a sacrament (p. 273). The presence does not conflict with the heavenly presence because the mode of the presence is not local (p. 285). No one can show a restriction to this local mode, and in default of this the whole argument from visibility and the heavenly presence falls to the ground (p. 286).

(3) Schwenkfeld. In 1527 Schwenkfeld intervened in the Eucharistic controversy with his *Ground and Cause of the Error*. Luther largely ignored this in *This Is My Body* but subjected it to devastating criticism in the *Confession*. Schwenkfeld corrupts scripture by changing the order "This is my body" to "My body is this" (p. 289). His claim that the Old Testament says nothing about impanation has no relevance (pp. 290–291). Nor has his spiritualizing of the object of faith and God's Word (pp. 292–293). Finally his argument that impanation is against Christ's kingship and God's glory is ludicrous, for the kingdom prevails wherever Christ is, and surely Christ is not disgraced by being "with us on earth in all the pangs of sin and death" instead of leaving us to the devil (p. 293).

(4) Wycliffe. Against a substantial presence Wycliffe had raised the problem that there can be "no identical predication of diverse natures." Hence "This is my body" has to be figurative, not identical predication. Wycliffe, then, retains the bread where transubstantiationists retain the body. Luther recognizes the difficulty but thinks it can be solved by retaining both, not as diverse substances, but as one substance in both name and reality. He gives the following reasons. (a) In these matters reason must be taught by God. (b) God's Word is plain and has to be accepted (p. 296). (c) The Trinity and the incarnation offer parallels of identical predication (p. 297). (d) So does the relating of the Holy Spirit to the dove, wind, or cloud (p. 299). (e) In the Eucharist two kinds of objects are united in what Luther calls "a sacramental union" in virtue of which one must even speak of crushing with teeth or tongue the body of Christ, since "what is done to the bread is rightly and properly attributed to the body of Christ" (p. 300). (f) When two things become one, grammar may speak of them either separately or interchangeably according to the familiar category of synecdoche (pp. 301–302). Identical predication is thus no problem, for with the sacramental union it does not even arise.

### c. Analysis

(1) Matthew. Turning to four passages for analysis, Luther first points out that his opponents do not take these passages literally, nor do they agree in their interpretations (pp. 304–305). He then begins with the words of institution in Matthew. These are "spoken by the mouth of God" and therefore we must be content with them and "cling to them as the perfectly clear, certain, sure words of God which can never deceive us or allow us to err" (p. 308). Nothing, Luther thinks, can be clearer or simpler.

(2) Mark. Only in non-essentials does Mark's text differ from Matthew's. It is unimportant that the disciples drank from the cup before Jesus said "This is my blood," for the words are virtually identical. "There certainly can be no figure of speech or any trope in them" (p. 313). The evangelists seem to be saying that no one can speak "more surely or more simply about this subject than to say 'This is my body' " (p. 314).

(3) Luke. Luke, as Luther sees it, preserves the correct order. A last cup is drunk before the Eucharistic cup, as if to show that the latter is no mere wine but "blood-wine" (p. 317). That the phrase is now "This is the new testament in my blood" Luther dismisses as of no significance. It means the same as "This is my blood of the new testament." Luther discerns Hebrew idiom in Luke here, but whatever explanation we adopt the words have to agree with Matthew and Mark. "This cup" in Luke has special significance. It ties us to a literal cup, not a spiritual one. This eliminates Schwenkfeld and entangles the Swiss. Hence Luther has a special liking for Luke: "Isn't Luke a nasty man, that with a single word he suddenly fells such mighty giants and heroes?" (p. 326).

(4) Paul. Luther finds additional support in Paul. (a) The bread and body are more closely related by the omission of "is" (pp. 331ff.). (b) Sacramental union is indicated plainly by the equation of wine, cup, testament, and blood (pp. 334ff.). (c) "This bread and this cup refer back to the specific bread and wine that are sacramentally united with Christ's body and blood." (d) Unworthy reception profanes the body and blood, not the bread and wine (pp. 341ff.). (e) Paul uses "bread and cup" interchangeably with "body and blood" and also says plainly that judgment falls when the bread and wine are not regarded and treated as the body and blood. The apostle's teaching in 1 Corinthians 10:16 is adduced in confirmation (pp. 348ff.).

*d. Confession*

To clarify his teaching, Luther appends a confession of his basic convictions. The Trinity and incarnation come first, followed by Christ's death and resurrection. Man's fall and condemnation and the bondage of the will come next. Such errors as Patripassianism, Arianism, Apollinarianism, rejection of the *theotokos*, and Pelagianism old and new are all denounced. Monasticism is set aside in favor of the orders of priesthood, marriage, civil government, and the supreme order of Christian love. A special article is devoted to the Holy Spirit and his ministry in relation to the Father and the Son. Baptism and the Lord's Supper are recognized next. Of the latter Luther says that in it "the true body and blood of Christ are eaten and drunk in the bread and wine" (p. 367). The church is confessed as the one community of all Christians "physically dispersed . . . but spiritually gathered in one gospel and faith under one head, Jesus Christ." Christ and his Spirit and God are present in it, and outside it is no salvation or forgiveness. Since forgiveness is not once and for all, voluntary penance is commended. Conditional prayer may be made for the dead but no masses are to be offered. Purgatory is "fabricated by goblins." There are no other than the two sacraments, and the mass is the greatest of all abominations (p. 370). Luther finds a place for biblical images or pictures, and he regards such things as bells, vestments, and altar lights as indifferent. Finally he affirms the general resurrection, the last judgment, eternal life for the godly, and eternal death for the wicked, the devil, and his angels. He concludes with the confident assertion that "so all Christians believe and so the holy scriptures teach us" (p. 372).

## D. CALVIN AND THE EUCHARIST

### 1. Role of Calvin

While the Swiss took one direction and Luther another, attempts at mediation were made. Bucer of Strassburg worked hard, but with little success, to find a comprehensive formula. Calvin then took over the part of the irenicist. In various tracts and successive editions of the *Institutes* he contended for a doctrine which would meet the concerns of Luther and yet accept the valid theses of Zwingli. Whether Luther could have been won over it is hard to say. Melanchthon, however, was impressed and Bullinger found it possible to go along with Calvin in the *Consensus of Zurich*. Peter Martyr was obviously working along the same lines, and to the same general area belong the Anglicans Ridley, Cranmer, and Jewel, who were no more satisfied with either Luther or Zwingli than they were with the medieval teaching.

### 2. Purpose and Fruit of the Sacrament

Calvin starts his exposition in the last edition of the *Institutes* with the truth that Christ has provided ongoing nourishment for his people. Since, however, we cannot grasp what union with Christ is, God gives signs, guarantees, and tokens which are "so adapted to our small capacity" that even the dullest people can get the point and be strengthened in faith by them (iv.17.1). The sacrament testifies to our growth into one body with Christ whereby what is his may be called ours in a wonderful exchange between qualities such as his divine sonship and our humanity, his strength and our weakness, his righteousness and our iniquity.

### 3. Christ's Spiritual Presence

The sacrament's testimony is so full that it is as if "Christ here

present were set before our eyes" and we were invited to take the body
and blood which he makes "one substance with us." As Calvin acutely
observes, the words "given and shed for you" give the sacrament its
force. The body and blood benefit us as they were given up for our
salvation. The analogical relation is also important: "As bread
nourishes . . . the life of our body, so Christ's body is the only food to
invigorate and enliven our soul" (sec. 3).

#### 4. Sacrament and Promise

The supper, then, does not just extend Christ's body to us. It seals
and confirms the promise by which Christ testifies that his flesh and
blood are our food and drink to eternal life (sec. 4). It sends us to the cross
where that promise was performed. Present feeding on Christ is not to
be isolated from the once-for-all act in which Christ became the bread of
life for us. "Once for all . . . he gave his body to be made bread. . . ; daily
he gives it when by the word of the gospel he offers it for us to partake . . . , when he seals such giving of himself by the sacred mystery of
the supper, and when he inwardly fulfills what he outwardly desig-
nates" (sec. 5).

#### 5. Sacrament and Faith

At this point Calvin warns us to avoid the extreme of distinguishing too rigidly between sign and mystery. Partaking of Christ is no mere
knowledge but involves a quickening of the soul to spiritual power.
Eating is not just believing, for "we eat Christ's flesh in believing." That
is, eating "seems rather to follow from faith" as the "remarkable effect"
of Christ's abiding (sec. 5).

#### 6. Sacrament and Spirit

In further criticism of the same extreme, Calvin claims that we do
not partake of the Spirit only, but also of flesh and blood, hard though it
may be to explain this. The life-giving Christ comes to abide in our flesh,
shows us that we are partakers of him, and "quickens our very flesh in
which he abides" (sec. 8). In his humanity dwells fullness of life, so that
partaking of his flesh and blood means enjoyment of participation in life
(sec. 9). How can this be? The answer lies with the Holy Spirit, whose
secret power "towers above our senses" and causes Christ's flesh, separated by a great distance, to penetrate to us and become our food. In the
supper, then, Christ seals "that sacred partaking of his flesh and blood,"
not by giving an empty sign but by "manifesting the effectiveness of his
Spirit to fulfill what he promises." Because of this work of the Spirit one
can be sure that in the supper Christ "truly presents and shows his

body." "With the sign the truth of the thing signified is surely present." With the symbol we may trust that "the body itself is also given to us" (sec. 10).

### 7. Signification, Matter, and Effect

Adopting traditional terminology, Calvin finds a. the signification in the implicit promises, b. the matter or substance in Christ with his death and resurrection, and c. the effect in such benefits as redemption and eternal life. These benefits are received through faith as participation in Christ, who has made himself ours.

### 8. Spatial Presence

If the sign and mystery are sundered at one extreme, the sign obscures the mystery at another. This happens when a local presence is postulated. Calvin follows Zwingli here. Locally, Christ's body is in heaven. A local presence is not needed for participation. We are taught that "the Spirit alone causes us to possess Christ completely and have him dwelling in us" (sec. 12). Transubstantiation comes in for severe criticism by Calvin. By making the bread the body it cancels the nature of the sacrament (sec. 14). Nor does Calvin see much merit in the Lutheran idea that the body is under the bread in virtue of its ubiquity, for this "assigns to the body a ubiquity contrary to nature" (secs. 17, 30). He rejects, too, the concept of a glorious and immortal body which can be in many places at once with no place or form. Docetism is suspected in these redefinitions of corporeality (sec. 17).

### 9. Word of Institution

Calvin accepts Zwingli's argument in his interpretation of the crucial saying "This is my body." The traditional view and the Lutheran exposition are grammatically impossible (sec. 20). The words are an instance of metonymy. "The name of the things was given to the symbol ... but not without a most fitting analogy" (sec. 21). The disciples obviously took it this way (sec. 23). Nor does Calvin think he is being rationalistic in adopting this interpretation, for the feeding that he teaches is plainly not learned "from physics." If it is urged that God could change the bread into the body, "the question is not what God could do but what he willed to do" (sec. 24). While Christ is always present in majesty, providence, and ineffable grace (Augustine), in the body he is in heaven from the ascension to the last day (secs. 26–27).

### 10. Participation by the Spirit

The key to a proper understanding is to be found in the ministry of the Spirit. The communion of Christ's body is bestowed by the Spirit's power. By the Spirit we are lifted up to heaven with our eyes and mind to seek Christ there (sec. 18). By the same Spirit Christ comes down to us to quicken our souls by the substance of his flesh and blood (sec. 24). Christ "substituted the Holy Spirit to supply . . . the defect of his absence" when he left his disciples (sec. 26). "A serious wrong is done to the Holy Spirit unless we believe that it is through his incomprehensible power that we come to partake of Christ's flesh and blood." Those devoid of the Spirit, of course, "can no more eat Christ's flesh than drink wine that has no taste." Christ "proffers this spiritual food" to all, but he can be received only with the "taste of faith," the wicked being condemned, not because they receive him unworthily, but because they refuse him and take only the outward symbols (sec. 33). Christ's presence, however, is not due to faith itself. Faith is the gift of the Spirit and participation is the work of the same Spirit, who is the mode of Christ's presence between the ascension and the coming again.

## 11. Mystery of the Sacrament

To say Spirit is to say mystery. Calvin realizes, then, that we have here a genuine biblical mystery. The ministry of the Spirit passes comprehension. We can only "break forth in wonder at this mystery, which plainly neither the mind is able to conceive nor the tongue to express" (iv.17.7). If anyone should ask how we can be taken up to Christ in heaven, Calvin replies: "I am not ashamed to confess that it is a secret too lofty for either my mind to comprehend or my words to declare. . . . I rather experience than understand it. . . . I offer my soul to him to be fed. . . . I do not doubt that he himself truly presents his body and blood and I receive them" (sec. 32). Is this mysticism? Is Calvin teaching a theology of experience? He himself would not think so. The Spirit's work is above reason, not contrary to it. Experience rests on the presence whose effect is so great as to give assurance of eternal life. We are not in the sphere of pure subjectivity nor of fusion with the divine. We are in the sphere of God's own operation according to the statement and promise of the gospel. The inexplicability is that of the divine mystery. As in all his theology of Word and sacrament Calvin is here the theologian, not of human experience, but of the Holy Spirit. For his "spiritual" is no vague term. It does not subjectively stand in contrast to "true" or "real." As he himself so finely says, "for us the manner is spiritual because the secret power of the Spirit is the bond of our union with Christ" (sec. 33).

## 12. The Mass

Calvin devotes a special chapter (chap. 18) to criticism of the mass. His objections are straightforward. The mass dishonors Christ (sec. 2), buries his cross and passion (sec. 3), effaces the true and unique death of Christ (sec. 5), "robs us of the benefit which was coming to us" from it (sec. 6), abolishes the Lord's Supper (sec. 7), repudiates communion (sec. 8), has neither biblical nor patristic support (sec. 9), and involves many corruptions (sec. 14). The basic error, he believes, is the failure to distinguish between sacrifice as expiation and sacrifice as praise or thanksgiving. Christ offered the one expiatory sacrifice (sec. 13). The sacrifice we now offer in worship is one of thanksgiving (sec. 16). This rests on the greater sacrifice by which we and all that is ours "ought to be consecrated and dedicated" to God. Its concern is the exalting of God. It is acceptable to God "only from the hands of those whom he has reconciled to himself by other means." It is necessary for the church and indeed embraces all its life and ministry, for sharing and good works are also acceptable sacrifices (sec. 16). The Lord's Supper includes sacrifice of this type, for in proclaiming Christ's death and giving thanks "we do nothing but offer a sacrifice of praise" (sec. 17).

## E. RIDLEY AND THE ANGLICAN VIEW

### 1. The Situation

Theologically the Reformation moved slowly in England. Gains were made for the doctrine of justification by faith in the Ten Articles of 1536 and the Bishops' Book of 1537. By the time of Edward VI, however, when the pace was quickening, the focus of debate was shifting to the Eucharistic presence. In the face of traditional, Lutheran, Swiss, and Anabaptist views the leading Anglicans seem not yet to have reached a definite view on the issue. Cranmer is often thought to have gone through a Lutheran phase but his own statements do not support this. The First Book of Common Prayer of 1549 helped to bring the issue to a head, for in it an attempt was made to rule out any thought of transubstantiation. The phrasing, however, still remained ambivalent and it was only with the Second Book of Common Prayer of 1552 that the Reformed view, which received more careful definition in the Forty-Two Articles of 1553, was expressed. The death of Edward and the accession of Mary, also in 1553, brought the matter into even sharper focus, for when theological charges were brought against such Reformation bishops as Cranmer and Ridley, their views on the Eucharist formed the central point of attack.

Ridley had played a key role in the development of the Anglican understanding. According to his own account, it was Ratramn's book that convinced him that the medieval teaching was neither biblical nor patristic. Once persuaded, Ridley helped to win over or to strengthen

Cranmer, and with the help of the exiles Bucer and Peter Martyr the two then brought about the Eucharistic revolution in official Anglican theology. While in prison in Oxford, Ridley took the opportunity to write a short *Treatise Against the Error of Transubstantiation,* in which he states his objections to the medieval view and clarifies his positive teaching. At much the same time he engaged in a verbal defense of his Eucharistic theology in the disputations of April 1555 which were the basis of his condemnation as a heretic and his execution in October of the same year.

## 2. The Treatise

### a. *The Points at Issue*

After a prayer for understanding and a reference to the basic biblical passages Ridley defines the points at issue. These are five in number but they may be reduced to two: (1) "whether there be any transubstantiation of the bread or no?" and (2) whether there be "any corporal and carnal presence of Christ or no?" Indeed, in the last analysis there is only one issue: "What is the matter of the sacrament, whether is it the natural substance of bread, or the natural substance of Christ's own body?" Ridley also points out, however, that to deny that the matter is Christ's own body is not to "take away simply and absolutely the presence of Christ's body and blood from the sacrament" (*Library of Christian Classics* 26, p. 299). Thus a further question arises. If Christ is not present "in the natural substance of his human and assumpt nature," then how is he present? At this juncture Ridley anticipates his positive teaching and explains briefly that the alternative is a presence "by grace" (p. 300).

### b. *The Scriptural Passages*

Like Luther, Ridley bases his presentation on those passages in the gospels and Paul which record the institution of the supper. As he sees it, the bread which Christ took remained bread in natural substance, but as a bread of remembrance it may be "by grace, and in a sacramental signification his body," Any other view involves a "confusion of substances" (p. 301). In spite of this, the claim is often made that the word "is" necessarily implies a change of the substance of bread to that of Christ's body. Ridley resists this claim for two reasons. (a) There is general agreement, supported by the distinction of literal and figurative speech, that when Paul says that "this cup is the new testament in my blood," the substance of cup is not changed into that of testament. It follows, then, that Christ "meant no more any such change of the substance of bread into the substance of his natural body, than he meant of the change and transubstantiation of the cup into the substance of the new testament" (p. 305). (b) Trying to take "is" literally involves insoluble logical and grammatical problems. For instance, what can "this" mean on such a view? Even more seriously, when does the supposed change take place as the words of institution are recited? It can hardly be with "blessed," for this comes too soon. Nor can it be with "is," for then the correct word would be "is changed into." If it comes with "my body," however, it is too late and the saying is not literally true. Transubstantiation and the like do not have the textual support that their champions think. Proper exegesis points to a different interpretation.

### 3. The Disputation

#### a. Arguments against a Substantial Presence

Presenting his own understanding in the *Disputation,* Ridley repeats that denial of a substantial presence does not have to be denial of a real presence, for the term "real" can have a general as well as a specific sense (pp. 311–312). Five arguments can be brought against a real presence in the sense of a substantial presence. (1) It is contrary to God's Word in John 16:7; Acts 3:21; Matthew 9:15; John 16:22; John 14:3; and Matthew 24:23,28; these verses tell us that in his incarnate body Christ is no longer present but is at the Father's right hand until the last day (p. 312). (2) "It varies from the articles of faith," which refer similarly to the ascension, session, and coming again (pp. 312–313). (3) "It destroyeth and taketh away the institution of the Lord's Supper," for remembrance is superfluous when there is presence (p. 313). (4) "It maketh precious things common to profane and ungodly persons," for if the bread be now Christ's body in material substance, not only the wicked but even "mice, rats also, and dogs may receive the very real and corporal body of the Lord" (p. 313). (5) "It confirmeth also and maintaineth . . . the devouring of man's flesh" — a cannibalistic implication which ought to warn us, as it did Augustine (pp. 305–306), that a different interpretation is to be sought (p. 313).

#### b. The True Presence

If the presence is not substantial, what is it? Both Tridentines and Lutherans found it hard to answer this question, although both left the door ajar, the former by distinguishing between substance and accidents, the latter by speaking of different modes of presence. Among the Reformed, Zwingli had hardly given a satisfactory reply, since his accepted presence of Christ after his deity seemed to imply a dubious separation of the person of Christ as well as the natures. Calvin approached the matter at a deeper level by recognizing the role of the Spirit in relation to all of Christ's present ministry, and it was along similar lines that Ridley worked out his concept of a real presence but not a presence in natural substance. He did so in five steps.

(1) Appealing to "the word of God and the ancient fathers," Ridley

saw the bread to be "the body of Christ in the remembrance of him and of his death" (p. 313). By remembrance he did not just mean the subjective act of recollection, for Christ makes the remembrance and by God's power "it far passeth all kinds of remembrance that any other man is able to make either of himself, or of any other thing" (PS, 8).

(2) Ridley also stressed, "with the ancient and the faithful fathers," that this broken bread is the "communion and partaking of Christ's body." He elsewhere calls this "communication": "he gave himself in a real communication." His point is that in the supper believers receive Christ's body truly and effectually in a spiritual communion, or a communion in the Spirit.

(3) This communion might also be described as a giving "to the godly and faithful the grace of Christ's body, that is, the food of life and immortality" (LCC 26, p. 314). Phrases from the fathers are adduced in elucidation: feeling Christ to be present in grace, receiving celestial food, the virtue of the very flesh of Christ, the life and grace of his body. What this amounts to is that in the sacrament the Christ who gave himself for us graciously gives himself and his grace to us who receive the Eucharistic bread and wine in faith and holiness (p. 314). The gift is grace and the communion is also grace.

(4) Ridley connects the presence in grace with the ministry of the Holy Spirit. He again adduces the fathers, who speak of receiving Christ's spiritual flesh, of the grace of the Spirit, and of the sacrament being the body because there is in it the Spirit of Christ (p. 314). Ridley can speak of spiritual eating: "Without the Spirit to eat the sacrament is to eat it unprofitably." Spiritual eating does not mean eating in the right frame of mind. It means eating in or by the Holy Spirit. To use the terminology of Luther, the body of Christ is present in the mode of the Holy Spirit.

(5) Finally, Christ's body can be described as really present because the power of God's word is in the sacrament and this "not only feedeth the soul but also cleanseth it." Ridley does not deny the power of the Word. He does not relate it, however, to a change in substance. He relates it to the effectual presence of Christ's body and blood by the Spirit even though bread remains bread and wine, wine. Thus the sacrament can be no naked sign, no purely human act of remembrance. Under the Holy Spirit it involves the presence of the whole Christ to his people in grace and power. What Ridley denies is what is for him the pseudo-miracle of substantial change. What he affirms is the true miracle of a real presence by the Word and Spirit.

# PART III
## Modern Theology

# CHAPTER XXI

# Reformed and Puritan: Theology and Covenant

## A. THE SETTING

Swiss Reformation theology, especially in its Genevan form, developed in different ways in the post-Reformation period. Arminianism, of course, introduced a decisive modification which the main body rejected at the international Synod of Dort (1619) but which still had important consequences. Orthodoxy itself, while attempting to retain the Reformation deposit, could not remain exactly as it was. New definitions had to be made in response to the Arminians. The growth of Arminianism and the development of theology as an academic task also brought significant changes in method, content, and ethos.

In addition to the influence of Arminianism and inner changes, a subtle distinction developed, too, between Reformed theology on the one side and its Puritan variant on the other. The situation here is complicated. Doctrinally it is difficult to see much difference between Reformed and Puritan statements. The Puritans themselves come in different forms. Thus we find Presbyterian Puritans, Anglican Puritans, and Independent Puritans, both English and American. Puritanism focused originally on matters of order, polity, and conduct rather than on theology. Yet life and theology cannot be isolated from one another. The emerging style of Puritan life inevitably affected at least the style and orientation of theology, if not to any high degree its dogmatic content. Ultimately it would influence the content, too.

A first point at which the Reformed and Puritan approaches can be compared and contrasted is in the understanding of theology itself. Time and again in theological history the question is asked: What is theology? How and why is it to be done? A comprehensive dogmatics clearly must devote attention to the crucial question of its own nature, method, and purpose. The seventeenth-century theologians certainly did not ignore this question, and two of them, Wollebius as a typical Reformed dogmatician and Ames (or Amesius) as an influential Puritan, have left us some interesting answers.

## B. THEOLOGY

### 1. Wollebius

#### a. Life and Work

Johannes Wollebius was born in Basel in 1586. He was ordained there in 1611 and succeeded to the chair of New Testament studies in 1618. He published his *Compendium of Christian Theology* in 1626. Its success may be measured by the fact that in addition to the many Latin editions it was translated into English (1650) and Dutch (1651). As a clear and concise statement of Reformed orthodoxy in the early seventeenth century it could hardly be excelled. Wollebius did not long survive the publication of the first edition. His relatively short life ended in 1529.

#### b. Definition of Theology

Wollebius opens his work with a brief prolegomenon. This consists of two sections, the second of which serves as a transition leading on to the body of the work. The first section contains a thesis which is then followed by twenty-two supporting or related propositions. In the thesis Wollebius offers his basic definition of theology as "the doctrine concerning God as he is known and worshipped for his glory and for our salvation." Four points should be noted in connection with this definition. (1) Wollebius recognizes that God is the main theme of theology. (2) He presupposes that God is known. (3) He relates the knowledge of God to the worship of God. (4) He also relates it to the salvation of man. For Wollebius theology has more of an expository than a speculative function. If its anthropological aspects are not ignored, they arise only within an authentically theological context.

#### c. Types of Theology

Under Proposition 1 Wollebius admits that the word "theology" might be used in other senses. Classical teachings could be loosely called theology, including the priestly or political teaching "through which the common people were kept under control by the requirements of religion." Wollebius himself, however, reserves the term for "that knowledge of God which a Christian may attain in this life from God's own Word." Two further points are made here. (1) The theology in view pertains to this life. (2) God's Word constitutes its source or norm. Wollebius then offers further elucidation by distinguishing between original and derived theology. "The original is the knowledge by which God knows himself." Derived theology is found first in the incarnate Christ and then in his members. Since, however, some of these members are in heaven and some on earth, a further distinction must be observed between the theology of the blessed and that of the militant or wayfarers. The latter is our present concern.

### d. Nature of Theology

In Proposition 2 Wollebius makes it plain that for him theology is not an intellectual faculty but a system of teachings. One can hardly define it as a faculty since it is broader than knowledge, understanding, or wisdom, consisting of action as well as contemplation. If defined as a faculty, then, it must embrace both the wisdom which results from understanding and knowledge and also the prudence which "directs the mind in action."

### e. Principles of Theology

In Proposition 3 Wollebius advances two principles of theology, the ontic and the noetic. The ontic principle, that of its being, is God himself. The noetic principle, that by which it is known, is the Word of God. The ontic principle is set aside for discussion in the body of the *Compendium*. Propositions 5–19 are devoted, however, to the doctrine of the Word of God and, more specifically, of holy scripture as the noetic principle of theology.

### f. Ends of Theology

Wollebius discerns three ends of theology. (1) As God is the primary and proper object of theology, so he is also its primary and final end (prop. 20). (2) God is the highest good and therefore "only Christians can rightly teach us concerning the highest good" (prop. 21). (3) Salvation is "a subordinate end" of theology. Wollebius avoids making salvation a supreme, and supremely self-centered, end. He offers a short but penetrating and wholly theocentric description of salvation; it consists "of communion with God and enjoyment of him" (prop. 22).

### g. Division of Theology

In his transitional thesis Wollebius divides theology into two parts, the knowledge of God and the service of God. The first consists of things to be believed (*ta pista*) and the second, of things to be done (*ta prakta*). In the full sense, therefore, theology embraces both dogmatics and ethics. In this regard Wollebius catches up his original definition. Theology has to do with both knowledge and worship. If dogmatics sets forth the knowledge of God, ethics sets forth his worship, for true worship of God consists of true holiness and righteousness, or the practice of good works (2.2).

## 2. Ames

### a. Life and Work

William Ames was born at Ipswich, England in 1576. Belonging to a Puritan family, he was sent to Christ College, Cambridge, where he came under the influence of William Perkins. He graduated in 1607, was elected to a fellowship, and might well have become master of the college but for his Puritan principles and practices. Instead, he resigned his fellowship, was appointed to Colchester, and when this appointment was blocked took refuge in Holland in 1610. After a brief stay in Rotterdam, where he met the pilgrim pastor John Robinson, he served as chaplain to the English merchants at The Hague from 1611 to 1618, when the English authorities engineered his dismissal. In 1619 he secured a professorial appointment at the university of Franeker, but again influential opponents stood in his path, and it was not until 1622 that he could take up his duties. Ames remained at Franeker until 1632. In that year, with a view to an eventual move to New England, he returned to Rotterdam as co-pastor of an independent congregation which had hopes of setting up an academy with Ames as president. In 1633, however, the river Maas overflowed into his Rotterdam home and led to his premature death by severe exposure.

Franeker afforded Ames the most favorable environment for his theological activity. At The Hague he had already become embroiled in the Arminian controversy, and with his *Coronis* of 1618 he earned a reputation as one of the most forceful advocates of orthodoxy. A whole series of works was then composed in the Franeker years, including his *Bellarmine Disarmed,* the famous work *On Conscience,* and posthumously published writings such as the *Philosophical Presuppositions* and *Principles of Logic.* Most influential of all these writings, however, was *The Marrow of True Divinity,* which, originally delivered as lectures in Leyden, appeared in Latin as the *Medulla theologica* in 1623 and went through several Latin and English editions as well as being translated into Dutch. In two ways the *Marrow* proved to be one of the most formative works of the immediate post-Reformation age. (1) It played a particularly important role in shaping New England theology. (2) It brought into theology a practical emphasis which had wide-ranging effects not only in Puritanism but also in Pietism and perhaps also in some forms of later Pietist liberalism.

### b. Definition of Theology

Ames sounds a new note in the very first sentence of the *Marrow.* Under the heading "The Definition and Nature of Theology" (Book 1) he defines theology as "the doctrine or teaching of living to God" (1.1). At the end of the same chapter he can thus suggest that theology might just as well as called *theozoia* ("living to God") or *theourgia* ("working toward God"). The shift here is apparent at once when comparison is made with the definition of Wollebius. God remains in the definition but is no longer the central point. Living or working to God replaces God himself as the principal theme. A disturbing anthropologizing is the unmistakable consequence.

### c. Source of Theology

Why is theology called doctrine? Not to distinguish it from understanding or knowledge, but to show that it "derives not from nature and human inquiry . . . but from divine revelation and appointment" (1.2). The principles of other arts are "developed through sense perception, observation, experience, and induction." The principles of theology can certainly be "advanced by study and industry," but they are not "in us by nature" (1.3).

### d. Practice of Theology

Theology is a practical, not a speculative, discipline (1.10). Ames argues this as follows. Living is the noblest work of all and thus the art of living is the most proper study (1.4). The highest kind of life is that which is nearest to the living and life-giving God (1.5). At this level good living takes precedence of happy living. Theology is to be defined as "that good life whereby we live to God," not as "that happy life whereby we live to ourselves" (1.8). For Ames, the will plays a decisive role in living. Hence the will is "the first and proper subject of theology" (1.9). All the disciplines, of course, aim at good living, but theology does so in a special way. Two deductions may be made. (1) Everything in theology refers either to the final end or to the related means, that is, to practice. (2) All truths relevant to living well in the various spheres of life can be said "rightly to pertain to theology" (1.12).

### e. Divisions of Theology

(1) Two Parts. Following the Scholastic distinction between being and working, Ames divides theology into faith and observance (2.1). The *Marrow* itself consists, then, of two books, with the introductory discussion forming the first two chapters of Book i. The division is not artificial for Ames; "it follows from the nature of the object." The object, of course, is not God but the spiritual life. Faith is the first act of this life, observance the second. In distinction from Wollebius, who also has doctrinal and practical sections, Ames gives his divisions a manward reference. Faith and observance replace the knowledge of God and the service of God as the two principal heads.

(2) Their Unity and Distinction. Ames does not want to imply that there might be faith without observance or observance without faith. He thus stresses the unity of the two parts in use and exercise (2.4). Yet three distinctions are also perceived: (a) a distinction of nature, (b) one of pertinent rules, and (c) one of order, "whereby faith holds the first place and spiritual observance the second," no acts of life being forthcoming "except where there is the vital principle of life" (2.5). In this regard Ames offers an excellent example. He avoids both abstract dogmatizing on the one side and empty moralizing on the other. Dogmatics and ethics are brought into integral relationship. If faith aims at action, action can have no other source than faith.

### 3. Comments

Solid areas of agreement may be discerned between Wollebius and Ames. They agree that theology has its basis in revelation. They both find in it two interrelated parts, knowledge or faith on the one side, service or observance on the other. While Ames does not discuss scripture in this context, they agree also that it is by scripture that revelation is mediated to us. Nor is Ames without an ultimate Godward reference, for in the body of the text faith is defined as "the resting of the heart on God" (i.3.1), and observance is "the submissive performance of the will of God" (ii.1.1). If practice is for him the end of theology, it has its own end in the doing of the will of God and the glory of God (i.1.1).

Nevertheless, a certain change in orientation is heralded by the change in definition. This must not be exaggerated. Ames is no early Schleiermacher transforming theology into a conceptualizing of Christian experience. At the same time his concern for action, his stress on the will, and his focusing of theology on the Christian life instead of on God carry with them implications which are not wholly unknown but which are undoubtedly new nuances in the Reformed world.

All this undoubtedly has a positive side. Ames would not let theological work be an end in itself. He nailed theologians to their responsibilities in Christian life and mission. Dogmatics could not become an intellectual game nor ethics an independent enterprise. The dogmatician should set an example of life as well as learning. If not, he might be doing many things, but he certainly could not be doing Christian theology. All the merit of Puritan seriousness may be seen in this emphasis of Ames.

Negatively, however, a price has to be paid. What Ames lost was not essential orthodoxy in detail but remembrance of the basic theological fact that the proper object of mankind's study is God. While God might still be the source and his glory the ultimate end in the *Marrow,* the Christian life becomes the immediate theme and goal. From an unexpected quarter, then, a powerful push is given to the anthropologizing of theology which would transform Puritanism, receive new impetus from Descartes, and finally produce a totally different theological style and approach. Ames himself had no such end in view. He aimed at relating theology more closely to life. In some sense he achieved this. In achieving it, however, he also helped to achieve other things. Wollebius, with his more careful definition, could achieve all that Ames wished to do. But in so doing he could also preserve theology itself as an authentic discipline.

### C. COVENANT

### 1. Covenant Theology

As we have noted in an earlier chapter, covenant theology came into prominence from the early days of the Reformation. If anything, however, its importance increased both theologically and practically in the seventeenth century. Much work was done on elaborating the doctrine of the covenant, and extensions of the covenant principle may be seen in several areas. Covenantal theology and practice would culminate in Cocceius of Leyden and the Puritans, but not before earlier dogmaticians such as Wollebius and Ames had made substantial contributions. In relation to each of these writers, the covenant forms another important point at which their divergent nuances may be studied, and note may also be taken of the new features in each as compared to the original teaching of the Reformation.

## 2. The Place of the Doctrine

Wollebius and Ames do not agree in their relating of the covenant to other doctrinal themes. Wollebius divides his discussion. He first introduces a covenant of works, which he connects with God's rule over man prior to the fall (i.8). Then, after dealing with Christ's saving work, he follows up his doctrine of common calling with a further chapter on the covenant of grace (i.21), which is in turn followed by his sacramental theology. Ames agrees with Wollebius insofar as he, too, first introduces the covenant of works under God's special government (i.10). But he then has another discussion of the covenant of works, and his main presentation is given under the head of "The Application of Christ" (i.24). As in Wollebius, this comes after the statement on Christ's work of mediation, but it precedes predestination (which Wollebius puts in 1.4), and it also comes before calling, which is for Ames the means by which the first part of application — namely, union with Christ — is attained (i.26).

## 3. The Covenant of Works

*a. Definition*

Both Wollebius and Ames speak of a covenant of works in the pre-fall period. The development of this concept is perhaps the most striking innovation in covenantal thinking. For Wollebius this covenant of works consists very simply in the promise of eternal life for obedience and the threat of death for disobedience (i.8.1). Ames, too, traces the first covenant, which he significantly calls a transaction, to the law that was established by command or prohibition and by promise or threat (i.10). For Ames, however, it seems that a covenant of works persists after the fall. He calls it a covenant of friendship. It involves an agreement between two parties and is universal in scope. It rests on the principle of divine sovereignty except in the grace of reward. It has its basis in the ability of man and is unconditional in the sense that its fulfillment depends on man's obedience. Much of what Ames is saying here seems properly to refer to what some theologians deal with separately as the covenant of the law, reserving the phrase "covenant of works" specifically for the situation prior to the fall.

### b. Sacraments

Both Wollebius and Ames rather fancifully regard the two trees in paradise as sacraments of the covenant of works. For Wollebius they serve the double purpose of both testing man and signifying life and evil. The trees are called the trees of life and knowledge because they signify these, not because they convey them (i.8.1, props. 2–5). Ames says much the same thing. "The reward for obedience was marked by a tree, namely, that of life, and the punishment for disobedience was marked by a tree, namely, that of the knowledge of good and evil. The one was the sacrament of life and the other the sacrament of death" (i.10.33).

## 4. The Covenant of Grace

### a. Definition

Wollebius describes the result of calling as the external fellowship of the covenant of grace (i.21.1.1). He defines this covenant as that which "God made with us, out of sheer mercy, after the fall" (prop. 1). He also thinks it is appropriately called a testament, since by it, through Christ's mediation, God has appointed a heavenly intercessor for his children (prop. 2). Ames offers a more precise definition when he calls the covenant "a firm promise" (i.24.11). In his view, however, "testament" is a more proper description than "covenant," for this covenant "is a free gift and is confirmed by the death of the giver" (i.24.12).

### b. Characteristics

(1) Cause and Efficacy. For both theologians, God is, of course, the author of the covenant. But whereas Ames finds its moving cause in God's mercy (i.24.16), Wollebius thinks in more personal terms and refers to "the entire Holy Trinity, in particular Christ the God-man, the angel of the covenant" (prop. 3). The unequal roles of God and man call for comment. Wollebius contrasts God's free self-obligating with the requirement laid on man (props. 4–5), while Ames says that in the new covenant God alone covenants: "God is a party assuming and constituting and man is a party assumed" (i.24.14).

(2) External and Internal. Both Wollebius and Ames distinguish between external and internal membership of the covenant. Wollebius relates this distinction to the parallel one between common and special calling. "Those who are called are considered a people of the covenant," but "some are really people of God and some only in external profession." The covenant is offered to all the called but only the elect enjoy its promise (prop. 7). Ames relates the external and internal membership to

the universal sufficiency of Christ's atonement on the one side and its limited intention of application on the other (i.24.9). "Although from the human standpoint the new covenant is often offered indiscriminately, by its nature it belongs, and with special propriety is directed, to those whom God intended."

(3) Unity. Wollebius and Ames both insist that the one covenant of grace extends across all ages after the fall. Wollebius talks of two testaments but only one covenant (prop. 4). The testaments "are the same in substance, Christ is the testator of both, both have the same promise of grace in him, and in each is the same requirement of faith and life" (prop. 15). Ames simply describes the free, saving covenant of God as "one and the same from the beginning" (i.38.1).

(4) First Administration. Wollebius differentiates two administrations, that of the Old Testament and that of the New. Within the first are three ages, from Adam to Abraham, Abraham to Moses, and Moses to Christ (props. 11–12). The third is "more truly testamentary" (prop. 13). Ames keeps the two administrations but within the first sees only two ages with Moses as the point of division (i.38.11). In practice, however, he finds many differences between the periods from Adam to Abraham and Abraham to Moses (i.38.13–28). Like Wollebius he sees "a progression from the imperfect to the more perfect" (i.38.2).

(5) Second Administration. Wollebius relates the new administration to the period after Christ's coming, but he does not elaborate on this (prop. 14). Ames, however, sees two divisions as in the first administration, the first from Christ to the end of the world, the second at the end itself (i.39.1). The first division covers the church age, so that Ames includes much of his ecclesiology under this head (i.39.14ff.), and his sacramental theology comes immediately after in Chapter 40. He has little to say about the covenant at the end except that the application will be perfected and the end of calling will achieve God's glory and our salvation (i.41.1–2) — the twofold purpose of the covenant according to the teaching of Wollebius as well (prop. 6).

(6) Differences of Administration. The two theologians see it as their chief task to enumerate the differences between the first and second administration. Wollebius discerns five areas of distinction: (a) time — the one temporal, the other eternal; (b) place — the one for Israel, the other for the world; (c) clarity — the one symbolical, the other plain; (d) simplicity — the one detailed, the other simple; and (e) agreeableness — the one with emphasis on law, the other with emphasis on gospel (prop. 17). Ames offers a similar list. The new testament is new in form, not in essence (i.39.4). It differs in quality, having a new clarity of matter and expression (1.39.7–8) and also a new freedom from the law (i.39.9). It also differs in quantity or measure, intensively in greater gifts of the Spirit (1.39.12) and extensively in respect of place and time (i.39.13). Like Wollebius, Ames stresses the perfection and permanence

of the new administration (i.39.3–4). Yet both insist that the covenant itself is one and the same. Ames repeats the familiar Reformation principle that "the old [testament] promises Christ to come, and the new testifies that he has come" (i.38.5).

(7) Sacraments. Like the covenant of works, the covenant of grace has its sacraments. These differ according to the administration. Wollebius picks out two primary and ordinary sacraments in the Old Testament, circumcision and the paschal lamb, and two in the New Testament, baptism and the Lord's Supper (i.22.2.2–3). The differences between them resemble those between the administrations, the former sacraments pointing to Christ yet to come and the latter to Christ already come. Ames realizes that the old sacraments do not exist in the first period or periods of the administration and so he finds an extraordinary sacrament in the ark and something like a sacrament in sacrificial banquets (i.38.19). Both Wollebius and Ames point out that since baptism is a covenant sign, infants may be baptized in view of their covenant membership (i.23.1, props. 14–17; *Marrow* i.40.12). As Ames acutely observes, faith and repentance do not constitute the covenant; it is the covenant of grace, and consequently both it and its first seal belong to infants (i.40.13–14).

### 5. Other Covenants

#### a. General Covenant

The covenantal principle becomes so important in the seventeenth century that other covenants are soon perceived in addition to the supposed initial covenant of works. Wollebius, for example, when differentiating the covenant of grace from that of works, refers without elaboration to a "universal covenant which God made with all creatures" (i.21.1, prop. 1). The main extension, however, comes from Ames.

#### b. Trinitarian Covenant

While Ames does not speak specifically of a covenant between the Father and the Son, he nevertheless brings the term into his discussion of the perfection of Christ's satisfaction. Grace is presupposed in Christ's undertaking of this work and the Father's acceptance of it for our good. Ames adds that "satisfaction also presupposes grace in that what was demanded by it was given in a remunerating covenant" (i.20.16). The emphasis here is on grace, but it is just a step from this presentation to the idea of an eternal compact or covenant within the Godhead itself.

#### c. Marriage Covenant

In view of the special relation between marriage on the one side and Christ and the church on the other, extension of the covenant principle to marriage might naturally be expected. Wollebius, however, does not move in this direction, although he talks of "contracting marriage" and of the consent of the partners (ii.11.3, props. 2, 6). Ames, too, refers to "the consent of the contracting parties" (ii.19.31), but he also goes further and, in view of the divine institution and perpetuity of marriage, calls it a "covenant of God" (ii.19.34). This bond or covenant can be dissolved only by adultery (ii.19.49).

### d. Church Covenant

Wollebius connects the church closely with the covenant, for the church is "the external fellowship of the covenant of grace" (i.21.1). Yet the idea of a church covenant seems to be alien to his thinking. This usage derives from the separatist tradition, which views the church or the individual congregation as a group of people mutually covenanted together. Ames, with his Independent background and connections, moves more easily in this direction. Discussing the instituted church in Book i, Chapter 32, he argues that believers constitute a particular church only when they are joined by a special bond. "This bond is a covenant, expressed or implicit, by which believers bind themselves" to perform all relevant duties toward God and one another. The goal distinguishes a church covenant from a civil or political covenant (i.32.15). The loose usage may be seen from this distinction. Churches may also enter into covenant to enjoy common agreement and mutual help, but not in the sense of forming a larger church (i.39.27).

### e. Minister's Covenant

As all members of a church are in covenant, so, for Ames, a special covenant exists between congregation and minister. In practice this means that the minister cannot leave by his own choice nor be ejected except for just cause, such as pluralism or non-residence (i.39.36). Ames does not spell out the covenantal obligations of the congregation. Indeed, he gives no detailed rules but simply establishes the principle.

### f. Covenant with the Devil

According to Ames, one can be in covenant with the devil as well as with God. This comes about when faith and hope are transferred from God to the enemy (ii.8.28). "If not openly and expressly, at least secretly and implicitly," this is entering into a kind of covenant with the devil (ii.8.30). Ames realizes, of course, that everything here is corrupt and counterfeit. The covenant is not properly a covenant and can lead only to bondage. It is extraordinary, however, that Ames should use the term at all in this context. He writes against a background of concern about witchcraft, the black arts, and satanic compacts. But only as the biblical covenant of grace is subsumed under the general category of contract can an arrangement with the devil be described, even improperly, in covenantal terms.

### 6. Questions

#### a. Legalism

Of the two questions which have to be put to this theology of the covenant, the first is whether a legalistic element has not begun to compete, in both Wollebius and Ames, with the fundamental understanding of the covenant in scripture. The covenant of works in paradise, while gracious in the sense that God did not have to set it up, becomes a contract with appropriate rewards and penalties for observance or non-observance. Again, the third form of the covenant of grace in its first administration becomes barely distinguishable from the covenant of works. This is especially true in Ames. To be sure, it is still insisted that the one covenant of grace covers the whole story from Genesis 3 to Revelation, but the contract principle introduces a confusing element in its interpretation and an unfortunate ambivalence in final understanding.

#### b. Illegitimate Extension

The second question, which must be put more narrowly to Ames, is whether the covenant can validly be extended to the point that covenants are seen almost everywhere one looks. A covenantal analogy might perhaps be legitimately seen in Christian marriage, since this reaches its true fulfillment only when modeled on the covenant of grace (Ephesians 5). The same might even be said of the relation between members of a congregation and the accompanying relation of people and pastor. Yet the distinguishing feature of the covenant of grace finds no obvious counterpart in many of the covenants that Ames so readily produces. Obligation lies at the heart of most of them, and the covenant is thus in constant danger of being reduced to a contract by this imaginative extension. Surely it would be a wiser, more instructive, and more beneficial course to reserve the term covenant for the biblical covenant of grace to which it properly belongs. Then the divine covenant could not so easily be misinterpreted in terms of human contracts. Instead, the relationships of Christians could be set in the light of the unique divine relationship, and their contracts could be rethought and reconstructed according to the criterion of the covenant of grace.

# CHAPTER XXII

# Lutheran and Reformed: Holy Scripture

## A. THE BACKGROUND

### 1. Developments

The Reformation churches emerged from the sixteenth century firmly committed to holy scripture as the supreme locus of authority in the church. During the Reformation crisis itself this position had not been uncontested. On the one hand an appeal had been made for more direct leading by the Holy Spirit. On the other hand the authority of the church and tradition had been set alongside that of scripture in a way which obviously involved the qualification and restriction of the latter. If by the turn of the century the direct appeal to the Holy Spirit had lost much of its force, the polemical thrust of reconstructed Roman Catholicism had become all the keener and a rationalistic approach to scripture was also gaining in strength. By the early seventeenth century, then, the theological heirs of the reformers had the difficult task of explaining and justifying their insistence on scripture as the supreme rule of faith and practice.

### 2. Responses

In undertaking this task they engaged in the systematization which marks all their endeavors. All possible aspects of the doctrine were considered. They adopted Scholastic forms of presentation which gave a different slant or flavor to the Reformation teaching. Themes which had received little place in the reformers themselves received new emphasis, so that different nuances were unavoidable. The thoroughness of the discussion justly claims our admiration, but something of the freshness and vigor of the original presentation is lost in the formalization.

Certain opponents of the emphasis on biblical authority tried to undermine confidence in holy scripture by pointing to its defects. The seventeenth-century dogmaticians thus felt constrained to ascribe a new importance to the reliability of scripture. Criteria by which its divine authorship might be known were now underlined. Individual theologians argued for the detailed inspiration of scripture and the inerrancy of its information in every area of knowledge. A few even took the bold step of espousing the inspiration of the Hebrew pointing.

Some commentators have found in this new approach evidence of a final insecurity, as though scripture had to be shored up by human arguments if its credibility were to be retained. Others perceive a normal course of intellectual formalization which processes the raw materials of the Reformation. Admirers of the seventeenth century read the situation differently. As they see it, rational tools are undoubtedly employed, but only to give added precision and intellectual force to substantially the same matter.

Support can easily be mustered for all these theses. In the last analysis, however, all of them are evaluations or hypotheses, not provable facts. That a change takes place between the reformers and their more scholastic successors can hardly be denied. It also need occasion no surprise. With a changing situation changes of some kind always take place, whether good, bad, or indifferent. What precisely the changes are in this instance may best be seen, not from interpretation, but from exposition of the actual teaching. This is where we begin. The possible implications may be sought elsewhere.

## B. LUTHERAN: QUENSTEDT

### 1. The Lutheran Dogmaticians

A long line of eminent Lutherans did extensive exegetical and dogmatic work during the later sixteenth and the seventeenth centuries. A. Hunnius played an important transitional role in the final years of the century of the Reformation. Gerhard and N. Hunnius were at work at the beginning of the seventeenth century, while Calov and Quenstedt dominated the middle and later years, and Baier and Hollaz were significant figures at the end of the period. All these theologians wrote a good deal on scripture, and by and large they held the same or very similar views, although not without variations in detail. Some arbitrariness is involved, then, in selecting one of them as a Lutheran spokesman, but J. A. Quenstedt, in his work *Theologia Didactico-Polemica sive Systema Theologicium,* will probably serve as well as any other to fill this role.

## 2. Scripture as Source and Rule

For Quenstedt scripture constitutes the noetic principle of theology. It is the unique and utterly reliable source of the knowledge of God. Nothing is known of the divine mysteries except through the divine revelation in scripture (1.12). As the source, scripture is also the norm. At first revelation was published by word of mouth, but once it was committed to writing the written word became the norm (1.35). Oral traditions could not and cannot compete with scripture as another source or rule of revelation.

## 3. Scripture as God's Word

Since God makes himself known in scripture, it may properly be defined as the voice and word of God (1.93). Scripture can, of course, be viewed simply in terms of its outward form as word, and at this level even the unregenerate can understand it. It can also be viewed, however, in terms of its inward form as God's Word, and at this level it can be received only by the enlightened mind (1.56). In its nature as the Word of God scripture has a fourfold function. (a) It distinguishes between true and false doctrine. (b) It brings us to faith in Christ. (c) It strengthens faith. (d) It calls the heathen to faith and salvation (2.62). Scripture cannot be replaced, for God has chosen no other means of revealing himself to us today (2.62).

## 4. Scripture and Inspiration

For Quenstedt the inspiration of scripture is an absolutely unique and extraordinary action of God (1.69). It may be considered from three angles: the act of inspiration, plenary inspiration, and verbal inspiration.

### a. The Act of Inspiration

When the authors of scripture are inspired they receive a supernatural enlightenment and also an impulse to write. Inspiration, then, involves illumination, incitement, and the supply of content and even words by the Holy Spirit (1.69). The whole Trinity, of course, is at work in inspiration. The voice of the Father is heard as well as that of Christ and the Spirit (1.92). Yet inspiration may be seen particularly as a ministry of the Holy Spirit. He inspires both the writers and the writings (1.70).

### b. Plenary Inspiration

Inspiration extends to everything recorded in scripture. Even the many things known or knowable to the authors before they wrote were inspired and dictated by the Spirit (1.68ff.). Things not of a spiritual nature are no less inspired than those that are (1.71). God has his own reasons for having even trivial matters (*levicula*) recorded; indeed, what seems trivial to us has its own importance in relation to the divine counsel (1.71). 2 Timothy 3:16 does not permit of any distinction between inspired and uninspired or merely superintended portions or classes of scripture. 2 Peter 1:21 is to the same effect. As Quenstedt observes, "the *lalia* pertains to all things that are contained in scripture." It does not refer merely to doctrinal matters, as though historical, ethical, and scientific matters "were added by their own [the authors'] free action and inspiration after the urge of the Spirit ceased" (1.70). For Quenstedt plenary inspiration is vital. Who is to distinguish what is merely human from what is also divine? To deny the inspiration of one verse is to deny the inspiration of all verses and thus to overthrow the authority of scripture.

### c. Verbal Inspiration

Plenary inspiration carries with it the implication of verbal inspiration. Quenstedt endorses this firmly: "The Holy Spirit not only inspired the content and sense, or the meaning of the words . . . but the Holy Spirit actually supplied, inspired and dictated the very words and each and every term individually" (1.72). This did not rule out the activity of the human authors, for they were the instrumental cause as the Holy Spirit was the first cause (1.72). Neither were the words inspired apart from their meaning, for, as Quenstedt points out, "the words apart from their sense are not truly and properly the Word of God" (1.157). Nevertheless, the converse is also true. The meaning is not inspired without the words (1.73). As words and content are inseparable, so they are inseparably inspired. Only as the words were also given by God can we be sure of the inspired meaning (1.75).

## 5. Autographs and Apographs

To what extent are copies of scripture inspired? The Lutherans differed on this matter. Some took the view that only the originals enjoy full inspiration. Others claimed no less inspiration for the apographs on the ground that they preserve the content of the autographs. Quenstedt, however, took the even more difficult position that the apographs are fully inspired because the words as well as the content of the autographs are substantially retained in them. When 2 Timothy 3:16 was written, only the apographs of the Old Testament were available, and it is to these that the term *theopneustos* applies. Inspiration and divine authority originally inhere in the autographs, but they now "belong to the apographs by reason of their derivation, since they were faithfully transcribed from them, so that not only the sense but also the words were exactly the same" (1.206). Whether Quenstedt is making the same claim for all apographs of all ages is not wholly clear. It hardly seems possible that he can have done so in the light of the many obvious variants even in the known manuscripts of his time.

## 6. Scripture and Inerrancy

The plenary and verbal inspiration of scripture leads on naturally to its inerrancy, which was increasingly underscored by the Lutherans as the century proceeded. It is not something which has to be proved to support inspiration. On the contrary, it is taken for granted as a correlate and consequence. As Quenstedt vigorously claims, if the biblical authors, although in themselves fallible, were moved by the Spirit of truth, "it follows that they could under no condition make mistakes in their writing, and no falsification, no error, no danger of error, no untruth existed or could exist in their preaching or writing" (1.79). This inerrancy means freedom from error of every kind, not only from lying and deceit, but from inaccuracy as well (1.77). It extends to words as well as content; "there is no error, even the slightest, either in content or words" (1.77). It also extends to every type of content: "Every single word . . . is most true, whether it relates to doctrine, ethics, history, chronology, typography, or onomastics" (1.77, cf. Calov, *Systema*, 1.564). Quenstedt can thus issue the solemn warning that "whatever fault or untruth, whatever error or lapse of memory, is attributed to the prophets or apostles is not imputed to them without blaspheming the Holy Spirit who spoke and wrote through them" and who "cannot be ignorant of anything, forget anything, . . . cannot deceive anyone, neither can he lead anyone into offence or error" (1.80).

## 7. Scripture and Dictation

If the Holy Spirit supplied the words and overruled the fallibility of the human authors, what room does this monergistic teaching leave for the humanity of scripture? Quenstedt makes various points which, as he sees it, help answer this question.

### a. Enlightenment

It must be recalled that inspiration embraces enlightenment. Thus the biblical authors write consciously and with an understanding of what they write. Mantic views are ruled out; indeed, they are to be specifically opposed (1.69).

### b. Human Will

At the level of origin and efficacy, it is true, the human will plays no role in the authorship. Yet it does have a part at the subjective and material level. Thus one can say that the penmen "wrote voluntarily, willingly, knowingly" (1.57).

### c. Accommodation

Futhermore, the Holy Spirit accommodated himself to the natural understanding and endowment of the holy writers so as to record the mysteries according to the usual mode of speech (1.76). This accommodation might allow for what pagans would describe as barbarisms and solecisms, although Quenstedt defensively resists the existence of such stylistic faults, as distinct from Hellenisms and Hebraisms. Indeed, he suggests that to charge scripture with barbarisms and solecisms is to pass impudent judgment on God, from whom the words and phrases of scripture derive. Accommodation, then, is of a carefully restricted nature.

### d. Dictation

Quenstedt does not equate the term "dictation" with a mechanical view of inspiration. He uses the term but qualifies it by parallels like suggestion (cf. 1.68). Thus the spontaneous operation of the faculties of the writers is also asserted. If a contradiction seems to emerge, the solution is found in the sovereign freedom of the Spirit to say what he wishes to be said through the words which come most naturally to those through whom he says it. In other words, the Spirit does not enforce his own words on the authors. He dictates in their style, not his. He is well able to do this.

## 8. Scripture and Authority

The ground of scriptural authority forms a crucial point in the seventeenth-century debate. Roman Catholics argue that scripture's authority rests on the witness of the church. Lutherans dissent. As Quenstedt says, human witness can result in no more than human faith (1.91). Scripture itself engenders faith in itself. He finds support for this in 1 Thessalonians 2:13, where the Thessalonians are convinced of the authority of the message by its divine authorship and effect, not by the fact that Paul preaches it. Like Christ, scripture needs no external testimony. The church can lead us to scripture but we accept it, not because of the church's word, but by the operation of the Holy Spirit, by which "we clearly perceive in our hearts the majesty and holiness and truth of the word" (1.88.92–93). Far from being guaranteed by the church's authority, self-authenticating scripture establishes the church's authority.

## 9. Scripture and the Criteria

What is meant by the self-authentication of scripture? The Lutherans find it in certain external and internal criteria which argue in favor of scripture's authority. The external criteria include such things as antiquity, accompanying miracles, the martyrs, and the growth of the church. Among the internal criteria are the truthfulness of scripture, its style, its harmony, and its spiritual power. It is agreed that the external criteria give only intellectual belief. Quenstedt takes what is perhaps the majority view when he says this applies to some of the internal criteria too (1.94), although Hollaz disputes this on the ground that essentially, if not formally, the inner criteria are the same as self-authenticating scripture itself.

### 10. Scripture and the Spirit

#### a. Inner Witness

The Spirit's role in inspiration has been noted already. In addition, however, the Spirit bears inner witness to the authority of scripture. Through scripture he grants certainty about scripture. Opinions vary slightly concerning the relation of this witness to the self-authenticating power of scripture and the criteria. It is generally accepted, however, that the Spirit alone gives true assurance of the authority of scripture, yet not in detachment from the reading of scripture itself.

#### b. Enlightenment

The Spirit's ministry relates also to the understanding of scripture. Scripture is clearly written, so that unbelievers know what it is saying. Yet it deals with divine mysteries which sinners do not comprehend, for their minds are darkened. The church alone cannot help here; only the Holy Spirit can illuminate the darkened mind through the "inherent light" of scripture itself (1.124).

#### c. Efficacy

Scripture as God's Word has intrinsic power to bring about spiritual results directly and properly. It does this, however, as means, not as principal cause. The Holy Spirit works in and with the Word in this regard to accomplish enlightenment and regeneration (1.176). It is argued by some, such as Calov, that scripture has this power inherently before and apart from its use. Quenstedt, however, prefers to speak of a first act — the potentiality — and a second act — the actuality (1.171). Either way the power is linked to the ongoing union of Word and Spirit: "God does not work separately without the Word nor the Word separately without God but God works with the Word and through the Word" (2.704). The work of the Word and that of the Spirit are one in a unity of energy and operation. It is the Holy Spirit who works with the Word and through it. Hence the power of the Word is the power of God (2.704–705).

### 11. Scripture and Christ

In relation to the efficacy of the Word Christ plays no less significant a role than the Spirit. There are three reasons for this. (a) Only
the gospel, of which Christ is the theme and center, acts efficaciously as
a means of grace. (b) The gospel is united both to the Holy Spirit and also
to the eternal Word. (c) In this union Christ himself comes to us, so that
he is bestowed as well as preached. The centrality of Christ is perhaps
not as plainly brought out here as it is by Luther. Nevertheless, scripture still has no autonomous importance or power. Christ and faith in
him take precedence of scripture and faith in it. Scripture may well be
called the noetic source of theology, but it is not the ontic source. God the
Father as source, Christ as theme, and the Holy Spirit as active cause
are not crowded out by the biblical word which is the means of grace
and power.


## C. REFORMED: WOLLEBIUS


### 1. Location

As noted in the previous chapter, Wollebius develops the doctrine
of scripture in his brief prolegomena. Indeed, he devotes most of the
prolegomena to this development. Having defined theology and discussed its divisions and nature (props. 1–2), he then states his ontic and
noetic principles (prop. 3). God is the principle of being, and "the principle by which he is known is the word of God" (prop. 3). Since scripture
has this noetic function, it seems logical to Wollebius that he should deal
with it before proceeding to the ontic principle. In contrast, Ames takes
a completely different course, placing scripture within the doctrine of
the ministry, which is subdivided into extraordinary ministry — the
inerrant work of the prophets and apostles (i.33.25–26) — and ordinary
ministry — the preaching and teaching of holy scripture (i.34).


### 2. The Unwritten and Written Word

Wollebius recognizes that the Word of God embraces more than
scripture. It first exists in unwritten form. The written form, however, is
not contingent but derives from God's command. Now that the unwritten form has been replaced, God's Word can be clearly equated with
scripture (prop. 4). Hence Wollebius concludes that theology finds its
only basis in scripture. Ames concurs, suggesting that "by divine writings there might be a perpetual use and fruit" of the extraordinary
ministry (i.34.1).

### 3. Divine Authorship

For Wollebius, the question of the status of scripture is quickly settled by its divine authorship and authority, which is held among all Christians (prop. 6). He dismisses as improper any question of whether scripture is God's Word. People who deny this ought not to be heard (prop. 7). Unlike Ames, Wollebius does not in this connection advance any specific doctrine of inerrancy (cf. Ames i.34). He does not dispute this, but feels no reason to stress it.

### 4. Witness to Scripture

How do we know the "divinity" of scripture? Wollebius differentiates what he calls a primary witness and a ministerial witness.

#### a. Primary Witness

The primary witness is that of the Holy Spirit, which again takes on a double form, the external and the internal. (1) External. Externally the Spirit witnesses in scripture itself to the divine origin and authority of the Word, in such phrases as "Thus says the Lord," or in verses like 2 Timothy 3:16 and 2 Peter 1:21. (2) Internal. Internally the Spirit speaks in the heart and mind of the believer, enlightening him so that he "recognizes the voice of God's Spirit speaking in the scriptures" (prop. 9).

#### b. Ministerial Witness

This is the witness of the church. The church does not form the basis of scripture's authority, nor does it confer "divinity" on scripture. The Spirit as author takes precedence here for four reasons. (1) He is his own best witness; (2) he is in intimate union with us; (3) he opens our eyes to the wonderful things of scripture; (4) he has the function of leading us into all truth. The church's witness, then, has a servant function. So, too, do the various aspects of scripture which confirm it as God's Word: the presentation of God as speaker, the supernatural gifts of the authors, the harmonious recording of events in different versions, and the effectiveness of the writings to God's glory and our salvation (prop. 9).

### 5. The Canon

Wollebius accepts as canonical the Hebrew Old Testament and the acknowledged books of the Greek New Testament (prop. 10). The Old Testament Apocrypha may be "read with profit" but cannot be accorded "the same authority for proving articles of faith as the canonical books." Four reasons are advanced for this: (a) the apocryphal books were written later and not by prophets; (b) they were not written in Hebrew;

(c) they are not quoted in the New Testament; (d) they contain myths, contradictions, and "many things at variance with the canonical records" (prop. 11). Ames, by the way, makes the useful point that omission of an author's name from a canonical book does not lessen its worth or authority. He also emphasizes the public giving of scripture to the church by God himself (i.34.8–9).

### 6. The Perfection of Scripture

When speaking of the perfection of scripture Wollebius has predominantly in mind its sufficiency, that is, its perfection for purposes of salvation, as mentioned in 2 Timothy 3:16. This is no abstract perfection but the full ability of scripture to do what it is designed to do, that is, to lead us to salvation and Christian maturity (prop. 12).

### 7. Ecclesiastical Rules

Wollebius does not insist, of course, on the exclusive authority of scripture. Many areas of Christian life in the church are not covered by biblical injunctions. Thus "rules of the church providing for conformity in external rites may be permitted in their proper place." On the other hand, no tradition is necessary to salvation nor is any of equal or superior authority to scripture (prop. 13).

### 8. Biblical Study

Wollebius takes the common Reformation view that scripture is meant to be studied by all Christians. He admits that "some passages are rather obscure" but pleads for perspicuity in the biblical presentation of "the primary articles of religion" (prop. 14).

### 9. Translation

To enable ordinary Christians to read scripture, scholars must translate it into "the common language of every nation." If the authenticity of a translation is to be accepted, the work must be in agreement with the Hebrew and Greek originals (prop. 15). Ames, in his discussion of translations, adds that inerrancy cannot be ascribed to them. They are authentic insofar as they express what is in the sources. They are thus to be tested by the sources. Ames admits that only copies of the sources are now available but believes that these have been preserved from serious defect. He agrees with Wollebius that versions are reliable so long as they agree with the sources in essentials (1.34.28–32).

### 10. Interpretation

While Wollebius states that the church has been given the task of interpretation, he insists that "the supreme judge of interpretation is the Holy Spirit speaking in scripture, not the Roman Church, its councils, or the pope" (prop. 17). The biblical text has only a single sense except that the meaning of some Old Testament prophecies is composite, that is, literal as well as typical or mystical. The typical sense is learned from the New Testament and has a christological reference (prop. 18). Wollebius suggests nine procedures by which the true sense may be discovered: prayer; linguistic study; investigation of the originals; inquiry into argument and purpose; distinction between the literal and figurative; understanding of causes, circumstances, and consequences; logical analysis; comparison of the clear and the obscure and the like and the like; and, finally, the rule of faith (prop. 19). Prayer obviously includes the enlightenment of the Spirit which Ames specifically mentions in a similar passage. Wollebius would also agree with Ames that while individual parts of scripture were written for special purposes and occasions, "in God's intention they are equally for the instruction of the faithful of all ages" (1.34.14). Interpretation aims at application.

## D. CONCLUSIONS

From our survey of Quenstedt and Wollebius, who, in spite of their different backgrounds, are clearly in substantial agreement on the doctrine of scripture, it may be accepted without demur that there is a distinction of form and nuance and emphasis between the seventeenth-century dogmaticians and their Reformation predecessors. On the other hand, one may legitimately question whether many of the criticisms that are brought against the new and more systematic presentation are justified. In particular, four of the sharpest charges seem to betray a considerable amount of exaggeration.

Mechanical inspiration, for instance, is not only not taught by Quenstedt or Wollebius but is specifically repudiated by the former and implicitly concluded by the latter, who does not even develop a detailed doctrine of inspiration. Inerrancy is unquestionably given prominence in Quenstedt, as it is also in Ames, but here again Wollebius provides some counterbalance, and Quenstedt neither defends inerrancy rationalistically nor makes it an apologetic basis for his belief in inspiration. Both Quenstedt and Wollebius stress the centrality of scripture as the source and noetic principle of faith. They also claim that it serves sufficiently and effectively to salvation. Yet here again they both keep in mind that God is the source and object of both scripture and faith and that scripture serves finally as a means instead of being a primary cause or end. Their strong emphasis on scripture does not exclude a careful delineation and distinction of its function. The objection that the criteria of scripture now play a bigger part in assurance of its authority has some merit. Nevertheless, both Quenstedt and Wollebius recognize that the testimony of the Spirit in and by the self-authenticating word can alone give final certainty regarding the divine authority and authorship. Indeed, Wollebius contends forcefully that the norm of faith and conduct is not scripture in isolation but the voice of the Spirit speaking through it. Similarly, Quenstedt ascribes the efficacious operation of scripture, not to the text alone, but to the ministry of the Spirit working in and through the text.

In these writers the doctrine of scripture is no doubt entering on a new phase. Tendencies may be discerned in the presentation which give evidence of some movement away from the Reformation emphases. The movement, however, has not yet proceeded very far. The tendencies are only tendencies. What change there has been is more in style, or, materially, in elaboration. The substance of the Reformation doctrine of scripture has not yet been altered, let alone abandoned.

# CHAPTER XXIII

# Reformed and Methodist: Predestination and Sanctification

## A. PREDESTINATION

### 1. Wollebius

#### a. Background

As early as the first part of the seventeenth century the Arminians, aided by the Lutherans and Roman Catholics, presented a serious challenge to the Reformation doctrine of election. A not unexpected result was the tightening of the doctrine at the Synod of Dort, from which emerged the five points of total depravity, unconditional election, limited atonement, irresistible grace, and perseverance that were to become the hallmark of Calvinism in later theologians and in documents such as the Westminster Confession. Arminianism, however, was by no means crushed. In particular it found a home in High Church Anglicanism, and in the middle of the eighteenth century John Wesley, the founder of Methodism, who had both a High Church and a Puritan heritage, became its unabashed and stalwart proponent. By this time, as the writings of Jonathan Edwards show, a philosophical issue had to some degree overshadowed and even replaced the theological one. Wesley, however, wished to deal with the matter at the biblical and theological level. It might be instructive, then, to contrast his Arminian criticism and reconstruction with an older Reformed statement such as that of Wollebius.

#### b. Place of the Doctrine

Under the general heading of predestination Wollebius finds an early place for the doctrine. After the prolegomena he first turns to the essence of God (1.1), then to the persons of the Godhead (i.2), and then to the words and the general decrees of God (i.3). Discussion of the decrees opens the door at once to predestination, which becomes the theme of i.4 and which is then followed by creation in i.5 and providence in i.6. Wollebius, by the way, distinguishes between God's eternal provi-dence and his actual providence. The decrees are "eternal providence," and in this sense predestination forms a part of providence (i.3.3, prop. 1). Eternal providence relates to the immanent or inner will of God as predestination does. Actual providence relates, of course, to the external works of God as the execution of the decrees. In this sense predestination and providence are to be considered apart.

### c. Definition

Wollebius defines predestination as a special decree of God by which "he has ordained that the glory of his grace, mercy, and justice shall be revealed in rational creatures" (i.4.1.3). It differs from a general decree in its application to rational creatures alone. In a general decree God wills to reveal his glory "in the creation and preservation of all things" (i.4.1.2).

### d. Distinctions

(1) Destiny and Means. To God, predestination is a single act, but for us a distinction arises between destiny and means. As Wollebius points out, predestination relates to both: "Anyone who is predestined as to destiny is also predestined as to means" (i.4.1, props. 1–2).

(2) Angels and Men. Following an ancient tradition Wollebius includes angels as well as men under predestination, since good angels are preserved and fallen angels condemned. But he does not relate the limited number of the elect to the vacancies left by fallen angels (i.4.2.1–3).

(3) Absolute and Non-absolute. Wollebius describes the cause of predestination as absolute, since God's free will is the efficient cause. As to object, however, it is not absolute, since the object is certain men, not man in general (i.4.2, props. 3–4). Nor is it absolute as to means, since the means are not the same in the case of the elect on the one side and the reprobate on the other.

(4) Election and Reprobation. Predestination covers both election and reprobation. God's grace and mercy are glorified by the unmerited salvation of some, while his justice is glorified by the merited condemna-tion of others. The two together constitute predestination as previously defined (prop. 4).

### e. Problems of Reprobation

Wollebius found three problems in reprobation. (1) Why does God reprobate his own creatures? To this the answer lies in the material cause — sinful and guilty man. (2) Why does not God elect all or reprobate all? The purpose of predestination, the glorifying of both mercy and justice, supplies the answer here. (3) Why does God elect this one and reprobate that one? The only answer in this case is to be found in the active cause: this is how God wills it (prop. 8).

## f. Christ and Election

(1) As Cause. Christ plays a twofold role in election. As the God-man he is with the Father and the Holy Spirit the efficient cause of our election. He is thus to be regarded as the electing God, to use the later phrase of Barth (prop. 9).

(2) As Means. As mediator Christ is also "the means of carrying out our election." Wollebius does not say specifically, as some of his contemporaries did, that we are elect only in Christ, but he quotes Romans 8:28-29 to show that we are predestined to conformity with Christ (props. 9–10). As mediator Christ is the cause of salvation, not of election (prop. 12).

## g. Reprobation

Wollebius does not think one can teach election and deny reprobation, for reprobation is no less plainly taught in scripture (prop. 11). No one can argue that lack of faith is the cause of reprobation. It causes damnation, the means whereby reprobation is executed, not reprobation itself (prop. 12). Wollebius agrees with those who object that God would not create man for damnation. He points out, however, that the glorifying of God's justice, not damnation, is the purpose of reprobation. Damnation serves as a means to achieve this, for by it "the person who has been rejected brings about evil for himself" (prop. 13). Within reprobation two acts may be assumed, preterition, or the denial of unmerited grace, and precondemnation, or deliverance to merited punishment. The fall provides the mechanism for the fulfillment of these acts, for only the guilty can be reprobated (or elected!) (prop. 4). Sin, while not the cause of reprobation, is its necessary condition and a cause of reprobability (as also of electability) (prop. 5). This is why the decree of predestination presupposes the decrees of creation, mutable divine likeness, and permission of the fall (prop. 6).

## h. Marks of Election

Wollebius gives evidence of an important shift when he discusses the marks of election. Instead of pointing, as Calvin did, to Christ as the mirror of election, he suggests that we "make a beginning from our sanctification" as a means of executing election. If by God's grace I know that I have the gift of sanctification, then I am "justified, called, and elect" (prop. 15). If good works must be subordinate to election, they cannot be "separated from it, since they are the means by which it is carried out, and certified to us" (prop. 16). Balanced and healthy though this is in itself, it opens the door to the almost morbid introspection which in many circles characterizes the pursuit of assurance of election through its necessary manifestation. While it is diabolical to say that works are useless if I am reprobate, it is contradictory "for anyone to be both reprobate and marked by good works" (prop. 16).

### i. Contrasting Features in Ames

(1) Place. While Ames agrees substantially with Wollebius in his understanding of predestination, he has some emphases of his own which merit brief attention. He places the doctrine under the general heading of the application of redemption and finds it intimated first by its application to some but not to all and by "the manifest difference which therefore arises between men in the dispensation of grace," although in itself it has existed from eternity (i.25.1).

(2) Relation of Means and Ends. Ames has a short but interesting section on the succession of means and ends. There is only one act of will in God because in him all things are simultaneous. Hence it is only a human way of speaking to put end before means or means before end. Both being willed by God, end and means do not succeed but concur (i.25.14).

(3) Christ and Election. If Ames weakens the christological aspect of election by not referring to Christ's role as the Son of God, he strengthens it by relating election primarily to Christ: "God made only one election in Christ. . . . Christ may be considered as first elected as head and then some men as members in him" (i.25.27).

(4) Reprobation and Election. Ames stresses more strongly than Wollebius the negative character of rejection compared with election. Salvation is an end in election, but damnation is not an end in reprobation (i.25.33). Indeed, since the negative setting apart of the reprobate depends on the positive setting apart of the elect, the remote end of reprobation is the same as that of election (i.25.36). If love in election bestows good directly, hatred in rejection only denies good and does not inflict evil, which is merited and self-inflicted (i.25.38). Election is a cause of salvation, reprobation an antecedent and not a cause of sin and damnation (i.25.40). Sin, not the permission to sin, causes "forsaking hardening, and punishment" (i.25.41). Ames, then, avoids the counterbalancing of election and rejection which has often been charged against seventeenth-century theology, but he plainly does so within the context of the teaching of Dort against which John Wesley so violently reacts. It would certainly be too much to claim that the Puritanism of Ames forms something like a bridge to the Arminianism of Wesley.

## 2. Wesley

### a. The Controversy

John Wesley became embroiled in debate about predestination almost from the very beginning of his evangelistic ministry in 1738. In November of that year George Whitefield invited him to share in the open-air work at Bristol. Wesley had doubts about the whole procedure, partly because of the field preaching and partly because of the prominence of the divine decrees in Whitefield's sermons. Overcoming his scruples, he joined Whitefield and was thus led to his true ministry. At the same time, however, he clearly taught a universal atonement and unfortunately initiated the conflict with Calvinists by publishing his sermon on *Free Grace*. Not unexpectedly, replies were issued and for the rest of his life Wesley devoted no little time and energy, whether in sermons, tracts, articles, or even hymns, to the refutation of Calvinism and the promotion of what he regarded as the true biblical teaching of election. An example of his approach may be found in the treatise *Predestination Calmly Considered (Library of Protestant Thought,* pp. 427–472), which he wrote and published in 1752.

### b. Irresistible Grace

(1) The Experience. Wesley opens this work by admitting that many believers experience a divine working which they have "no power to 'resist' " (sec. 1). God graciously upholds and corrects them in such a way that they realize that everything is of him and nothing of self, even faith being a gift of God "before which no good work can be done" (2–3).

(2) The Inference. From this fact of experience the inference is often drawn "that the true grace of God *always* works *irresistibly* in every believer." This leads to the doctrine of double predestination, as in Calvin and the Reformed confessions. God works irresistibly in those whom he has elected and does not work in the reprobate (4–7).

### c. A Compromise

A compromise Wesley will not accept is that whereas irresistible grace gives evidence of election, one cannot speak of a corresponding reprobation. To assert election without reprobation is inconsistent: "In holding one you must hold both" (8). Calvin himself taught that "election cannot stand without reprobation" (9). This, he thinks, is self-evident and should be candidly admitted (9–15).

### d. Two Elections

(1) Unconditional. Wesley himself sees two elections in scripture. The first is indeed unconditional, but it has to do with service, not salvation. It is "a divine appointment of some particular men to do some particular work." It may not always be an election to salvation, as one can see from the case of Judas (16).

(2) Conditional. The second election, which is "a divine appointment of some men to eternal happiness," is conditional, as is the corresponding rejection. The condition of election is faith, of reprobation, unbelief. All believers are elect, all unbelievers are reprobate (17). If believers can be called elect before they believe, this is because God "sees all eternity at one view" (18), and not because of a prior and unconditional decree (18–19).

### e. Reprobation and Scripture

Wesley concedes that he cannot accept unconditional election because he cannot accept unconditional reprobation. Why not? Because so many scriptures rule it out, such as those which speak of God's universal willingness to save (20), those which refer to Christ's death for all (21), and those which "declare the justice of God" (22). Scripture does not say that God in his justice might have let all sinners perish, nor does it single out the sovereignty of God as a possible ground of reprobation, for "all his attributes are inseparably joined" (23). In the condemnation of impenitent sinners "God proceeds according to the known rules of his justice and mercy." Sovereignty is never given as the cause why any man is punished with everlasting destruction (29).

### f. Problems of Reprobation and Justice

(1) Ground of Condemnation. Pursuing the matter of justice in greater detail, Wesley sees a conflict between unconditional reprobation and justice, since on this view the condemned are in the last analysis lost because they are reprobate, not because they have done evil (31).

(2) Inability Not to Sin. To be sure, outer and inner sins have been committed. These merit punishment. Yet in default of grace sinners are said to have no power not to commit them. How, then, can a man be condemned for what "God could have saved him from but would not"? (33).

(3) Original Sin. If it is argued that original sin is the basis of judgment, Wesley has two questions: first, "What do you mean by this term?" and second, Where does scripture say that "any will be damned for this alone"? (24).

(4) Unbelief. Unbelief might be cited as the ground of punishment, but here again the problem of inability arises (25). This problem is compounded in that if Christ died for the elect alone, the reprobate have no object for their faith: "There never was any object for thy faith. . . . God himself . . . could not make thee believe Christ atoned for thy sins, unless he had made thee believe a lie" (36). Parenthetically, Wesley claims that reprobation is fully and finally refuted by the threefold fact that Christ died for all, that he is the propitiation for the sins of the whole world, and that he died for all that they might be saved (39).

### g. Problems of Reprobation and Sincerity

(1) God's Good Will. Many scriptures testify to the good will of God toward sinners. How can these be sincere, Wesley asks, if in fact some who are addressed are eternally excluded from penitence and salvation? (40–41).

(2) Christ's Invitation. Similarly Christ issues a general invitation which is repeated in the preaching of the gospel. How can release be preached to captives if God is "unalterably determined in himself never to open the doors for them"? (42).

### h. Problems of Reprobation and Love

(1) Eternal Love. As Wesley sees it, scripture says plainly that God's love "extends even to those who neither love nor fear him" (43). What can this mean, however, if from all eternity he withholds his salvation from the reprobate?

(2) Temporal Love. Can it mean merely that he gives them "gifts of nature and of providence"? Wesley sees no love here if the recipients of these blessings are merely like oxen which God is "fatting" for the slaughter" (43). Grace of this kind is "damning grace." It is unthinkable that God should deal thus "with any soul which he had made" (45).

### i. Free Will and God's Glory

Much of the difficulty arises because a false conflict is seen between man's freedom and God's glory. Oddly, natural freedom has never been seen as a threat in this regard. Furthermore, Wesley himself contends only for "a measure of free will supernaturally restored to every man" (46), so that he, too, ascribes "to God alone the whole glory of our salvation" (47). The core of the matter, however, is whether God is more glorified by unconditional reprobation than by freedom of the will (51). In terms of God's wisdom (52), justice (53), love (54), and even sovereignty (55), unchangeableness (59), and faithfulness (60), freedom surely does more to enhance his glory than reprobation.

### j. The Problem of Divine Sovereignty

(1) Pharaoh. The hardening of Pharaoh might be adduced as an instance of God acting in sheer sovereignty. Wesley, however, raises two important points here. (a) Can we be sure that the reference is to eternal condemnation? (b) If it is, is not Pharaoh punished "because of his own stubbornness and impenitence"? (56).

(2) Esau. Esau is also quoted as a typical reprobate, but again Wesley has two reservations. (a) Scripture depicts his awareness of sin and his reconciliation with Jacob, so that there is hope of his salvation (57). (b) The passages in Romans 9:12–13 and Malachi 1:2–3 obviously refer to his posterity, not to his person (58).

### k. Perseverance

(1) The covenant. The covenant is often cited in relation to unconditional election. Wesley rejects as totally unbiblical the idea of a covenant between the Father and the Son for the election of some and the rejection of others (61). He regards faith as the pivot of the biblical covenant (62) so that the covenant is conditional, as various scriptures from Genesis, Exodus, Leviticus, and Romans suggest (63–67). God will certainly keep his side, but only if man's side is kept, too.

(2) Preservation. Will believers be kept from falling away by the faithfulness of God? Wesley finds no scriptural support for this and the witness of experience is ambivalent (68). Some verses, however, seem to

indicate that "one who is a true believer . . . may nevertheless finally fall from grace." Here Wesley discusses a long list ranging from Ezekiel 18 to Hebrews 10 (69–78), and he adds more references for readers "to weigh farther at their leisure" (79). Against the charge that he is making salvation conditional Wesley retorts that he is not making it anything but is simply reporting what he finds.

### l. Antinomianism

Wesley's final problem with unconditional election and rejection is that it "tends to hinder the inward work of God in every stage" (86). On this view no warning or promise can help those who live carelessly. If they are reprobate they are lost anyway, and if elect they will be brought to salvation by God. Again, the believer with an assurance of salvation "grows a little and a little slacker till ere long he falls again into the sin from which he was clean escaped." Thinking he is in grace, "he sins on, and sleeps on till he awakes in hell" (87). Wesley's ultimate concern is pastoral. "The doctrine of absolute predestination leads to the chambers of death." I "oppose it from the same principle whereon I labour to save souls from destruction" (88). It is condemned by its evil effects (89). He thus concludes with an appeal for unity in the pursuit of holiness. Whether one can agree or not on other matters, scripture states plainly that "without holiness no man shall see the Lord." Mutual assistance is unquestionably needed if we are to grow in grace, in service, and in the knowledge of Christ (90). Sanctification, not predestination, is ultimately the dominating and controlling issue.

## B. SANCTIFICATION

### 1. Ames

#### a. Preliminary Considerations

As we have just seen, Wesley had a practical concern for holiness in his criticism of the Reformed doctrine of predestination. The example of Ames, however, shows that incompatibility did not have to exist between Reformed teaching and Christian practice. Ames no less than Wesley had a concern for sanctification. Where the difference arose was not in concern, or even in degree of concern, but in understanding.

#### b. Location of Sanctification

Ames places sanctification, like predestination, in the context of the application of redemption. It is dealt with here as an aspect of communion. A relative communion, that is, a communion of relation, is seen in justification. An absolute or real communion is achieved in sanctification and glorification, which manifest justification and bring its consequences into being in an alteration of qualities (i.29.1–3).

### c. Definition

In this connection sanctification does not denote separation or consecration but "the real change in man from the sordidness of sin to the purity of God's image" (i.29.4). This is not a change of relation or intent but "a change of quality and disposition as the gift of inherent grace" (i.29.7–8). It affects the whole man, although it begins in the soul, and within the soul in the will (i.29.10–11).

### d. Starting Point and End

Sanctification starts from the stain of sin and ends with the purity of God's image (i.29.13–14). The sanctification of the Christian differs here from that of Christ's human nature, which "was never defiled by unholiness" (i.29.12).

### e. Degrees

Ames posits two degrees of sanctification, that of infancy and that of maturity. The former is a first beginning, the latter a higher stage. Yet even the latter is "only a beginning of the holiness promised and expected." When completion is achieved in the life to come, sanctity will replace sanctification (i.29.16).

### f. Parts

(1) Mortification. Ames follows the familiar line of Reformation teaching when he considers the two parts of sanctification. The first part is "the wasting away of sin" (i.29.18). He finds three causes for this: Christ's death, the meritorious cause; God's spirit, the principally effective cause; faith, the serving cause (i.29.19–21). Denial of self and the world follows, and although sin remains, it is broken, not regnant as in unbelievers (i.29.22–23).

(2) Vivification. Restoration of the divine image constitutes the second and positive part of sanctification. Christ's resurrection is in this instance the exemplary cause, while the effective and serving causes are the same (i.29.26–27). Vivification implies "total commitment, to God and Christ" (i.29.28).

### g. Conflict

"All that are sanctified tend to perfection" but they do not attain to perfect sanctification in this life (i.29.29). Hence the Christian life is marked by a "spiritual war" between the corrupted part of believers (sin) and the renewed part (grace). The sinful part, the flesh, does not lie merely in the appetites but "in the will and reason itself" (i.29.32). The struggle continues throughout the present life, so that "a daily renewal of repentance" is required (i.29.31).

### h. Good Works

Because of the persistence of the corrupted part, "even the best

works of the saints are so corrupted . . . that some remission is needed"
(i.29.34). Nevertheless, "the good works of the regenerate are not to be
called sins; rather, they are said to be defiled with sin" (i.29.35). In
virtue of justification, this defilement does not prevent them from being
"accepted and rewarded by God" (i.29.36). "The taking away of every
imperfection from soul and body and the bestowal of total perfection"
will come for the soul on its separation from the body and for soul and
body together at the last day (i.30.33–34). Perfection in this life exists
only "in the dreams of some fanatics" (i.29.29).

### i. Survey

It will be seen, then, that Ames has little new to offer, only a new
presentation of the basic Reformation understanding. He sees in
sanctification the usual twofold movement of putting off and putting on.
No hope of perfection is held out, but movement toward it is expected.
Sanctification is not stationary but progressive. Assurance of ultimate
sanctity forms a motivating force. This rests, of course, on the fact that
God himself is the sanctifier. Justification without the manifestation
and consequence of sanctification is inconceivable, just as sanctification
constantly reposes in justification. Change of relation means change of
reality, but there can be no change of reality without change of relation.
Quietism is excluded, for in sanctification it is not God's ordaining will,
but his commanding will, which is at issue (ii.1.3). A link is retained
with creation, for sanctification finds its goal in the restoration of the
divine image. An eschatological link is also maintained, for sanctification in this life will issue in sanctity, first of the soul and then of both
soul and body, in the life to come, when the absolute communion of
glorification brings with it the total and perfect good (i.30.1).

### 2. Wesley

#### a. Introduction

If Ames evidences a deep concern for Christian observance, the
same may certainly be said of Wesley. Released by the Aldersgate
experience from attempted works-righteousness, he retained his belief
that sanctification is the goal of justification. This led him, as we have
seen, to oppose a doctrine of predestination which seemed to induce
indolence and passivity. It also led him to resist the common view, held
by Ames, that sanctification cannot in any sense be completed in this
life. Surely, he thought, sin, or the sinful disposition, is not as invincible
as all that. On the other hand, he keenly sensed the danger of illusions
of perfection. Across the years, then, he wrestled with the problem of
perfection (that is, entire sanctification) not without criticism and not
without variations in his own thinking. Two pieces from different
periods, *Christian Perfection* (1741; *LPT*, pp. 254–271) and *The Scripture
Way of Salvation* (1765; *LPT*, pp. 271–282), will serve to illustrate his
teaching.

*b. Christian Perfection*

(1) The Semantic Problem. Wesley acknowledges that the word "perfect" offends many people (1). Yet we cannot abandon it, for it is used in scripture (2). What is needed is an explanation, especially as Paul almost in the same breath calls himself both perfect and imperfect (3). In what sense, we must ask, are Christians imperfect, and in what sense are they perfect? (4).

(2) Imperfection

(a) Ignorance. Wesley learns from both scripture and experience that Christians are not perfect in knowledge. They know many things. They have a basic knowledge of God (1.1). But even apart from natural matters, they still do not know many things about either God (1.2) or his ways and works (1.3).

(b) Mistakes. Ignorance breeds mistakes. Christians are not mistaken about the essentials of salvation, but they can be mistaken as to facts (1.4) and also in "the interpretation of holy writ." This does not prove that they are not God's children but "it is a proof that we are no more to expect any living man to be infallible than omniscient" (1.5).

(c) Infirmities. Christians are also imperfect in the sense that they suffer from infirmities, not as sins, nor merely as physical disabilities, but as mental and social defects, too: "weakness or slowness of understanding . . . incoherency of thought . . . the want of a ready or retentive memory . . . ungracefulness of pronunciation . . . a thousand nameless defects either in conversation or behaviour." Perfection is not given and is not to be looked for in this area (1.7).

(d) Temptations. Christians are not "wholly free from temptation." Some may not feel tempted, but this is due to non-resistance. Others may enjoy periods of freedom. But temptation will recur. Thus the perfection attainable on earth differs from that of heaven. Wesley concludes that there is "no absolute perfection on earth . . . none which does not admit of a continual increase." For perfection, after all, is "only another term for holiness" (1.9).

(3) Perfection

(a) Young Christians. Like Ames, Wesley sees different stages of Christian life. Each has its own perfection (2.1). That of young Christians is not to commit deliberate sin (2.2). They do not continue in sin (2.3). "All real Christians . . . are made free from outward sin" (2.4). Being born of God, they are so far perfect as not to commit sin (2.5).

Wesley will not allow the saying in 1 John to be blunted by qualifications such as that those who are born of God do not sin "habitually" (2.6). Nor does he see the relevance of Old Testament examples of sinful believers: "We cannot measure the privileges of real Christians by those formerly given to the Jews" (2.8). After Pentecost the apostles were made more than conquerors by the Holy Spirit (2.11). If it is argued that Peter and Paul sinned, Wesley thinks it poor logic to infer that all the apostles, or all Christians of the apostolic age, or of all ages, "do and will commit sin as long as they live." Paul's thorn in the flesh he construes, not as sin, but as a physical disability. James teaches that we offend all, but contextually this does not in Wesley's view apply to true believers. 1 John 1:8, he thinks, is demanding confession for the past sin that all have committed. It has no bearing on whether we sin or commit sin now (2.19–20).

(b) Mature Christians. If young Christians are so far perfect as not to commit sin, mature Christians have the added perfection of being "freed from evil thoughts and evil tempers" (2.21). Evil thoughts are not thoughts about evil, such as the evil of others or suggested evil, but thoughts that are themselves evil (2.21). The heart from which such thoughts proceed is cleansed (2.22). Every thought is brought into captivity to the obedience of Christ (2.23). Evil tempers include pride, self-will, and anger "in the common sense of the word, which does not exclude an indignation at sin accompanied by love and tender compassion to the offender" (2.26).

(c) Present Perfection. Wesley closes his treatise with an insistence that one does not have to wait until death for freedom from evil thoughts and tempers. "As he is, so are we in this world" (2.27). Through the cleansing of Christ's blood the Old Testament prophecies have been fulfilled for Christians. In a somewhat paradoxical peroration, then, Wesley encourages his hearers to cleanse themselves from all filthiness of flesh and spirit, perfecting holiness in the fear of God.

### c. The Scripture Way of Salvation

(1) Faith and Salvation. A sense of perfection could give rise to the antinomianism which Wesley so greatly feared. To guard against the idea of assured perfection he thus preached and published *The Scripture Way of Salvation* in which, on the basis of Ephesians 2:8, he aimed to explain the two words which "include the substance of all the Bible . . . namely, faith and salvation." He divided his work into three sections: What is salvation? What is faith? How are we saved by faith? (3).

(2) What Is Salvation? Wesley defines salvation broadly, not just as going to heaven, but also as "a present thing," a blessing we already possess. Since it has a past aspect, too, it "ought to be extended to the entire work of God, from the first dawning of grace in the soul till it is consummated in glory" (1.1).

More specifically, salvation embraces justification and sanctification. The first means pardon, forgiveness, and acceptance on account of Christ's work, with peace, joy, and hope as immediate effects (1.3). The second refers to the real change which comes with the relative one (the same terminology used by Ames) and it begins "at the same time that we are justified" (1.4). The first experience of change, however, soon yields to a realization that "sin was only suspended, not destroyed." Thus two principles are felt to be at war; pride, self-will, anger, and unbelief stir in the heart even though they do not conquer (1.6). What is begun with the new birth is "the gradual work of sanctification" through mortification and renewal (1.8). We "wait for entire sanctification, for a full salvation from all sin, for the perfection of Hebrews 6:1 which is perfect love" (1.9).

(3) What Is Faith? As the evidence of things not seen, faith in a general sense can be equated with the opening of the understanding to the invisible things of God, the spiritual and eternal world, the glory which shall be revealed (2.1). More particularly, however, faith is "divine evidence" that God was in Christ reconciling the world to himself, and that Christ loved me and gave himself for me (2.2). It is by this faith that we receive Christ as prophet, priest, and king (2.2). Faith, then, is the assurance of divine sonship which leads to a "childlike confidence in God" (2.3).

(4) How Are We Saved by Faith? In relation to justification, faith saves because it "is the condition, and the only condition. . . . No man is justified till he believes; every man, when he believes, is justified" (3.1). Repentance and fruits are necessary, too, but not conditionally so. In default of time or opportunity one may be saved without them, but "one cannot be justified without faith. This is impossible." "Repentance and its fruits are only remotely necessary . . . whereas faith is immediately and directly necessary to justification" (3.2).

As regards sanctification, Wesley refutes the common charge that he teaches sanctification by works. As we are justified by faith, so we are sanctified by faith. Faith "is the condition, and the only condition. . . . No man is sanctified till he believes. Every man, when he believes, is sanctified" (3.3). Repentance and fruits, of course, "are, in some sense, necessary," too. This repentance is the repentance consequent to justification whereby we are conscious of sin remaining in the heart and of our utter dependence on free prevenient and accompanying grace to overcome it (3.7–8). The fruits include all works of piety and mercy (3.9–10). A false doctrine claiming the destruction of all sin at justification blocks the way to sanctification by preventing consequent repentance. Hence no place is left for being perfected in love (3.11). Wesley still insists, however, that "there is no possible danger in thus expecting full salvation" (3.12).

In sanctification, too, repentance and fruits are not necessary in the same sense as faith. "A man may be sanctified without them. But he cannot be sanctified without faith." They are only remotely necessary, whereas "faith is immediately and directly necessary to sanctification" (3.13). Faith sanctifies as "a divine evidence and conviction" that God has promised it, that he can do it, that he is willing and able to do it now, and that he does it (3.14–17). The "nowness" of sanctification is underlined here. "God cannot want more time to accomplish whatever is his will." He does not have to wait for us to be more ready or fit. When we realize that he will and can do it now, and are thus confident that he does it, "in that hour it is done" (3.17).

Is sanctification instantaneous, then, or is it gradual? Wesley leaves the matter open, but with a bias to instantaneous sanctification, which he calls "infinitely desirable" if God so wills it. In his exhortation, then, he urges that we should look for this work "every day, every hour, every moment. Why not this hour, this moment? Certainly you may look for it now, if you believe it is by faith." Three things alone are needed: "Expect it by faith; expect it as you are; expect it now." If these things are present, Christ is ready and waiting, and the work of sanctification can be done (3.18).

### d. Questions and Insights

(1) Questions. Obvious questions arise out of Wesley's presentations. The correlation of his views presents a problem. His exegetical procedures can hardly pass unchallenged. Ambiguity, if not incredibility, haunts his attempt to show that Christians are free from sin. His teaching on the different necessity of faith on the one side and repentance and fruits on the other raises complications in regard to both the relative change and the real change. Exactly how present sanctification might be either instantaneous or gradual is not immediately plain. Nor is it plain whether his appeal for present sanctification involves a second work of God — the work of full salvation — or whether it has to do with the first work of God as both justification and sanctification by faith. Either way, will not the present sanctification produce the very assurance of holiness which it is Wesley's intention to shatter?

(2) Insights. To end with questions would be to do a serious injustice to Wesley, who after all was a preacher and pastor, not an exegete and dogmatician. In his work there are insights and concerns which the church can ill afford to ignore. For instance, he maintains a healthy stress on the role of faith and grace in sanctification. His fear of antinomianism does not stampede him into legalism. He also has an especially acute awareness that salvation embraces holiness, the achievement of which is a chief part of Christianity for most believers. If he does not attain clarity in his understanding of perfection, he reminds us constantly both that degrees of perfection can be attained and also that perfection, and nothing less, is the goal. The peril in insisting that perfection can never be attained is a defeatist acceptance of sin. Wesley will have none of this. He does not regard it as an authentic mark of humility. It implies a slothful acceptance of less than the best. To be sure, absolute perfection will not come in this life. But such perfection as may be had is rightly held up as a goal which may be achieved, or at least approximated, as a stage, or a series of stages, on the way to that total fulfillment of the saving work of God which is the final end.

Wesley often was on love. This not made clear.

# CHAPTER XXIV
## *Liberal Pioneers*

If a rationalization of theology may be seen in the Protestant orthodoxy of the seventeenth century, it failed to halt and possibly even helped to promote the development of an autonomy of reason in the century which followed. Orthodoxy itself now came to rely increasingly on rational apologetics. Where Christian doctrines seemed not to measure up to the criteria of reason, neologizers tried to give them a more acceptable content. The deists took the more radical line of reducing Christianity to a natural religion. Miracles in particular constituted a stumbling block in a causally understood universe, and the question of their rational credibility necessarily raised in an acuter form the question of their historical credibility. The new surge of empirical study gave added point to the historical question. The orthodox made a valiant attempt to turn the use of reason and research in their favor, but their pivotal argument for a good universe received a devastating blow from the Lisbon earthquake, and they were hampered in any case by their very acceptance of unregenerate reason as the final judge in matters of God. Theology, it seemed, could no longer give the old answers to new questions. A reduced or reconstructed version of Christianity would have to replace that which had come down from the reformers and their seventeenth-century successors.

## A. LESSING

### 1. Editor of Reimarus

An important figure at this juncture was Gotthold Ephraim Lessing. The son of a pastor, Lessing took up a literary career, but an underlying theological interest surfaced again in 1769 when he became the librarian at Wolfenbüttel. Here, after some early essays in which he aimed to undercut the mediating neology of Halle, Lessing published in

1774 and 1776 some extracts from the *Apology for Rational Worshippers of God* of Hermann Samuel Reimarus. Essentially the six extracts contain little that had not been said already by the English deists. The simple and rational teaching of Jesus, the extracts argue, has been corrupted by dogmatic views of revelation and scripture which will not stand up to investigation. A special revelation which is also universal is pragmatically impossible. The biblical records involve at many points mathematical absurdities. The resurrection narratives cannot be reconciled in detail, and therefore the resurrection itself cannot be accepted as a historical fact. All this is, in Lessing's eyes, superficial. The importance of the extracts does not consist in what they say. Indeed, as editor Lessing himself makes some criticisms and issues some prudential disclaimers. The extracts are important to Lessing because they help to open the door to his own more searching investigation of orthodoxy and more significant reinterpretation of Christianity.

## 2. The Demonstration of the Spirit and of Power

### a. Historical Mediacy

In reply to the Reimarus extracts, J.D. Schumann of Hanover wrote an essay *On the Evidence of the Proofs of the Truth of Christianity*. To this argument based on the miracles and prophecy, Lessing made his own answer in a short but pregnant pamphlet *On the Demonstration of the Spirit and of Power* (1777). His first point here is that since we ourselves did not see the miracles, we are asked to believe not only the miracles but also the witness of those who say they did see them. The proof from miracles has true power only for the first generation. "Miracles which I see with my own eyes . . . are one thing; miracles of which I know only from history that others say they have seen them and verified them are another." "The reports of miracles are not miracles."

### b. Historical Relativism

Historical reports, no matter how well supported, can have only a relative and not an absolute certainty. No one has ever asserted that "what I read in reputable historians is just as certain for me as what I myself experience." Certainly there is no reason to deny that the reports of miracles "are as reliable as historical truths ever can be." But they cannot be treated as absolutely reliable, as they must be, Lessing thinks, if eternal truth is to be proved from them.

### c. History and Truth

In this way Lessing arrives at his famous rejection of historical revelation. "If no historical truth can be demonstrated, then nothing can be demonstrated by means of historical truths." Nor does this mean merely that truth may be historical but cannot be proved historically.

Different types of truth are at issue. "Accidental truths of history can never become the proof of necessary truths of reason." The gap is not just at the level of proof, although that is how Lessing comes at the matter. For, as he admits, even if we believe that a person rose from the dead, this does not mean that he is the Son of God. Already presupposed in the whole discussion, and supposedly forming its conclusion, is the distinction between rational truth which is necessary and historical truth which is contingent.

### d. The Ugly Ditch

It might be argued, of course, that the resurrection is connected to belief in Jesus as the Son of God because Jesus himself taught this and "inspired historians, who cannot make a mistake," recorded it. Here Lessing falls back on his original position. That Jesus taught his deity and historians recorded it may be known only with historical or relative certainty. This, Lessing says, is "the ugly broad ditch which I cannot get across." But what precisely is the ditch? Is it the mediacy of historical knowledge? Is it the relativity of all historical truth? Is it the nature of historical truth in comparison to necessary truth? In any case Lessing is not just rejecting historical fact as a basis of rational truth. He is presupposing that truth in the absolute sense cannot be historical. No jump can be made from historical to necessary truth.

## 3. The Education of the Human Race

### a. The Role of Revelation

At the end of the *Demonstration* Lessing concedes that miracles can be helpful in getting ordinary folk to accept the essential message of Christianity. He develops this thought more fully in his aphorisms on *The Education of the Human Race* (1777–1780). Here he compares revelation to education. All that we gain by education we might acquire for ourselves, but education brings it to us more easily and more quickly. Revelation plays a similar role in religious matters (4).

### b. The Three Ages

As education follows a progressive syllabus, so Lessing perceives three ages or stages in revelation. In neological fashion he gives these a trinitarian slant. The first age is that of the Father, the second that of the Son, the third that of the Spirit.

(1) Age of the Father. The age of the Father is identical with that of the Old Testament. Its task is to impress monotheism on polytheistic and idolatrous peoples (6).

(2) Age of the Son. When the first age passes, the primer of the Old Testament may be set aside (51–53). Christ replaces it as "the first reliable, practical teacher of the immortality of the soul" (58–61). Hence

the New Testament becomes "the second, better primer for the race of man" (64).

(3) Age of the Spirit. Finally, the age of the Spirit is coming in place of that of the Son. No primer will be needed in this final age. Things learned by revelation will now be known without it. The rational meaning of such mysteries as the Trinity (73) and the Son's satisfaction (75) will be understood. Apart from a few pioneers this age has not yet arrived but Lessing has no doubts: "It will assuredly come, the time of a new eternal gospel which is promised in the primers of the new covenant itself" (86). Nor will those who have gone before be left out, for possibly individuals "may be present more than once in this world" (94). Providence, in its "eternal and inscrutable way," will finally bring the whole of mankind to perfection.

### c. Revelation and Reason

In this essay Lessing does not set revelation over against reason. Revelation has guided reason, and reason gave clearness to revelation (36). There might even be some things that reason could not have reached on its own (77). Revelation, however, is hardly understood as God's personal self-disclosure. Nor does it constitute more than an external and disposable packaging by which abstract truth is more readily learned. As packaging, revelation does not prove this truth; nor is it finally necessary to it. Thus the educational concept does not change Lessing's basic thinking. Certain historical developments have providentially accelerated and broadened the apprehension of rational truth. In so doing they have outdated themselves, or will outdate themselves, as teachers always do. Reason remains when revelation has served its turn and can be set aside.

## 4. The Rule of Faith and Holy Scripture

### a. A Necessary Answer

As the Reimarus debate continued, J. M. Goeze of Hamburg became Lessing's most serious critic. A heated debate developed in which Lessing accused Goeze of bibliolatry and Goeze asked what Lessing understood by the Christianity which, he thought, could easily exist apart from the Bible. In his *Necessary Answer to a Very Unnecessary Question* (1778) Lessing replied with the thesis that the rule of faith predates scripture (1ff.), that its authenticity is more easily proved than that of the New Testament (15), and that "its divine nature can be proved with far greater certainty than the inspiration of the New Testament writings" (16). What scripture teaches in addition to the creed, "in the opinion of the first four centuries is not necessary to salvation; it may be true or false, it may be interpreted one way or another" (20). According to Lessing, then, the Bible is not needed either to prove Christianity or to supply its substance, and not everything that it teaches need be accepted or defended.

### b. A New Hypothesis

At the time when Lessing was so heavily engaged polemically, he was also digging into the origins of the gospels at the human level. The result was his *New Hypothesis concerning the Evangelists as Merely Human Historians,* which was written in 1777 and 1778 but published only in 1784. Not bothering about scripture as revelation, Lessing is able here to make an early attempt at historico-literary analysis. As he sees it, original oral accounts of the gospel quickly took written form (4). They resulted in a Jewish-oriented Hebrew or Aramaic Gospel (11ff.) which the three synoptists all used in different ways (26–50). John also drew on it, as did the so-called heretical gospels (44). John, however, wrote with a Gentile orientation and a new theological and christological emphasis (51–63) which gave true consistency to Christianity. The importance of this essay does not lie so much in its conclusions as in its principle and method. Historical questions are tackled at a historical level, and scripture is studied, not as a repository of divinely given truths, but as a set of writings of human provenance.

## 5. Christianity and Religion

### a. The Origin of Revealed Religion

In his work *On the Origin of Revealed Religion* Lessing follows what will be a common line by distinguishing between religion and the religions. Acknowledgment of one God and commensurate action form the natural religion to which everyone is committed according to his capacity (1–2). This capacity varies, and so a positive religion must be constructed, just as positive law is constructed out of natural law (5). The positive religions are named after their founders (6). They are all true insofar as they embody the agreement necessary for unity in public religion (9). They are all false, however, to the extent that the matters agreed upon "not only stand beside what is essential but also weaken and supplant it" (10). The best positive or revealed religion is that which has fewest conventional additions to natural religion and least hampers its good effect (11). Lessing in this fragmentary work does not tell us which this is.

### b. The Religion of Christ

The religion of Christ would possibly have qualified as the best positive religion, but if so, Lessing wants to distinguish it from the Christian religion. The difference, as he states it in his short work *The Religion of Christ,* lies in whether Christ is viewed as a man, which is incontrovertible, or as more than a man (2–4). The religion of Christ is that which he himself practiced, which every man has in common with him, and which every man wants to have in common with him as he sees his exalted character as mere man (3). The Christian religion, in contrast, makes Christ more than a man and views him as an object of worship (4). How the two religions "can exist in Christ in one and the same person is inconceivable" to Lessing (5). The religion of Christ is clearly and lucidly taught in the gospels (7) but the Christian religion is so ambiguous and uncertain that there has never been an agreed interpretation of the passages on which it supposedly rests (8).

## 6. Lessing's Contribution

Much of Lessing's importance rests on the simple and forceful way he presents a rationalistic position which he essentially shares with others. At one point, however, he stands out above his contemporaries, namely, in relation to the question of historicity. Possibly Lessing was confusing different issues in his *Demonstration,* yet he raised a decisive question when he asked whether eternal truth can be based on historical facts or in any way related to them. For him, it seems, the world of absolute truth is an abstract and timeless world, whereas that of history is relative and contingent. Christianity might be studied at both levels, but no transition can be made from the one to the other except in the sense that the historical might serve as a temporary dress for the rational and absolute. In advancing this thesis with its wide-ranging implications, Lessing posed a question with which theology has had to wrestle ever since and which has produced the most varied and, for the most part, not very satisfactory answers.

Other points in Lessing, of course, have also had importance: the idea of progress in religion, the distinction between religion and the religions, the differentiation of the simple teaching of Jesus from the more complicated doctrine of Christianity, and the historical analysis of the biblical documents. Behind them all, however, there looms the ugly ditch which Lessing could not or would not jump. Is there in fact a way to leap over this ditch? If so, how? If not, what does this mean for the confession of Christ? Can Christ be confessed on this side? Can he be confessed in different ways on both sides? Or is there, perhaps, no real ditch there at all? The radical questioning of the historical truth of Christianity, or, more basically, of revelation as history, undoubtedly forms Lessing's most intriguing and influential contribution to subsequent theological discussion even though concentration on the issue of historical proof obscured for a time its wider significance.

## B. HERDER

### 1. The Influence of Hamann

While rationalism was a dominant force in the eighteenth-century world, emotionalism proved to be an effective parallel and counterpoise. Thus even as Lessing with his rationalistic concept of truth was raising the historical question, Herder, another pioneer of modern German literature and theology, was busily working out one possible answer with his poetic concept of truth.

At an impressionable age in Königsberg Herder came under the spell of J. G. Hamann, the so-called magus of the north. From Hamann he learned that if knowledge is through the senses, as Locke had shown, the knowledge of God is also in and through the sensory world. As the vehicle of the knowledge of God, nature plays the part of a figure or symbol. Symbolism, however, is of the essence of poetry. Hence a threefold relation exists between revelation, nature, and poetry. Like nature, poetry is an instrument of revelation, for it conveys truth in symbolical form. It is precisely in its human quality as literature that scripture serves as the revelation or word of God.

Hamann could agree with Lessing in dismissing miracles as evidences, or even as supernatural events, for all events are a manifestation of God. Nor did he have to regard the Bible as a special book. Its revelatory character consisted in its nature as true poetry, which was for Hamann the mother speech of the race. Only negatively, however, did Lessing and Hamann agree, for Hamann clearly did not accept Lessing's view of truth, and his own concept of revelation left no ugly ditch between truth and natural, historical, or literary fact. God, who is himself a supreme creative genius, manifests himself in nature and poetry, and supremely and finally in the incarnation. Properly to know God's symbolical works is to know God himself.

### 2. The Riga Sermon

#### a. Occasion

In 1764, after two years in Königsberg, Herder took up a teaching position in the cathedral school at Riga. Here he quickly proved his worth and in 1766, when he received an invitation from St. Petersburg, an additional post was found for him as curate. Thus far Herder's interests had been chiefly literary, but commitment to an ecclesiastical career led him to Old Testament study, in preparation for which he learned Hebrew. His Riga sermon *On the Divine Nature and Use of the Bible* is a direct result of this new turn in his career and a basic statement of his accompanying understanding of scripture.

#### b. Indirect Revelation

Herder begins the sermon with the orthodox thesis that the Bible underlies our knowledge of divine truth. He points out, however, that it does so indirectly. God's thoughts and speech differ from ours and hence we could not comprehend a direct statement. God communicates with us in a way that we can understand. He cannot speak to us in a divine way; he has to speak in human fashion.

### c. Historical Exegesis

Since scripture necessarily has human form, it follows that exegesis must be historical and literary. Absolute exposition is impossible; nor can scripture do its work if it is artificially interpreted in terms of one's own age. All the biblical speakers and writers, including Jesus, used the language and thought forms of their time. Isolation from background is impossible. Hence all the rules of literary and historical criticism must be applied to the biblical books too.

### d. Biblical Errancy

A further inference from the humanity of scripture is that the books, written by different authors at different times, bear evident marks of the individualities and limitations of the writers. Inspiration brings gracious direction but it does not obliterate personality or historical rootage. If contemporary forms are to be found in the books, so, too, are mistakes in historical and scientific matters such as cosmology. The authority of scripture remains, for through this human instrument God speaks. Infallible information is not given, however, in every area of knowledge.

### e. Devotional Reading

At the end of the sermon Herder finds one exception to his rule of indirectness. At the emotional or devotional level scripture can speak with immediacy. God fills the soul and holds direct converse with those who read the Bible in simplicity of heart. This hearing, however, has to be the active and reflective one of an ongoing dialogue with God. No magical effect is to be expected.

## 3. Provincial Papers and Theological Letters

### a. Provincial Papers

(1) Scripture. In two later writings Herder reiterated his principles of biblical approach and understanding. He wrote his *Provincial Papers* in a refutation of the rationalistic view of the pastor's office and function. Basically he sees the pastor as a man of deep human insight, not as a clever philosopher. The Bible must not be dismissed as an imperfect guide to conduct. Nor must it be read as a dead book of doctrine and morality. If pastoral work rests on scripture, scripture has to be read as God's living Word which is allowed to speak its own message. This entails a study of the genre and setting of each book. Above all, Jesus himself must be presented, not as the "rainbow" figure of contemporary piety, but as the vital personality of the gospels, "a Galilean with the Galileans," who "loved the spirit of religion and not the letter."

(2) Revelation. In the *Papers* Herder relates his concept of the

Bible to the understanding of revelation as a progressive education of the race. He handles this theme, however, in sharp contrast to Lessing. The divine education comes, not through discourses, sermons, or lectures, but through seed-thoughts whose planting is recorded in scripture, "the first and dearest and only book of culture." An ascent is traced from the patriarchs by way of the prophets to Christ himself. The modern pastor now bears responsibility for fulfilling the divine program.

### b. Theological Letters

(1) Biblical Study. Having moved to Weimar in 1776 to serve as general superintendent of the church there, Herder attempted large-scale reforms in all areas of ecclesiastical life. The training of clergy became a special concern of his. He cherished the ambition of founding a proper theological seminary. In default of this he worked out a scheme of reading and study which he published in his Letters to Young Pastors concerning the Study of Theology. Here again Herder sees biblical investigation as the main business of the pastor. He thus devotes two of the four parts of the work to the Bible, one to the Old Testament and another to the New. His fundamental principle is stated very simply in the introduction. The Bible must be read as a human book written for men by men. "Its language is human . . . its meaning, its whole purpose and use." As the parchment, ink, and characters are human, so are the composition and matter. The methods and insights of literary and historical research are thus to be used by the expositor, although, as Herder judiciously warns, he must not confuse "the scaffolding and the building."

(2) The Old Testament. In the Old Testament section Herder points out that the language of each people has its own genius. Hebrew has the qualities of naturalness, simplicity, and symbolical force. These the reader must appreciate. Literary genre must also be understood. The paradise story, for example, is neither prose narrative nor allegory, but poetry, and as such is "true history told in childlike fashion." Youthful unsophistication characterizes much of the Pentateuch with its vivid and imaginative accounts of real events or experiences. The story of Balaam's ass ceases to be a difficulty once its poetic form is perceived.

Turning from the Pentateuch to the rest of the Old Testament, Herder shows a high regard for the historical books, describing them as "masterpieces of historico-poetic narration." The prophets are to be related to the situations of their day, for primarily they are not dogmatic teachers or foretellers but "speakers of God's will for this age, this city, these circumstances." The psalms should obviously be interpreted as the hymnbook of Hebrew religion, and it is most important to remember that they were originally sung. Apocalyptic language is discerned in Daniel, Job is called "an ancient and lofty book for all nations," and Ecclesiastes should perhaps be divided into a teacher's column and a questioner's column with some possibility of composite authorship. For true study it is essential to enter into the spirit of each book. Part of scripture's self-understanding is that God speaks through it. Herder accepts this but also interprets it. God wills to speak to us in scripture as he does in nature. "What is not natural is not divine." The naturalness of the Bible means that the message belongs integrally to the literary and historical form, so that the latter must be investigated if the former is to be received and understood.

(3) The New Testament. Similar procedures apply to New Testament study, too. Herder recognizes the differences between the gospels, and especially between the synoptic gospels and John. Yet he contends for a common origin and an underlying unity. No fragment or fragments can be isolated and said to be alone authentic. The parables commend themselves to Herder. They have the vivid directness of true poetry. To appreciate them, however, one must read Jewish writings. The fulfillment of prophecy constitutes a problem. Herder cannot accept this as a proof of Christianity; yet he cannot deny that Jesus related Old Testament sayings to his own life and ministry. His solution is that while the prophetic oracles relate to situations of their own time, there may also be traced "a true chain of prophecy, of the promise of salvation or blessing" which, by a process of narrowing down, leads finally to the one person of Christ. The epistles Herder sees as part of the working ministry of the apostles, so that they must not be read too academically. As the books of scripture record events, they are themselves events. The epistles, as the living letters of living men, are to be comparatively related to their individual authors and the specific situations in which they wrote. We miss the point if we read them as abstract doctrinal and moral dissertations.

(4) Revelation, Reason, and Nature. An important theme in Herder's discussion of theology is the relation of revelation, reason, and nature. Theology is described as "the most liberal of all the sciences," for its subject matter embraces man, the universe, and God. It has two main authorities, reason and scripture. Both are "gifts of the one God" and they "lead to the same goal." Scripture should not be equated with revelation. Revelation comes first; it is the divine activity which scripture records and witnesses. Revelation in this sense is God's fatherly education which includes all his dealings with man through history and experience. Scripture gives permanent form to these acts while reason, which is developed by revelation, is essential to its apprehension. Yet scripture is not the only book of revelation, for God has manifested himself in nature, too. Nature is "a very readable and lofty book of God" which has its own authority. Yet scripture and nature are not rivals. In the biblical tradition we have an explanatory commentary on nature. Jesus "taught and showed the one God, the Father of all, through both nature and scripture." Nature and the Bible are complementary, "the one for the eye, the other for the ear."

## 4. Biblical Studies

### a. Gospel Expositions

Herder did not merely offer theoretical principles of exegesis. He also attempted their practical application. As early as 1775 he was impelled by the discovery of the Zend Avesta to write his *Expositions from a Newly Discovered Source,* in which he dealt chiefly with John's gospel. He began this work with a sketch of the intermingling of religious thought prior to the coming of Christ. "The barriers between national forms of thought had fallen." The picture presented was that of "a sea of intermingling thought and language." The diversity of the New Testament bears witness to this. Matthew is oriented to the Chaldeans, Luke to the Hellenists, John to the Dispersion, Paul to different groups as occasion demands. Herder acknowledges that he cannot fill in the whole picture, but he will make a contribution by trying to trace the relation between the New Testament and the Zend Avesta. He is aware of the danger of over-concentration, for "in the broken Greek of the apostles ideas and series of ideas have flowed together." He also senses the danger of too close analysis: "He who digs at the roots can easily kill the tree." Yet the work must be done, and he thus devotes most of the book to a study of the way in which the Zend Avesta sheds light on such important biblical terms as "logos," "light," and "fire"; such incidents as the visit of the magi and the exorcisms; such concepts as bread and wine, the poor in spirit, and the name; and such events as the descent into hell, the ascension, and the last judgment. The details of the investigation need not concern us, but the approach is obviously of the highest significance for ensuing biblical work.

### b. The Spirit of Hebrew Poetry

In 1781 Herder definitively stated and illustrated his methods of Old Testament criticism in a notable pioneering book, *The Spirit of Hebrew Poetry.* He opens this study by pleading yet again for an appreciation of the Old Testament as "a human book full of ancient poetry." He then counters the objection that Hebrew is a poor literary medium by stressing its merits. "Among the Hebrews the verb predominates, so that all is life and action." Hebrew resembles "a poor but pure and beautiful village girl." If there is some monotony, the concentration of sound gives force and vigor. The lack of tenses puts everything in "the poetic present." Parallelism is "emotion catching its breath," and in any case rhyme is only another form of parallelism. If Hebrew poetry is primitive, it has the virtues of childlikeness and simplicity essential to all great literature. Beyond it lies, not a rationalistic view of things, but a sense of God immanent and active in all creation.

Herder goes on to examine in detail the various literary groupings of the Old Testament: the pentateuchal material, Job, individual poetic pieces such as the Song of Deborah, parables, riddles, Hebrew names, the prophets, the Psalms, and Canticles. Time and again, however, he comes back to his basic theme. For a true understanding, the poetic structure must be understood, So, too, must the function of poetry. Poetry is a symbolical expression of eternal truth. Even in recording historical events it brings out their ultimate meaning. It must be understood on its own terms and in its own setting. In this regard the Old Testament does not finally differ from other poetry except for its more pronounced religious and theological orientation. Thus, as miracles are simply a spiritual interpretation of ordinary events, the inspiration of scripture is simply a term by which to express the divine aspect of all authentic literature. God makes himself known through Hebrew poetry, yet not uniquely. The divine message is perceived through an appreciation of the human medium.

### 5. The Redeemer of Man

In his final years Herder wrote persistently on biblical and theological themes. In 1794 he offered a neological explanation of glossolalia in *The Gift of Tongues*. An essay on *The Resurrection* followed in which, after a long and evasive discussion, Herder finally rejects a miraculous restoration of Jesus and locates the true point of the resurrection in its effects, "the rebirth of the apostles to new ideas and hopes." The next work, *The Redeemer of Man,* has, perhaps, greater interest because here Herder tackles the question of the historicity and interrelationship of the gospels. The gospels are not, he thinks, history or biography, but apostolic records, semi-poetical by nature, which are based on the gospel message and related to the needs of the readers. The rule of faith precedes the written documents. An Aramaic Matthew probably comes next, but Herder sees no way to isolate it from the present Matthew. Various "historical commentaries on the confession of faith" are then written, and those with an apostolic association finally establish themselves. Herder thinks Mark is the first of these. Luke and Matthew expand a Marcan original with special purposes in view. The background of the day accounts for the emphasis on miracles and fulfilled prophecies. The teaching of Jesus himself centers on the divine fatherhood and human brotherhood. This is the kernel or spirit of Christianity, and while dogmatic forms are necessary they are so only as the husk or letter. What about the person of Jesus? Herder deals with this in a separate treatment of John's gospel under the title *The Saviour of the World*. Here Herder finds in Jesus a supreme religious genius who proclaims and indeed embodies "what is most divine in man" in the form of "the purest and most comprehensive humanity." At the end of *The Saviour of the World* Herder gives a genealogical tree of the gospels: the rule of faith, the Palestinian gospel, Mark, Luke, Matthew, John. He ends his biblical work as he began it by insisting that criticism must be just as impartial and discriminating "in relation to these historical writings as in relation to any other historical writings."

### 6. Survey

Herder is so rich in ideas that it is best to let the summaries of his work speak for themselves. The revelation of God in nature and history may perhaps be singled out as his fundamental tenet. Jesus sums this up, for it is precisely in his full humanity that he is divine. To achieve a recognition of his deity one must study his humanity. Scripture conforms to the same pattern. In its poetic quality it follows God himself by presenting eternal truth in material dress. As God's instrument to this end, it, too, is fully human and has thus to be investigated and appreciated in its literary and historical humanity. The pattern of eternal truth and historical expression duplicates itself yet again in the relation between Christianity and its changing expression in the dogmatic and practical forms of the succeeding generations. Herder agrees with Lessing that a rational proof for Christianity cannot be found in miracles and prophecies. He does not agree at all, however, that there is no way from the historical to the eternal. God is not known in abstractions but in nature and history. It is by the study of the natural and the human that we know the divine. The problem for Herder is not the rationalist's problem of jumping a ditch from history to truth, for in Herder's poetic understanding no such ditch exists. The problem is that of keeping apart the symbol and what it symbolizes, the literary and historical expression of the reality and the reality expressed. Knowing the kernel by the husk, yet not confusing the two, constitutes the ultimate task and difficulty of interpretation.

# CHAPTER XXV
## *Religious A Priori and Positive Revelation*

### A. KANT AND THE MORAL A PRIORI

#### 1. The Critiques

*a. Pure Reason*

At the very time when Lessing was putting his critical questions to historicity and Herder was busy finding divinity in humanity, Kant unexpectedly accomplished an intellectual *coup d'etat* with his *Critique of Pure Reason*. The details of Kant's epistemological analysis need not concern us here, but the theological effects of the analysis call for notice. At one point or another it seemed to undermine or destroy all the existing options.

(1) Rational Orthodoxy. Using the philosophical proofs of God as its foundation, rational orthodoxy ran up against Kant's severe criticism of these proofs. The ontological argument was dismissed as a kind of conjuring trick in which existence suddenly appears as an attribute of being. The cosmological and teleological proofs carried more weight but failed to achieve the desired end of an indispensable God. If Kant's objections did not destroy the orthodox arguments, they introduced an element of serious doubt which robbed them of their appeal, especially when the comforting support of supposed innate ideas was also removed.

(2) Lessing. It might seem that Lessing's questioning of a movement from historical to eternal truth was confirmed by Kant, but in Lessing's case, unfortunately, the assumption of rational truths crumbled before the thoroughgoing empiricism of Kant. Religion could no longer find an alternative starting point in a rational a priori, as rationalists and neologists alike had believed. The rationalistic reconstruction of religion was demolished along with the traditional structure defended by rational orthodoxy.

(3) Herder. Herder's principle of revelation through nature and history was also endangered by Kant's epistemology. If knowledge

356

comes through the senses, only sensory things may be apprehended. A pattern may be imposed on these by the knowing subject, but access to the noumenal as distinct from the phenomenal world is blocked. Thus, to talk of God being known through sensory objects makes no sense. To be sure, the possibility that God might be known cannot be ruled out. The fact of such knowledge, however, cannot be asserted. What is confidently thought to be God might simply be a hypothesis or construct of human thought. Real knowledge is confined to the sensory data.

### b. Practical Reason

To many of Kant's contemporaries, especially the younger among them, it seemed as though his analysis removed all possibility of a real knowledge of God. Kant, however, did not see himself as merely a destroyer. If the *Critique of Pure Reason* had shattered some illusions, other religious possibilities remained. As he saw it, rationalism had been on the right track when it looked for a religious starting point on the inside rather than the outside. It had simply looked in the wrong place in its careless assumption of innate ideas. More helpful was its concept of natural law. For if pure reason teaches us that there are no innate ideas, we learn from practical reason that there is an innate moral sense, the categorical imperative. By an odd and convoluted argument Kant can even arrive at God and immortality from this moral a priori. The desire for happiness, as well as the moral demand, is innate in man. Since, however, right and happiness do not coincide in this life, a future life is needed for their common realization, and God is needed to guarantee this final result. God and immortality, however, come on the scene only inferentially and not axiomatically. The religious a priori is to be found in the moral law within. Only on the basis of this universal moral sense can religion — a religion of practical reason — be built.

## 2. Religion Within the Limits of Reason Alone

### a. Starting Point

Kant himself attempted a moral reconstruction of religion in his work *Religion Within the Limits of Reason Alone*. The starting point, of course, is the moral sense. Innate in man, as distinct from other possible rational beings, lies the character of having "an ultimate ground of the adoption of good maxims or of evil maxims," which for Kant is "the ground antecedent to every use of freedom in experience" (p. 17). In the specific use of freedom Kant discerns that evil maxims are adopted as well as good. He thus formulates a doctrine of radical evil, not in the sense of original sin (p. 35), but in the sense of a transgression of the moral command (p. 37) which involves the frailty of human nature (p. 24), the impurity of the human heart (p. 25), and also its perversity (p. 25). This propensity to evil, as Kant calls it, . . . is "woven into human nature" (p. 25). Nevertheless, it is counterbalanced by an original pre-disposition to good which Kant traces at three ascending levels as a predisposition to animality or mechanical self-love, to human or physical self-love, and to personality or "simple respect for the moral law." In his final assessment of the human problem, then, Kant faces up to the reality of moral evil; and yet he cannot allow that man is "basically corrupt" (p. 35). "Despite a corrupted heart he yet possesses a good will." Hence "there remains hope of a return to the good from which he has strayed" (p. 39).

### b. The Essence of Religion

For Kant the essence of religion consists in "the restoration to its power of the original predisposition to good." In his general observations on this point (pp. 40–49) one quickly finds confirmation of the fact that Kant's radical evil is not so radical after all. Having spoken already of a corrupted heart but a good will, he now comes out with the blunt assertion that "man himself must make or have made himself into whatever, in a moral sense, whether good or evil, he is or is to become." He uses the old Pelagian argument here. We cannot be held responsible for what is not an effect of free choice. If supernatural cooperation may be needed, "man must first make himself worthy to receive it, and must lay hold of this aid." Since we ought to become better, impossible though it may seem, "this must be within our power" (p. 40). It is so because we have never been able to lose the incentive for good. The required revolution in disposition cannot be impossible, for "duty bids it, and duty demands nothing of us which we cannot do." Quoting John 3:5, Kant oddly concludes that self-regeneration is the essence of moral religion (p. 43). Time and again he questions the possibility of this. Innate corruption unfits man for all good. Yet time and again he argues that in morality, as distinct from nature, the demand that "we *ought* now to be better men" implies that "we must be *able* to be better men" (p. 46). God does not do this for us. He helps, but only when we make ourselves worthy of help. For Kant the essential point in moral religion is not to know what God has done for our salvation but to know what man must do to be worthy of divine assistance (p. 47).

### c. Conflict of the Good and Evil Principles

Kant certainly sees that becoming better means a struggle both against natural inclinations and also against the evil disposition. Some interesting points in his discussion of this struggle may be noted. (1) Moral perfection does not spring from us. Hence its archetype may be thought of as having come down and assumed humanity. The human Christ enters the picture here. Practical faith in him brings accept-ability with God as man's "consciousness of such a moral disposition as enables him to have a well-grounded confidence in himself that he can follow Christ as an example" (p. 55). (2) If no act can claim perfection, God looks on the heart. Similarly, if assurance of advance in good is hard to come by, the prospect of eternal progress or regress either "strengthens in goodness" or raises a call for a "break with evil so far as it is possible" (p. 63). (3) Even granted an inner revolution, does not past guilt demand satisfaction? Indeed it does, but the pain of transition from the old man to the new constitutes the required punishment. The moral disposition, which might be equated with the divine Son, bears the guilt as divine substitute, "the suffering which the new man . . . must accept throughout life being pictured as a death endured once for all by the representative of mankind" (p. 69). (4) Discussing the legal claim of the evil principle and its defeat, Kant neologizes the ransom theory of the atonement. Christ as the exemplar of moral good suffers physical death but gains a legal victory which "opens the portals of freedom to all who, like him, choose to become dead to everything that holds them fettered to life on earth to the detriment of morality" (p. 77).

### d. The Kingdom of God

Kant equates the victory of the good principle with the founding of God's kingdom on earth. He gives a philosophical account of this and then a historical account. In the former he sees a need to move on from an ethical state of nature to an ethical commonwealth (pp. 87–88), which is the concept of the people of God under ethical laws (p. 90) and which can be realized only as a church (p. 91). "Pure religious faith alone can found a universal church," but by a quirk of human nature this needs ecclesiastical faith as its instrument (p. 94). Faith and the faiths are thus distinguished. The faiths based on revelation and scripture serve a temporary purpose, and God's kingdom comes with the transition from these to the exclusive sovereignty of pure religious faith or the "universal religion of reason" (pp. 105, 113). In the historical account Kant is interested only in the area in which there is awareness of the tension between liturgical and moral faith and development of the predisposition to the unity of the universal church. He dismisses Judaism as irrelevant in this regard and begins with Christianity, which in intention introduces pure religious faith. Only in Kant's day, however, is this understood with a moral reinterpretation of what was formerly thought to be historical revelation (pp. 121–126). The Book of Revelation presents a beautiful picture of the moral world-epoch brought about with the introduction of true universal religion and faith (p. 126). Luke 17:21–22 offers good support for the proposed moralization.

### e. Religion and Clericalism

Kant distinguishes between service and pseudo-service under the sovereignty of the good. Church officials render the latter when they regard their teachings and rules as ends in themselves. If Christianity is viewed as a revealed or learned religion, not as a natural religion in which I know something as my duty before I accept it as a divine injunction, the danger arises that leaders will reject reason as the commanding principle, claim an exclusive right of biblical interpretation, and change the service of the church into a domination, so that revealed religion is no longer a means of explication and diffusion as it ought to be (pp. 152–155). Another form of pseudo-service is the imposition of additional practices as a way of securing divine approval. Kant calls this fetishism. Fetishism leads to clericalism. Its essence consists, not in "principles of morality," but in "statutory commands, rules of faith, and observances" (pp. 167–168).

### f. Self-salvation

Self-salvation characterizes the religion of the moral a priori. Even if man's situation is one of corruption, by a free choice he can set himself on the way to virtue. "It must be possible to overcome evil, since it is found in man, a being whose actions are free" (p. 32). We begin, not "with a faith in what God has done on our behalf," but "with what we are to do to become worthy of God's assistance" (p. 108). Man's improvement of his life is "the supreme condition under which alone a saving faith can exist" (p. 109). Vicarious atonement can be made only by "the moral disposition which in all its purity . . . man has made his own" (p. 69). No "reasonable man, who knows himself to merit punishment, can in all seriousness believe that he needs only to credit the news of an atonement rendered for him . . . in order to regard his guilt as annihilated" (p. 107). Theoretically it might seem that "faith in a merit not [one's] own . . . must precede every effort to do good works," but the necessity for good works to precede faith is "practical, and indeed, purely moral" (p. 108). The truth, then, is not that "we must believe that there was once a man . . . who through his holiness and merit rendered satisfaction both for himself . . . and for all others," but that "with all our strength we must strive after the holy disposition of a course of life well pleasing to God, to be able to believe that the love . . . of God toward man . . . will make good, in consideration of an upright disposition, the deficiency of the deed" (p. 110). What finally counts for Kant is what is done by us, not what is done for us.

### g. Scripture

In his moralized Christianity Kant seems to give scripture a high rank. He offers his own religion of reason in biblical dress (pp. 73ff.). Scripture also provides the best foundation for the ecclesiastical faith which serves true religious faith (p. 97). For "a holy book arouses the greatest respect." Again, "the most sophisticated reasoning avails nothing in face of the decisive assertion." Moreover, Christian scripture contains "the purest moral doctrine of religion in its completeness" (p. 98). Kant recognizes, however, the crucial role of interpretation. Two forms are valid, the rational and the scholarly. But the scholarly, which argues for the authority of scripture and presents doctrinal exposition, must be subordinate to the rational, for according to 2 Timothy 3:16 scripture is given for moral improvement and this, then, "will comprise the highest principle of all scriptural exegesis." Scholarly exegesis serves ecclesiastical faith in a given situation, but the pure religion of reason is the authentic and universally valid expositor (pp. 102–105). The aim of scripture is "to make men better." The historical element "contributes nothing to this end," and we may thus "do with it what we like" (p. 102). The wax of scripture is thus shaped to the moralistic nose of Kant.

### h. Theology

Behind Kant's whole presentation lurks the impossibility of any knowledge of God which comes from outside of man. No real place is left, then, for "special revelation, which, being historical, can never be required of everyone" (p. 99). Divine triunity can be moralized, but if it is thought to denote what God is in himself it leads us into the sphere of a mystery transcending all human concepts and thus "unsuited to man's powers of comprehension" (pp. 132–133). As Kant sees it, faith is illusory if it involves "the possibility of our overstepping the bounds of our reason in the direction of the supernatural (which is not, according to the laws of reason, an object either of theoretical or practical use)" (p. 182). God, of course, figures a great deal in Kant's moral reconstruction of religion. God commands, assents, and so forth. In the last resort, however, Kant is not really talking about God. In his epistemology God cannot be known by man. He cannot even make himself known. He is no less imprisoned by epistemological impossibility than man. If Kant cannot know him, he cannot be known. Instead, the word "God" becomes a cipher for something that Kant and all of us can and do know and whose existence we cannot contest. This is the moral disposition within us which is "the basis and interpreter of all religion." When this finally frees religion "from all empirically determining grounds and from all statutes which rest on history," "God will be all in all." Theology is thus swallowed up in moral anthropology. Not only is nothing done for us, but neither do we know anyone who can do anything for us. Beginning with ourselves, we act by ourselves, and finally end with ourselves. The all-in-allness of God is the all-in-allness of the moral self-realization of man.

## B. SCHLEIERMACHER AND THE EMOTIONAL A PRIORI

If Kant hoped that his moralistic reinterpretation would fill the void left by his epistemological exclusion of God, events quickly showed him to be wrong. His negative assessment of religion had a powerful effect. In particular, his closing of man to the knowledge of God hypnotized his contemporaries into acceptance not only of God's incompetence in communication but also of his virtual non-existence. His moral alternative, however, had little appeal for a younger generation in which the powers of feeling and imagination were increasingly at work. If some sense of moral imperative could hardly be denied, few could regard this as a genuinely religious a priori. The prosy rationalism of Kant, made even more unattractive by his clumsy style, provided little field of exercise for latent religious impulses. Now that God could not be known apart from man, a beginning might have to be made with something in man — but surely a better starting point would have to be found. If Kant had taught the educated of his day to despise religion intellectually, he could not bring them to reaccept it morally. A new approach or apologetic was needed for the rehabilitation of religion. It was to supply this new approach or apologetic that in 1799 the young Friedrich Schleiermacher, chaplain at a Berlin hospital and member of the group known as the Berlin Romantics, published his remarkable work *On Religion: Speeches to its Cultured Despisers.*

In assessing the *Speeches,* one should remember that this is not a work of formal theology. Later, as a theological professor, Schleiermacher was to write a more carefully formulated statement in *The Christian Faith.* Now, however, he was writing as an apologist, searching for a religious a priori which his disillusioned generation could accept. He wanted to avoid the technical phrases of Christian faith and practice, omitting even the word "God" in the first edition. He wanted to put everything in a new and exciting way. He aimed to persuade, not to instruct. How far the final substance of Schleiermacher's own faith is accurately expressed is a matter for debate. In another time and other circumstances he might have done it all differently, as he did in some of his later sermons. This is a book for the hour, not a definitive confession. Nevertheless, it is perhaps in some ways his most vital and revealing work. It lies behind the revolution associated with his name. For that reason it will amply repay the time spent in its analysis and evaluation.

### 1. First Speech

#### a. The Triadic Principle

After asking for a hearing, Schleiermacher provides a general background for his presentation in the common triadic principle of

Romanticism. Everything in the universe is "made up by melting together two opposite activities" (p. 3). In the spiritual life this takes place through gifted people who are "interpreters of Deity . . . and reconcilers of things that otherwise would be eternally divided" (p. 6). Through them others learn to enjoy the One in All and All in One. True priests, they "strive to awaken the slumbering germ of a better humanity" and finally to merge their own priesthood into "a universal priesthood of humanity" (p. 7).

### b. The Emotional A Priori

This ministry presupposes that religion is an authentic human constituent. Like others of his day, Schleiermacher distinguishes between inner religion, "an expression of human nature," and outer religion, "a product of time and history" (p. 13). His concern is with the former, a reality which cannot be dismissed. Religions might be viewed skeptically, but one needs to go deeper and "find the kernel within this shell" (p. 15). This kernel is defined as "the immediate feeling of the Infinite and Eternal" (p. 16). Only with the discovery of this a priori can religion be seen in its external manifestations. Alone, systems can easily be "mere habitations and nurseries of the dead letter" (p. 16) which do not come from "the heroes of religion" (p. 17). Religion must also be distinguished from morality, of which it neither can nor should be viewed as a useful prop (pp. 18–19). Religion does not have to justify itself by serving something else (pp. 20–21). If no assured starting point for it can be found in God and revelation, an adequate alternative is the religious sense which is an inalienable part of humanity. "Piety springs necessarily by itself . . . a province of its own in the mind belongs to it, in which it has unlimited sway . . . it is worthy to animate most profoundly the noblest and the best and to be fully accepted and known by them" (p. 21).

### 2. Second Speech

#### a. Religion, Metaphysics, and Ethics

Having posited man's innate religiousness, Scheiermacher attempts a closer definition. He dismisses the common notion that religion is a way of thinking and a way of acting (p. 27). Piety is no "craving for a mess of metaphysical and ethical crumbs" (p. 31). Since religion never appears without impurities, the sacred writings include metaphysical and ethical conceptions, but these are baser substances alloyed with the precious metals. They are for beginners who are endeavoring "to break through from a lower region to a higher," that is, to the religion that has nothing to do with science or morality (pp. 34, 35).

### b. Pure Religion

What, then, is pure religion? It is essentially contemplation as immediate awareness of the "universal existence of finite things in and through the infinite, and of all temporal things in and through the Eternal" (p. 36). It is a seeing of God's activity in man's (pp. 36–37). As the original relation of intuition and feeling it thus achieves the unity in difference of thought and action which its elimination excludes (p. 41). "Feeling is piety in so far as it expresses the being and life common to you and to the All, . . . in so far as it is the result of the operation of God in you by means of the operation of the world upon you" (p. 45). No healthy sensation is not pious (p. 46). Religion may be fostered by nature, but normally the universe first "portrays itself in the inner life, and then the corporeal is comprehensible from the spiritual" (p. 71). True religion is found especially in true humanity. To have it man must first "have found humanity" (p. 72). Only in "the feeling of a religious disposition" (p. 80) can one see the true meaning of history in the twofold insight, first, that spiritual renewal comes out of decomposition, and, second, that the whole follows a uniform course as "the high World-Spirit smilingly marches past all that furiously opposes him" (p. 81).

### c. Religion and Dogma

How do dogmas or doctrines stand in relation to pure religion? They are "the result of the contemplation of feeling . . . general expressions for definite feelings" (p. 87). Not necessary to religion itself, they are necessarily created by reflection. Miracle, for example, is a religious term for event; an event is a miracle once "the religious view of it can be dominant" (p. 88). Similarly, any "original and new communication of the Universe to man is a revelation." Inspiration "is simply the general expression for the feeling of true morality and freedom" in "action which springs from the heart of man" (p. 89). Grace is "the common expression . . . for interchange between the entrance of the world into man, through intuition and feeling, and the outgoing of man into the world, through action and culture" (p. 90). A sacred writing is "a speaking monument from the heroic time of religion." Mere belief in it does not imply true religion, but only he who best understands it "could most easily do without it" (p. 91). God and immortality are not "the principal things in religion." Whether God be viewed as personal or as "the universal, productive, connecting necessity of all thought and existence" (p. 95), we have him in our feeling only by the emotions produced in us by the world, since God is "the highest, the only unity" (p. 94). The concept of immortality as a reward is "inconsistent with the nature of piety" (p. 99) and is "irreligious" (p. 100). True immortality consists, not in the preservation of sharply cut personality, but in surrender of life from love of God, and life in the One and All. It comes through sinking oneself in as much of the whole universe as one can, and this immortality we may have already. "In every moment to be eternal is the immortality of religion" (p. 101).

### 3. Third Speech

*a. Innateness of Religion*

In many people the "noble capacity of religion" exists only as "a slumbering spark" (p. 120). It cannot be kindled, however, by mere "teaching and imparting." Teaching religion is "absurd and unmeaning." One can teach doctrines, but these are just "the shadows of our religious emotions" (p. 122). Imitation will not produce true religion. The master-disciple relation helps, but when the spark of religion ignites, it "spreads to a free and living flame, fed by its own atmosphere" (p. 123). "Man is born with a religious capacity" which is more thwarted by moralism, analysis, and explanation than by scepticism (pp. 124–125). The great prerequisite for its development is the presence of "heroes of religion, holy souls, . . . entirely permeated by religion." Steps must be taken that these may appear as "natural if rare products of their age" (p. 135).

*b. Spheres of the Sense of the Infinite*

What steps? Schleiermacher replies by pointing to three spheres of the sense of the infinite: the interior of the ego which produces mysticism, the outer world which produces a religion of elemental nature, and art, which unites and adorns the first two. In his own time, however, religion and art have been divided, and hence the two forms of religion have lost their force. By a restored cooperation of religion and art they need to be "united in one channel" to bring religion to completion. Even philosophy and ethics can help here by relating man to the world, and science by relating the powers of nature to man. Along these lines religion will be rekindled, for after all "the greatest work of art has for its material humanity itself, and the Deity directly fashions it." God is now working "with bold and effective art," and "the heavenly growth flourishes in the midst of [our] plantings" (p. 142).

### 4. Fourth Speech

*a. The Religious Society*

As an innate feeling or sense or capacity, religion is a very personal thing having as many expressions as people have. Yet Schleiermacher recognizes that "if there is religion at all it must be social, for that is the nature of man." Man has "a spiritual nature . . . which demands that he express and communicate all that is in him." In religion this cannot be done merely through books or ordinary conversation. The need exists, then, for "a higher style and another kind of society entirely consecrated to religion" (p. 151). This is the city of God and by it an "eternal union" and "a heavenly bond" are produced (p. 152). This society is not a proselytizing agency. Its religion is the collective religion of all the pious (pp. 152–153).

### b. The Organized Church

In contrast, the organized church is "only an association of persons who are but seeking religion" (p. 157). Even if this is a far cry from the true church, however, the latter must have some bond of union with it (p. 161). In particular its leaders should be taken from the true church. The problem is that the thousands who try to follow soon lose their enthusiasm (p. 165) and politicians interfere in a prostitution of religion to other interests (pp. 167ff.). In answer Scheiermacher proposes an unorganized auxiliary ministry of "truly priestly souls" (p. 175). He rapturously portrays the possible outcome of their work — an "exalted fellowship of truly religious souls," "an academy of priests" among whom "all that is human is holy, for all is divine," "a band of brothers" who are "no longer men, but mankind also," "on the way to true immortality and eternity" (pp. 179–180).

## 5. Fifth Speech

### a. Religion and the Religions

If Schleiermacher differentiates religion and the religions, he sees that religion may be in the religions, since "these display the same form of heavenly beauty" (p. 211). Indeed, it is good as well as necessary that religion should take form in the religions. "Everyone in the religion of others may see and share what he cannot find in his own." Similarly "everyone may seek ... religion in the form best fitted to awake the germ that lies asleep in him." The "multiplicity of the religions is based on the nature of religion" (p. 212). The only question is whether a specific religion is agreeable to the principle of religion (p. 213).

### b. The Positive Religions

The main forms of religion are called positive religions. These arise when one of the great relations of mankind to the Highest Being is selected and made the center to which all the others refer. Attachment to these religions is not essential, but a form of religion is, and since few can develop their own, adherence to a given religion will be the common rule (p. 225). Natural religion offers only a sorry alternative, for it slips quickly into metaphysics and morals and lacks the cohesion given by a definite view (pp. 232–233). Historicity marks positive religions and their founders, for the moment of first filling with the consciousness that is made the center of religion is always sacred, as is also the moment of the first setting up of this intuition "as the foundation and center of one peculiar religion" (p. 236). At this point a danger arises of confusing the intuition itself with the historical facts relating to the founder or the sacred sources (p. 237). Positive religion consists essentially in "some intuition of the finite and the infinite, some one universal religious relation . . . placed in the center" (p. 237).

### c. Judaism

Two of the positive religions are singled out for special treatment. The first, Judaism, is somewhat prematurely described as long since dead. This is not because it was a mere forerunner of Christianity, for "each religion has in itself its own eternal necessity" (p. 238). It is because its center no longer has the same force. This center is a childlike view of the relation between God and man, especially in the form of "universal immediate retribution" (p. 239). All history is thus a colloquy in word and deed between God and man. Prophecy tries to apply this view to the wider sphere of the nations. "The belief in the Messiah was its highest product" (p. 240). One might note in passing that Schleiermacher never achieved renown for his understanding of the Old Testament.

### d. Christianity

A more glorious intuition is perceived in Christianity — that of the universal resistance of finite things to the unity of the whole and of the way in which the deity reconciles this hostility to himself. At this point Schleiermacher takes up again the triadic principle with which he began. To resolve the antithesis of finite and infinite, "ever more exalted mediators" are set up in whom "the deity unites with humanity ever more closely" until finally reconciliation is achieved in Christ. Christ is "the author of the noblest that there has yet been in religion" (p. 246). The divine element in him is the "clarity to which the great idea he came to exhibit attained in his soul" (p. 246). He fulfills perfectly the conditions of mediation. "What mediates must not again require mediation. . . . It must belong to both sides, participating in the divine essence in the same way and in the same sense in which it participates in human nature" (p. 247). Yet Christ did not claim to be the only mediator; Christians should be mediators, too. He did not exclude any "who got out from the same cardinal point" (p. 248). Similarly, scripture forbids "no other book to be or become a bible" (p. 249). The basic intuition of Christianity — that of resistance and reconciliation — has enduring validity (p. 251). Hence the living spirit of Christianity will constantly renew itself (p. 250). Nevertheless, Christianity is comprehensive, not exclusive. It makes no claim to be the sole type of religion. "In all ways the deity is to be contemplated and worshipped" (p. 252). In his peroration, then, Schleiermacher asks his readers to let whatever type of religion develops in them flourish in "the indivisible fellowship of the saints which embraces all religions." His closing sentence could hardly be more characteristic or revealing: "To worship the God that is in you, do you not refuse us." (p. 253).


## C. SCHLEGEL AND POSITIVE REVELATION

### 1. Introduction

It must not be supposed, of course, that all theology abandoned the revelational a priori in favor of a religious a priori. In fact, the early nineteenth century saw some important developments in positive theology. This may be seen in the case of Friedrich Schlegel. Schlegel, the able theoretician of the Berlin Romanticism, had been a very close friend and associate of Schleiermacher at the time of the composition of the *Speeches*. Later, however, he gravitated toward Roman Catholicism. Behind this movement lay a realization that God cannot be known through something innate in man nor can he be abstractly equated with the sum total of reality. To begin with man and the world is to end with man and the world. If God is to be known at all, it must be as the personal God in his self-revelation as such. In 1811 Schlegel expressed his thinking on this matter in two reviews of Jacobi's *Of the Things of God and Their Revelation*.


### 2. First Review

As Schlegel understands him, Jacobi espouses the common thought of his day that speculative reason is useless in theology and that we are thus dependent on some form of inner revelation. As in Kant, God is here ushered out by the front door and then smuggled in again by the back door. The reference to inner revelation, however, leads Schlegel to analyze and assess the various types of revelation and it is here that the interest of his work lies.

Schlegel notes three types of revelation — general, inward, and positive. He defines the first as the revelation "by which God glorifies himself in the whole of creation and in all creatures, the eternal Word by which all things were created . . . being considered . . . as a self-revelation and manifestation of God." "Inward or moral revelation, active in the voice of conscience and in moral feeling," he finds in many of the better religions which "recognize the First One and seek it only in inward feeling, rejecting or dismissing as unnecessary the outward forms or distinctive shapes which it must assume." Finally, positive revelation is that which is given in Christianity, and of this Schlegel goes on to give a fuller description.

Positive revelation "was imparted by the Redeemer of mankind, was proclaimed in the spoken and written words of the apostles and prophets as inspired by the Spirit of God, and has been guarded, broadened and published abroad in the church. In contrast with the metaphysical revelation on the one side and the inward or moral on the other it might also be called the historical revelation, since it rests upon the historical fact of redemption." For Schlegel this fact is "the central point of history." It also "explains the beginning and the end of history, bringing for the first time both unity and meaning to the whole." No account can do this, "however rich in artistic skill, that does not set out from this central point."

Positive revelation as such, however, cannot be the starting point, for it rests on the presupposition of the living personal God who reveals himself. God, then, is the real theological a priori who makes nonsense of the theological inferences drawn from Kant's epistemological analysis. He alone, not a necessary but impersonal being known from general or inward revelation, is the true first cause. This self-revealing God is known, however, by revelation — not by reason, either pure or practical. In the approach to the knowledge of God revelation and reason cannot be joined.

Why not? "If reason is the source of all being and of all knowledge, there can be no hope of reaching the living God." Reason might demonstrate or explain God, but it cannot attain to him. It can produce only an absolute in the form of "an artistic system of dynamic law," "the lofty feeling of autonomous power," or fate or destiny. But for Schlegel this is simply a "lifeless It" or the endlessly repetitive "I am I." Unaided, reason cannot take us to any true Thou. In a remarkable passage Schlegel shows the difference between an It knowledge — that of reason — and a He or Thou knowledge — that of revelation. "It might be said that any true Thou presupposes a love which is something more than reason and different from it. How much more is this so with the highest Thou. . . . Only in the person of this Thou does the dead It, the necessary being of reason, become the He. . . . And only thus is the I, revolving relentlessly around itself, lifted out of itself and united with that aweful He in the loving Thou."

In and of itself, then, reason knows nothing of God. It leads only to an empty void. Thus far Kant is right even if his reasoning is wrong. But Kant is wrong in supposing that God can be known by practical reason. God himself fills the void by imparting himself in revelation. He is known as this is grasped in faith. Schlegel cannot believe that ignorance of God is natural to man. Nor does he attribute this ignorance to a clash between God and nature. It is due to a "foreign infection" which God's self-revelation is designed to overcome. He admits, however, that knowledge of God and knowledge of the world stand on different planes. Reason, the form of knowledge in relation to creatures, proves inadequate in relation to the Creator. The difference in knowledge corresponds to the difference in the object of knowledge. Hence one need not conclude from the inadequacy of reason either that God is unknowable or that he may be known only by inner revelation. He himself brings knowledge of himself by way of historical self-revelation.

### 3. Second Review

In the second review Schlegel deals with the important objection that personality means limitation, so that the personal God is a contradiction in terms. In his reply Schlegel argues that the objection arises out of a false procedure. Beginning with what personality is for us, it then lets itself be bounded by abstract notions of what God can and cannot be. The proper course is wholeheartedly to grasp and acknowledge positive revelation in which God himself will teach us who and what he is. There, to our astonishment, we find in fact a divine self-limitation of condescension. We also find that this is "the peculiar characteristic of the concept of the living God." Nowhere, indeed, is God's deity more essentially manifested. Let us listen to Schlegel himself on this important point: "In Christianity is found the concept which everyone can understand, the concept of the loving condescension and mercy of God ... in which all doubts as to the limitation apparently involved in the personality of God are easily resolved. What is this condescension of God but a voluntary self-limitation in love, a miraculous restraint of almightiness. At what point would the being and love of God be demonstrated more essentially and more appropriately or more powerfully than in this restraint of almightiness. . . . So little does this loving condescension of free self-limitation in love seem to us to be not in accord with the being of God or commensurate with his dignity that it is rather this very condescension, this very mercy of God, which is the peculiar characteristic of the concept of the living God as it is taught by Christianity; every god, on the other hand, who is not merciful in himself and who does not directly condescend, be he presented in abstractions never so lofty, is nothing but blind fate, a false idol, the mere phantom of the absolute."

Here again, of course, a difference emerges between two types of knowledge. The philosophical type aims at coherence, perfection of form, and certainty, but it breaks down in relation to God, since it wants to cut him down to the size of its own conceptions. The second type is a free and personal knowledge with faith as its basis. It is with this knowledge that in faith's response to his positive historical revelation God is known — not the god of the philosophers but the God of Abraham, Isaac, and Jacob.

Schlegel ends the review with a not unjustified complaint against the arrogance of philosophy and an affirmation of the ultimate centrality of theological knowledge. Philosophy, or false philosophy, makes mathematical certainty the norm in all branches of human cognition. Hence it divides faith from knowledge, since faith does not offer this type of certainty. It also banishes positive revelation from serious epistemological discussion on the ground that it, too, lacks the certainty required. For Schlegel, however, faith brings the understanding which is real knowledge of the living God in his self-revelation. Indeed, it does more. We are not to say that God may be left to faith while man belongs to the sphere of (rational) knowledge. For man himself cannot be known alone and apart from God. The certainty which philosophical knowledge gives is the certainty of a very restricted and inadequate knowledge. The knowledge of God through revelation and faith, which is true theological knowledge, plays the determinative role in the knowledge of man too, and not of man only, but of all creation insofar as it stands in the decisive relation to its Creator.

# CHAPTER XXVI
## *Incarnation and Inspiration*


## A. INCARNATION

### 1. Introduction

Superficially it might seem strange that with the surge of anthropologizing the nineteenth century should be one of the great centuries of christological study. But perhaps the situation has its own
logic. The preceding period had brought a new focus on man. It was
natural, then, that the humanity of Jesus should call for notice. What
does it mean to confess Jesus, true God, as also true man? Does not a
problem arise here? Can the humanity stand the pressure of deity?
What does it entail that the deity is now also humanity? What is implied
by this humanity? New thinking and formulation seem to be demanded
if the historic confession is still to be made.

There is another side to it as well. The development of scientific
study of the world favors a new stress on the immanence of God as
distinct from his transcendence. The principle of immanence, however,
lies close to that of incarnation. It is by no means illogical, then, that a
cosmic significance should be sought for the incarnation and its role in
theology enhanced and extended.

Exploration of the relation of Christ's humanity to his deity was
carried out especially by the so-called kenosis theologians Thomasius
and Dorner. Thomasius (1802–1875) may be selected as the spokesman.
A professor at Erlangen from 1842, he published his *Person and Work of
Christ* between 1853 and 1861, a revised edition appearing between
1856 and 1863. In this study we shall be using Part 2 on "The Person of
the Mediator." As regards the incarnational principle, Anglican
theology under the impulse of F. D. Maurice played an important part,
as may be seen in the essays edited by Charles Gore of Oxford in 1889
under the title *Lux Mundi*. An influential statement is given in this volume by J. R. Illingworth in his essay on "Incarnation and Development."

## 2. Thomasius: The Person of the Mediator

### a. Introduction § 34

Thomasius opens his study with three significant affirmations. (1) The fact of Christ's coming is "the center of salvation history implanted in the midst of time." As such it may also be called "the inner ground of the entire saving revelation." (2) The only necessity of the incarnation is "the free compassionate love of God for the irretrievably lost race." (3) Christ's person and work are "interwoven," so that even if we have to study them apart "there is at bottom the same subject."

### b. Foundation § 35

The Christian's personal union with God rests on the fact that the Mediator "is personally one with God on the one hand and with us reconciled ones on the other . . . belonging essentially to both." Correspondingly his work, being human, has the necessary historical reality, and, being divine, it has also "world-reconciling power." Three essential elements may thus be seen, Christ's deity, his humanity, and the unity of the two. A fourth essential is the distinction of the twofold state, the condition "from which he continually mediates the communion with God to us," and the condition "in which he established it objectively for us." Identity of substance, of course, persists through the difference of conditions.

### c. Basis § 36

Thomasius offers a fourfold basis for the incarnation: the preexistence of the divine which became man in Christ, the pretemporal triune decree of redemption, the immanent trinitarian relations of Father, Son, and Spirit, and, more immediately, the self-determination of the Son which activates this relation for the purpose of mediating salvation.

### d. Possibility § 37

Thomasius acutely finds the possibility of the incarnation in the relation between God and humanity established at creation. Made in God's image and for a divine destiny, human nature is capable of the divine (natura humana capax divinae). In itself, of course, this constitutes only a general possibility, since our union with God falls far short of the union of God and man in Christ. Nevertheless, it means that there is no hindrance in human nature as such to the divine humanity of Christ which God willed for our salvation.

### e. Act § 38

Speaking of the specific act of incarnation, Thomasius first says what it is not. It is not the union of the Son of God with an existing individual and the resultant transformation of this individual. It is not the transmuting of the Son "out of himself, or himself into, the humanity in which he historically appeared," as though the Logos were already man, or changed himself into human nature. A delicate balance has to be maintained in understanding the incarnation. The distinction of divine and human must not be erased in a false identity. Yet no external juxtaposition must be set up which would destroy personal unity. In the act of incarnation the Son of God took and made his own "the human kind common to us all."

### f. Assumption of Human Nature § 39

This taking or assuming of human nature is to be defined both negatively and positively. Negatively it is not the producing of a new person, nor is it the assuming of sinful flesh, although Thomasius insists that the assumed nature was human nature "as it had come to be in consequence of the fall." He explains this by saying that while the nature, or human substrate, was effected *out of* the substance of Adamic humanity, it was not effected *by* this, but by a supernatural purifying activity on it. The assumption of human nature means the penetration of the human by the divine and the participation of the divine in the human.

### g. Self-limitation of the Son § 40

Thus far Thomasius has for the most part followed the lines of orthodoxy. It is when he moves on to an explanation of the historical person of the God-man that he takes a more innovative course. He does so because he feels traditional Christology does not leave enough room for the truly historical life of Christ. The only possibility, he thinks, is to postulate a "self-limitation of the divine." Without this, he can see no solution to two inherent problems. First, if the Logos remains in the divine mode with no self-limitation, the divine and human natures never come together in a true unity of person. The universal activity of the Logos does not coincide with the divine-human action. We have "a double life, a doubled consciousness." Second, if unity is achieved by the imparting of divine fullness to human nature, so that this is stripped of its inherent limitation, then humanity is divinized, a normal human life of development is excluded, and Christ cannot be the historical person through whom followship with God is mediated. No option remains, then, but that of a "self-limitation of the eternal Son of God."

Self-limitation, however, needs careful handling. It cannot be a setting aside of what is essential to deity. If it were, Christ's divine nature would be extinguished. What it entails is laying aside of the divine mode of being and adoption of a human creaturely form of existence. It is a renunciation of the divine glory: "Mild he laid his glory by," as the Christmas hymn of Charles Wesley has it. Two points are made then: (1) as the assumption of human nature the incarnation is the self-limitation of the Son, and (2) this self-limitation mediates the assumption of the flesh. These two moments are coincident in time and deed as two sides of the same act. In the biblical evidence which Thomasius adduces for his position, he puts it as follows. The Son's self-limitation is an act of free self-denial in love. It embraces the renunciation of due divine glory and "assumption of the humanly limited and conditioned pattern of life." All this is closely connected with the two states, that of exaltation on the one hand and that of humiliation on the other.

### h. Person of the God-Man § 41

The ego of the Son is that of the eternal Logos with the characteristics of a human ego, so that the divine-human ego is the proper subject of the person. This has two implications. (1) The Son has not reserved a distinctive being outside his human nature; there is no Word outside the flesh *(Verbum extra carnem)*. (2) The Word enters totally into the human, and the human is totally taken up into the Word in a self-divestment which is an act of both will and love. The possibility of this union lies in dependence on God on the one side and possession of the fullness of humanity on the other.

### i. Divine-Human States § 42

Two general points are made here. (1) There is essential identity: "From the divine-human ego the two streams of divine and human life flow together in an organic movement." (2) There is formal distinction; for the purpose of redemption the unity has a "twofold configuration" which divides Christ's life into the two states, which Thomasius goes on to discuss separately.

### j. The State of Humiliation § 43

A developing sense of divine sonship and vocation is discerned in Jesus. This is mediated by the Spirit and carries with it a sense of determination by the divine decree which leads to voluntary submission to the Father's will and the fulfillment of earthly life as "one great act of suffering obedience." Unlike the self-limitation, the humiliation is an act of the incarnate, not the discarnate Logos. Continuing the self-limitation, it has the two aspects of revealing and divesting. Revealed are the immanent divine attributes, such as power, holiness, and love, which, being essential to deity, are retained and used. Divested are the relative attributes, such as omniscience and omnipresence, which the incarnate Mediator neither has nor uses. The humiliation is "an actual kenosis" of these attributes, "and surely not merely of their use but of their possession." This applies to "the whole undivided person of the redeemer." If the Logos laid aside his glory as God-*man,* he also surrendered it as *God*-man. Against objections Thomasius points out (1) that this is a self-determination, (2) that it is for a brief span, and (3) that it ends with the exaltation. Birth and death raise problems, for they imply cessation of self-consciousness, but even in their passivity they are high points of redemptive activity in which, mysteriously, the subject remains integrally itself in what is not very clearly called a "withdrawal of potence."

### k. The State of Exaltation § 45

After a short intermediate stage of passage through death (§ 44) Christ enters the exalted state of freedom, power, and fullness of divine glory. In this he has unlimited personal fellowship with his people as both man and God and takes up again the relative divine attributes which he had set aside. The exaltation, which is the work of the Father at the resurrection, entails an exaltation of humanity on the basis of the hypostatic union and by the mediation of the humiliation. Humanity being exalted, any antithesis between it and the relative divine attributes is done away, for these contradict only the present and not the intrinsic essence of humanity. Christ shared our limitation for a moment in order that in him we might enjoy a fulfilled and transfigured humanity forever.

### l. Observations

We must be grateful to Thomasius for a reverent, profound, and thought-provoking discussion. In the classical tradition he keeps the incarnation in constant touch with reconciliation. The full biblical and historical materials which he supplies are especially noteworthy. Thomasius forces us to consider the full implications of the old formula of two natures and one person. He also faces squarely the problems in his own position, even if he does not always have satisfactory answers. His concept of self-limitation is surely on the right lines, and he is to be commended for his insistence that the true humanity of Christ, which is no less essential to salvation, must not be absorbed in his deity.

Nevertheless, the teaching of Thomasius is beset by questions. How far or in what sense, for example, can one say that there is no hindrance in humanity to real fellowship with God? Ought the states of humiliation and exaltation to be so rigidly separated? Can one really say, in the light of John's Gospel, that Christ divests himself of the glory of God in his earthly life and ministry? What is the basis of the distinction between immanent and relative attributes? Can God really be God without the relative attributes? And what about the concept of divesting itself? Does it have a solid exegetical basis? Even if it does, can one say that for thirty years or so the Logos exists totally only in the man Jesus, and that he suffers some kind of extinction in the womb and the tomb? How does an evasive term like "withdrawal of potence" help us here?

To raise these questions is not to condemn Thomasius. It is not to say that he is wrong, or wholly wrong, in any or all of these matters. Perhaps his main fault is to speak too confidently in things which all of us so little understand. The questions simply show that serious difficulties arise in his treatment and that the so-called kenotic Christology must not be accepted too readily, even if it does offer what many seem to have regarded as the welcome relief of a fallible Jesus.

### 3. Illingworth: Incarnation and Development

#### a. Lux Mundi

The essays edited by Gore and published under the title of *Lux Mundi* (1889) were also in different ways studies in the religion of the incarnation. They were composed at a time when the human Jesus was being increasingly investigated, when kenotic Christology was exploring afresh the implications of divine humanity, and when natural science was opening up the concept of cosmic development on a new and ascending scale. Many different aspects of incarnation were covered in the essays, but perhaps the most ambitious treatment is that by J. R. Illingworth, fellow of Jesus College, Oxford, who in addition to his piece on "The Problem of Pain" contributed the notable essay on "Incarnation and Development."

#### b. Historical Basis

Illingworth first lays a historical foundation in scripture, the fathers, and especially the Schoolmen, all of whom hint at the cosmic significance of the incarnation. Bonaventura says that "every creature is a Divine word" (p. 135). Thomas, too, describes the incarnation as "the exaltation of human nature," and according to him, "every intellectual process has its origin in the Word of God who is the divine reason." Thus, if we are taught the sciences by philosophers, "God revealed them to them" (p. 136).

#### c. Science and Theological Immanence

The last quotation from Thomas leads Illingworth to look at the developing science of his time. He accepts the maxim that the finite intellect cannot transcend the limits of finitude. Hence science can enhance our knowledge at the finite level but cannot solve the ultimate problems of origin and development (p. 137). Yet science need not be in conflict with the discipline which deals with such matters, namely, theology. Evolutionary science might seem to have played a hostile role, but in overthrowing a utilitarian teleology it has established a more comprehensive one which sits well with the Christian doctrine not only of the creation of all things by divine reason but also of God's "indwelling presence in the things of His creation" (pp. 138ff.). Even in its hypothesis concerning man, evolutionary science does not contradict immanence, for God "is not only present behind the beginning of matter but immanent in its every phase" (p. 142), and on the intellectual side "the objects of our thought . . . are ideas of the Divine Wisdom" (p. 143). Thus "all the great teachers of whatever kind are vehicles of revelation," although "we reject them the moment they transgress their limits" (p. 145). Atheists, too, may be assisted by God in his divine immanence (p. 143).

### d. Philosophy and Religion

This principle has important ramifications for philosophy and religion. Greek philosophy in particular was "vitally inspired by the light that is the life of men" (p. 147), and it was thus "capable of assimilation by the Christian organism" (p. 147). The details are of little relevance from this standpoint: "It is merely a question of the degree in which the eternal Word chose to reveal himself through one agency rather than another" (pp. 148–149). The same applies to religion. The world religions manifest religious universality, progressiveness, and incompleteness, but all this is in harmony with the fact that God has not left himself without a witness (pp. 149–150). Religion was "the agelong prayer. The Incarnation was the answer." Pre-Christian religion, like pre-Christian philosophy, is "a long preparation for the Gospel" (p. 150).

### e. Miracle

In a third part Illingworth acknowledges a difficulty. The incarnation sounds very well as an obscure generality, but a genuine historical incarnation means the miraculous, and this "contradicts experience" (p. 152). Illingworth has two answers. (1) Experience does not cover all fact. (2) Experience includes awareness of moral evil and liberation from it through "the personal influence . . . of Jesus Christ" (p. 153). The atonement, however, must not be severed from the incarnation. Illingworth closes with a striking passage on the significance of the latter. It "opened heaven . . . but also reconsecrated earth." "The religion of the Incarnation has been a religion of humanity. . . ." "Secular investigation is . . . nothing less than the correlative and counterpart of the Incarnation." The religion of the incarnation does justice to the material "by the creative import which it assigns to the human body" while still excluding its "perversion." "Though its own first vocation is to seek and save one by one, it consecrates in passing every field of thought and action." "We can conceive no phase of progress which has not the Incarnation for its guiding star" (pp. 155ff.).

### f. Appreciation

To appreciate Illingworth's essay its apologetic intent must be understood. In the critical situation at the end of the nineteenth century he was trying to soften the clash between science and religion by appealing to divine immanence, not evolution, as a master principle. If he enjoyed only limited success in this effort, he deployed no little learning and stylistic force in making it. Nor can there be any final contesting of his appeal to the immanence of God, although many theologians prefer to work this out in terms of the divine providence or concursus. Whether Illingworth does so well in detailed areas is debatable. His emphasis on design is perhaps an overemphasis, and what he says about miracle falls short of adequacy. Nor does he tackle properly the epistemological problem posed by Kant. More generally, however, his thesis carries no little weight in virtue of its material merit and the skill with which he presented it.

Unfortunately it also raises some more serious difficulties. (1) The biblical and historical evidence, which he offers only very selectively, hardly seems to support the structure which he erects upon it. (2) Philosophy and religion cannot be so easily swept under the rug of preparation for the gospel as Illingworth assumes. (3) The specific connection between immanence and the Logos, not the Father or the Spirit, does not have the strength which Illingworth needs for his thesis, for after all he is writing on incarnation and development, not immanence and development. (4) Illingworth takes a difficult path when he chooses to present incarnation as a special form of immanence and then advance it as a general principle instead of pointing directly to Christ as the incarnate Word. (5) While one must concur with his refusal to separate incarnation and atonement, he surely falls into the very error that he condemns by detaching a generalized incarnation from the very specific purpose of the atonement. His extravagant rhetoric betrays this. The incarnation, while universal in scope and ramifications, was after all a very specific historical event. Poor service is finally done to it if in a confused equation with the divine immanence or concursus it is transformed into a grandiose cosmic principle with some very questionable theological implications.

## B. INSPIRATION

### 1. Introduction

Concern for Christ's humanity was very naturally accompanied by a new interest in the humanity of scripture. This manifested itself in the burgeoning of textual, lexical, exegetical, historical, and literary studies. It also raised new questions about the inspiration and authority of scripture as a divine and not just a human book. On the one side were those who felt that the older doctrine, especially in its tight seventeenth-century form, could not be harmonized with the new outlook and the new findings. On the other side a fresh statement of the older teaching was attempted, although not without certain modifications under the pressure of more recent developments. On a broader view, the isolation of scripture from other activities of the Spirit was seen as the main stumbling block, and integration of inspiration into the general working of the Spirit was regarded as the major task.

## 2. Schleiermacher

### a. Scripture and Spirit

In this matter, as in so many others, Schleiermacher offers some interesting insights, not just in the poetic flights of the *Speeches* but also in the more sober discussion of *The Christian Faith*. While denying that scripture is the basis of faith, since faith is needed to read it (§ 128), Schleiermacher is ready to accept its normativity both formally and materially. He does so, however, because it is the first in a series of presentations of the Christian faith (§ 129). The New Testament books are inspired in the sense of being self-derived and then collected under the guidance of the Spirit (§ 130). It is emphasized, however, that the Spirit is the spirit of the community, which is the source of all its gifts and works. Thus the theology of the apostles may be superior to that of others, but not qualitatively so, just as their writing is not qualitatively different from their other work. Authorship, then, has little bearing on authenticity. To know what is canonical we need only Christian experience and the Spirit's witness, which in practice amount to much the same thing. Through a use of scripture which is both critical and constructive the Spirit will lead us into all truth (§ 131).

### b. The Old Testament

It is worth noting that all this applies only to the New Testament. Schleiermacher accepts the canonicity of the Old Testament because of the witness of the New and the relation between church and synagogue. Nevertheless, he does not accord it the same dignity or inspiration, since the law differs from the gospel, and Christian piety senses the distinction. As he sees it, the Old Testament should not be put in front of the New but added to it as a kind of bulky appendix (§ 132).

### c. Contribution

The significant point in Schleiermacher, however, is that the New Testament writings, although normative, constitute only one of the works of the Spirit in the church. Hence they do not enjoy a unique status and no special qualities need be claimed for them. Inspiration is a general term which applies to the whole of scripture, not the detailed parts, so that not every part is to be equally ascribed to the Spirit, nor does any question of a special inerrancy arise. Schleiermacher leaves us with one especially interesting and instructive suggestion when he compares the relation of the Spirit and the authors of scripture to the hypostatic union, that is, the union of the divine and human natures in the one person of Jesus Christ (§ 130).

### 3. Alexander

#### a. The New Orthodoxy

As a representative of the attempted restatement of orthodoxy in the light of a changed situation, we might take a brief glance at Archibald Alexander, the father of the Princeton School. Alexander is very conscious of the problems of epistemology raised by Kant, and it is not surprising to find in his *Thoughts on Christian Experience* (1841) some shift to a religious a priori as the basis or guarantee of Christianity. Nevertheless, his chief focus is on the problem of scripture — the mustering of evidence in its support and the more precise examination and categorization of its inspiration. This is the theme of his important *Evidences on the Authenticity, Inspiration and Canonical Authority of the Holy Scripture* (1836).

#### b. Scripture and Reason

Alexander accepts the sensory basis of reasoning, but he does not see why this rules out a rational knowledge of God or necessitates a special theological epistemology. In this regard he stays close to the rational orthodoxy of the previous century. All truth has to be rational, for "without reason we can form no conception of a truth of any kind." If a thing is true, its reception is reasonable irrespective of the kind of evidence on which it is based. "Truth and reason are so intimately connected that they can never with propriety be separated" (*Evidences*, p. 10). It follows, then, that if scripture is true it cannot contradict reason nor can the knowledge which it imparts be other than rational. If the evidences are sufficient to show that scripture is true, its conformity to reason cannot be challenged.

#### c. Scripture and Experience

While Alexander finds a place for experience, he does not think it should come first. Unlike Schleiermacher, who argues that faith is the basis, not scripture, Alexander compares scriptural truth to "the inscription or image on a seal" and its apprehension in the human mind to "the impression made by the seal on the wax." He allows, however, that "if that impression is clearly and distinctly made, we can understand . . . the true inscription on the seal more satisfactorily than by a direct view of the seal itself." He attributes the making of the impression to the Holy Spirit, so that, as in Schleiermacher, we find at least a tendency to merge experience and the Spirit's inner work: "Genuine religious ex-

perience is nothing but the impression of divine truth on the mind, by
the energy of the Holy Spirit" (*Thoughts,* 1.8).

### d. Biblical Evidences

Since truth rests on evidences, Alexander thinks it important to
supply arguments for the biblical revelation. He agrees with earlier
writers that miracles and fulfilled prophecies supply the main external
evidences. In addition, however, he suggests three important internal
evidences. (1) What scripture says about God accords with what reason
expects. (2) What it says about man accords with both reason and
experience. (3) Scripture gives instruction in areas where it is most
needed, such as the area of human sin or divine forgiveness. The reasonableness of scripture is thus shown by its conformity to criteria which
themselves are extraneous to it.

### e. Inspiration

Alexander defines inspiration mainly in terms of function. In it
new truth about God is disclosed, or obscured truth is clarified. Illumination accompanies it as the work of the Holy Spirit which makes understanding possible. As regards the relation between inspiration and revelation, Alexander rejects a narrow equation. Revelation is a broader
term; inspiration applies properly only to the biblical authors.

If inspiration is defined in terms of function, Alexander investi-
gates its nature, too. He discovers three forms: superintendence, suggestion, and elevation. In the first, which mostly characterizes the historical books, the Holy Spirit directs the selection of "facts and circumstances which will answer the end proposed" and gives such help as
to preserve the writers "from all error and mistake." Suggestion, the
central form of inspiration, means the presentation to and through the
authors of new truth which they could not reach or know on their own.
Elevation, perhaps the least important of the three, denotes a divine
enhancement of the sublimity of the authors' utterances.

### f. Verbal Inspiration

In Alexander's view this differentiation in inspiration does not
work against verbal inspiration. To be sure, words are suggested only
where inspiration has the form of suggestion. In superintendence and
elevation human words are controlled or given an added intensity. Yet
in every case the word is the powerful and inerrant Word of God. "As in
the narration of well-known facts, the writer did not need a continual
suggestion of every idea, but only to be so superintended as to be
preserved from error; so in the use of language in recording familiar
things, there existed no necessity that every word should be inspired;
but there was the same need of a directing and superintending influence
as in regard to the things themselves" (*Evidences,* pp. 226–227). This

means, not a rejection of verbal inspiration, but three types of verbal inspiration corresponding to the three types of inspiration in general.

Since all scripture is inspired, no distinction can be made between important things and trivial things. Alexander cannot agree with Schleiermacher that not all parts of scripture are equally inspired. He does not, indeed, find any objection to this in principle, but the practical problem of drawing a line between inspired and uninspired parts cannot be overcome.

### g. Inerrancy

What about errors or mistakes? Little credence can be attached to scripture if it is wrong in basic matters, but does it matter if there are more trivial errors? Alexander thinks it does. Scripture stands or falls as a unit. Hence one must be able to trust it in every matter. Alexander holds what has often been called a "domino" theory here. If one piece falls, all pieces fall. "Could it be shown that the evangelists had fallen into palpable mistakes in facts of minor importance, it would be impossible to demonstrate that they wrote anything by inspiration" (*Evidences*, pp. 228–229). Inspiration implies inerrancy, but by the same token, proven error refutes inspiration. Alexander himself is confident that no palpable mistake will in fact be proved, but his teaching here undoubtedly produces a slight uncertainty and a feeling that some kind of solution, however artificial, has to be produced for every suggested problem.

### h. Conclusion

Three points may be noted in Alexander. (1) He clings to the rational orthodoxy which sets so great store by human evidence for biblical truth and authority. (2) He finds a way of allowing for the human factor in biblical authorship, that is, the differentiation of inspiration, without compromising verbal inspiration or inerrancy. (3) He yields a little to the new emphasis on experience by tending to equate it with the former inner testimony of the Holy Spirit.

### 4. Charles Gore

### a. Experience

It is natural that in the symposium *Lux Mundi* inspiration should be an important topic for discussion. The editor himself, Charles Gore of Trinity, Oxford, selects it as the theme of his own contribution. Like Schleiermacher, he believes that inspiration should be related to the other activities of the Holy Spirit. Unlike Schleiermacher, however, he depicts these activities on a wider canvas and only at the end takes up the narrower subject of the inspiration of scripture.

Gore first discusses the appeal to Christian experience. In the

fuller sense he can accept the validity of this, for Christianity is a
"manifested life," first in Christ, then in the church. As such, it is the
sphere in which the Spirit, the Lifegiver, "finds his freest and most
unhindered activity." "Last in the eternal order of the divine being . . .
the Holy Spirit is the first point of contact with God in the order of
human experience" (pp. 230–231).

### b. The Cosmic and Human Aspects

Gore next points to the cosmic work of the Spirit. The one life of
nature is "the universal evidence of the one Spirit." The Spirit works
especially in rational creatures and finds his "chiefest joy" in humanity.
Humanity's rebellion against God brought disappointment, but in God's
ongoing purpose the Spirit finds in the Son of Man "the perfect realization of the destiny of man." The church then becomes, not the exclusive,
but "the special and covenanted sphere of His regular and uniform
operation" (p. 235).

### c. Marks of the Spirit's Work

Four marks of the work of the Spirit in the church are noted. (1)
The work is social, for man "cannot realize himself in isolation" (p. 235).
(2) It is individual, for with his different charisms the Spirit gives "more
individualized life" within the common faith (pp. 236–239). (3) It claims
and consecrates the whole of nature. Sin has brought apparent discord
between "the divine operation and human freedom," between the
spiritual and the material, but this is overcome by the Spirit in Christ
and the church. The visible church and the sacraments show how the
Spirit's operation covers physical as well as spiritual life (pp. 239–240).
(4) The Spirit's work is gradual. This may be seen in the Old Testament,
which in its imperfection is a "gradual process of education" justified by
its total result (p. 240). The same gradualness characterizes Christian
experience. Christians are often vulgar, ignorant, and sinful. The
church offers only "a very troubled and imperfect home" (pp. 242–243).
Nevertheless, the Spirit is gradually at work, he himself being present
as "the 'Vicar of Christ' in whose presence Christ himself is with them"
(p. 243).

### d. The Person of the Spirit

For Gore the doctrine of the Spirit rests partly on this experience
and partly on the revelation in Christ recorded in the New Testament (p.
244). The Spirit is here known as the third person of the Trinity, distinct
from Father and Son yet no less truly God. As Gore finely puts it:
"Wherever the Father works, He works essentially and inevitably
through the Son and the Spirit; wherever the Son acts, he acts from the
Father and by the Holy Spirit; wherever the Holy Spirit comes, He

brings with Him in His coming the Son and the Father." Unhappily he tends to spoil the effect of this by commending the triune character of man's spiritual nature as an apt if inadequate image of the divine relationships (p. 246).

### e. Scripture and Spirit

Turning to inspiration, Gore lays down two principles. (1) Inspiration of scripture is not a qualitatively different work of the Spirit but is part of his general operation. Hence belief in it must be held in the context of "belief in the general action of the Holy Spirit upon the Christian society and the [Christian] soul" (p. 248). (2) Scripture and church belong closely together. If the apostles have unique authority, they write to those who also have the Spirit, so that "the spirit in which the church lives" cooperates with and even limits the spirit in which the apostles speak and write (p. 248). Scripture is "the highest utterance of the Spirit," but "the Spirit in the church" interprets the meaning of scripture (p. 249).

### f. Scripture and Faith

Gore agrees with Schleiermacher that scripture, or at least its inspiration, is not the basis of faith. The facts of Christianity are accepted because of their general credibility. Belief in inspiration "follows, does not precede, belief in Christ" (p. 250). Objections to this belief do not affect the historicity of the gospel narratives. "Christianity brings with it indeed a doctrine of the inspiration of Holy Scriptures, but is not based upon it" (p. 250).

### g. Meaning of Inspiration

What does inspiration mean? Gore in his answer points to the Jews. As "every race has its inspiration" the Jews, being chosen to restore man's broken relationship with God, have a supernatural one which is "more direct and more intense" and which "involves a direct consciousness on the part of its subjects" (p. 251). Yet there are different degrees of inspiration in the different sorts of literature. Human freedom is important here, but it involves no clash with the Spirit's ministry. "The human activity is none the less free, conscious, rational, because the Spirit inspires it" (p. 251).

### h. The Old and New Testaments

(1) Old. In the Old Testament inspiration denotes more specifically a "point of view." The writers go to work like others but with the aim of keeping before the chosen people "the record of how God has dealt with them" (p. 252). Thus the prophets, while not always predicting with accuracy, interpret "what God is doing and commanding in their own age" and "forecast what in judgment and redemptive mercy God means

to do and must do in the Divine event" (p. 254). Once this is seen, no Christian need find it hard to accept the inspiration of the Old Testament.

(2) New. In relation to the New Testament Gore has four points. (a) The apostles' inspiration for writing is the same as their inspiration for teaching. (b) The New Testament rests on Christ's training of his apostles to perpetuate his revelation. (c) It consists in an endowment for "representing, and not misrepresenting, [Christ's] teaching and himself" (p. 255). (d) In secondhand writers like Luke it is part of their whole spiritual endowment, and tradition helps to keep out material errors (pp. 255–256).

### i. Inerrancy

Does inspiration entail inerrancy? Gore thinks not. The general historicity of scripture may be accepted, and inspiration undoubtedly means illumination of judgment (p. 260). But there is no "miraculous communication of facts not . . . otherwise known"; illumination does not lift us out of "the natural conditions of knowledge" (p. 260). Different genres occur in the Bible, and accuracy is not always an issue. Even myth can have a place with no detriment to inspiration (p. 262). The advance in literary criticism, then, "does not constitute any threat to the doctrine of inspiration, only to particular definitions of it to which the church is not tied" (pp. 262–263).

### j. Christ and Scripture

What about Christ's position in debated matters? Gore makes three points here. (1) Often Christ is not pronouncing on authorship or historicity. (2) He makes no claim to give information on such matters. (3) He did not reveal his deity by anticipating natural knowledge. "The incarnation was a self-emptying of God to reveal himself under conditions of human nature" (p. 264). To reconcile man to God Christ "used human nature" and "willed so to restrain the beams of Deity as to observe the limits of the science of His age," and similarly of its historical knowledge (p. 265). This limitation, Gore insists, must not be confused with fallibility but is simply a refusal to employ "the unveiled omniscience of deity" to "anticipate or foreclose a development of natural knowledge" (p. 265).

### k. Scripture and Criticism

Gore concludes that while much criticism may be arbitrary and irreverent, the church must not rule out free discussion. As regards the New Testament writings Gore feels that research has "fortified and enriched the sense of their inspiration." The same might happen in relation to the Old Testament if it were asked how much might "legitimately and without real loss be conceded." Opposition, however, leaves obstacles in the path of many who want to believe (p. 266). In Gore's view, a verbal and inerrant inspiration can no longer be retained. With suitable redefinition, however, inspiration need not be at odds with a critical approach so long as it does not go to extremes. This is achieved by placing inspiration in the context of the total work of the Spirit, equating it with a particular standpoint or teaching, and removing Christ from debates about historicity by means of insights from kenotic Christology.

## 5. Nevin

### a. Mercersburg Emphases

An interesting development in Reformed theology took place when Philip Schaff and John Nevin became colleagues at the small college of Mercersburg in the late nineteenth century. Like the *Lux Mundi* school, the Mercersburg theology made Christ's incarnation a focus. Christ was seen as faith's basis and object. Note was taken of the christological significance of the Creed and the church. Christ's mystical presence at the Eucharist was strongly affirmed. The evils of sectarianism, especially of private interpretation, were deplored. From a staunchly Reformed angle, these theologians sought a christologically centered catholicity as the basis of evangelical and more broadly ecumenical unity.

Inevitably, the general thinking of Mercersburg had ramifications for the understanding of scripture. Nevin in particular was concerned, not so much about inspiration, but more about the relation of scripture to revelation and faith. He developed some of his fresh and instructive insights in a work entitled *The Meaning of Protestantism* (*LPT*, pp. 182ff.).

### b. Faith and Its Object

In this essay Nevin has a section, "The Principle of Protestantism," in which he first examines the question of the objectivity of faith. The subjective experience of faith cannot exist in a vacuum. Faith in isolation cannot be decisive. No true faith "can exist without embracing its object" (p. 187). In the last analysis what is believed counts for more than the believing itself.

What, then, is the object of Christian faith? In a general way one might call it the "substance of divine truth." But what does that mean? For some the biblical record provides this substance. Nevin demurs, for behind the documentary form (the inspired pages of scripture) lies "the living fact of revelation" mediated through these pages (p. 188). Others seem to take the even narrower view that inspiration, whether as a fact or a doctrine, is the substance of divine truth and the proper object of faith. Now Nevin neither denies the fact of inspiration nor rejects the doctrine. He cannot agree, however, that the inspiration of the documentary record is the object of faith. Faith's object lies in the substantive matter which the record makes known.

### c. Christ as Faith's Object

So far, Nevin has spoken very generally. He has defined the object of faith as the living fact of revelation and the substance of divine truth. He has said what these are not, but has not yet explained what they are. When he goes on to this more specific positive definition, he is led at once to Jesus Christ. For Christ, as "the root and principle . . . of the whole Christian salvation" (p. 188), is clearly the center of revelation. Thus the true object of faith is Christ himself.

Here, however, a subtle danger arises, for Christ might very easily be equated with the subjective experience of Christ, and experience itself could then become the real object and basis of faith. Nevin guards against this, for he sees that with Christ come the objective realities of the Bible and the church. Faith cannot break free from these in subjective autonomy (pp. 188ff.). If the objective Christ is "primordial" for salvation, it is through the Bible and the church that Christ is known and present. Nor does the problem of heteronomy arise. Objective Christianity in the form of the Bible and the church, and supremely of Christ himself, is essential to faith. Faith and its object belong together, and authentic faith is attained only with a union of subjectivity and objectivity.

### d. The Role of Scripture

Nevin's main target in this work is the misplaced stress on faith which occurs at the expense of the object of faith. Nevertheless, he has some important things to say about the role of scripture, too. Scripture is not revelation itself but its instrument. Christ, not scripture, constitutes the real object of faith. Yet with the church scripture has high significance as an objective reality which faith cannot bypass or ignore as though Christ could be known and believed in some mysterious emotional or mystical way. To know Christ, faith must go by the route of church and scripture. Only thus can it be authentic Christian faith.

### e. The Apostles' Creed

Nevin has some further discussion of the relation of Christ and scripture in a little work called The Apostles' Creed (LPT, pp. 309–317). Once more he starts with Christ as "the one only principle of Christianity" (p. 310). This means the subjection of scripture to Christ. Its validity derives from its proclamation of Christ as the fundamental principle. Yet it also means the indispensability and normativity of scripture for us. Only through scripture can we authentically know Christ and come to faith in him.

### f. Inspiration

All this has for Nevin an important bearing on inspiration. Nevin does not agree that when inspiration is being attacked, as in his day, rational evidences have to be found and marshaled in its support. Proving inspiration is not a primary task. Whether or not we can prove inspiration, the presence of the Word is "the true substratum" of Christianity. It is as we can prove the reality of revelation that we shall also be able to prove the inspiration of scripture. We are to begin, then, with the truth of Christianity itself, not with inspiration. Inspiration is an implication, not a basic principle. For Christianity itself is not only "a written word" but "a new creation . . . starting from its founder Jesus Christ" (p. 310). As such it has a real historical substance. This is where the Apostles' Creed enters the picture as representing the primary substance. But the further details of the argument need not detain us. Already Nevin's understanding of the role of scripture and inspiration has emerged with sufficient clarity. Like Schleiermacher and Gore, he puts scripture and its inspiration in a larger setting of which the true and proper center and focus is Christ himself.

# CHAPTER XXVII
## *Two Liberals*

### A. HARNACK

#### 1. Introduction

As the nineteenth century ended and the twentieth century began, the so-called Liberal Protestant theology reached a climax in two brilliant and influential thinkers, Adolf von Harnack and Johann Wilhelm Herrmann. Harnack was an accomplished historian, writer, and lecturer. His *History of Dogma,* for all its shortcomings, can still hold its own with any rivals. His detailed studies, while obviously outdated, still retain their value as reference works for consultation on many matters. So great was his stature that even when Karl Barth revolted against Harnack's theology he could never bring himself to subject it to the public criticism which he aimed so effectively against the work of others.

#### 2. What Is Christianity?

Much of the essence of Harnack's theology is conveniently summed up for us in the little volume *Das Wesen des Christentums*, which was put into English under the title *What Is Christianity?* The book arose out of a series of lectures which he gave extemporaneously at the University of Berlin to an audience of some six hundred students drawn from all the faculties. These lectures were taken down in shorthand, and only a few changes were needed to prepare them for publication. For the English version Harnack himself wrote a brief preface in which he states that theologians "only half discharge their duties if they think it enough to treat of the Gospel in the recondite language of learning and bury it in scholarly folios." Hence he presents his own "short and plain statement of the Gospel and its history."

### 3. Scope of the Lectures

Defining the scope of his lectures, Harnack says that he will not engage in apologetics, which cries up religion by showing how it serves something else (p. 8). Nor will he offer philosophical theory, since a thing cannot be known in general conceptions. His approach will be that of a historian who rests on the records of Jesus, the disciples, and the early church. He points out, however, that the historian has to decide what is essential (p. 14). Jesus and the disciples were "situated in their day just as we are situated in ours" (p. 13). They were bound to their nation and its conditions. Hence "the kernel has to be separated from the husk" (p. 13). The gospel cannot be identical with its earliest form. It contains something which under changing forms is of permanent validity. Harnack's task is to single out that something, which he takes to be simple and unmistakable. He remembers, of course, that "in history absolute judgments are impossible." The assigning of value, as a "creation only of feeling and will," is "a subjective act" (p. 19).

### 4. The Message of Jesus

#### a. Preliminary Points

Harnack divides his sixteen lectures into two main sections, "The Gospel" and "The Gospel in History." The first section, which will be our concern here, has two subdivisions, "The Leading Features of Jesus' Message" and "The Gospel in Relation to Certain Problems." Before giving his account of the teaching of Jesus, however, Harnack makes some introductory observations which shed a good deal of light on his own theological outlook.

(1) Synoptic Basis. Harnack is convinced that "our authorities for the message which Jesus Christ delivered are . . . the first three gospels" (p. 21). John, while containing a "real, if scarcely recognizable, traditional element," has little historical worth (p. 22). The synoptics are not history but "are not altogether useless as sources of history" (p. 22). Harnack does not mean to be patronizing. He sees that the gospels have a unique character. Fortunately this coincides, if imperfectly, with the presentation of a firsthand tradition (pp. 22ff.).

(2) Miracles. Reports of miracles constitute a problem which Harnack tries to solve in four ways. (a) In an age when natural laws are little understood "there are no miracles in the strict sense," and miracles have no real significance (pp. 27–28). (b) Purported miracles do not mean that the witness is from a later age (p. 28). (c) Miracles remind us that natural laws serve "higher ends" (p. 29). (d) Our knowledge of natural law is incomplete, especially at the psychological level, so that while we do not believe that the earth stood still we cannot dismiss the physical healings as illusions (pp. 30–31).

(3) The First Years of Jesus. Since we are told nothing of the first thirty years of Jesus' life, we cannot study his teaching against its background. It seems that he had no rabbinical training (pp. 34–35), had no connection with the Essenes (p. 35), went through no violent crisis (pp. 35–36), and, surprisingly, did not come under Greek influence (pp. 36–37). His teaching, however, suggests that "he lived in religion" in a natural way (pp. 38–39), so that "he strikes the mightiest notes" "yet clothes the strongest emotion in the language in which a mother speaks to her child" (p. 40).

### b. The Kingdom of God

(1) Nature. Trying to pierce to the valid kernel of Jesus' teaching, Harnack fixes on God's kingdom and its coming as the first of three predominant elements. For Jesus the kingdom is not just a future event, but "something inward, something which is already present" (p. 56), "the rule of the holy God in the hearts of individuals" (p. 60). The dramatic, external, and historical aspects are the husk, the mode of statement. Finally at issue are "God and the soul, the soul and its God" (p. 61).

(2) Expressions. As the rule of God which is a victory over evil, the kingdom finds two expressions in the ministry of Jesus. (a) The external expression consists of exorcisms and healings (pp. 62–65). (b) The internal expression consists of the forgiveness of sins. For Harnack "this is the first complete transition to the conception of the kingdom of God as the power that works inwardly" (p. 65). The external is abandoned here; the individual is redeemed.

(3) Meaning. Understood thus, the kingdom has a threefold meaning. (a) It is a supernatural gift. (b) It is a purely religious blessing, the inner link with the living God. (c) It is the most determinative experience of life which permeates and dominates all else (p. 67). As the entry of the eternal into time, the kingdom gives meaning to life, which can have no meaning as long as death is the end.

### c. The Fatherhood of God
### and the Infinite Value of the Human Soul

(1) The Fatherhood of God. Also intrinsic to Jesus' message is the fatherhood of God and the consequent value of the soul. At this level the gospel is not "a positive religion . . . it is . . . religion itself" (pp. 68–69). The most important witness to the divine fatherhood is the Lord's Prayer. Here the gospel is God's fatherhood applied to all life. Implied are "an inner union with God's will" and "a joyous certainty of the possession of eternal blessings" (p. 71).

(2) The Value of the Soul. The soul's value follows naturally from its relation to "the Being who rules heaven and earth." A child of God "has a value which is higher than all the fabric of this world" (p. 72). The

endowing of the soul with infinite value rests on "a transvaluation of all values" in which the whole world counts for nothing if the soul is lost. Others had dimly felt this before Jesus. It was his peculiar genius "to give perfectly simple expression to profound and all-important truths . . . as though he were only reminding men of what they all knew already" (p. 74).

### d. The Higher Righteousness and the Commandment of Love

In what Jesus says about the higher righteousness and love Harnack finds four themes. (1) Jesus severs ethics from "the external forms of religious worship and technical observance" (p. 77). (2) He goes to the root of moral questions by insisting on the primacy of "disposition and intention" (pp. 77–78). (3) He finds one root and motive of truly ethical conduct — that of love (p. 78). Love is of one kind, whether shown to neighbor or enemy. It is the new life already begun. "It is always the love which serves" (p. 78). (4) Jesus combines religion and morality in a new way by uniting love and humility in the love of God. Hence in his teaching "religion may be called the soul of morality and morality the body of religion" (p. 79). The Beatitudes bring this out very clearly.

## 5. Implications of the Gospel

### a. The Gospel and the World

Having presented the essence of the message, Harnack goes on to discuss its implications in six areas of debate. The first is that of the relation between the gospel and the world, especially in the matter of asceticism. Does the transvaluation of all values mean that "the gospel is a world-denying creed"? (p. 87). From Christ's own life-style, the conduct of the disciples, and the stress which Jesus put on trusting God, he concludes that it is not world-denying, although he recognizes that self-denial in relation to mammon, care, and selfishness forms an integral part of "the love that serves and is self-sacrificing" (p. 95).

### b. The Gospel and the Poor

In discussing what he calls the social question, Harnack contrasts the views of Jesus as a great social reformer (pp. 95–96) and as a purely religious teacher who is concerned about the poor but aims at no improvement in their earthly lot (p. 97). He himself takes a middle course. Jesus "laid down no social programme for the suppression of poverty and distress." He did not interfere in economic and political matters (p. 105). On the other hand, "no religion ever went to work with such an energetic social message" (p. 106). The gospel means solidarity with others. It aims at a "socialism which rests on the consciousness of a spiritual unity." In this sense its social message "can never be outbid" (p. 108).

### c. The Gospel and the Law

Harnack follows a similar line in relation to public order. Jesus was "no political revolutionary" and had "no political programme" (p. 111). He attacked the unconstituted authority of parties (p. 112) but respected the division of power between God and Caesar (p. 113). Jesus did not disparage law but saw its limitations and dangers. He thus taught his followers to transcend law by love, at any rate at the individual level (pp. 119–120).

### d. The Gospel and Work

What is the relation of the gospel to work and civilization? Some complain of a lack of teaching here, while others see in Jesus an ideal for every type of human activity (pp. 126ff.). Harnack thinks that a distinction must be observed between the affairs of the gospel and those of the world. The church errs if it ties itself to a particular epoch of civilization. Work and civilization "do not comprise the highest ideal" (p. 129). "There is a great deal of hypocritical twaddle talked about work," but most of it is "stupefying toil" (p. 129). Progress does not alter man's basic position. Jesus came with a greater ideal, that of the kingdom of justice and peace created by the forces of love. He thus tells us of "the real work which humanity has to accomplish" (p. 133).

### e. The Gospel and Christology

Here Harnack suddenly switches to the doctrinal sphere. In his teaching, how does Jesus "wish himself to be understood"? Harnack begins with two points: (1) his person must not be detached from his commandments (p. 135) and (2) he "described the Lord of heaven and earth as his God and his Father" (p. 136). He then considers the two designations "Son of God" and "Messiah." Jesus has a unique sense of sonship resting on his unique knowledge of God and his unique mission to communicate it. Once the kernel is separated from the husk of contemporary form we find that this uniqueness lies in its unsurpassable perfection (pp. 139–140). As for "Messiah," Jesus adopts this title in order "to gain an absolute recognition within the lines of Jewish religious history, . . . the true religious history for all mankind" (p. 151). What, then, of his own place in his message? On the one hand, "the gospel has to do with the Father only and not with the Son" (p. 154). On the other hand, "he is the way to the Father" as "the personal realization" of the gospel (p. 156). Accepting the gospel, we are forced to affirm "that here the divine appeared in as pure a form as it can appear on earth" (pp. 156–157).

### f. The Gospel and Doctrine

Harnack concludes this whole section with some brief remarks on the Creed. The gospel is no "theoretical system of doctrine" (p. 157). True creedal confession means doing God's will (pp. 157–158). Knowledge varies, but to possess God "as a Father is an experience to which nothing else approaches," and "the poorest soul" can have this. Only experienced religion is to be confessed (p. 159). But have not changes in the world and its history outdated the gospel? No, for its essentials are timeless and so is the man to whom it is addressed (p. 160). Individual doctrines may need restatement. Thus the vicarious theory of Christ's death and the story of the empty tomb will have to go, but the reality of expiation stands. As to the empty tomb Harnack has two things to say: (1) "the New Testament itself distinguishes between the Easter message of the empty grave and the appearances of Jesus on the one side, and the Easter faith on the other" (p. 173); (2) "this grave was the birthplace of the indestructible belief that death is vanquished" (p. 175). Starting with the New Testament itself, Harnack thus engages in a relativizing of all doctrines in which the Holy Spirit, for example, really signifies the "independence and immediacy of religious life and feeling" (p. 178). A simple essence of truth, or ultimately of experience, finds varying expression in the changing forms of life and thought. The forms may be discarded; the unchanging essence is to be sought, retained, and re-expressed.

## 6. Three Observations

### a. The Husk and Kernel Thesis

The obvious merits of Harnack's work should not blind us to the dubious feature that everything finally rests on the thesis that in Christ's teaching, the apostolic records, and all Christian doctrine we have an imperishable kernel which is contained in an impermanent and dispensable husk. Now there may be truth in this concept as applied to the church's dogmatic formulations, although even here it needs careful handling. In relation to the original teachings, however, it depends on a prior decision regarding the nature of historical revelation. Does this imply contingency, so that it is only by chance, or as the product of purely historical forces, that the gospel takes one form and not another? Is there some providential ordering so that one form is chosen that is at least the best adapted to express the inner message? Or does historical revelation carry with it a divine particularity whereby the form is integral not only to the understanding but also to the very essence of the message? Harnack took the first or, at most, the second view, but even in his day it had not escaped the most radical and searching of opposition. For behind the whole matter lies one of the most basic of all theological questions. Are God and his word and work to be interpreted in terms of humanity, or are humanity and the world to be understood in God's terms? Are the teachings and facts of Christianity generalizations, or do they have divine specificity? Do we have a best or an authentically and divinely unique work? Has a general word been spoken or a supremely particular word? A simplistic acceptance of the husk and kernel metaphor such as one finds in Harnack ignores these most profound questions.

### b. The Nature of the Kernel

Even if one were to agree to the general concept, however, the question still arises whether Harnack's supposed kernel really does represent the essence of the message of Jesus. Contemporary researches were already suggesting that Harnack was doing at least as much reading in as reading out when he expounded God's kingdom or fatherhood as the true kernel. No doubt God's kingdom does in fact stand at the heart of the gospel but what is here stripped away as husk surely belongs to the essence of the kingdom as Jesus understood and preached it. As Harnack perceives, he has made a very subjective judgment in singling out the inner aspect of the kingdom as the true essence. No one can deny that this is the essence for Harnack. It is the essence of Harnack's own gospel. Something else, however, might be the essence for someone else. No criterion exists by which to say what is truly the essence of the gospel once some part of the historical record is regarded as kernel and the rest as husk. The same applies to the divine fatherhood and all the rest. Harnack, liberated by his husk and kernel principle, engages in large-scale and highly subjective neologizing. He does not even concede that his own statement is simply a new twentieth-century husk. He claims to present the inner kernel itself. Might it not be that in discarding the husk he has in fact discarded the kernel, too?

### c. Individualism

The surprisingly strong individualism of Harnack's presentation also calls for comment. Christianity is ultimately a matter of "the soul and its God." Even the Christian fellowship is finally a society of individuals. The organizational or institutional sphere is that of world, law, and state. Distinguishing so sharply between the inner and the outer spheres, Harnack shows extraordinary timidity in assessing the social, legal, political, and cultural implications of the gospel. He displays a judicious grasp of the tensions but finally leaves his society of loving service at the mercy of the establishment in large areas of public life. Barth need not have been so surprised that Harnack joined up with other German intellectuals in support of the German position in 1914. With his individualistic understanding of discipleship he could see no inconsistency. But is he right? Do the public and external things — the church as an institution, the means of grace, correct doctrine, concrete action in state and society — not matter? Is it perhaps that at root Harnack has failed to set the objectivity of revelation in necessary and healthy juxtaposition with the inner experience of faith? Harnack's individualism, which is one important strand in Liberal Protestantism just as the social gospel is another, has some obvious elements of truth which should not be neglected or disparaged. Nevertheless, it plainly needs to be set in a broader objective and external context if it is to correspond to the faith and discipleship of the New Testament.

## B. HERRMANN

### 1. Communion with God

Perhaps the most illustrious contemporary of Harnack in the world of German scholarship was Johann Wilhelm Herrmann of Marburg. A great biblical scholar, Herrmann exercised an influence which would extend to Bultmann and beyond. Like Harnack, he hoped not merely to engage in critical work but also to give his age a positive presentation of the gospel. He did this especially in his work *The Communion of the Christian with God*, which was first published in 1886 and went through many editions in the years that followed.

### 2. Preface

In a preface written for the fourth edition of 1903 Herrmann makes some important points. a. We must steer a middle course between the reduction of the gospel to mere ideas, which "do not transform us," and full assent to everything taught in the New Testament, which makes the gospel a law (p. viii). b. Faith is an inner experience of pure trust created by a personal Spirit "when we listen to the sacred tradition of the Christian community" (p. ix). c. The scriptures are properly reverenced when (1) "they are investigated in their historically determined reality" and (2) "they are used . . . to seek out the revelation of God" (p. x). For the Christian the Bible should be "the means by which with his own vision he lays hold of the Person of Jesus" (p. x).

### 3. Introduction

In an introductory survey of "The Present Situation of Protestant Theology" Herrmann argues that to accept the biblical tradition as law is not the way to inherit or appropriate salvation (p. 2). One must begin with the one saving fact, the personal life of Jesus (p. 7). Personal Christianity is what counts — "a communion of the soul with the living God through the mediation of Christ" (p. 9). This "can arise in spite of wrong teaching, and can remain alive amid obsolete ecclesiastical forms" (p. 11). Faith is the common factor in all Christians. Doctrines, as the thoughts of faith, vary widely even in the New Testament, and no consensus can or should be demanded (pp. 14–15). This does not entail subjectivism, for there is "a true objectivity" which must be "protected by clear views concerning the life of faith" (p. 17). The main task is exposition of the new life "which we know to be a Christian reality" (p. 18).

## 4. Christianity, Mysticism, and Luther

### a. Mysticism

In Chapter 1 Herrmann first lays down the principle that "the inner life of religion is a secret in the soul" and cannot be handed on (p. 19). This seems to imply mysticism, but Herrmann rejects this because it gives Christ only a dispensable role (p. 30) and cannot take him "into the inmost experiences of the [Christian] life" (p. 34). "The Christian has a positive vision of God in the personal life of Jesus Christ" (p. 33). He is thus rooted in history (p. 36). "In the human Jesus we have met with a fact whose content is incomparably richer than that of any feelings which arise within ourselves" and which gives certainty to "our conviction of being in communion with [God]" (pp. 36–37).

### b. Dogma

On the other hand, dogma and its exposition cannot communicate the salvation which is communion with God. Dogmas or doctrines are thoughts of faith that arise in this communion (p. 40). They do not offer salvation. "The thoughts of others who are redeemed cannot redeem me." I have to be put in the state of mind in which such thoughts are generated, and "this happens only when God lifts me into communion with himself" (p. 42). When I am, then the witness of all the redeemed helps, and this is found "in scripture as nowhere else" (p. 43).

### c. The Older Orthodoxy

Herrmann agrees with the older Protestant orthodoxy on three points. (1) Subjective experience is not to be severed from the objective power which leads to it. (2) It cannot be confined to feeling and hence cannot be cut off from the thoughts of faith which doctrine formulates as the content of faith. (3) These thoughts express not only what is already experienced but also what is promised by God, "who has awakened our faith within us." Yet he also disagrees at three points. (1) The objective power behind experience is not a sum of thoughts about faith but the man Jesus. (2) The thoughts of faith arise within the communion with God into which the personal power of Jesus lifts us. (3) It is not the sum of thoughts of faith, even if biblical, which makes a person a Christian, but the faculty of producing such thoughts (p. 47).

### d. Luther

Luther plays an important role in meeting the longing for an objective reality in support of faith. But we must distinguish between what is essential and what is dispensable in Luther. His acceptance of the authority of scripture as an infallible word of God is dispensable. This "is no expression of his religious experience." It is the "chariot" on which his Christianity made its entrance into the church (p. 51). This chariot is now "broken." "No one can still hold to the idea that all the words of scripture, being the word of God, are infallible expressions of the truth" (p. 52). The same applies to Luther's reverence for dogma. Yet Luther's experience of communion with God through Christ is of inestimable value. His witness to what makes a Christian to be a Christian is "incomparably more precious than his theology" (p. 56). It is this witness, Herrmann thinks, which can help those who have a yearning for God but will not profess to hold ideas "to which in reality they are strangers."

## 5. Communion and Revelation

### a. Communion and Revelation in Jesus

Communion with God means certainty that "God speaks clearly to us and also hears and considers our speech in his operations" (p. 57). To establish communion with us, God makes himself known, not by giving information about himself (p. 57), but by a fact that is both within our experience and also outside us — the fact of the appearance of Jesus in history (p. 59) and of our encounter with him as "an undoubted reality" (pp. 60–61), through whom "we are first lifted into a true fellowship with God" (p. 60).

### b. Two Aspects of Jesus

Herrmann next considers two aspects of the person of Jesus. (1) It is the only revelation that can convince those who sense the need for unconditional obedience, for in it God shows himself to us in our moral struggle as "the power to which our souls are really subject" (p. 63). (2) It is the most important sphere of reality on which to reflect. God cannot be sought in nature, for "we do not find our whole selves there." "It is only out of life in history that God can come to meet us." "In history there is no fact more important for each individual than Jesus Christ" (p. 65).

### c. Jesus and Historical Knowledge

Is not the real fact the tradition about Jesus, not Jesus himself? Are we not dependent on the New Testament for our knowledge of Jesus, and is not the New Testament subject to criticism, so that decisions as to its reliability "do not give us facts on which our religious faith could be based"? (p. 69). Herrmann acknowledges the truth behind these questions. While some features in the record may be generally accepted, one cannot base faith on these. "No historical judgment . . . ever attains anything more than probability." "Here Lessing is right" (p. 72). What, then, is the answer?

### d. The Power and Inner Life of Jesus

Certainty as to the fact of the person of Jesus rests, not on historical judgment, but on the power of Jesus himself. The New Testament portrays not only the outer life of Jesus but also his inner life. This is preserved in his church and interpreted "when we meet with men on whom it has wrought its effect" (p. 73). In relation to it we do not depend on the "mere record," for it presses in on us as "a power that is present through its work on us" (p. 74). Experience of this power means that "the inner life of Jesus becomes part of our own sphere of reality" (p. 74). Hence Jesus himself, and not just the story of Jesus, is a real thing for us.

This being so, the truth of all the details of the gospels has little significance. Historical criticism can have full play. The power of Jesus may be seen, indeed, in the fact that, through every imperfection of the record, the inner life of Jesus shines out plainly. The results of historical study change, but when we see the inner life of Jesus and this personal spirit wins power over us, an unshakable basis is established for faith (p. 76). Historical research can remove false props and also increase our knowledge of the inner life of Jesus. But it can neither give us, nor take away from us, "the personal life of Jesus which speaks to us from the New Testament" and "which, when we perceive it, always comes home to us as a miraculous revelation" (p. 78).

Experience of communion with God through apprehending the person of Jesus in the power of his inner life constitutes for Herrmann the uniqueness of Christianity (pp. 78–79). The saving fact is the personal life of Jesus grasped as a reality. This comes through the New Testament read as witness to Jesus, not as a set of doctrines (p. 81). It comes supremely through the transforming power of the inner life of Jesus. "Only something which transforms a man can constitute a saving fact," and "this effect can be exercised . . . only by something which he has himself experienced." Thus the inner life of Jesus is the saving fact (p. 83).

### e. Features of the Person of Jesus

Various features of the person of Jesus are now described. (1) He is conscious that he himself is not inferior to the ideal for which he dies (p. 89). (2) He points to himself as the redeemer. "The advent of the kingdom of God is bound up with his own appearance in history" (p. 94). (3) His person is God's revelation (pp. 97–98). The force of his character makes undeniable the reality of the God who is not only his but ours and who so loves us that in communion with him he forgives us our sins (p. 99).

### f. Objective Grounds of Certainty

For the certainty that God does in fact commune with us Herrmann finds two objective grounds. (1) First is the fact of the person of Jesus as an element and force in our own sphere of reality (p. 102). (2) Second, in odd Kantian fashion, is the fact that "we hear within ourselves the demand of the moral law." When we experience God in the power of Jesus this demand takes the form of a personal life, so that doing good is no longer a painful problem but begins to be "the very atmosphere in which we live" (p. 103). No other objective ground exists for Herrmann, but these are enough, he thinks, to keep the beginning of the religious life from being "a purely subjective experience" (p. 105).

In contrast Herrmann finds pure (and false) subjectivity in an acceptance of conceptions that does not arise out of the fact that God comes into communion with us. Assent of this kind does not mean fitting oneself to facts but following "an arbitrary and subjective will" (p. 107). The only protection against this is "joy in the objective reality of the personal life of Jesus and in his power to make us feel God working upon us." Doctrines which do not express facts that are sure for us do not offer us the objectivity for which those who reject such creedal affirmations "are athirst" (p. 108).

### g. The Christianity of Children and Adults

Children are led to God, not by the inner life of Jesus, but by persons placed in their lives by God. Adults, however, are authentic Christians, not by thoughts of God's love, but by God's revelation in Jesus. The certainty of adult Christianity lies in the real fact of Jesus, which convinces "by the power of its own content," not in thoughts about Jesus, to which assent must be given (p. 125).

Along these lines the deity of Christ may be firmly confessed. We know Jesus when we experience him as "redeeming power . . . which actually works upon us." We also know God "when we experience God's communion in the influence which Jesus has upon us" (p. 128). Similarly, the work of Jesus, rightly understood, teaches us to see in him "the divine act of forgiveness" and "the message through which God comes into communion with us," so that "we recognize in his human appearance God himself drawing us to himself." In what Jesus does we grasp God as "a Personal Spirit working upon us" (p. 143). When Christ's deity is accepted in this full sense, Herrmann believes that the dogma must be rejected "as an utterly inadequate effort at thought" (p. 181).

## 6. Communion and Its Exercise

In a final chapter Herrmann works out for faith and moral action the implications of communion with God. The chapter is too long and varied for analysis here, and in any case it repeats in essence much of what has been said already. Faith is not assent to doctrines but receiving and using "what God gives us when he comes inwardly near us" (pp. 214ff.). Theology does its proper work when it shows that we can understand our present existence only when we take into account the appearance of Jesus (p. 237). Communion with God, which is faith, means knowing God in his creative power (p. 245). Communion with Christ is communion, not with an idealized Christ, but with the historical Christ in whom we see the living God and have his true presence in our hearts (p. 283). Faith works itself out in conduct, which "itself belongs to the communion of the Christian with God" (p. 320). The life of faith, as communion with God, is simple prayer (p. 331) in which we realize that God is present in power "by the entrance of the historical Christ into our life" (p. 335). The thoughts of faith are fruitful when faith is awakened in us by the actual power of the real historical revelation. They cannot be built into a philosophical scheme, but when they arise out of faith they have worth, for the soul that conceives them is set free from the world and rises to God. Everything depends, however, on our first "running up against an undeniable fact which compels [us] . . . to recognize that in it God is touching [our] life." Religious faith is not concerned with the establishment of eternal truth but with the actual elevation of men out of life according to the flesh into eternal life. When this is seen, "we can no longer think of gaining certainty of faith in any other way" (p. 355).

### 7. The Influence of Herrmann

More so than Harnack, Herrmann helped to shape the course of theological thinking beyond his own time and even among those who in varying degrees revolted against him. Some of the points at which he did so may be briefly listed.

a. He accepted the impossibility, but also the dispensability, of a historical demonstration of Christianity.

b. He distinguished sharply between doctrines, which are secondary, and the experience of communion with God through Christ's impact, which is primary.

c. Since the detailed errors of fact or doctrine in the New Testament did not in his view invalidate its character as witness to the inner life of Jesus, he could see no incompatibility between a high estimation of scripture and its vulnerability.

d. While rejecting historical demonstration and inerrancy, Herrmann regarded the historical character of revelation — the knowledge of God through the inner life of Jesus and its effect upon us — as of the utmost importance. On this ground he strenuously resisted all charges of subjectivity.

e. The centrality of faith went hand in hand with this stress on historicity. Faith is itself, not assent, but communion with God. All aspects of life in communion with God are referred to faith, and theology consists of the thoughts of faith.

f. Finally Hermann dismissed the concept of eternal truths in favor of a definition of Christianity as elevation from the life of the flesh to eternal life. Theology, then, cannot be presented as part of a comprehensive philosophy but only as reflection on the real event of communion which takes place under the impact of the real fact of the inner life of Jesus.

### 8. Problems in Herrmann

Formative though it has been, the theology of Herrmann raises some serious problems. Ironically, these arise at the very points where it perhaps exercises its strongest appeal.

a. In his haste to deny the possibility of a historical demonstration of Christianity, Herrmann leads us very close to historical skepticism. This is not so easily offset as perhaps he imagines by his acceptance of the general accuracy of the story of Jesus: "Every reasonable man will hold the more general features of the common story of his life to be correct" (p. 71).

b. Herrmann appeals to the fact of the inner life of Jesus, but what cogency does this appeal have according to his own canons of historicity? What is this inner life? How do we know about it? How do we know about the inner life of anybody? Why should we trust the records here and not elsewhere? Or are we just accepting an impression the records make on us? Do we know what we call the inner life of Jesus only through some impact on our own lives? In the last analysis is his historical fact the subjective fact of our experience in reading the records and not the objective fact of an actual life of Jesus some two thousand years ago?

c. If it is, Herrmann has no effective safeguard against the subjectivism with which he is charged. In fact, the term "experience" probably emerges as the key term of the book and this is the secret of its appeal. But Herrmann wants it both ways. Experiencing the impact of Jesus means that his inner life is a saving fact; thus an apparent objectivity is established by subjectivity. Experiential demonstrability replaces the dismissed historical demonstrability. How far that which is demonstrated is a real factor with an authentic reality of its own, however, does not so easily appear.

d. Depreciation of the written word does not help Herrmann's case. He sees our need for knowledge of the person of Jesus. Hence apostolic tradition serves as an important witness, and "hearing the gospel" is a phrase that Herrmann likes and uses. But he makes the normativity of scripture yield to its vulnerability. The records are unreliable in detail (p. 75). The stories of the birth, miracles, resurrection, and ascension of Christ are not gospel (p. 80). One need not assent to all that the apostles believed (p. 81); in fact, their beliefs vary so greatly and allow of such different interpretations that they give rise to endless dispute (pp. 14–15). Herrmann thinks, of course, that with all this he is promoting the true authority of scripture as a guide to communion with God through Christ. All too plainly, however, he seems to be bringing scripture within the orbit of Christian experience and preventing scripture from discharging its objectively normative function. He affords the Old Testament no consideration at all in this whole context.

e. The final problem in Herrmann, perhaps, is that he does not let God be God. He accepts God sincerely, but only "God as I experience him in some impact of a supposed inner life of Jesus." Theology, then, becomes the thinking out of this experience of God, not the thinking out of what God tells us about himself. Herrmann begins with a religious, not a divine, a priori. Seeing the need for a fact outside us, he finds no proper way to meet that need. Faith, and not its object, becomes the starting point. The inner life of Jesus offers no true object, for it is known only in its impact upon us. Herrmann will not boldly start with the implication of faith, namely, that God is, quite apart from me and my faith, that he has made himself known in the person of Jesus, quite apart from me and my faith, and that I and my faith must be oriented to this God and this person through the scriptures which God has raised up for this purpose. In practice God is no true object for Herrmann and therefore no true subject. He undoubtedly writes an appealing and influential book. Nevertheless he fails at the two most vital points, neither recapturing the authentic gospel nor pointing the way back to authentic theology.

# CHAPTER XXVIII

# Barth and the Word of God

## A. BACKGROUND

### 1. The State of Theology

The first years of the twentieth century presented a confused and disquieting picture in theology. Liberalism held the field in the Protestant world in forms which included not only the reductionism of Harnack and the experientialism of Herrmann but also the relativism of Troeltsch and the social gospel of Rauschenbusch. In opposition a strong conservatism might be found in the ongoing positivism of Europe, the orthodoxy of Princeton, and American fundamentalism. Roman Catholic conservatism checked but did not wholly destroy the modernism of Loisy and his associates. Some more constructive movements such as those of the *Lux Mundi* and Mercersburg schools exerted only a limited influence, while the message of an authentic pioneer such as P. T. Forsyth was largely lost in the cacophany of competing voices. Protestantism, as well as Roman Catholicism, stood in need of positive reconstruction, but prior to the first world war there seemed to be little likelihood of this need being met.

### 2. The Emergence of Barth

Relief came from an unexpected source, a young Swiss pastor with neither doctorate nor university chair. To be sure, Karl Barth came from an academic family and had studied under Harnack and Herrmann. But he had moved off into a parish and was devoting himself to social, economic, and political issues, earning for himself the title of "the red parson" of Safenwil. Nevertheless, many forces were already pressuring Barth the pastor into drastic theological rethinking. Perhaps the most powerful of all was the problem of the pulpit: How are we to preach God's Word as we are commissioned to do? The first world war

**405**

exposed the bankruptcy of the liberal message. In his search for an answer Barth came increasingly under the influence of scripture, which he had begun to study with a new depth and seriousness. Along with scripture other voices took on new significance, the reformers, of course, but also modern prophets like Kierkegaard and Dostoevski. The result was the astonishing theological bombshell which marked the end of the military conflict in Europe: Barth's *Epistle to the Romans*.

## 3. The Dialectical Theology

Three emphases in particular secured for this commentary an attention which no ordinary exposition could have commanded. a. Barth magnified the divine transcendence with his adoption of Kierkegaard's infinite, qualitative distinction between God and man. b. In contrast to the safe humanizing of God's work in Herrmann he insisted on the wonder and yet also the sharp historical particularity of the divine intervention which culminated in Jesus Christ. c. He pointed to the strange new world of the Bible which it is not our business to appropriate to us but to which we must be appropriated if we are to understand and proclaim its message. Barth put all this in new forms of thought and language — sharp paradoxes and strange mathematical images — which broke the familiar patterns and claimed attention by their very newness and strangeness.

## 4. The Theology of the Word of God

Barth's life was drastically changed by the success of his commentary on Romans. He became the center of a movement. Lectures and writings filled his time. A professorship opened up new possibilities of study, reflection, and discussion. But the commentary posed a problem for him. What he was really getting at was perhaps not wholly clear to himself and was certainly misunderstood even by his admirers and disciples. After attempts at revision, he embarked, as every professor of dogmatics should, on a more extended theological exposition which began as *Christian Dogmatics* and then became the massive *Church Dogmatics*. Positively, he aimed here at three things: the centrality of the object of faith; the concentration of the object of faith in the Word of God; and the church-relatedness of theology. Negatively, he saw a need of distinction from two extremes, on the one side that of Liberal Protestantism, representing subjectivism and existentialism, and on the other side Roman Catholicism, representing the analogy of being. In the course of its development across some forty years, of course, the *Church Dogmatics* was to deal with many other central issues. These, however, might be called the initially determinative concerns, and since the object of faith and theology is God, the ultimate aim is the restoration of

God to his place as the starting point, theme, center, and goal — not only of theology and faith, but of all the church's life and mission and finally of all God's handiwork in nature and history.

## B. THEOLOGY

### 1. Nature of Theology

In the plan of his *Church Dogmatics* Barth devotes a first volume, divided into two parts, to theological prolegomena. He does this under the title "The Doctrine of the Word of God." He begins by defining theology and saying what is meant by theological prolegomena. Like Herrmann, but on different grounds, he thinks that only believers can do theology. At its simplest, theology is the talk of believers about God (1.1, p. 3). Believers do not exist in isolation, however, and so theology is the church's talk about God. Talking about God poses the question of correctness or purity. Hence theology in a technical sense becomes the critical and constructive scrutiny of what the church says about God. This scrutiny is the theologian's task (p. 4).

### 2. Theology and Science

Thinkers like Herrmann distinguished between the thoughts of faith and secular knowledge and denied the possibility of any embracing world view. Barth agrees, but he also feels the need for a fuller discussion of the relation between theology and other disciplines (pp. 5ff.). Theology shares the methodology of other disciplines at vital points (p. 7). Its uniqueness lies in the uniqueness of its object — God in his self-revelation — and in the uniqueness of its presupposition — an act of faith based on God's free grace.

### 3. Types of Theology

Theology can be done in two ways, regularly by those who teach and study in the schools, irregularly by those engaged in the church's general ministry (pp. 275ff.). Somewhat wryly Barth concedes that irregular theologians, among whom are Anselm and Luther, have on the whole been the rule in the church and have shown more of the seriousness, vitality, and joy of Christian insight (p. 278).

### 4. Theological Prolegomena

Apologetics and polemics have traditionally been linked with prolegomena. Barth rejects this understanding. Theology, he thinks, is genuinely apologetic and polemical when it does its proper work (p. 25). The need for prolegomena arises only out of the need to distinguish between truth and heresy when the themes of theology are discussed. Heresy is found by Barth in Liberal Protestantism on the one side (pp. 36–37) and Roman Catholicism on the other (pp. 40–41). In answer to these extremes prolegomena must present the authority of scripture within "the context of an embracing doctrine of the Word of God" (p. 43).

## 5. The Criterion of Theology

Having stated his norm in general, Barth now explains it in detail. The church's talk about God is to be defined more specifically by proclamation (preaching) and sacrament (pp. 49ff.). In this regard Barth makes the sound observation that when social work tries to be proclamation it can only become propaganda! Proclamation is itself God's Word, but since it will always be man's word, too, it must come under dogmatic scrutiny (p. 72). Professed non-theologians are not exempt from this scrutiny, nor are theologians themselves; dogmatics neither sets out all Christian truth, nor does it constitute its own criterion. It has the servant role of testing and correcting what the church says in order that God's Word may sound forth in man's word (pp. 82ff.). The criterion by which dogmatics tests proclamation cannot be dogmatic teaching itself. It can only be the substance and source of proclamation, namely, the Word of God.

## C. THE WORD OF GOD

### 1. Its Threefold Form

Locating the criterion of dogmatics in the Word of God raises the question "What is meant by the Word of God?" Functionally one might simply equate it with scripture. In Barth's view, however, heresy can be properly met only if scripture is set in the full context of God's Word. Following suggestions of the reformers he thus presents the Word in its threefold form as Word preached, Word written, and Word revealed (pp. 88–124). The Word preached is real proclamation on the presupposition that God's Word is the commission (pp. 89–90), the theme (pp. 91–92), the judgment (pp. 92–93), and the event (pp. 93–94). The Word written implies that proclamation rests on the Word already spoken by the prophets and apostles as a given factor, that is, the canon, by which the church is called, empowered, and guided (pp. 99ff.). The Word revealed is the revelation which scripture recollects as written, and proclamation points forward to as promise (p. 111). "In revelation our concern is with the coming Jesus Christ, God's own Word spoken by God Himself" (p.

113). "Revelation does not differ from the person of Jesus Christ" (p. 119). Materially, this third form is the first. Yet the Word, although threefold in form, is the one Word in a perichoresis which forms an important analogy to the divine triunity. We know the revealed Word only from scripture adopted by proclamation, the written Word only through the revelation which fulfills proclamation, and the preached Word only through the revelation attested in scripture (pp. 120–121).

### 2. Its Nature

#### a. Speech

Correcting the existentialism and anthropocentricity of his own *Christian Dogmatics* (pp. 125ff.), Barth now considers, not the recipient of the Word, but its nature. His first main point is that the Word is speech. (1) It is thus spiritual, although not in a disembodied sense (pp. 133–134). (2) It is also personal, for *God* speaks (pp. 136–139). (3) It is purposive, that is, it has a direction and goal (pp. 139–142). (4) It carries with it the presence of the speaker (pp. 142–143).

#### b. Act

The Word is not only speech but also act. (1) This means that it has contingent contemporaneity (pp. 145–149). (2) It means further that it has power to rule (pp. 149–156). (3) It also implies that the Word is decision (pp. 156–162).

#### c. Mystery

Finally, the Word is mystery. (1) This implies its secularity. It enters into the world, so that the unveiling of God entails his veiling, and his veiling, his unveiling (pp. 165–174). (2) This secularity is accompanied by a one-sidedness in which the Word is either veiled or unveiled but not partly the one and partly the other (pp. 174–181). (3) The Word as mystery again means its spirituality, not now in the general sense, but with a specific reference to the Holy Spirit (pp. 181–186). The Holy Spirit is God as the Lord of our hearing as well as the Lord of speech (p. 182). If we hear, receive, believe, and obey the Word, as we do, then this takes place only as the miracle of the Spirit and not as our own work.

### 3. Its Knowability

#### a. Possibility

Barth takes it for granted that the Word is known in the church. Hence he asks only concerning the possibility, not the reality, of knowing it (p. 190). The fact that the Word is spoken carries with it the fact that it is known (p. 191). But how? The possibility of knowing the Word does not rest primarily on any epistemological faculty in us (pp. 191–193). The Word brings its own possibility (pp. 193–194). This takes the form of experience in the sense of a determination by God's Word that becomes also a self-determination (pp. 199–200) involving all the anthropological centers such as intellect, will, and feeling.

### b. Acknowledgment

But in what does this determination lie? Barth finds it focally in acknowledgment, which covers knowledge, personal relation, control, respect, necessity, decision, and submission. He does not find it in an enhancement of man, his endowment with a new aptitude, or the drawing out of the special capacity of a few. This would imply a human as well as the divine ground or fulfillment of the possibility (pp. 209ff.). "The possibility of the knowledge of God's Word lies in God's Word and nowhere else" (p. 222). Hence "it is in faith, as the possibility given in faith, that we have to understand the knowability of the Word of God" (p. 229). Knowledge of God's Word, as acknowledgment, is put into effect in faith. In faith we have real experience of the Word, even on the assumption of our own total incapacity (pp. 238ff.). This takes place as the believer exists wholly and utterly by the object of faith (pp. 244ff.). Barth concludes, then, that "the Word of God becomes knowable by making itself known" (p. 246). God is "the original subject, the primary power, the creator of the possibility of the knowledge of God's Word" (p. 247).

## D. THE REVELATION OF GOD: THE TRIUNE GOD

### 1. The Doctrine of the Trinity

#### a. Setting

After a further discussion of the problem, the nature, and the function of dogmatics, Barth devotes the rest of the Prolegomena (1.1 and 1.2) to a material presentation of the three forms of the Word of God. He now reverses the order, beginning with the Word revealed, or the revelation of God, in a three-part discussion which deals first with the Triune God. This raises, of course, the whole question of the doctrine of the Trinity, and Barth begins by saying something about its place, root, and so-called vestiges.

#### b. Place

As regards place, Barth thinks that if we ask who is the self-revealing God, we are forced by scripture to ask about the mode of revelation. We then find that God is, in unimpaired unity, revealer, revelation, and revealing (p. 299). But this implies the Trinity. Hence, if the primary question of theology is *Who is the self-revealing God?*, the doctrine of the Trinity is the proper place to begin.

### c. Root

Barth locates the root of the doctrine in the fact that "God reveals himself as the Lord" (p. 307). Statements about revelation are not identical with it; nor is the doctrine of the Trinity identical with the text of the biblical witness. It is a translation and exegesis of it. Nevertheless, there is an indirect identity, and therefore the doctrine is a good interpretation of revelation. Indeed, some passages point strongly in this direction. The true root, however, lies in God's revelation of himself as the Lord, revelation meaning the historical self-unveiling (pp. 315–320) of the God who by nature cannot be unveiled (pp. 320–321). This revelation is called historical because it occurs at a specific time and place to specific people (p. 324), and no distinction can be made between content and vehicle (p. 329). Biblical revelation is the root of the doctrine because it has the three elements of unveiling, veiling, and impartation, of form, freedom, and historicity, of Easter, Good Friday, and Pentecost — the same thing said three different times in three different ways (p. 332). Thus the doctrine deals with a problem that is posed directly by the biblical witness to revelation.

### d. Vestiges

Traditional theology has also looked for vestiges or traces of the Trinity in nature, culture, history, religion, and psychology (pp. 336–338). Barth allows that illustrations may be found in these spheres. Commandeering ideas and facts in the world to speak about God is not intrinsically wrong. Yet the danger arises that a second root, and even a proof, might supposedly be found here (pp. 342–343). When this occurs, he thinks, we are no longer speaking about the true God of revelation. The ambivalence of illustration may be seen here, namely, the crowding out of that which is illustrated by that which illustrates. Hence it is best to stick to the one true and reliable vestige of the Trinity which need not be sought out, since it is the Word itself as revelation, scripture, and proclamation, or, by derivation, Christian theology as exegetical, dogmatic, and practical theology (p. 347).

## 2. The Triunity of God

### a. Unity

The divine triunity first involves unity in trinity. We are baptized into one name. The creed refers to one God. God is one in threefold repetition (p. 350). Monotheism is precisely the point in the doctrine of the Trinity (p. 351). But what kind of monotheism?

### b. Trinity

In answer, we have to speak of trinity in unity. In God unity is neither singleness nor isolation. God is the one God in three "modes of being" (pp. 355ff.). For persons Barth prefers here, not the modalistic concept, but the ancient term of Greek and Latin orthodoxy (pp. 360–361). The three modes are not attributes of God but three different ways in which God is God — ways which correspond to the three aspects of revelation as unveiling, veiling, and imparting. God is God in threefold relationship, that of fatherhood, sonship, and procession.

### c. Triunity

Unity in trinity and trinity in unity come together in triunity. This adds nothing materially but keeps the tension of unity and trinity. Relation means distinction but not separation. "The one God may be known only in the Three and the Three only as the one God" (p. 370). This is reflected in God's outward works, such as the appropriation of creation to the Father, redemption to the Son, and sanctification to the Spirit, even though creation, redemption, and sanctification are, of course, works of the one God (pp. 373–374), for the external works of the Trinity are undivided. To be sure, God is not to be understood from his works. Nevertheless, a reference to God may be seen in his works.

### d. Significance

As regards the contemporary significance of the Trinity, Barth insists that it answers the necessary question concerning who it is that reveals himself (p. 380). In its express statements the doctrine may say more than scripture does. Yet it rules out the false hypotheses of subordinationism and modalism. The triunity cannot leave any place for the idea that one mode or person is more God, or less God, than the others (p. 381), nor does it permit of the notion that the modes or persons are intrinsically alien to God (p. 382). More positively, the doctrine tells us that the God who reveals himself in scripture can in fact be our God, and it also tells us how far he can be our God.

## 3. God the Father, Son, and Holy Spirit

Barth concludes his discussion with three sections in which, on the basis of the Nicene Creed, he presents God as Creator and Eternal Father, God as Reconciler and Eternal Son, and God as Redeemer and Eternal Spirit. In each case he begins with God's revelation of himself in relation to us, as the Lord of our existence, the Lord in the midst of our enmity against him, the Lord who frees us. But far from deducing God's inner being from his outer relation, he argues that God is Father, Word, and Lifegiver to us because he is Father, Son, and Spirit antecedently in himself. If the operations point us in this direction, they do so because he who is already the Triune God is the Lord of the operations.

## E. HOLY SCRIPTURE

### 1. The Word for the Church

*a. Witness*

The discussion of the Trinity forms only the first part of Barth's long chapter on the first form of the Word of God as the revelation of God. It is followed by two more parts, the first on the incarnation and the second on the outpouring of the Spirit. Each of these merits careful study, but within the brief compass of the present exposition we may pass on to the treatment of the second form of the Word of God under the title of "Holy Scripture." Barth divides this into three sections, "The Word for the Church," "Authority in the Church," and "Freedom in the Church," each of which consists of two subsections. It is in the first sub-section of "The Word for the Church" that Barth develops his famous concept of holy scripture as witness.

Barth likes the term "witness" for three reasons. (1) It is fully biblical. (2) It is a limiting concept, distinguishing "the Bible as such from revelation" (1.2, p. 463). Witness is not the same as that to which it witnesses. (3) Yet there is a more positive side, too, for the Bible as witness is not separate from revelation. "It is simply revelation as it comes to us." It sets before us that to which it witnesses (p. 463). It does this, of course, in its humanity, and this poses the demand for good hermeneutics (pp. 463–464). Every human word points to an object and is properly heard only if the object is perceived. In the biblical word the object is divine revelation. Naturally, since the word is human, we can understand it only in the light of what it says (p. 466). Thus historical exegesis is valid and necessary as a tool. But since the object is revelation, it runs the risk of missing the true point by assuming that what the Bible expresses is simply the religious teaching of the authors. In this regard it may fail even to be authentically historical (pp. 468–469). At the same time, one must realize that since the content is revelation "it is only by revelation that revelation can be spoken in the Bible and . . . heard as the real substance of the Bible" (p. 469). Here biblical hermeneutics can serve as a good model for general hermeneutics, which continually talks and interrupts instead of genuinely listening.

*b. The Word of God*

By revelation, revelation is in fact spoken and heard in scripture. This means that in its positive function as witness the Bible is itself the Word of God. Barth feels the need of a gradual approach to this truth, and he thus advances a series of propositions to clarify its meaning and scope.

(1) In and with the church we acknowledge as scripture the writings of the canon, witnesses to which revelation itself attests and which the church recognizes and confirms (pp. 473–481).

(2) We thus accept the witness of expectation in the Old Testament and of recollection in the New, a witness which is one, not in virtue of a unified theology, but in virtue of a common center of revelation in Jesus Christ (pp. 481–485).

(3) The Bible bears witness to itself as scripture, not merely in the uniqueness of revelation as its theme, but also in the uniqueness of the relation set up within it whereby certain people have the function of being the first witnesses of this revelation, namely, the prophetic and apostolic authors. As first witnesses, these authors have the passive role of witnessing what takes place and the active one of telling others of it. Only in this function, not as specially gifted people in the moral or religious sphere, are they unique as the writers of scripture (pp. 485–492).

(4) The union of matter and form in the Bible's self-witness means that form and content cannot be separated: "We cannot have revelation except through this witness." "We are tied to these texts" (pp. 492ff.). No content is to be sought behind the form. Criticism must not treat the biblical records as "sources," nor must it foolishly try to mediate a "historical truth lying behind the texts." The texts must be studied "for their own sake," for "revelation does not stand or occur, and is not to be sought, behind or above them but in them." Christianity is a book-religion (pp. 494–495).

(5) Apart from the divine distinction of its authors as witnesses, the Bible is a very human book. Its uniqueness lies, not in intrinsic qualities, but in its function, in which it is both "divine" and human (pp. 497ff.). The incarnational analogy must not be pressed, for there is no personal union of God and the humanity of the authors (p. 500), but it must be recognized, for scripture is both "a witness to revelation which belongs to revelation" and also "a very human literary document" (p. 501). In virtue of its function it has priority over all other writings and authorities in the church; to acknowledge this can hurt neither God nor faith but will contribute to the greater health and vitality of the church (p. 502).

(6) Barth now comes to his decisive statement that scripture "as the original legitimate witness of divine revelation is itself the Word of God." It is so in the present tense by "a divine disposing, action and decision" (p. 502). Scripture as God's Word has always to be believed (p. 506). We do not walk by sight. Seen in itself scripture is the work of fallible men. It can be read as a human word, subjected to criticism, shown to have gaps and overemphases, found to be a source of offense (pp. 507–508). It is God's Word, not as an inherently inerrant compendium of knowledge, but as an act of revelation which has to be believed (pp. 508–509). Nevertheless, despite its human vulnerability, it is God's Word, the one Word of God and not "a lesser, less potent, less ineffable and majestic word" (p. 512). Being God's Word is not one of the Bible's

many attributes. The Word is not tied to the Bible but the Bible to the Word in the free decision of God. Yet this decision does not stand in doubt. Praying that the Bible may be God's Word and may be perceived as such, we confess that it is in acknowledgment of God and his grace and the freedom of his grace (pp. 512–513).

### c. Inspiration

Barth now formulates in eight propositions what he thinks can be believed about inspiration. (1) First and very simply the Word is God's. To say the Bible is God's Word is to speak primarily about God, not the Bible. It is to speak about his being and rule in and through the Bible and thus to give him the glory (p. 527).

(2) God's Word is also work. We refer to an act, not a state. If the Word is eternal, it also takes place in time as something new (pp. 527–528).

(3) God's act is God's miracle. It is initiatory. It is not under our control. Its very content is grace. It is truly honored, then, if it is set outside the sphere of human competence and seen as miracle (p. 528).

(4) This Word has human form. The offense that fallible men speak God's Word in fallible words must be accepted precisely because it is by God's gracious sovereignty that it happens. The miracle lies in the very fact that scripture is God's Word in true humanity (pp. 528–530).

(5) God's Word is not an inherent and manifest attribute of scripture. Something specific happens as and when the Bible is God's Word. The speaking and hearing of the Word is not identical with the existence of the book as such. A human word is present at the center of God's Word but only because God takes and uses it as such (p. 530).

(6) God, not man, decides how and when the Bible is his Word to us. This has two implications. It is not for us to decide what parts of scripture are, or are adapted to be, God's Word. Neither is it a matter of our sense of the presence of God's Word (pp. 530–532).

(7) The Bible as God's Word involves a twofold reality. On the one hand "God . . . says what the text says." "The work of God is done through this text." Hence real inspiration is verbal inspiration. On the other hand, God's presence is our present, which we accept in faith, and in the acceptance of which we are forced into the concrete effort of exegesis (pp. 532–534).

(8) Finally, inspiration "cannot be reduced to our faith in it." Too easily we think that faith is what makes the Bible God's Word. In this regard we must beware of trying to establish on our own the objectivity of inspiration (p. 534). Ultimately the fact that the Bible *is* God's Word lies behind its recognition as such (p. 537). For Barth this, and not subjective experience, is what the witness of the Spirit implies. In experience the self is subject, in the Spirit's witness God is the subject (p. 537).

## 2. Authority in the Church

### a. Of the Word

(1) Divine and Human Authority. Turning to the authority of scripture Barth first makes an important distinction between direct, absolute, and material authority on the one side and indirect, relative, and formal authority on the other. The former authority is divine, the latter human. On the human side scripture might claim precedence as the oldest record. At this level, however, it stands alongside other authorities and does not enjoy the absolute authority which is to be ascribed to it as God's Word (pp. 540ff.).

(2) Revelation and Scripture. Revelation constitutes supreme authority. But revelation is uniquely related to the biblical authors. These men stand in obedience to revelation in the specific time of God's revealing work, so that their function can be neither continued nor repeated (pp. 543–544). Their witness in scripture is for us what Jesus Christ was for them. Therefore, although scripture has in itself only indirect, relative, and formal authority, in virtue of this function of its authors it confronts the church as a direct, absolute, and material authority. The church obeys it because it obeys him who commissioned its writers. Hearing them, it hears him (p. 544). Here is the scripture principle of the reformers, held with some ambivalence by the fathers, and replaced by papal infallibility in the Roman Catholic development which culminated at Vatican I (pp. 544–572).

(3) Scripture and Church. The authority of scripture carries with it that of the church. It does so by defining and directing as well as instituting that authority (p. 574). Hence the church's authority is one of obedience, not of autonomy as in Liberal Protestantism and Roman Catholicism. Jesus Christ is Lord of the church. This Lordship cannot be vested directly in the church (pp. 574–575) for between it and him stands the fact of holy scripture. By the Holy Spirit Christ is present to us in his Word, and this Word is that of the biblical witnesses (p. 579). His revelation is revelation in this primary sign, "the reality of the apostles and prophets," which "has the form of book and letter in which the apostles and prophets continue to live for the church" (p. 581). This authority is not dead because it stands in the book and letter, for it is not the authority of the book and letter but of "the voice of the men apprehended through the book and letter" (p. 581). To see and hear Christ the church has to go to scripture (p. 583). No matter what the church says about it, scripture "is always autonomous and independent of all that is said" (p. 583). When it ceases to live by scripture the church dies (p. 584). When it obeys this superior authority it is snatched from the solitariness of self-authority and it "must and can live" (p. 585).

### b. Under the Word

(1) Subsidiary Authority. Just as the first commandment does not

exclude the fifth, so the primary authority of scripture does not exclude subsidiary authority. On the contrary, it establishes indirect, relative, and formal authority. In particular it establishes that of the church as a reflection of God's authority in his revelation (pp. 586–587). This authority depends, of course, on obedience to scripture and rejection of all attempts "to be and exercise the essential authority of God" (p. 587).

(2) Church and Confession. The church's authority arises "in a common hearing and receiving of the Word of God" and in common confession. We have to hear and receive with others and enter into the church's confession (pp. 588–589). Even if the church is wrong, we have to begin with trust and respect (p. 589), and hence the authority of the church arises. Through every debate in the church this authority consists primarily in the common confession of faith which, however fallible or tentative, still has a claim to be heard before we make our own confession (pp. 592–593).

(3) Forms of Authority. Historically the church's authority takes form in (a) the canon (pp. 597–603), (b) the fathers old and new (pp. 603–620), and (c) the creeds and confessions (pp. 620ff.). As regards the fathers, Barth suggests four criteria by which a true ecclesiastical teacher may be recognized: his expository work, his relation to Reformation teaching, his responsibility to the church, and his speaking of a word that demands decision (pp. 613–620). He has some parallel criteria by which to know true creeds or confessions: their relation to scripture, their expression of insights given to the church, their character as event in encounter with scripture, their specificity in time, space, and substance, and their origination and ratification in the church (pp. 620–649). Barth issues a closing reminder that the church's confession in the general sense is not itself scripture but a "first commentary" on it. Hence it cannot replace scripture but is subject to it and reformable by it (p. 649). Nor can it rule out our own expositions of scripture which may contribute to its reform or correction (pp. 650–660). Every confession can be succeeded by an altered one (p. 659). Before alterations are made, however, "all the voices of the now effective confession have to be seriously heard," and above all it must be under the constraint of the Word of God in holy scripture "that we have now to speak . . . differently from the fathers and brethren" who have gone before us in the faith (pp. 659–660).

### 3. Freedom in the Church

*a. Of the Word*

(1) Authority and Freedom. Authority and freedom seem to stand in antithesis. Barth argues, however, that the authority of the Word calls for free obedience, not subjection (pp. 661ff.). Authoritarian churches do not see this because they have a wrong view of authority. Similarly churches which boast of freedom do not see it because they

have a false idea of freedom (pp. 666ff.). True authority and true freedom have both to be learned from the authority and freedom of the Word. Freedom means first the freedom of the Word. Then those who believe it and obey it participate in its freedom (pp. 669–670).

(2) The Nature of the Freedom of the Word. (a) The freedom of the Word, when analyzed, is seen to consist first in its unique theme. Divinely given to divinely appointed witnesses, this theme makes scripture a unique subject, "a truly living, acting and speaking subject" whose authority in the church is accompanied by and exercised in freedom (pp. 672ff.).

(b) The freedom of the Word is then seen to consist in its peculiar power in relation and opposition to all other subjects. Barth considers four aspects of this power. It is the power of the Word to maintain itself in face of every direct or indirect attack (pp. 680–681), to "distinguish itself from the elements of the world which crowd upon it" (pp. 681–682), to assimilate and make "serviceable to itself the alien elements it encounters" (pp. 682–683), and to "change its own form and therefore its effect upon the world" (pp. 683–684).

(3) The Work of the Freedom of the Word. The particular sphere of the Word is the church, and it is here that we look for its work, which consists in the founding, preserving, and ruling of the church. The Word in its freedom founds the church by procuring from people of all nations "the hearing of obedience" (pp. 687–688). It preserves the church by maintaining itself against all opposition, so that the church shares its ongoing course so long as it occupies itself with scripture and keeps itself under its authority (pp. 688ff.). Finally, it rules the church in spite of being constantly impeded by false forms of ecclesiastical government. It does this when the church gives itself to exegesis, gives thanks "for the reality" of the government of the church by the Word, and prays "that it may never cease to be a reality" (pp. 692ff.).

### b. Under the Word

(1) Characteristics. Freedom under the Word does not mean license to think and speak and do as we please. It means freedom of conscience defined as "readiness and willingness to make one's own the responsibility for understanding of the Word of God" (p. 696). This freedom has a twofold limit (a) in readiness to listen to other church members and (b) in the freedom of the Word itself. It is established, however, by this freedom. Freely founding, preserving, and ruling the church, the Word gives its members a new freedom, not as a capability, permission, or reward, but as a gift which is continually to be received as such (p. 697). In response to the Word that comes to us as a human word, our self-determination, spontaneity, and activity are engaged in its service (p. 701). This applies to the church, but to individuals within it, not

the church en masse (p. 703). In this freedom individuals are led to see themselves in the totality of their being as they decide "in self-identification with the decision of the Word of God" about them (p. 705).

(2) Expression. How exactly does this freedom express itself? In his fivefold answer Barth first suggests (a) that by the interpretation of scripture it expresses itself in participation in the Word's own freedom to found, preserve, and rule the church (pp. 710–715). (b) This participation means subordination of "all human concepts, ideas and convictions to the witness of revelation supplied to us in scripture" (pp. 715–722) on the assumption that even in the most debatable parts the biblical message is "truer and more important" than anything we ourselves can say (p. 719). (c) Explication, the first aspect of interpretation, constitutes the next expression of freedom. This means observation of the sense of scripture — with historico-critical research as a primary tool — and focus on the object of the biblical word, in which it can speak for itself, as the ultimate demand (pp. 722–726). (d) Meditation, the next stage of interpretation, follows. This is reflection in which "we accompany what is written . . . with our own thinking" (pp. 727–736). In it systems of thought are unavoidably and rightly used, but they must have no independent interest and should not be allowed to distort what scripture says (pp. 730ff.). (e) Application, the culmination of interpretation, forms the final expression of Christian freedom under the Word. Barth variously defines this as appropriation, assimilation, contemporaneity, homogeneity, and "the indirect identification of the hearer and reader . . . with the witness of the revelation" (pp. 736–740). Strictly, however, application means our appropriation to the Word, not our appropriation of it (pp. 738–739). In it we do not come to the Bible looking for answers to our own questions, the relevant concerns of modern man, but we come to learn what the real questions are, who modern man is, and what are his genuine concerns. In the last resort application, like exposition and meditation, involves a "perfect confidence" in scripture which is actually faith in its object, Jesus Christ. Hence "faith itself, obedient faith," fittingly sums up for us "the activity which is demanded of us as members of the church, the exercise of the freedom which is granted to us under the Word" (p. 740).

## F. PROVISIONAL COMMENTS

Since important sections of Volume 1 have been omitted, and no section has been examined in detail, any comments on Barth's presentation must obviously be tentative. All the same, certain features call for favorable notice while others no less evidently call for question or dissent.

## 1. Areas of Strength

Barth displays a healthy understanding of what theology is all about, boldly proclaiming its integrity as a discipline and refusing to merge it into the various humanities that masquerade as divinity today. His comprehensive grasp of the Word of God is also refreshing and constructive, the more so as he retains the essential relationship of the forms on a trinitarian model. His connecting of revelation more closely to the Trinity, even to the point of a trinitarian analogy, has obvious merit, as has his brilliant exposition of revelation in terms of unveiling, veiling, and imparting. Perhaps the climax of 1.1, if not of the whole of Volume 1, lies in the emphasis given to the Triune God and the masterly treatment both of the Trinity itself and also of the three persons according to the creedal affirmations. Yet the doctrine of scripture, while it has drawn heavy criticism, has some valuable aspects too, especially the focus on the ongoing ministry of the Holy Spirit and on the unique authority and freedom of the Word of God. Few theologians have written so magisterially on the scripture principle of the Reformation, namely, the supreme normativity of scripture, which is in fact the working principle of Barth himself in the *Church Dogmatics*.

## 2. Problem Areas

If there is a pervading weakness in Barth, however, it is the tendency of his nimble mind to depart from this working principle and to go far beyond what the data of scripture legitimately allow. Thus the Word of God undoubtedly has a threefold form in scripture, but Barth's account of the interrelationship, while fascinating, has little in the way of textual basis. Similarly his exposition of unveiling, veiling, and imparting, while not manifestly untrue or unhelpful, sounds a little too good to be altogether true, especially as so excellent an analogy of the Trinity finally results. The discussion of the root of the doctrine of the Trinity has value in that it shows the church's teaching not to be just an intellectual abstraction, but it also leaves us wondering whether Barth's approach is not too generalized and circuitous. Finally, the doctrine of scripture, for all its unquestionable merits, raises some no less incontestable problems. Barth's category of the vulnerability of scripture is itself highly vulnerable by reason of its ambivalence. Is there not also a failure in logic in the assumption that the fallibility of the authors necessarily involves the fallibility of all their acts or writings? And why should God's speaking through fallible words mean a more authentic miracle? Is it a principle that the greater the fallibility the more authentic the miracle? Where does scripture itself tell us anything of this? One might also wonder whether it is not a mistake to stress the present ministry of the Spirit in the use of scripture at the expense of the once-for-all work of the Spirit in its authorship. Barth would later resist a similar imbalance in the matter of reconciliation. Is there not also a need for some rethinking in the matter of inspiration?

CHAPTER XXIX
# *Barth and the Doctrine of God*


## A. THE KNOWLEDGE OF GOD


### 1. Orientation

In the previous chapter we looked only at the Prolegomena of Barth's *Church Dogmatics* in Volume 1, Parts 1 and 2. Barth projected the work in five volumes, four of which would be devoted to the main dogmatic content. His plan for these four took a trinitarian form. Volume 2 was to deal with the doctrine of God, Volume 3 with the doctrine of God the Creator, Volume 4 with the doctrine of God the Reconciler, and Volume 5 with the doctrine of God the Redeemer. Barth completed Volume 2 in two parts, the first dealing with the knowledge and reality of God, the second with his election and command. He also finished Volume 3, this time in four parts dealing with creation, man, providence, and the ethics of creation. Volume 4 also had four parts, but only the first three of these, dealing with the three aspects of reconciliation, were published. The fourth part on the ethics of reconciliation was drafted, but apart from a fragment on baptism was not revised for publication. No part of Volume 5 appeared.

For a comprehensive understanding of Barth it is essential that the *Church Dogmatics* be read and pondered as a unity as well as in its detailed sections. Clearly, however, our present purpose does not allow a full presentation of Barth's teaching. A very sketchy outline might of course be given, but perhaps it will be better, by way of introduction, to take two samples, the first from 2.1 on the knowledge of God and the second from 2.2 on the election of God. These selections do not imply, of course, that the other materials in Volume 2, let alone those in 3 and 4, are of less interest or importance. They will simply serve as working examples with the help of which students may feel their way into the rest of the *Church Dogmatics*.

## 2. Starting Point

Barth's discussion of the knowledge of God starts out from the fact that through his Word "God is actually known and will be known again" in the church (2.1, pp. 3–4). This means that the first question is that of the reality of the knowledge of God, not of its possibility. "Where God is known He is also in some way or other knowable" (p. 5). Not the fact, but the extent and, consequently, the manner of knowledge forms the true issue (p. 5). Since real knowledge of God comes through the Word, its object cannot be regarded as an open question. The God of the Word, not some other god, is the God who is known and knowable in the church (p. 6). This knowledge which is under the constraint of the Word is under no fear of attack (p. 7). Any battle against doubt will be a victorious one. The constraint of the Word entails certainty of knowledge, whereas free choice of this or that god inevitably brings uncertainty. All apologetics that begin with an open question are false, but there can, of course, be a true apologetic consisting of an exposition of the rationality of the knowledge of God through the Word (pp. 8–9).

## 3. The Knowledge of God

### a. Man Before God

(1) God as the Object of Knowledge. In the true knowledge of God through the Word, God is the one distinct object, but he is so by giving himself to be known (p. 9). God is thus "the real and primary acting subject of all real knowledge of God." As such, however, he makes us the subjects of the knowledge of himself as object. In his Word he comes as object before man as subject. By his Spirit he makes the human subject capable of considering and conceiving himself as object (p. 10). The upward flight of the mystic is thus ruled out. It is a flight to non-objectivity, and as he ascends, the mystic passes the God who descends to make himself the object of human knowledge (pp. 10–12).

(2) Knowledge of God as Faith Knowledge. Real knowledge of God is a knowledge of faith, for faith is the total relation to the God who makes himself known (p. 12). It is man's orientation to God as object (p. 13). The knowledge of faith differs from other knowledge because of the difference of object. God has genuine objectivity like all objects, but his objectivity is unique in the whole range of knowledge (pp. 14–15). Knowledge of faith means union with the God who is distinct from all objects, including the knower; it is thus a distinct knowledge (p. 15).

(3) The Objectivity of God. In what sense is God's objectivity different? Barth distinguishes three different forms of the divine objectivity. (a) First is what he calls the primary objectivity wherein God in his triune life is eternally objective to himself. (b) Then comes the secondary objectivity wherein he gives himself to be known by us. (c)

This is, however, a mediated objectivity, and it thus involves the objectivity of other objects which serve as "signs or veils" representing the objectivity of God (pp. 16ff.). In knowing God, therefore, man stands indirectly before God and directly before another object which is "the medium by which God gives Himself to be known and in which man knows God" (p. 17). God himself, of course, chooses this object; it is not left to man to find God's objectivity in objects of his own arbitrary selection.

(4) Knowledge of God as Grace and Obedience. The knowledge of God does not presuppose our own qualification to be subjects of this knowledge. God himself makes us so, and for us this means, not precedence, but the subsequence which is dependence on grace (p. 21). This subsequence implies the obedience of faith. God acts first to make himself object and us subjects. We then follow God in his act. Truth may be had only as grace, and grace is received only in the decision of obedience (p. 27).

### b. God Before Man

(1) God as Subject. Setting man before himself as object, God sets himself before man as subject. He shows himself as object, awakening man to faith and opening man's eyes to his objectivity. He meets man in such a way that he is always God, and therefore man can truly know him. How, then, does he meet him? How does he present himself? What is the basic content of this knowledge of God in which he presents himself? To this question Barth has two answers (pp. 31–32).

(2) The Love and Fear of God. The first answer is that God presents himself as him "whom we must fear above all things because we may love Him above all things" (p. 32). Bound to the Word, we may love him because he is worthy of our love, he wills it, and he enables us so to know him as not to be without him (p. 33). Thus loving him, we are commanded to fear him, for he is in himself to be feared, he wills to be so, and he opens our eyes to his fearfulness (p. 34). This fear is not the terror that love expels but the recognition that apart from God's love and the freedom to love God in return nothing but destruction could await us (p. 35).

(3) The Clarity and Mystery of God. In his second answer Barth takes another pair of contrasting concepts. God meets us as the one "who remains a mystery to us because He Himself has made Himself so clear and certain to us" (p. 38). We may love God above all things because he has made himself so clear to us. He has done this, however, by showing himself as object. Precisely in so doing he remains a mystery to us in the sense that "He is and remains the One whom we know only because He gives Himself to be known" (p. 41).

(4) Knowledge and Word. How can we say all this about God? Barth's answer is simple. To know God we learn from God. "God is

known through God and through God alone." God makes himself known in his Word (p. 44). Here he declares himself. He speaks about himself as the one true Lord (p. 45), the Triune God, as whom he primarily knows himself in direct objectivity (pp. 47–49). Ours, of course, is not this primary knowledge. It is derived knowledge and as such it carries three limitations. (a) By reason of the mediation of a creaturely object, supremely in the incarnation, there is veiling as well as unveiling in the knowledge of God. The veiling can be unveiling only because of God's lordship in and above the sign (pp. 53–57). (b) God is always "I" — the incomparable "I" — and yet in the knowledge of himself he is also "Thou" and "He." He has made a world and creaturely objects of knowledge. In grace he has made himself an object for these objects. We cannot know him as he knows himself or us. We know him only through his name, in which his "I" is veiled as "Thou" and "He" (pp. 57–61). (c) God makes himself known to us in time, not eternity, and this involves a movement of cognition from one present to another. Each cognition "exists in complete truth," but "the whole truth is always truth for us temporarily" and has always to be repeated (pp. 61–62). Yet time is also to be seen as given by God, as divine time or revelation time. If this means limitation, it is also to be understood as a concession which makes possible our participation in the self-knowledge of God (p. 62).

### 4. The Knowability of God

#### a. The Readiness of God

(1) Knowability and Readiness. Knowability can be discussed only on the basis of real knowledge. The question of knowledge, however, was not that of facticity but of extent and manner. Similarly, knowability does not come into question as a fact. If God is known, he obviously can be. The theological question is that of the way of knowability. How can God be known and how far? The answer, Barth suggests, lies primarily in the readiness of God to be known by us. This readiness is grounded in God's own being and activity and is itself the ground of the corresponding readiness of man to know God.

(2) God's Readiness and Self-knowledge. God's readiness implies first his readiness for self-knowledge. Little as we know about it, God is eternally knowable to himself. Because of this eternal divine knowability, his knowability for us is no abstraction. Concretely actualized by God, it is a participation in God's self-knowability (p. 68).

(3) Readiness, Truth, and Grace. God's readiness to be known by us may be simply defined by the statement that God is the truth. Truth means openness, and all openness is originally God's. God's readiness means grace, too, for only by grace do we refer ourselves to God, to God as the truth, to God in his revelation. Only by the truth itself do we have to do with the truth (p. 69). If God's readiness is not understood as grace

and as the mystery of his good pleasure, it is not understood at all (p. 75).

(4) Grace and Analogy. God's readiness as grace may be seen most clearly in his choice of the terms by which we may know him. We ourselves have no analogies by which to know God's being and nature as Lord (pp. 75–76), Creator (pp. 76–77), Reconciler (pp. 77–78), and Redeemer (pp. 78–79). If God is known and knowable as Lord, Creator, Reconciler, and Redeemer, it is only in an analogy to be created by God's grace, not in an already existent analogy (p. 85).

(5) Natural Theology. Natural theology takes the opposite view and suggests existent analogies in an attempted demonstration of the knowability of God. Barth regards the theological impossibility of this course as self-evident. To explain why it is so persistently taken he advances three reasons. (a) It is thought to be possible and practicable (pp. 85–88). (b) It is thought to be pedagogically useful at least as an introduction to theology (pp. 88–97). (c) It is thought to have biblical sanction in that strand of scripture which appeals to man's confirming witness with creation (pp. 97–126). Yet Barth thinks these reasons are inadequate because the assumptions on which they rest are so ill-founded and unconvincing. He thus claims that a fourth reason is the real one but postpones discussion of this until the next section.

### b. The Readiness of Man

(1) Man's Readiness and God's. The knowability of God implies readiness on man's part as well as God's. Man's readiness, however, cannot be independent or self-grounded. It is included in God's, and as God's is a readiness *of* grace, man's must be a readiness *for* grace (pp. 128–129).

(2) Need and Grace. As a readiness for grace, man's readiness seems to have three simple implications: (a) need of grace if man is to know God: (b) knowledge of this need and of the reality of grace; and (c) willingness to accept God's grace for the need (pp. 129–130). Taken alone, however, these things do not in Barth's view constitute the authentic readiness of man for God, for they presuppose a human openness to grace and thus evade the real problem of human readiness (pp. 130–131). An idea of openness is not the same as the reality of it. Even in apparent need, knowledge, and willingness, the openness which is man's readiness is still lacking. When man is seen as the object of openness, even in the church, true openness is not attained (pp. 133ff.). The real reason for the ongoing vitality of natural theology comes to light at this point. Natural theology expresses the belief that man in himself is open to grace, so that even in the affirmation of need and grace he is really affirming himself and doing that which is more natural and gratifying for him to do.

(3) Readiness and Christ. To say that man is not open, however, is surely to rule out the readiness of man which God's own readiness

establishes and includes. And to negate man's readiness is to negate God's, and with it the knowledge and knowability of God. Is there any alternative? Barth thinks there is. We should not begin with the need, knowledge, and willingness of man, even of regenerate man. Man's readiness is to be sought and found, not anthropologically or ecclesiologically, but christologically in the one man Jesus in whom alone man has real and not just abstract existence (pp. 142ff.). Jesus Christ alone, true man, God who is man, is in himself ready for God (pp. 150–151).

(4) Christ's Readiness and Ours. Jesus Christ bore and bore away our own enmity and resistance to grace (pp. 151–152). In him our old man is buried and our new man rises up as the man who is ready for God. Not simply in virtue of our need, knowledge, and willingness, but in virtue of our participation in Christ, we, too, may be ready for God. This participation has two sides. (a) Objectively Christ executes our readiness for God by his external work of intercession and representation before the Father (p. 156). (b) Subjectively the Holy Spirit works out the participation in us as a life which is the life of faith (pp. 157–158). The ultimate error of natural theology is the attempt to dodge Jesus Christ and the Holy Spirit or to compromise with them in relation to the readiness of man (pp. 164–165). Its vitality is the vitality of man's illusion that he can stand on his own even in his readiness for God (pp. 166ff.). The right way to meet it is by the proclamation of faith and a theology of the Word which has a proper understanding of itself (p. 168). Even in the matter of human readiness God is knowable only in his grace. By this positive truth natural theology is already rejected (pp. 172–178).

### 5. The Limits of the Knowledge of God

#### a. The Hiddenness of God

(1) The Terminus a Quo. The knowledge of God in which God is known by God is an event. As such it has two limits, the *terminus a quo* and the *terminus ad quem* (pp. 178–183). The *terminus a quo,* the point of departure, is the hiddenness of God, not as a general epistemological conclusion, but as the content of a statement of faith (p. 183) in which we confess that "knowing God, we do not comprehend how we come to know him" (p. 184).

(2) The Negative Side. Negatively this implies the divine incomprehensibility, not in the sense of our inability to conceive of God, but in the sense that he is not an object that we can bring into the process of our conceiving, that is, of our apprehension (p. 187). As Barth sees it, what we apprehend we resemble, master, and are one with. But we neither resemble God, master him, nor are originally and properly one with him. We ourselves, then, cannot initiate our knowledge of God. God initiates it. In so doing he judges our conceiving and leaves us only the conceiving of faith.

(3) The Positive Side. The positive side is that in confessing God's judgment we confess his grace. If God's hiddenness means our inability to conceive of him; it also means his revelation and, therefore, our conceiving of him in faith. Indeed, conceiving of God's hiddenness is the beginning of knowing God. Man cannot apprehend God on his own. But God is apprehensible in his revelation to those who cannot apprehend him on their own (pp. 195–199). He is so, not directly, but indirectly, not in his being to sight, but in a sign to faith — and supremely in the incarnation as the sign of all signs (p. 199). Thus, even as we recognize God's hiddenness we are authorized and commanded, in gratitude and obedience, to think and speak about God (pp. 201–204).

### b. The Authenticity of Knowledge

(1) The Terminus ad Quem. The *terminus ad quem,* or forward limit, is the authenticity of the knowledge of God. Knowledge is the goal as well as the presupposition, but not in the sense of a goal that might not be achieved. Authentic knowledge of God is that to which we move as the hiddenness of God is that from which we come. It is authentic knowledge because our movement within the limits is instituted and directed by God himself (p. 204).

(2) God as Object. Authenticity is guaranteed by the fact that the Triune God is the object of our knowledge. Making himself object to us, he catches us up into his own knowledge of himself as object (p. 205). True knowledge depends primarily on our having to do with God as subject (p. 208). It thus depends on his revelation as the revelation of himself (p. 209) which as such is trustworthy and which claims our thought and speech (p. 210) according to his own will and power.

(3) Participation. If authenticity is the goal, how do we participate in it? Barth has two answers. Participation takes place in thanksgiving (pp. 216–220) and in wondering awe (pp. 220–224), for it implies a gracious relationship between our words and concepts on the one side and God as object on the other (p. 224). The fact of this relationship leads Barth into a renewed discussion of analogy.

(4) Analogy. Human words are obviously inadequate when used about God. There can be no connection between their use for creatures on the one side and the Creator on the other. This is why we speak of analogy, which implies both parity and disparity (p. 225). But how can analogy arise in this field? One might say that words which are applied properly to the human sphere are applied improperly to God, but Barth will have none of this. Analogy is possible only because God takes certain words and restores them to their proper use (pp. 229–231). God, not man, establishes analogy by his free and gracious decision. Analogy in this sense corresponds to the unveiling and veiling of God in self-revelation. Hence the disparity in analogy must be understood as revelation — the veiling or hiddenness of God — no less than the parity —

the unveiling or authenticity (p. 236). What we have here, then, is not the intrinsic analogy of being but the extrinsic analogy of grace.

(5) Christ. If it is asked what final confirmation there can be for the authenticity of the knowledge of God, the answer does not lie in external arguments. Yet it does lie outside us, not in the sense that we must grasp it, but in the sense that it lies in Jesus Christ. For confirmation we must look to him in faith (pp. 243ff.). He is the first and proper subject of the knowledge of God as object (p. 252). His own confirmation by testing may also be ours (p. 253).

## B. THE ELECTION OF GOD

### 1. Election

#### a. Features of Election

(1) God in Covenant Relation. Barth breaks comparatively new ground in Chapter 7 by including election in the doctrine of God. Why he does so becomes fully apparent only as he proceeds, but already in the first section (§ 32) he makes some important statements which show in what direction he is moving. The first is that the God who is the subject of the doctrine of God is disclosed in Jesus Christ to be in relation to someone else (pp. 5–6). This relation is that of the election of grace which Barth calls the "sum of the gospel" (p. 10) and which involves a covenant partnership between God and the people represented in Jesus (p. 11).

(2) Election and Predestination. As the election of grace, election is not to be subsumed under a general concept of predestination which includes in counterpoise both election and reprobation (pp. 12–18). Election implies the freedom of God (pp. 19–20; 27–30), his mystery (pp. 20–21; 30–32), and his righteousness (pp. 22–23; 32–34).

#### b. Source of the Doctrine

(1) False Sources. Considering the question whence our doctrine of election is to be derived, Barth rejects various sources on which theologians have commonly drawn. These include tradition (pp. 35–36), usefulness (pp. 37–38), experience (pp. 38–44), and a general concept of God as omnipotent will (pp. 44–51).

(2) The True Source. Election, like all else, is to be developed out of the self-revelation of God according to the witness of scripture (p. 52). Concretely this means it must have its source in Jesus Christ (pp. 53ff.), the one man to whom the human race is finally narrowed down in a process which led from Adam by way of Abraham, Isaac, Jacob, Judah, and the remnant until at last Jesus came as very man (pp. 55–58). The election, then, is primarily that of Christ and of others only in him (pp.

60–76), so that while one has to consider the election of the community and that of the individual, and the order of treatment may vary, the election can be materially understood and presented only as the election of Christ.

### c. Election and the Doctrine of God

(1) The Material Relation. It is because the election is primarily that of Christ that election forms part of the doctrine of God (pp. 76ff.). Christ is God, and therefore his election "is the primal and basic decision in which God wills to be and actually is God, . . . God is none other than the One who in his Son and Word elects Himself, and in and with Himself elects His people" (p. 76). From all eternity God in his love and freedom is the electing God. "God does not will to be God, and is not God, except as the One who elects." The doctrine of election, then, stands at the head of all doctrines as an integral part of the doctrine of God.

(2) Other Arrangements. Barth candidly admits that his order of treatment stands almost alone in dogmatic and confessional history. He offers a survey of the various arrangements and the place of election in them, noting that even so strong an advocate as Calvin found difficulty in putting the doctrine in a suitable context (pp. 77–88). From this study he concludes that only as part of the doctrine of God can election assume the function proper to it in the biblical witness (p. 91). For election speaks of the self-determination of the gracious God, upon which all else rests, which is his will to be God solely in Jesus Christ, and in terms of which he is Lord of Israel and the church, the Creator, Reconciler, and Redeemer. Election denotes God himself at the beginning of all his ways and works as ways and works of grace (p. 92).

## 2. The Election of Jesus Christ

### a. The Role of Jesus Christ

Jesus Christ mediates between God and man. In him as God, God reveals God to man. In him as man, man sees and knows God (p. 94). In him, God joins himself to man. God's being is his and man's is originally his, too. He is the beginning of God without whom God does not will or elect anything. He is himself, in fact, God's free grace. He is grace in its outward operation. He is God's Word, his decree and beginning. He is himself the divine election of grace (p. 95). This may be seen from John 1:1–2 (pp. 95–99).

### b. Concrete Election

Election, of course, leads us beyond time to a sphere where God is with himself in his freedom and good pleasure (p. 100). This sphere, however, is not an empty one. The electing God must not be thought of as an abstractly electing God, as in the concept of an absolute decree (pp.

100–101). Grace is no abstract exercise of freedom. It is the divine self-ordination to being as Jesus Christ, the beginning of all God's outward ways and works, the beginning of the covenant of grace (pp. 101–102). Election, then, is the election of Jesus Christ.

### c. Jesus Christ Electing God

Election, of course, can refer both to the one who elects and also to the one who is elected. Similarly the name of Jesus Christ can refer both to God and man. The election of Jesus Christ means, then, that Jesus Christ is himself the electing God (p. 103). Hence the divine decree of election, while omnipotent and incontrovertible, is not unknown but known (pp. 103–104). Jesus Christ is not just an object or standard of the divine will or freedom. He is this will or freedom in action (p. 104). He himself posits the beginning of the ways and works of God. He is not just the object of election. With the Father and the Holy Spirit, he is its subject (p. 105). There is no will of God apart from his will. If he also reveals and executes the election, this does not mean that he has a secondary role compared to the Father or the Holy Spirit. The election that he reveals and executes is the election that is made by him, too. The election that he reveals and executes is thus the one full and basic election of God. No ultimate and hidden will of God lies behind the decision which he not only executes and manifests, but also takes (p. 115).

### d. Jesus Christ Elected Man

(1) Lord and Head. Traditional theology, on the basis of the "in him" of Ephesians 1:4, has found a larger place for Jesus as elected man than as electing God. Nevertheless, the full force of election "in him" is missed if it is not seen that Christ is also the electing God. For only as such can he be also, as the man Jesus, the object and content of the eternal divine decision in whom, and not just through whom, all others are elected, so that he is the Lord and Head of the elect and the revelation and reflection of their election (pp. 116–118). In other words the election of Jesus Christ, as acceptance by grace, is the election of him who is himself the beginning of all God's outward ways and works (pp. 118–120).

(2) Election to Suffering. Equally basic is the fact that the election of the man Jesus is the primary act of election because it is his election to vicarious suffering (p. 120). Herein it may be seen that God's inconceivable grace is the grace of self-giving (p. 121). In the divine predestination, judgment, wrath, and rejection are foreseen as the creature yields to the shadow of evil that accompanies the light of God's good creation (p. 122). God in self-giving grace transfers this rejection to the one man Jesus who in obedience to God rejects the evil and does the good (p. 123). The rejection of evil — and all that has its source therein — has

to take place. Hence God must and does reject man as he is in himself. But God does so in the person of the elected man Jesus, whom he elects "at the head and in the place of all others" (p. 124). Jesus is elected to rejection so that we who are rejected in ourselves might be elected in him. In Jesus "God who is the Judge takes the place of the judged, and they are fully acquitted from sin and its guilt and penalty" (p. 125). In the one in whom they are elected they die as sinners and are set apart for divine sonship as the grace for which they were elected from all eternity in the election of the man Jesus (p. 125). Election in him means election to believe in him, to love and honor him, so that our election may be achieved in him and our rejection may be fulfilled in his rejection. This understanding involves a christologically reconstructed supralapsarianism which Barth develops in a long excursus (pp. 127–145) at the end of § 33.1.

*e. God's Eternal Will in the Election of Christ*

(1) God's Decree. If Jesus Christ is the electing God and elected man, the subject and object of election are both known, not unknown (pp. 145–155). Hence there is no obscurity about the good-pleasure of the will of the electing God (pp. 156–161). If the element of mystery remains, God's decree cannot be the hidden and absolute decree of tradition (pp. 158–161). Its content, the divine self-giving, is manifest in Jesus Christ (p. 161). This self-giving in the incarnation of the Son as death and resurrection has two sides. Negatively, God elected himself to be man's covenant partner, that is, to suffer death in the bearing of man's rejection (pp. 162–168). "He elected our rejection" (p. 164). Thus his decree includes no rejection for us. We deserved it, but God did not will it. "He willed the rejection of His Son in our stead" (p. 168). Positively, the divine self-giving in Christ means that God elected to have man as his covenant partner (pp. 168–175). With his own rejection he thus decreed in Christ man's exaltation to God's glory as the bearer of his image. We have, then, a double decree, but only as the decree of self-giving love fulfilled in Jesus Christ and with a positive purpose alone for man.

(2) God's History. For Barth God's eternal will in the election of Christ is no decree in an abstract sense. It has the form of divine action in a history between God and man (pp. 175ff.). If God always has the initiative in this, inaugurating it in eternity in the election of his Son to union with the man Jesus, he exercises this initiative in love, so that it finds a counterpart in the response or decision of man's election of God. God's freedom does not negate man's; it establishes it. The man Jesus, the primary object of election, makes this response of man's free election of God (pp. 177–178). One sees in him that God's election of grace "has as its sole content the fact that God elects man in order that man may be awakened and summoned to elect God" (p. 180). In this electing man can exist in freedom before God.

(3) God's Will in Action. Barth sums up this whole line of thought by identifying the divine will and the divine action. Election is a living act. It is God's will in action (pp. 180ff.). Tradition has often presented it as an abstraction from God's will or as a state resulting from it. On this view, God in his present acts is, at it were, deistically bound by a prior decision of predestination. As Barth himself sees it, however, election, being genuinely eternal, does not cease with time. It is the presupposition of all that now takes place between God and man, but it is a living and moving and powerful presupposition (p. 184). It is a free electing and rejecting in time (p. 186). This activist understanding of election, however, can be seen to be true only if election is identified with the election of Jesus Christ.

### 3. The Election of the Community

#### a. The Elect Community

While the election of grace finds its focus in Jesus Christ, this does not mean exclusion of the election of the community and the individual. A few hints may be given, then, of the way in which Barth develops these further aspects. His mention of the community reminds us that we should avoid the common practice of overemphasizing the individual here. In scripture God chooses a people. His covenant is with a people. This people is ultimately the one community of both the Old Testament and the New. It is elected not merely for salvation but also for service. By its existence witness to Jesus Christ is to be carried to the whole world and all people are to be summoned to faith in him (§ 34.1).

#### b. The Two Forms

Although one, the community has the two forms of Israel, which includes post-New Testament Jews, and the church, which consists of all believers from Pentecost to the second coming. Israel is the passing form of the community which resists its election, while the church is the coming form which is called on the ground of its election. Jesus Christ constitutes the point of union. He comes out of Israel and in him takes place the passing of the old man and coming of the new which produces the church.

#### c. The Two Functions

Christ executes both the judgment and the mercy of God, and the community in which he dwells is elected to represent Christ and his work of judgment and mercy as a witness and summons to the whole world. Within the common task Israel has specifically the function of representing God's judgment, and the church, his mercy (§ 34.2). Similarly the one community is elected to serve the promise of God in Jesus Christ which is to be heard and believed by man. Within the common task Israel has the special function of hearing and receiving the promise, the church of believing it (§ 34.3). Finally, the one community is elected to represent to the world the death that God has taken away from man and the new life that he has given him. Within this common task the specific function of Israel is to represent the death which God chose for himself in order to take it from man, while that of the church is to represent the risen life of Jesus Christ by which newness of life is divinely given to man (§ 34.4). It may be noted that at the conclusion of the main points in this section Barth adduces exegetical support from Romans 9–11. He relates 9:1–5 to § 34.1, 9:6–29 to § 34.2, 9:30 and chapter 10 to § 34.3, and chapter 11 to § 34.4.

### 4. The Election of the Individual

*a. The Individual Aspect*

At the beginning of § 35 on individual election Barth discusses the relation of this aspect to election as a whole. Whereas traditional teaching has made individual election the center, he himself sets it in the broader context of the election of Christ and the community. Yet this does not relativize it. The election of individuals is indeed established in and with that of Christ (pp. 306ff.). In his new individuality as forgiven man, the individual finds in Christ's election his own election (p. 314).

*b. The Message to the Individual*

The church's witness to the individual brings out four important aspects of this.

(1) Man in his old and ungodly individuality wills, posits, and chooses his rejection by God (pp. 316–317).

(2) God, however, has elected this ungodly individual and he has himself carried his rejection in Jesus Christ (p. 317).

(3) For all its terrible effects, the perverse choice of rejection on the part of the ungodly individual is invalidated in and by the vicarious rejection of Jesus Christ (pp. 317–318).

(4) The old individual is thus elected through the bearing of his rejection and the forgiveness of his revolt against God (pp. 318–320).

This message must go out as a call for decision. If the promise of election is not received and believed by the individual a gap will open between the being and the life of the elect. "He will live as one rejected in spite of his election" (p. 321). This call for decision cannot be a statement in the third person but must be a powerful address in the second person: Thou art the man! (pp. 322–323).

*c. The Mission of the Elect*

Acquiring a new and authentic individuality as they respond in faith to their election, the elect receive a special calling. In and with the community they are to proclaim the election of Jesus Christ as their election of which they have assurance in faith (pp. 345–347). For them this is a witness to the truth. They bear this witness recollecting that they have this election in Christ and expecting that others too will find their own election in Christ (pp. 347ff.) even though they are as yet still lying against the truth and therefore against their true being and calling.

### d. The Mission of the Rejected

Since all are rejected in themselves and all are elected in Christ, Barth finds a solidarity between the individual elect who believe the truth and the individual rejected who deny it. The rejected, even as they isolate themselves from God by resisting their election, fulfill God's purpose by witnessing to it in a negative mode (pp. 449ff.). Persisting in their false denial of Christ's rejection for them and their own election in Christ, they represent the sinner who is not willed by the holy, omnipotent, and compassionate God. As such, they remind the elect, of course, that they are not elected in and for themselves. They also testify indirectly to election, for their denial cannot exist independently but has to be a lie against the gospel (p. 453). It may all be summed up in three points.

(1) The rejected manifest those to whom the gospel comes, lost and ungodly people who are rejected in themselves and elect only in virtue of the vicarious rejection to which God's Son was elected (pp. 455–456).

(2) The rejected manifest what is denied and overcome by the gospel — the false choice, freedom, and service of sinful man under the judgment of God (pp. 456–457).

(3) The rejected indirectly manifest the purpose of the gospel — a future in covenant with God — for, having no future of their own, they point us to the one real hope which lies in the positive will of God directly disclosed in the resurrection of Jesus Christ and the new life of the elect in him (pp. 457–458).

In spite of themselves the rejected discharge this function, but they achieve their true destiny only if they come to faith and are changed from reluctant and indirect witnesses into willing and direct witnesses to the election of Jesus Christ and his community (p 458). The whole sub-section (§ 35.4) closes with a long and striking exposition of the indirect apostleship of Judas and the particular form in which he, too, fulfilled the will of God in the handing over of Jesus (pp. 458–506).

## C. INSIGHTS AND PROBLEMS

### 1. Insights

In his handling of both the knowledge of God and the election of

God Barth has many valuable things to teach us. He develops with unusual rigor what ought to be the truism that God is known through God. He boldly grasps the nettle and says that God makes himself object. He brilliantly ties in God's secondary objectivity with the self-revelation of the Creator in and by the creaturely. His rejection of natural theology applies strictly to natural theology, not to natural revelation. The development of the analogy of grace shows both discernment and profundity, and the distinction between the revealed divine hiddenness and general epistemological agnosticism is well drawn. The ongoing stress on Christ's vicariousness merits attention, while the insistence that assurance of authenticity lies not in external arguments but in Christ and faith's self-identification with him has the ring of biblical truth.

As regards election, the rethinking of Christ's role deserves special commendation. In his development of the vicariousness of Christ's person and work Barth has seldom been excelled. His understanding obviates the problem of a particular atonement which led Dort to distinguish universal sufficiency and limited efficacy. The insight that universal sufficiency means universal reality calls for closer consideration than it has normally received. Things really are as God wills them, even if those who defy this truth may achieve a negative and false reality of their own. Barth also shows in this area, as in that of providence (3.3) and reconciliation (4.1), a fine sense of God's teleological overruling, by which all things in different ways serve his purpose. This would be a frightening thought if that purpose were obscure. It is a comforting one, however, when in the election of Jesus Christ we know that purpose as one not only of wisdom and power but also of grace and self-giving love.

## 2. Problems

For all the insights, problems also arise in Barth's teaching. In the chapter on the knowledge of God his interpretation of scripture seems often to consist of a good deal more meditation than exposition. What exegesis there is falls easy victim to criticism, especially in relation to the "natural theology" of scripture. The whole handling of natural theology suffers from a failure to come to grips with natural or general revelation. Because of this, one often wonders whether finitude or fall is in Barth's view responsible for our ignorance of God. Is this ignorance intrinsic to creatureliness as such or to the fallenness of the creature? Surely clarification can come here only with some discussion of general revelation or the grace of creation. A more general difficulty possibly lies behind this particular one. The movement of Barth's thought is not always as clear to his readers as it was no doubt to himself. His basic points are simple but their force is blunted by surrounding complexities which lead to confusion and (often unnecessary) disagreement.

The doctrine of election raises problems of another order. Its inclusion in the doctrine of God has not gone uncontested, for no less cogent reasons might be found for placing other doctrines here, too. The resultant supralapsarianism runs into the same difficulty, for if election means service why should not election serve creation as creation serves election? The strong concentration on Christ poses difficulties, too. A lurking universalism is the most serious of these. If Christ bore the rejection of all, why should there be any other rejection? Barth argues that there can still be a living in rejection as though Christ had not borne it, but this thought is hard to grasp and Barth is not strongly committed to it, as his hope for Judas shows. He finally leaves it all to the sovereignty of the Spirit (4.3), but in this case a dark corner remains which is not illumined by the spotlight on Christ. The Father wills the election of all, the Son accomplishes it, but unaccountably the Spirit may not bring all to election. Finally it may be asked whether Barth does not allow his imagination a little too much freedom in the christological exposition of the Old Testament at the end of § 35.2. That the church is right to read the Old Testament christologically need not be contested. Could it not be, however, that Barth with his lively and constructive mind sees more than is really there? Indeed, do we not have to ask again whether in his whole doctrine he has not built too large a structure on too slender a foundation?

# CHAPTER XXX

# *Thielicke and the Evangelical Faith*

## A. THE EVANGELICAL FAITH

On the Lutheran side a powerful dogmatic restatement in the light of modern issues may be found in *The Evangelical Faith* by Helmut Thielicke, professor of systematic theology at the University of Hamburg in West Germany. Thielicke, an opponent of the German Christian movement under Hitler, achieved prominence as a preacher during and after the second world war and even as a professor kept up his interest in evangelistic mission. His first large-scale venture into theology came with his multi-volumed *Theological Ethics*, of which three volumes are available in English with some condensation and rearrangement. After completing the ethical series he projected a dogmatics in three volumes, the first devoted to prolegomena, the second to the Father and the Son, and the third to the Holy Spirit. The first volume came out in 1968, followed by an English translation in 1974. The subtitle, *The Relation of Theology to Modern Thought Forms,* conveys the scope and purpose of the volume, and the preface may be consulted for a clear statement of the author's understanding of his task, method, and theme in relation to *The Evangelical Faith* as a whole.

## B. CARTESIAN AND NON-CARTESIAN THEOLOGY

### 1. Address and Accommodation

*a. Address*

As Thielicke sees it, address belongs constitutively to the Word of God (p. 23). Since the Word is necessarily clothed in the means of expression of its day, contemporary address presupposes restatement. Address also presupposes some analogy between what is said and those to whom it is said, for without this there could be no possibility of understanding (p. 24). For these reasons theology has to focus not only on the message but also on the recipient or addressee.

### b. Accommodation

This focus on the recipient may take two forms. The first is the good one of actualization, the reinterpretation or readdressing of the message in such a way that it reaches its hearer (pp. 26–27). The second, however, is the bad one of accommodation in which the message is brought under the rule or measure of the recipient. Theology has to engage in actualization, but this will carry with it the polemical task of repudiating accommodation, as in the Barmen Declaration of 1934. (It may be noted in passing that Thielicke is not using the term "accommodation" in the same way as Calvin, for whom it describes God's own action of putting his self-revelation in human terms adjusted to our weakness and ignorance.)

## 2. Modern and Conservative

Following up an insight of Barth's in *Church Dogmatics* 1.1, pp. 197, 211ff., Thielicke suggests that the theological conflict today is best defined as a conflict, not between moderns and conservatives, but between Cartesians and non-Cartesians. On close analysis the words modern and conservative both prove to be ambivalent (pp. 30–37). In contrast, a common feature of all the variations of so-called modern theology is the Cartesian starting point (p. 34), whereas what is called conservative theology is always marked by a non-Cartesian orientation.

## 3. Cartesian Theology

### a. Concentration on Appropriation

Essential to Cartesian theology is a focusing on the act of appropriation (pp. 38ff.). In relation to address the dominant interest is not in what is addressed but in the addressee. Recognizing that one cannot do theology without anthropology, the Cartesian begins with anthropology. What point of contact does the message find in my existing conceptions? (p. 39). In their different ways Lessing, Schleiermacher, Bultmann, and Tillich all offer examples of this Cartesian emphasis (pp. 40ff.).

### b. Adulthood

The sense that man has now come of age contributes heavily to this stress on the addressee. Previously the divine message might have been accepted uncritically and on pure authority. Today, however, adulthood means autonomy. Before the message can be accepted, the question must be put how we can understand and appropriate it on our own responsibility (p. 39). Thus attention is necessarily shifted to the addressee as a theme of primary religious importance (pp. 39, 49ff.).

### c. Existential Analysis

Once this step is taken, a whole host of preliminary questions arises in relation to the recipient of the message. What elements in him will either meet the message or reject it? What about the clash between modern thought and the outmoded concepts in which the message was first delivered? What steps must be taken to relate the message to modern questions and concerns? The result of all this is the domination of the existential analysis of man which in its attempt to open up access to the theological content runs a serious risk of prejudicing what is said about that content, so that "in the last analysis theology is reduced to a mere chapter in anthropology" (p. 53).

### d. Method and Matter

Thielicke does not agree with those who argue that the Cartesian approach, or at least the questions it raises, should be dropped altogether because of the risks that are involved. The method as such is legitimate, and the questions need to be faced. At the same time the matter of almost all Cartesian theology must be challenged, for in spite of the original intention what usually happens in this theology is that, by what Thielicke calls "a tragic entanglement" initiated by the premises, the autonomy regulates the kerygma (p. 55). Thus the desired and attempted actualization becomes a harmful accommodation. This is illustrated by a more extended analysis and criticism of the theology of Bultmann (pp. 55–65).

### e. The Key Hermeneutical Question

In Cartesian theology the form of theological statement plays a crucial role, not merely in the valid sense that there must be translation into familiar terms, but also in the more dubious one that a kerygmatic content has to be extracted out of the outmoded form (pp. 66–67). For here a problem arises at once: What is form and what is content? In the resurrection, for example, do the empty tomb and the resurrection appearances belong constitutively to the kerygma, or are they the mere form of some other truth, a mere manner of speaking? This is the issue in the demythologization debate, which Thielicke goes on to discuss in detail (pp. 67ff., 84ff.). In its extreme form, which is the ineluctable consequence if not the intention of Cartesian theology, two fatal steps are taken. First, the kerygma is robbed of its historical facticity, existentialized, and thereby destroyed as genuine kerygma (pp. 110–111). Second, the elevation of the subjective consciousness virtually destroys all that transcends this consciousness, so that no dialogue is possible, everything is monologue, and prayer, for instance, loses any authentic meaning (pp. 111–114). "Monolithic commitment to contemporary recipients of the message" leads to a rule of the contemporary and his consciousness which is "a total perversion" (p. 114). The question of the recipient is certainly a valid one. In principle one might even start out from it. But to press this to the point where self-understanding becomes normative for all else is to initiate a movement of which this sorry perversion of the message is the inevitable end.

### 4. Non-Cartesian Theology

#### a. Primacy of Proclamation

Except for very rigid and reactionary groups, non-Cartesian theologians do not deny the need for an actualization or contemporary statement of the gospel. In contrast to Cartesians, however, they do not begin with the addressee and human subjectivity. They begin instead with the kerygma itself. According to Thielicke, then, the first and material characteristic of non-Cartesian theology is the precedence which it gives to that proclamation centered on the Word of God which by the Holy Spirit discloses itself and also creates its own hearers (p. 212). Since proclamation aims at man, existential analysis undoubtedly has a place. Nevertheless, it does not have a primary or normative place, nor can it ever be a central or final word (pp. 213–214).

#### b. Appropriation

Appropriation of the message is no less important in non-Cartesian than Cartesian theology, but it is understood very differently. What is appropriated in Cartesian theology, under conditions laid down by the self-understanding, is the gospel itself. In non-Cartesian theology, however, God's Word cannot be appropriated by any present state of existence. Instead "the Word itself sets up the conditions under which it may be heard and received." In so doing, it integrates the recipients into God's history (p. 216). In other words, we ourselves are appropriated to the message.

#### c. Newness

When the message is presented in terms relevant to a given age or culture, an element of newness will necessarily be present. In Cartesian theology this newness has both a negative and a positive side. Negatively it means the exclusion of parts of the truth which are no longer thought to be acceptable to modern ears. Positively it means a transposition of the truth itself into the new terms and concepts which are designed to express it (pp. 125–126). In contrast, non-Cartesian theology retains old truth (p. 127). There is for it nothing new in either the faith or the life of the church (p. 218). Yet "acceptance of the old does not imply rigid and unchanged quotation." Instead there is what

Thielicke calls "reproduction" (p. 127). Old truth is put in "the linguistic medium of the contemporary age" (p. 125). What is transformed, however, is not the message but the medium. As current terms are impressed into the service of the kerygma, "they must shed their ideological content." They must undergo a dying and renewing and emerge with a new sense. The term "logos" is instructive here. Justin Martyr tends to give this term a normative role by identifying Jesus with the Logos. This is Cartesian theology. In contrast, John's Gospel takes the non-Cartesian course. It de-ideologizes the term and gives it kerygmatic content by identifying the Logos with Jesus (pp. 125–126). Hence the newness in non-Cartesian theology is simply that of expression. The present situation and its questions are considered, but they do not become a normative principle, nor do they prejudice the answers. "They are recast and transcended in encounter with the text" (p. 127).

### d. Newness of the Spirit

While all this is true, it is not yet the whole truth. There is in fact an authentic newness beyond that of expression. This newness, however, is not that of a human reconstruction of the gospel to fit contemporary thought or need. It is actualization in the form of genuine re-presentation by the creative ministry of the Holy Spirit, for whom little or no place can be found in Cartesian theology. The work of the Holy Spirit is to bring us to faith by referring us back to the salvation event and thus orienting us to Christ. It is as he kindles faith in us that we are integrated into the divine acts and thereby achieve our new and true identity which is determined by that which God addresses to us. This theme of the renewing work of the Holy Spirit, the special mark of non-Cartesian theology, forms, of course, a theme apart. The development of this theme is the second great contribution of Thielicke in the first volume of his *Evangelical Faith*.

## C. THE WORK OF THE HOLY SPIRIT

### 1. The Role of the Spirit

#### a. New Creation

As we have seen, authentic appropriation as Thielicke understands it is not appropriation of message to recipient but of recipient to message. Study of the recipient in himself and as such can play only a limited role, for precisely in his receiving the recipient is himself created again by the Word and Spirit. This is the vital point which Cartesian theology misses. It can engage in existential analysis. It may go on to speak of existential encounter and even transformation through the message as it is adjusted to this analysis. But it does not find any serious place for the new creation of the subject by the message itself in the power of the Spirit — the new creation by which alone he can be an authentic recipient.

### b. Continuity

The question arises, however, whether the concept of new creation is not too strong. Does no self at all exist prior to the work of the Spirit? If such a self does exist, what continuity is there between this old self and the new? Can one think of the receiving of the gospel simply as the filling of a vacuum? If not, if the Word "is to encounter a concrete man with a specific self-understanding, then theological relevance must be ascribed to what is already there" (p. 138). Thielicke admits this. An element of continuity remains through the work of the Spirit. Man's prior understanding of himself is not ignored (p. 138). There is, in a sense, a point of contact for the gospel. The only thing is that in view of the creative work of the Spirit the prior self-understanding is not to be accorded the same rank as in Cartesian theology (p. 139).

### c. Examples

(1) Philosophical. To illustrate his point Thielicke offers a philosophical example. The categorical imperative of Kant provides a point of contact inasmuch as it may be equated with the radical and unconditional law of God. Yet the law of God, unlike Kant's imperative, exposes the inability of natural man to fulfill it. Human reality is not that of the "I ought and therefore I can" of Kant. The man who entertains this view of himself fights the gospel. The point of contact is the point of the divine assault on self-incurved man, and if contact is successfully made a new creation takes place in which this man is lifted out of his illusion and given true reality as a child of God (pp. 140ff.). In this respect, Thielicke observes, contact is an improper term. It tries to answer the wrong question, that of the "how" of God's work. It is thus to be "written with chalk on the board and then at once rubbed out again" (p. 146).

(2) Biblical. The parable of the prodigal son is taken as a biblical example. Here the point of contact is the ontic or biological sonship of the prodigal, which symbolizes the divine imago. Relationally this sonship can be and is disrupted. If identity remains even in extreme alienation, it is not in itself a ground of restoration. The prodigal cannot appeal to it. It has to go through a process of dying and rising again. The son has not fulfilled the obligation of sonship, and therefore he has lost his claim to it. No change in himself can as such alter this. Sonship can be restored only by the father's act. To be sure, it is the same son who is reaccepted. Nevertheless, reacceptance is not his own work (pp. 146–151). Divine likeness, Thielicke suggests, does not lie "in an indestructible continuity of human nature. . . . It is finally the image that God has of us."

Our dignity is not our own but the alien dignity which consists in "what is done on us and to us" through the redemptive work of Christ and the inner ministry of the Holy Spirit (p. 151).

## 2. The Death of the Cartesian Self

### a. The Death of the Old Self

Although identity remains, "the self is relativized as a theme of theology" (p. 152). Hence the real question is not "Who am I and what can I appropriate?" For "I learn who I am only from what happens to me and changes me" (p. 153). Hence the question of the self can have only a preliminary role. This self does not draw God into its own existence. By the Word it is drawn out of itself and into God. The self-centered self dies and is born again as "I am integrated into the salvation history enacted preveniently outside me and before me" (p. 153).

### b. The Salvation Event and Its Possibility

This integration means that the possibilities of this event, which cannot be calculated, replace the potentialities of the self, which are all that Nicodemus has in mind with his question in John 3:4. We do not look back on achieved possibilities nor try to elicit new ones from within in Socratic fashion. At this level continuing identity is not the point, as though regeneration were simply a mutation of the same self. Experiencing God's possibilities means the death of the former self and the raising of the new one. Nor does interest focus on the self that is raised but on the God who raises it (p. 155).

### c. Identity of God's Faithfulness

When interest still focuses on the old self, a wrong relation arises between faith and understanding, for the Word of God is regarded as interpretative, not creative (pp. 155–156). Being creative, the Word changes the self instead of merely disclosing it (p. 156). Thus continuity is to be sought, not in the self and its principles of understanding, but in the faithfulness of God and his tenacious image of the human self (p. 156). The Word, being active, establishes facts, not just meaning. The faith which acknowledges these facts is itself a creation of the Word, so that salvation history is no mere value judgment of faith. Salvation constitutes itself as such, breaking the continuity of the ordinary nexus of events (p. 158), as in the incarnation and resurrection of Christ (pp. 158–159). In the light of the creativity of the Word "the Cartesian self cannot serve as the point of reference in theological thinking," for "it allows no place for death and resurrection." Identity and continuity consist in "the faithfulness of God" (p. 159). To illustrate the distinction Thielicke concludes this section with an incisive analysis of the theology of Herbert Braun (pp. 160–173).

### 3. New Creation by the Spirit: Anthropological Aspect

*a. Survey*

The question of identity or continuity pinpoints the difference between Cartesian and non-Cartesian theology. The former defines identity as an ongoing identity in terms of self-understanding. The latter defines it as a new identity in terms of death and resurrection. On the former definition the ongoing self forms a primary theme of theology. On the latter the theme is determined by "the whence of the new identity" (pp. 174–175).

*b. Spirit and Letter*

The new self is re-created by the Word, but by the Word as Spirit, not letter. As letter, or law, the Word provokes, divides, and kills me. It announces God's claim but does not impart the new being which alone can meet it (pp. 175f.). As Spirit, however, the Word is creative. By the presence of the Spirit it gives me what I do not have. The Spirit confers the new birth. A process is involved here, not a state in which I might say that I in myself am the new I. Thus the Spirit should not be thought to give an immanent quality, nor should we speak of "having" the Spirit (pp. 177–178). The Holy Spirit lays hold of me in the form of faith. Faith looks to Christ, not to the new self. Through it the works of the Spirit are produced, the new self being as it were a by-product and not the goal (pp. 178–179). Gifts are certainly given by the Spirit, but his relation to Christ and the Word should be remembered. "The gift of the Spirit and the Spirit as the giver are one and the same" (p. 180). If the Spirit works as an imparted power, he himself is personal and he is to be defined in terms of what he is, not of his mode of manifestation (p. 181).

*c. Spirit and Identity*

The implication of creation by the Spirit for human identity may be summed up very quickly. The autonomy of "I am I" is undercut. So, too, is the falsification: "I am the I that has the Spirit." Instead, "I am" now denotes the relation which constitutes my new being. The new identity is expressed when I say: "By the Spirit I am in Christ," or: "Christ is in me by the Spirit." Love, the fulfilling of the law, is a total movement of the I. Yet even in love I am not an autonomous subject, for my ability to love is released by God's love for me (pp. 183–184). What I am as the new being in Christ by the Spirit is at all points the correlate of what God is for me (p. 184).

*d. Flesh and Spirit*

The new life is spiritual. Implied here is a discontinuity between the Spirit and the flesh, not flesh in its innocuous sense as the locus of earthly life but in its normative sense as an orientation of life (pp.

184–185). The Spirit effects a complete reorientation of life which entails discontinuity with both the carnal past and the carnal future. The break with the carnal past takes place because of God's forgiveness. "In the forgiving mind of God I am no longer the man I was" (p. 186). Continuity with the carnal future is broken because the empirical incalculability which we meet with mingled hope and fear is replaced by the incalculability of divine possibility which brings us under the control and care of God. A change of lordship constitutes the essence of this reorientation.

Some ambivalence remains in this life, for at one and the same time "I am the old man and I am also the new man." Nevertheless, the true locus of what I am is to be found in the second "I am" — the man I am for God (p. 189). If conscience still accuses me, forcing me to say "I am" in identification with my carnal self, God protects me against the accusation because "I am covered by the name of Christ." A change in identity has taken place. Yet, as faith perceives, continuity persists through all the discontinuity. This continuity lies in God. Its basis is faith in his faithfulness (p. 190).

### e. Imperative and Indicative

Discussing the development of the new man, Thielicke sees this as neither the unfolding of infused qualities nor as an increasing occupation of carnal territory by the Spirit. Instead we begin with the indicative that the new man is already fully in being. Thus development, or conflict, consists in following imperatives which relate, not to a future form of existence, but to a determination of it that is already past. Progress in the Christian life does not come by advancing beyond faith. It is not cooperation. It is not an end in itself. It is a simple going, or going back, to "the place where God is at work, where I am brought to faith by his Word and receive his Spirit as a pledge." Thus faith never outgrows its beginning, which is the creative and regenerative Word. Becoming begins here too, and it is here that the conflict between Spirit and flesh takes place.

## 4. New Creation by the Spirit:  Hermeneutical Aspect

### a. Hermeneutical Implications

If a new creation takes place by the Word and Spirit this obviously has a hermeneutical dimension. Whereas an interpretative word can be drawn into the human self-consciousness, a creative word first creates the possibilities of understanding and acceptance. Negatively this points to the fact that because of our inauthentic being we do not have our own possibilities of acceptance. "The ontic state of man shatters his noetic possibilities." Positively it means that truth is revealed only by an active Word which itself brings about the ontic change to true reality that we ourselves can never achieve (p. 194).

### b. Discontinuity

For the mediation of divine truth a break in continuity is thus required. The truth would still be the truth, of course, even if it were never imparted or understood. It would be the truth for God in the divine self-knowledge. It can be the truth for us, however, only as God by the Spirit gives us a share in himself, his self-knowledge, and his analogy (p. 195). This analogy has to be one of being before it can be one of understanding. The Spirit gives authentic being in order that there may be authentic understanding.

### c. Proclamation and Theology

Where does the creative Word meet and transform us? Thielicke argues that it does so in proclamation. An important implication of this is that theology does not fulfill its proper task if it precedes proclamation in the form of pre-discussion, as in Cartesian theology. Theology should follow proclamation in the form of reflection. A true understanding can be achieved only when a true being has been restored. Apprehension of this simple truth would quickly show how pointless are most of the unending hermeneutical and methodological debates in a good deal of modern theology.

### d. Unique Truth

Behind much of the discussion thus far lies the fact that the truth of proclamation is unique. It is, of course, analogous to truth in general. Nevertheless, we cannot describe it merely as truth that we can know or as truth that applies to us. We have to see in it a truth that understands us before we understand it. It is, in fact, truth in person. This truth in person is the truth into which we have to be called and in which we have to be (pp. 202ff.).

### e. Revelation and Accessibility

The unique truth of proclamation does not stand at our disposal. It requires revelation in the sense of a divinely imparted accessibility or a divinely given participation in God's self-knowledge. This implies, not an epistemological critique of pure reason, but a theological critique of impure reason (p. 208). Reason can see and assess the words and events of salvation history on its own level, but it cannot relate them to their true reality because it cannot relate them to their true object. A special category of knowledge is needed if these words and events are to be seen, not as mere history, but as the work of the Lord of history himself acting as a figure in history (pp. 209–210).

### f. The Spirit and Understanding

This special category of knowledge is faith. It is present, however, only if an analogue is present between the knowing subject and the known object. But where is this analogue to come from? Sin has brought a breach in communication which means a loss of the analogy and therefore exclusion from the knowledge of God. Hence Christ stands incognito within the facts relating to him. Understanding can come only when the analogy is "re-established in an act of new creation." The Holy Spirit performs this creative act by creating the hearer and believer. Hence theological epistemology can never be heteronomous. Faith arises spontaneously for those whom the Spirit sets in the new analogy. For this reason theological statements do not depend on proof. As proclamation, address, and appeal "they can be made . . . only in confidence in the awakening and creative and effectual power of the Word entrusted to them" (p. 211).

## D. INTERIM ASSESSMENT

### 1. Incompleteness

The first volume of *The Evangelical Faith* forms a totality in itself. It is, however, part of a series, and thus far the third volume on the Holy Spirit is not available. Here Thielicke might expand or even modify what he has said about the Spirit's ministry. Thus only an interim and not a definitive assessment can be attempted.

### 2. Influence of Barth

Worth noting in passing is Thielicke's indebtedness to Barth, but this should not be exaggerated. Thielicke disagrees sharply with Barth on many matters, especially the sensitive one of the relation of law and gospel. He also makes his points in a highly distinctive way. Yet affinities are unmistakable, especially the distinction between Cartesian and non-Cartesian theology, the virtual elimination of a point of contact for the gospel, and the essential insight that the Word creates its own hearers and gives its own understanding through the ministry of the Spirit. As regards the latter point a common source may be found in scripture and Reformation theology.

### 3. Cartesian Theology

Thielicke shows considerable strength in his dissection of Cartesian theology. While accepting its methodological possibility he shows clearly that it leads materially either into an impasse or to a distorted accommodation of the gospel. Through self-understanding the hearer can achieve only confusion and illusion. Self-understanding can never be more than understanding of an inauthentic identity, so that an accommodated gospel will be inauthentic too. To know who I really am I have to die to my own idea of who I am, being shown who I am in my inauthentic existence and also who I am in my true existence as one who is forgiven and regenerated by God. The autonomous Cartesian self can never be a recipient of the gospel. Hence a true theology cannot start with the analysis of this self. Nothing can be achieved by relating the gospel to it. A radical discontinuity is demanded which means the death of this self and abandonment of the theology centered upon it.

## 4. The Ministry of the Spirit

By stressing the role of the Spirit Thielicke sharpens his thesis, for the Spirit is the neglected factor in Cartesian theology. In this whole area Thielicke renders good service by reviving biblical emphases. Regeneration is taken seriously as the introducing of a new identity which in God entails continuity as well as discontinuity with the old one. This new being is the true recipient of the gospel in and through appropriation to it. True understanding comes with this new being in a distinctive theological epistemology. This being has its roots in the vicarious humanity of Christ and is thus to be seen as a divine gift of participation which is neither autonomous nor heteronomous but, as Barth would say, theonomous.

This emphasis on the Spirit's work has several implications which Thielicke perceives and works out with commendable skill. In the question of the recipient of revelation one need not be held up or dominated by analysis of the present self. Nor need proclamation await the results of such analysis in order to find out what is to be proclaimed. The old self will be replaced when the gospel is proclaimed and received. Only terminologically does there need to be any accommodation to the existing I, and in this accommodation the new terms, like the existing I, will be appropriated to the gospel and not vice versa. In no case can the Cartesian self understand and accept divine truth on its own, for only the Holy Spirit can supply the analogy by which it is known and received, and it is by revelation and faith, not by human investigation, that there is access to God and that God's inaccessibility apart from revelation and faith is known. The revealed words and facts of revelation are not open to the natural man on his own. Their true facticity and meaning are brought to light by the creative ministry of the Spirit. It is the Spirit, too, who in this ministry gives the only answer to the anguished modern question of identity: Who am I? By the Spirit one learns to say: I am the creature of God, the victim of inauthenticity through alienation from God, the child of God through the vicarious death and resurrection of Christ and the regenerative work of the Spirit. The creation of the new self is at the same time a restoration of the self as God created it. Thus continuity remains, not in the creature, but in God's faithfulness to it and in his purpose for it.

## 5. Significance

In all this Thielicke has made a valuable contribution to the modern theological debate. He perhaps interweaves too many themes, so that his points do not come through as forcefully as they should. His repetitiveness also points to a lack of rigor in planning and composition which robs the work of some of its effectiveness. Nevertheless, his analysis leads through the methodological questions to the most profound of theological issues. He gives new emphasis to biblical and Reformation teaching which it has been a fault of most Cartesian theology to ignore. He does not plead for a rationalistic orthodoxy in place of rationalistic unorthodoxy but uses some of the insights of the present to reconstitute what he believes to be genuine biblical orthodoxy. Not all non-Cartesians, let alone Cartesians, can be expected to agree with all his theses. Nevertheless, if they are given the serious consideration they deserve, in many areas they can help to give a new vitality, a new seriousness, and an authentic biblical content to the theological enterprise.

# Conclusion

How does one conclude an introduction? Perhaps the best way is just to stop and let the readers go ahead on their own, or, if they have had enough, to let them stop, too. An introduction does not call for the author's own intrusive thoughts or concerns. Nor should too much time be spent on an introduction, which should lead on as quickly as possible to the real speakers. But even an introduction needs to be rounded off, and hence some brief reflections will be helpful by way of conclusion.

A first and self-evident reflection is that the whole work might easily be written again with a different set of theologians or even with different works, or portions of works, from the same theologians. As we have proceeded, the gaps have become increasingly noticeable. Who ever heard of a history of theology that included no Scots, Baptists, or Roman Catholics, only a couple of Americans (rather obscure ones, at that), and fewer modern Anglicans than heretics? Well, the method of the work was explained in the Introduction, so that its selectivity need not now be defended. The point is, however, that as in the traditional understanding of predestination, the election of some has meant the passing over of many more who might equally well have been chosen.

These very gaps, however, point us to the vast theological resources which the church has at its disposal. Perhaps the most valuable lesson that younger readers can learn is that if wisdom did not die with the last generation, it certainly was not born with the new one. Only the most hopeless ignorance or appalling conceit can casually write off the thinking and authorship of the past as unworthy of attention. The work of the past, no less than that of the present, is no doubt uneven in both correctness and quality. Nevertheless, great minds have wrestled here with great themes. They have done so in the context of their own times and the particular concepts and problems of those times. Even the way in which they have responded to their times is instructive, but more so is the material teaching they have given and the material questions they have raised. To attempt a comprehensive new beginning when all this wealth of thought, inquiry, and scholarship is available can only be described as foolish and irresponsible as well as impossible.

Along the same lines, it is humbling to notice that so much of the supposedly original thinking of our modern teachers and writers has been anticipated by the theologians of the remoter or more recent past. Sometimes it may be simple ignorance that has led someone to suppose that he is the first to have and enunciate a brilliant insight. In such cases the insight is indeed a genuinely new one for those who proclaim it, but they would do well not to boast too loudly of its newness, lest others might have come across it already in the fathers or the schoolmen. Did not Herder speak of religion as the opiate of the people almost a century before Karl Marx, and who can say whether he himself did not pick up the phrase from some other thinker? In other instances a process of assimilation has taken place in which a thought of the past is read and adopted and then reappears in a distinctive form or context. One often finds this in the *Church Dogmatics*. Barth has often studied and digested an earlier writing and then has produced one or more of its striking thoughts in an unmistakable Barthian mode. In such cases critics need to be careful, for unless they are adequately versed in historical theology they may easily dissent from a "novelty" which has a long and respectable history in the church. Barth's "modes of being" for "persons" offers an instructive example. Somewhere along the line all of us are likely to be caught proclaiming our original thought in blissful ignorance of its prior history or failing to recognize the process of assimilation that lies behind an apparently offensive term or teaching. The wider the reading, the greater will be the modesty. As Ecclesiastes warns us, there is nothing new under the sun. And in one sense, at least, that goes for Christian theology, too.

Encouragement may be found by realizing that in and through and in spite of every deviation theology gives evidence of an ongoing attachment to its true theme and center as they are normatively presented in scripture. Revolts and innovations have succeeded one another, and continue to do so, but even in the worst extremes there is usually a recognizable core of the gospel and a plea is made that what is being sought is the authentic message. Furthermore, the revolts and innovations have always been brought under the scrutiny of scripture and tradition and have been accompanied, with varying measures of success, by an equalizing counterthrust. It is tempting to be speculative here, and to agree with Tertullian, or, more recently, Thielicke, that heresy performs a necessary service to truth, not only by testing it, but also by bringing its implications to light. Be that as it may, the fact remains that the gospel as it was first understood has remained substantially the same gospel across the centuries. Neither by revolution nor evolution has it been definitively changed into something else. No one so far has managed to get away with the "other gospel" against which Paul issued so passionate a warning even in the apostolic age. We can have good hope that no one ever will.

Theology has not done too bad a job in putting Christian truth into the changing terms of different patterns of language, thought, and culture. This task of translation clearly presents the church with its most serious task and danger, not only in life and conduct, but also in proclamation and the theology which serves it. Proclamation cannot consist merely in reading scripture or the creeds, nor can theology be merely a presentation of biblical themes in biblical terms. The work of translation cannot be avoided. Its indispensability, however, is matched by its difficulty. So many errors are possible. One can do too little, failing to achieve genuine contemporary expression. One can do the wrong thing, producing new terms which miss the mark and mislead. One can fall into a happy ambivalence, so that the precise meaning cannot be pinned down. One can do too much, losing much or most of the gospel by forcing it into an alien form or by relativizing even its normative expression in scripture. Naturally, examples of all these mistakes can easily be found in historical theology. It might be stated, indeed, that the task is never executed perfectly, as the arguability of any contemporary translation of scripture so plainly shows. Nevertheless, the story has on the whole been one of relative success rather than relative failure. The changing shape of theological expression and presentation makes this apparent. Theologians, of course, are forced into the task whether they like it or not. Even when they themselves are naively unaware of it and think they are being purely biblical, they belong to their time. Yet on balance they have neither fought too hard against this in misguided conservatism nor yielded so weakly to it as to lose the tradition in surrender to contemporary thought and culture. The secret of this partial success undoubtedly lies in the attachment to the main theme and center of theology to which reference has already been made. Or perhaps Barth sees the matter more clearly when he ascribes it to the divine disposing in human confusion, or, more specifically, to the freedom and sovereignty of the Word and Spirit. As the reformers so wisely remarked, individuals and churches may err, but the whole church will never be in complete error all at once. The medium will not absorb the message.

It has become clear, one might think, that a schematization of historical movement is hardly possible. Different attempts have been made by different scholars to trace a pattern across the centuries. A highly favored thesis has been that trinitarian and christological themes are handled especially by the early church, soteriological themes by the Reformation period, and anthropological and possibly pneumatological themes by the modern church. Now obviously this and similar schemes contain elements of truth. Different emphases can indeed be discerned in different periods. At the same time, however, our introduction has surely made it clear beyond dispute that all the important themes arise in every age. Does not the christological work of the early church have a soteriological core? Have the reformers nothing to say about Christology, anthropology, or pneumatology? Do not post-Reformation theologians deal with sacrament as well as scripture, with election as well as the doctrine of man? Indeed, are not all the themes so intimately related that one can hardly deal with one without dealing with the others, too? Our selected representatives surely teach us to tread warily as we move into the area of speculative systematizing. Perhaps that is a pity, for a good deal of the fun of history lies in putting out one's own hypothesis and knocking down the hypotheses of others. Well, we can have our fun, but let us not be too serious about it. Ultimate truth is not at stake here, only opinion, and perhaps, if we get too serious, reputation. If we want to play the game, let us do so with the final recognition that it is only a game. No one need go to the stake for it. If there is a final pattern in theology, a pattern that corresponds to all the facts, then this is the pattern being woven by God himself. Revelation unfortunately seems not to include the disclosure of this pattern, especially to historical theologians.

Finally, we remember again that there is no conclusion. This does not apply only to students, who will find that achieving any degree of mastery in this field is an endless task. It also applies to those who make theology, for theologians are constantly faced with new situations in which their work has to be done afresh. The questions and concerns of the past and the available tools of thought and expression can never be precisely the same even if resemblances exist. Hence theology can never be solely and simply historical in the sense of merely having to repeat what has been said before. As the gospel must be preached in different and changing circumstances, so theology must find the right forms in which the theme of proclamation can still be expressed. What has been done before can be of the greatest help here materially as well as methodologically. But neither in general nor in detail can it ever be a final word. It may achieve the rank of a secondary or subsidiary standard, as have the creeds and confessions and many passages in the fathers of all generations. Nevertheless, some degree of restatement will still be required. To be sure, scripture can very well be called a final word. In content and indeed in wording, too, it has finality in the sense that pure theology will always consist in an exposition of what is said in scripture. Yet even scripture itself does require exposition and this can never be a once-for-all task. If theology is in an extended sense contemporary exposition of the definitive biblical word, it can never itself be described as truly definitive. Perhaps it may be possible to write the definitive book that reviewers like to speak about. What is certain, however, is that no theology can ever be described as definitive, although some theologies come closer to it than others. The making of theological books will be without end, and the study of these books which can have no conclusion will be a weariness to the flesh as well as a great excitement. Only when we know as we are known will there be a conclusion — a conclusion which will also be a new beginning.

# Bibliography

Ames, W. *Marrow of Theology,* trans and ed. J. D. Eusden. Pilgrim Press, Philadelphia, 1968.

Barth, K. *Church Dogmatics,* ed. G. W. Bromiley and T. F. Torrance. T. and T. Clark, Edinburgh, 1956ff.

    Vol. 1.1, trans. G. W. Bromiley, 1975

        1.2, trans. G. T. Thomson and H. Knight, 1956

        2.1, trans. T. H. L. Parker, W. B. Johnston, H. Knight, and J. L. M. Haire, 1957

        2.2, trans G. W. Bromiley, J. C. Campbell, I. Wilson, J. S. McNab, H. Knight, and R. A. Stewart, 1957

Fathers and Early Writers of the English Reformed Church. Parker Society, Cambridge University Press, Cambridge.

    H. Bullinger. *Decades* I-II, ed. T. Harding, 1849

    *Decades* V, ed. T. Harding, 1852

    T. Cranmer. *Miscellaneous Writings (Homily of Salvation),* ed. J. E. Cox, 1846

    N. Ridley. *Works,* ed. H. Christmas, 1841: *Brief Declaration or Treatise against Transubstantiation* and *Disputation*

Fathers of the Church, ed. R. J. Deferrari. The Catholic University of America Press, Washington, D.C.

    Vol. 25 Hilary, *On the Trinity,* trans. S. McKenna, 1954

    Vol. 33 Chrysostom. *Homilies on John,* trans. T. A. Goggin, 1960

    Vol. 37 John of Damascus. *The Orthodox Faith,* trans. F. H. Chase, 1958

    Vol. 61, 64 Cyril of Jerusalem. *Catechetical Lectures,* trans. L. P. McCauley and A. A. Stephenson, 1969, 1970

Harnack, A. von. *What is Christianity?* trans. T. B. Saunders. G. P. Putnam's, New York, 1902.

Herrmann, W. *Communion with God,* trans. J. S. Stanyon. G. P. Putnam's, New York, 1906.

Kant, I. *Religion within the Limits of Reason Alone,* trans. T. M. Green and H. H. Hudson. Harper and Row, New York, 1960.

Lessing, G. E. *Theological Writings,* ed. H. Chadwick. Stanford University Press, Stanford, 1956.

Library of Christian Classics, ed. J. Baillie, J. T. McNeill, and H. P. van Dusen. Westminster Press, Philadelphia, 1953ff.

Vol. I *Christian Fathers,* ed. C. C. Richardson, 1953
  Ignatius. *Epistles*
  II Clement
  *Epistle to Diognetus*
  Justin Martyr. *First Apology*
  Irenaeus. *Against Heresies* III and V
Vol. II *Alexandrian Christianity,* ed. H. Chadwick and J. E. L. Oulton, 1954
  Clement. *Stromateis* VII (On Christian Perfection)
  Origen. *On Prayer*
            *Dialogue with Heraclides*
Vol. III *Christology of the Later Fathers,* ed. E. R. Hardy, 1954
  Athanasius. *On the Incarnation of the Word*
  Gregory of Nyssa. *An Address on Religious Instruction*
  Cyril of Alexandria. *Third Dogmatic Letter*
Vol. V *Early Latin Theology,* ed. S. L. Greenslade, 1956
  Tertullian. *The Prescriptions of the Heretics*
                *On Idolatry*
  Cyprian. *On the Unity of the Catholic Church*
  Jerome. *Letters*
Vol. VII *Augustine: Confessions and Enchiridion,* ed. A. C. Outler, 1955
  *Enchiridion*
Vol. VIII *Augustine: Later Works,* ed. J. Burnaby, 1955
  *The Trinity*
  *The Spirit and the Letter*
  *Homilies on I John*
Vol. IX *Early Medieval Theology,* ed. G. E. McCracken
  Radbertus. *The Lord's Body and Blood*
  Ratramnus. *Christ's Body and Blood*
  Remigius. *Reply to the Three Letters*
Vol. X *A Scholastic Miscellany,* ed. E. R. Fairweather, 1956
  Anselm. *Proslogion*
            *Letter on the Incarnation of the Word*
            *Cur deus homo*
            *The Virgin Conception and Original Sin*
  Abelard. *Exposition of Romans*
  Lombard. *Sentences*
Vol. XI *Nature and Grace,* ed. A. M. Fairweather, 1954
  Thomas Aquinas. *Summa theologica*
Vol. XIX *Melanchthon and Bucer,* ed. W. Pauck, 1969
  Melanchthon. *Loci communes theologici*
Vol. XX-XXI *Calvin's Institutes,* ed. J. T. McNeill and F. L. Battles, 1960
  Calvin. *Institutes of the Christian Religion*
Vol. XXIV *Zwingli and Bullinger,* ed. G. W. Bromiley, 1953
  Zwingli. *Of the Clarity and Certainty of the Word of God*
            *Of Baptism*
            *Of the Lord's Supper*
            *An Exposition of the Faith*
Vol. XXV *Spiritual and Anabaptist Writers,* ed. G. H. Williams, 1957
  Grebel. *Letter to Thomas Müntzer*
  Hofmann. *The Ordinance of God*
  Hubmaier. *On Free Will*
  D. Philips. *The Church of God*
  M. Simons. *On the Ban*
Vol. XXVI *English Reformers,* ed. T. H. L. Parker, 1966
  N. Ridley. *Treatise against the Error of Transubstantiation*

Library of Protestant Thought. Oxford University Press, New York.
*God and Incarnation,* ed. C. Welch, 1965
Thomasius. *Christ's Person and Work*
*Mercersburg Theology,* ed. J. H. Nichols, 1966
J. W. Nevin. *The Meaning of Protestantism*
*The Apostles' Creed*
*Reformed Dogmatics,* ed. J. W. Beardslee, 1965
Wollebius. *Compendium of Christian Theology*
*John Wesley,* ed. A. C. Outler, 1964
*Christian Perfection*
*Predestination Calmly Considered*
*The Scripture Way of Salvation*
Luther's Works, ed. T. H. Lehman and J. Pelikan. Concordia and Fortress.
Vol. 25 *Lectures on Romans,* ed. H. C. Oswald, 1972
Vol. 35 *Word and Sacrament,* ed. E. T. Bachmann, 1961
*The Holy and Blessed Sacrament of Baptism*
Vol. 37 *Word and Sacrament,* ed. R. H. Fischer, 1961
*This is my Body*
*Confession concerning Christ's Supper*
Lux Mundi, ed. C. Gore. Murray, London, 1913.
J. R. Illingworth. *The Incarnation in Relation to Development*
C. Gore. *The Holy Spirit and Inspiration*
Schleiermacher, F. E. D. *The Christian Faith.*
——————————. *On Religion: Speeches to Its Cultured Despisers,* trans. J. Oman. Harper and Row, New York, 1958.
Simons, M. *Complete Writings,* ed. J. C. Wenger. Herald Press, Scottdale, Pa., 1956.
——————————. *Foundation of Christian Doctrine.*
Thielicke, H. *The Evangelical Faith,* Vol. I, trans. and ed. G. W. Bromiley. Eerdmans, Grand Rapids, 1974.

# *Indexes*

## I. NAMES

## II. SCRIPTURE REFERENCES